SOLDERING IN ELECTRONICS

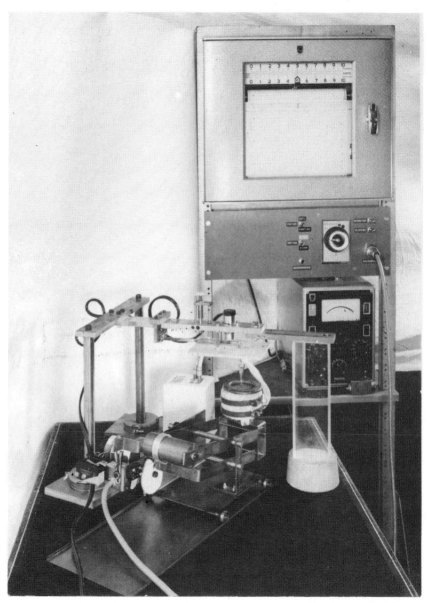

The original wetting balance, as developed by J.A. ten Duis in 1967 (see Chapter 7).

SOLDERING IN ELECTRONICS

by

R. J. KLEIN WASSINK

ELECTROCHEMICAL PUBLICATIONS LIMITED
1984

ELECTROCHEMICAL PUBLICATIONS LIMITED
8 Barns Street, Ayr, Scotland

ISBN 0 901150 14 2

Photo typesetting by Brian Robinson,
North Marston, Bucks
Printed in Great Britain by The Anchor Press Ltd
and bound by Wm Brendon & Son Ltd,
both of Tiptree, Essex

UNITS

Throughout the book the SI system of units has been used, and numbers have been given with the decimal comma on the line according to the recent International Standard ISO 31/0-1981(E). Some quantities and units as used in the text are given below.

Symbol Used	Quantity	SI Unit	Other Unit Equivalents
	thermal diffusivity	m^2/s	1550 sq.in/s
	surface area	m^2	10,75 sq.ft
	heat transfer coefficient	$W/(m^2.K)$	0,86 kcal/(m^2.h.°C)
	specific heat capacity	$J/(kg.K)$	$2,4 \times 10^{-4}$ cal/(g.°C)
	surface tension	J/m^2	10^3 erg/cm^2
	modulus of elasticity	N/m^2	$1,02 \times 10^{-5}$ kgf/cm^2
	force	N	0,102 kgf
	heat flux	W/m^2	0,316 Btu/(h.sq.ft)
	acceleration of gravity	m/s^2	
d,l,L,x,y	length, thickness, distance	m	39,4 in
	viscosity	Pa.s	10^3 cP
	heat conductivity	$W/(m.K)$	$2,4 \times 10^{-3}$ cal/(cm.s.°C)
	mass	kg	2,2 lb
	pressure	N/m^2 (= Pa)	$1,45 \times 10^{-4}$ psi;
	density	kg/m^3	0,0624 lb/cu.ft
	time	s	
	temperature	°C	
T	temperature interval	K	degC
	velocity	m/s	3,28 ft/s
	volume	m^3	$6,1 \times 10^4$ cu.in

Preface

The subject of this book is rather specialised; yet it has proved difficult to keep treatment of the matter within reasonable bounds, as soldering in electronics exhibits many characteristics unknown in other soldering applications.

The book has been written mainly for those involved in the electronics industry, for example, design engineers, process engineers, production engineers, quality engineers, metallurgists and chemists. During my prolonged contact with these specialists I have learnt that they need both background knowledge and in-depth technical information, and in compiling this text I have tried to achieve a reasonable balance between the two. In so doing I have not only dealt with established know-how, but have also given my own opinion on those items which are still a matter of controversy. These personal views are based on my experience as a research worker, as a co-ordinator of soldering development activities and as a member of various consultative and standardisation committees inside as well as outside my company.

Some chapters of this book constitute rewritten 'Information Sheets' on soldering which I originally published within my company in collaboration with several colleagues. Other chapters bear the mark of extensive deliberations.

I gladly avail myself of this opportunity to thank all my colleagues for their interest, advice and support, and would like to mention explicitly Messrs J.A. ten Duis, J.H.J. van Dijk, H.M.J. Hermans, M. Leenaerts, G. Schouten and F.G.M. Wolters. Mr E.E. de Kluizenaar was kind enough to read the whole manuscript and to suggest many improvements. I also gratefully acknowledge the help of Mr B.M. Allen in checking the entire manuscript for correct English usage and in giving his comments on many topics; moreover, I appreciate having been allowed to incorporate his valuable bibliography on soldering.

Finally, I should like to record the useful and pleasant co-operation with Mr W. Goldie of Electrochemical Publications Ltd. in transferring my manuscript into an attractive printed book.

January, 1984.

R.J. Klein Wassink
Centre for manufacturing Technology
Nederlandse Philips Bedrijven B.V.
Eindhoven, The Netherlands

CONTENTS

ix

CHAPTER THREE   **Thermal Aspects of Soldering**

CHAPTER FOUR   **Solder Alloys**

CHAPTER SIX   Solderable Materials

CHAPTER SEVEN   **Assessment of Solderability**

CHAPTER TEN   Reflow Soldering

CHAPTER ELEVEN   Manual Soldering

CHAPTER TWELVE   The Quality of Soldered Joints

Chapter 1

SOLDERING IN ELECTRONICS

Soldering is an important technique in the assembly of electronic products. Many people, such as the designers of electronic products, process engineers and production engineers, have to deal with the various aspects of soldering in the successive steps of the manufacturing process. The decisions which they take in their respective fields influence the soldering result at a later stage.

Since soldering technology occupies an intermediate position among various sciences such as mechanics, chemistry and metallurgy, it is understandable that in practice many different people are involved in discussions on its technicalities.

Soldering in electronics is in many respects different from soldering in other branches of industry. Although the physical principles of all soldering (and brazing) processes are the same, the features specific to their use in electronics are so numerous that it is possible to speak of soldering in electronics as a subject in its own right. This book deals with the technology of soldering in electronics, attempting to give not only a basic knowledge and comprehension of soldering phenomena, but also to deal with the systematic application of this knowledge to the practical manufacturing of electronic products.

1 THE POSITION OF SOLDERING

Efficient functioning of electrical equipment is dependent on the correct interaction of electrical components. For their interconnection, these still rely for the most part on soldering, which has maintained a dominant position even in the face of the many other connecting techniques currently appearing on the scene.

In electronic mass production hundreds of millions of soldered joints are being formed daily. A standard radio receiver contains about 500 joints, a black and white television set about 1000, and a colour television set about 2000. Large computers and telephone systems have over 10^5 soldered joints. With the correct joint design and the application of a good process, reliable joints are obtained, having a negligible contact resistance and an acceptable strength. Reliability implies that the joints not only have the desired properties immediately after production, but can also be expected to ensure failure-free working during the life of the equipment.

Soldering is a simple operation. It consists of the relative positioning of the parts to be joined, of wetting the surfaces with molten solder and allowing the solder to cool down until it has solidified. For soldering in electronics, tin-lead alloys with a melting point of about 185°C are the most often used. Hand soldering with the aid of a soldering iron is a very long-established technique

[Allen] which is still used in electronics, although for mass production purpos
several machine techniques have been developed. Machine soldering methods a
discussed in Chapters 9 and 10, and hand soldering techniques in Chapter 11.

The adoption of mechanised methods is stimulated on the one hand t
considerations of efficiency, and on the other hand by the desire to obtain a mo
closely controlled quality than is realisable by manual soldering technique
Machine soldering affords a gain in quality because the machine, unlike ma
never relaxes its attention. However, at the same time, the machine involv
losses because it is incapable of adapting to extreme situations. No machir
method is able to cope with such contingencies as inadequate solderability (
component terminations or deficiencies in the soldering process.

Soldering has some clear advantages over competitive joining techniques suc
as welding or fixing with conductive adhesives:

(i)   the solder joint forms itself by the nature of the wetting process, even whe
      the heat and the solder are not directed precisely to the places to t
      soldered. Because solder does not adhere to insulating materials it may i
      many cases be applied in excess quantities (*cf.* conductive adhesives). As tl
      soldering temperature is relatively low there is no need for the heat to t
      applied locally (*cf.* welding);
(ii) soldering allows considerable freedom in the dimensioning of the joints, s
      that it is possible to obtain good results even if a large variety (
      components are used on the same soldered product;
(iii) the soldered connections can be disconnected if necessary, which impli
      that repair is easy;
(iv) the equipment for both hand soldering and machine soldering is relative
      simple;
(v)   the soldering process can easily be automated, offering the possibility of ii
      line arrangements of soldering machines with other machines.

The basic difference between soldering and welding is that, in welding, tl
metals to be joined themselves melt, whereas in soldering no fusion occurs, bi
only wetting by the solder alloy, which must therefore have a lower melting poir
than the parts to be joined. In general, welds are stronger than soldered joints ar
do not creep under moderate mechanical loads.

A practical difference between welding and soldering is that welds have to t
made consecutively, whereas soldered joints can be made simultaneously in or
single operation. This factor in principle makes soldering a cheap connectir
method.

1.1.1   Soldering as a System

Many factors influence the outcome of the soldering operation, these beir
related both to the components or parts to be joined, and to the soldering proce
applied.

1.1.1.1   SOLDERING PARAMETERS

In the interrelation of the main variables for soldering of components t inted boards, three stages can be discerned (Figure 1.1), namely, design, anufacture and use.

The quality of the end product, which becomes clear in service, depends on the easures taken during the design and manufacturing stages of the electronic oduct. These measures concern the complete set of soldering variables given in gure 1.1. The phrase 'soldering as a system' intends to convey that these easures should be adapted to one another in such a way that together they form coherent system to yield an optimum overall result.

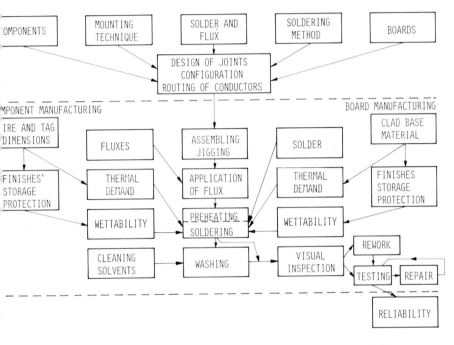

Fig. 1.1   Diagram showing the interactions between the main soldering variables.

At the design stage the foundations of the suitability of the components for achine soldering in the manufacturing stage are laid. The design concerns, *inter ia*, the shape of components and the configuration of the conductors to which e components must be soldered, as well as surface treatments such as ectroplating of component terminations to assure satisfactory wettability at the oment of soldering.

The component leads to be soldered may consist of various materials. Thus, in single soldering operation, tinned copper wires, tin-lead plated or gold plated ickel-iron wires, and Kovar wires may all have to be joined to a printed board.

The components also differ as regards their thermal behaviour, some having a rge heat capacity, others small. Components and printed boards are often ensitive to the elevated temperatures associated with the soldering operation, us incurring the risk of thermal damage. These effects of materials and heat ust be taken into account right at the design stage.

Mounting technique, soldering method, applied materials and process onditions should be chosen bearing in mind the characteristics of the electronic components and the conductor pattern designed for a full realisation of the electronic functions. Conversely, the design of the conductors must be adapted to the possibilities and limits of the processes to be used.

At the manufacturing stage the components as specified come together in the soldering machine under the selected process conditions. The solderability (wettability and thermal demand) of the parts to be connected should match the characteristics of the solder alloy, the soldering flux and the thermal load during soldering. Figure 1.1 shows these interactions in relation to the following process steps: assembly, flux application, preheating and soldering.

The time lapse between the date of manufacture of the components and the printed board on the one hand, and of the soldering operation on the other can be considerable. Consequently, ageing effects associated with storage must be taken into account before embarking upon soldering.

Figure 1.2 shows the course of a production process for printed circuit assemblies. The total throughput time may easily exceed a period of one year because of the long storage and waiting times between the separate steps of the process. This renders feedback and in-line correction of inadequate earlier treatments nearly always impossible. The alternative is to specify the products on each step of the process in such a way that the later process steps can be carried out successfully. This implies forward specification instead of backward correction.

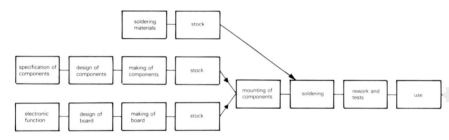

Fig. 1.2   Various steps in the production process in the manufacture of soldered printed board

Printed boards inhibiting intrinsic deficiencies from the soldering point of view lead to more or less systematic errors in soldering. When those employed in the production department are confronted with such boards, they will attempt to meet product quality requirements by modifying the process conditions of the soldering machine. However, even if the problems can be solved in this way, the result of modifying process conditions will be suboptimal at best. If such a state of affairs is permanently accepted, this implies suboptimal soldering quality and thereby inferior end products. With accurate forward specification, there is no need for these modifications.

The importance of the process parameters is often over-emphasised at the expense of the parameters of design of printed board and components, which have been shown statistically to be the dominant factors governing soldering quality. Therefore the major engineering effort should be directed towards the application of correct design of parts to be joined. In this way, a sound foundation can be laid for product effectiveness in that, from the start, printed board designs and components that are suspect (or even known to generate faults) can be avoided.

1.1.1.2 THE SOLDERING SYSTEM

Good soldering quality as a prerequisite for reliable joints is achievable only through a soldering process in which a great many variables both with respect to materials and to techniques have been optimised in an integrated system Thwaites]. This implies that, in design and manufacture, coherent measures are taken that are controlled systematically [Anon. Ref. 21]. Clearly, this is a matter of organisation and planning throughout the whole production period, which may last for more than a year (Figure 1.2).

A complete and coherent soldering system can only be set up successfully by combining knowledge, information, co-operation, specification and evaluation.

Knowledge

This comprises not only fundamental knowledge, but also knowledge about design possibilities and production methods. The existing gaps in knowledge are currently filled by the results of experimental work on soldering technology. Although research and development on specific details remain to be carried out, lack of knowledge is seldom the source of poor soldering results at the present time.

Information

The available knowledge, however, must be channelled to the relevant people in the form of manageable information, which is not a simple task.

Co-operation

The soldering system presupposes a fruitful co-operation between the various departments or companies participating in the work. Co-operation can only be achieved if the information needed is adequately distributed.

Specification

Specification of the soldering variables and process steps will assist in the proper organisation of the soldering system. Leading as it does to standardisation, specification at an early stage can prevent problems in soldering and will save subsequent additional and needless costs. It also makes it possible to evaluate whether delivered materials and components conform to intended quality requirements.

Evaluation

Evaluation implies incoming inspection, materials testing and final inspection. Solderability is an important property to examine, because it is not constant but decreases with time. Solderability and its susceptibility to decay are closely related to the thicknesses of electrodeposits on the parts to be soldered. However, a complete specification of layer thicknesses is not sufficient to guarantee solderability, because the electroplating processing also exerts its own influence. Therefore solderability testing cannot be dispensed with.

The implementation of specifications and standards will produce a positive response from suppliers. The initial extension of the testing activities can then be left increasingly to them. When, after some time and as a result of this delegation of responsibility, the suppliers' processes have been established at the correct level, it will be possible to reduce the test activities for the entire process. The extra costs of quality improvement will then be offset to a large extent.

In principle, more than one good solution exists to the problem of constructing an integrated soldering system, the particular choice itself being less important than the coherence of the measures involved. In isolation, each of the measures has limited significance. Only when employed jointly in a complete array with all other relevant provisions will the resulting integrated soldering system become a powerful means towards establishing reliable soldering.

The soldering system is completely undermined when attempts are made to obtain incidental price reductions by deviating from the requirements set out in the specifications or standards, *e.g.*, when using cheap components with poor solderability. The same can be said if the soldering process conditions are shifted outside the common operating range for the sake of only a few components.

1.1.2 Parameters of the Soldering System

In the soldering system each of the following items in the Section must be considered to ensure that the product will meet the required reliability level.

1.1.2.1. DESIGN

Components
  (i) dimensions and shapes (terminations, leadless);
 (ii) thermal demand (thermal adaptation);
(iii) resistance to soldering heat;
 (iv) sensitivity to static charges;
  (v) density of components on the board (vertical, horizontal mounting);
 (vi) packaging of components (reel, bulk).

Boards
  (i) configuration of components on the board;
 (ii) thickness of board (stiffness);
(iii) single-sided, double-sided, multilayer;
 (iv) pattern of conductors (electrical design);
  (v) thermal requirements and adaptations;
 (vi) hole plating and plating thickness;
(vii) hole flanging.

1.1.2.2 MATERIALS

Components
  (i) basis materials of terminations;
 (ii) solderable platings (tin, solder, noble metals);
(iii) electrodeposition, hot tinning;
 (iv) storage;
  (v) wettability (requirements, testing methods);
 (vi) whiskers.

Boards
  (i) choice of laminate materials;
 (ii) plating of conductors (under-etching, fusing, levelling);

iii) plating of end connectors;
iv) solder resist;
(v) surface resistivity;
vi) storage (preserving coating);
vii) conformal coating after soldering.

olsder Alloy
 (i) composition (melting point/range);
(ii) impurities;
iii) dissolution of plating materials;
iv) form (solid, flux-cored wire, cream, preforms).

luxes
 (i) type of flux (rosin type, water-washable type);
(ii) density and control of density;
iii) efficacy versus corrosion;
iv) corrosion testing;
 (v) cleanliness testing.

olvents
 (i) cleaning solvents;
(ii) environmental effects;
(iii) interaction with components.

.1.2.3 PROCESSES

Components
 (i) handling of components;
(ii) pre-bending of leads;
(iii) clinching of leads (insertion);
(iv) pretinning of terminations.

Boards
 (i) drying of double-sided boards with plated holes;
(ii) soldering jigs and aids;
(iii) stiffening strips on the boards.

Soldering
 (i) method and equipment (wave, drag, reflow, cutting);
(ii) conveyance and in-line arrangements;
(iii) process conditions (times, temperature);
(iv) fluxing method and preheating method;
 (v) flux removal method, if any;
(vi) application of solder in reflow soldering;
vii) dross formation, oil application;
viii) maintenance.

.1.2.4 INSPECTION AND REWORK

 (i) rework criteria;
(ii) rework facilities;

(iii) criteria for the final inspection;
(iv) testing of the final products.

1.1.3 Standardisation

Standards are indispensable for attaining controlled conditions in all parts of
soldering system and many companies have set up their own standards on variou
aspects of soldering. If this approach is followed consistently, standards can b
grouped together to cover an entire soldering system. A general coverage of a
soldering methods is too wide and therefore such groups of standards should b
restricted to specific systems, for instance the soldering of components with lead
to laminated printed boards provided with holes. The items to be covered in suc
a group of standards follow from Figure 1.1 and could include:

(i) design directives for joints and configuration of conductors;
(ii) requirements for solderability of the parts to be joined, both thermal
requirements and wettability requirements;
(iii) requirements for the materials used in the process, such as solder alloys,
fluxes and cleaning liquids;
(iv) soldering methods and soldering parameters;
(v) inspection criteria.

Apart from company standards, national and international standards hav
been drafted, but only for separate areas of soldering technology. The situation i
still rather confused because in many cases the differences between variou
national standards are quite substantial, even concerning apparently simpl
matters [Gamalski].

The international organisations for electronics are not well suited to coverin
an extended field of soldering technology. There exists no single authoritativ
organisation that has established general requirements for soldering [Becker]. Fo
instance, the IEC (International Electrotechnical Commission, Central Office i
Geneva, Switzerland) is split into Technical Committees for separate aspects
these committees working in their own fields with only tenuous links betwee
them. For soldering, the following Technical Committees and Sub-Committee
are the most significant: TC 40 for passive components, TC 47 fo
semiconductors, TC 48 for electromechanical parts, SC 50C for environmenta
testing methods including solderability, and TC 52 for printed boards. Each o
these committees gives recommendations for its specific group of components
including solderability requirements and resistance to soldering heat, but
systematic co-ordination of all recommendations to achieve an optima
connecting technique for these different components does not exist.

The CECC (Cenelec Electronic Component Committee, General Secretariat i
Frankfurt am Main, Germany), forming a part of CENELEC (Europea
Commission for Electrotechnical Standardisation), has as its aim the facilitatio
of international trade by harmonising the specifications and quality assessmen
procedures for electronic components. The CECC has adopted IEC publicatio
68 for environmental testing procedures, so that for solderability, for instance
IEC Publ. 68-2-20 [Spec. Ref. 1] applies.

In the IIW (International Institute of Welding, Central Bureau in Paris

France) soft soldering is also dealt with, but with a much wider scope than simply soldering for mass production in electronics.

Currently, ISO Standards exist in draft form, but so far these cover only a part of the technology for electronics. In 1980 work was started in IIW to co-ordinate the separate fields of soldering and to promote relevant ISO standards.

At national level many National Standards are available, prominent among them being the American MIL standards, some of which are mentioned in the following chapters.

Institutes such as the ITRI (International Tin Research Institute, London, UK) and the IPC (Institute for Interconnecting and Packaging Electronic Circuits, Evanstown, Ill., US) have contributed valuable documents on various items.

Finally, it should be made perfectly clear that specification and standardisation must not be allowed to cause needless rigidity in the technology.

1.1.4 Reliability of Soldering

Two meanings of the word 'reliability' are used in connection with soldering:

(i) the reliability of the soldered joints in terms of life-expectancy of soldered and reworked products. Part of Chapter 8 deals with joint design, related to strength and life-expectancy of joints;

(ii) the reliability of the soldering process, related to the amount of rework that is necessary to bring the product within the required specification after the product has been subjected to the actual soldering operation. Aspects of inspection and rework are discussed in Chapter 12.

The two types of reliability are connected since an inverse relationship exists between the amount of rework during production and the quality level ultimately reached. Improving the soldering process is accompanied by an enhancement of product quality. This is a clear case in which spending money on prevention is more prudent than spending money on cure.

1.2 BASIC ASPECTS OF THE SOLDERING PROCESS

The various mass-soldering processes all have their own particular characteristics. They differ in the way in which the solder flux and the solder alloy are applied to the parts to be joined and in the manner by which the heat is supplied. Despite these differences, each soldering process must meet a number of basic prerequisites in order to produce good soldered joints. These basic aspects are illustrated in Figure 1.3 where they are placed in a central position. They derive from the basic knowledge on soldering, and have definite implications for the design and manufacture of the products to be soldered. In many cases the basic aspects have been worked out as specifications or standards with which design and manufacture should comply.

The electronic design, the hardware design and the manufacturing process together determine the end product. Co-ordination throughout the entire design and production period is imperative for success.

Sections 1.2.1 to 1.2.5 deal briefly with the basic aspects of soldering processes, whilst the ensuing chapters go into more detail.

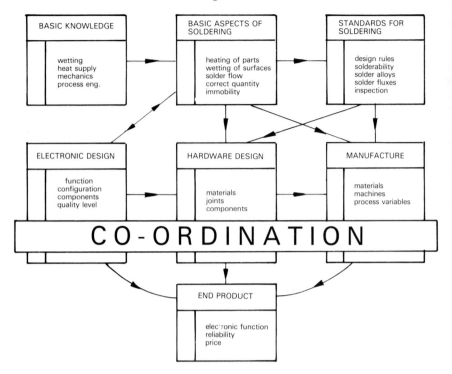

Fig. 1.3 Diagram showing the interrelation of the basic aspects of soldering processes with design and manufacture.

1.2.1 Heating

From the thermal point of view the soldering process must satisfy two conflicting requirements:

(i) the surface to be soldered must be sufficiently hot to permit wetting by the solder;

(ii) the components to be soldered should not be heated to a temperature at which they will be damaged.

Many examples exist in which, on the face of it, the wetting properties of the surfaces are insufficient, but where a detailed analysis reveals that the thermal conditions are to blame.

The thermal design must be such that the solder flowing to the area to be soldered does not cool down so rapidly that solder flow is impaired before the joint has been effected. This is part of the thermal aspect of solderability called 'thermal demand', which is discussed in Chapter 7. Further, the heat considerations lead to an area of operation for specific soldering processes between a minimum and maximum heating time and soldering temperature. Various thermal aspects are discussed extensively in Chapter 3.

1.2.2   Wetting of Surfaces

The metal surfaces to be joined must exhibit good wettability. They must be so clean that metallic contact can be established between solder and metal to be soldered, as will be discussed in Chapter 2. The component with poorest wettability determines the activity of the flux to be used and hence has a strong effect upon the whole soldering technology, because corrosion risks, requirements for washing after soldering, *etc.*, are closely associated with it (see Chapter 5).

If wettability is insufficient, soldering engineers tend to increase the flux activity and the soldering temperature despite the known risks. Technologically speaking, this is not necessary. There are well known methods for obtaining metal surfaces that are readily wettable by solder at normal soldering temperatures using only mildly activated fluxes. Solderable metallic coatings which serve this purpose are discussed in Chapter 6.

The wettability of many parts has been greatly improved during recent decades with the result that nowadays this need not be the major problem in soldering. Consequently, more attention can be paid to the other aspects of soldering, in particular to those related to joint design. It is important to maintain a high level of wettability by selecting appropriate metals and solderable coatings, and by applying approved materials processing. The level of wettability is verified by performing suitable tests for which established procedures exist. Wettability is one aspect of solderability, assessment of the latter relating to components and boards being discussed in detail in Chapter 7.

It is the task of the component manufacturer to ensure solderability and this is certainly achievable for nearly all parts to be soldered. Hence, wettability must be built in at an early stage in the component production process, if the circuit manufacturer is to avoid being forced to apply highly active, and thus corrosive, fluxes.

Wettability is an essential parameter of the complete soldering system shown in Figure 1.1, and one which cannot be left to chance.

1.2.3   Solder Flow

The solder must be brought into contact with both metal surfaces to be joined, and in addition the flow of the solder into the joint must be possible.

Extreme situations tend to arise here. In wave soldering the solder for the joint is obtained from a volume that is more than 10^7 times the joint volume, whilst in reflow soldering only a small amount of solder of predetermined volume is applied at or near the place where the joint is to be formed.

In the first case, the solder flow is influenced by the specific fluid dynamic characteristics of the soldering machine, to which further attention is devoted in Chapter 9. Once the liquid solder is in contact with the clean surfaces, any capillary gap is filled automatically with solder by capillary action. Hence the solder joint connections are made spontaneously, provided that in the set-up no trivial obstructions to solder flow are present, such as distorted boards, flux-vapour cushions and solder oxide skins. In reflow soldering, the solder has to flow over a small distance only, and this flow is influenced by the local configuration of the parts to be joined as well as by the temperature and the temperature distribution. Reflow soldering methods are discussed in Chapter 10 in which special emphasis is placed on the heating of the parts to be connected.

1.2.4 Adequate Quantity of Solder

The soldered joints must retain the correct amount of solder. In reflow soldering processes the amount of solder is chosen such that the correct amount is retained automatically in the joints. In processes like wave soldering the situation is much more complicated. On the one hand it is necessary for solder fillets to be formed of such a size that they bridge the spaces between the component leads and the solder lands, whereas on the other hand conductors intended to remain separate must not be allowed to be connected by bridges. This is largely determined by the shape of the solder lands and conductive pattern on the board, and to a lesser extent by the process conditions during soldering. Shape and volume of the soldered joints, given certain dimensions of the holes and solder lands, are the net result of an intricate interaction of surface tension and gravity, as is discussed in Chapter 2.

For boards with plated holes the capillary rise between component leads and hole walls substantially promotes the formation of good joints. Holes without plating, however, only constitute a very short capillary space, so that here joints of a sufficient volume are obtained less readily.

The board design and configuration of conductors suitable for machine soldering are discussed in Chapter 8, where practical directives are given.

1.2.5 Immobility of Parts During Solidification of the Solder

Although solidification is a rapid phenomenon its duration cannot be neglected in practical soldering. During the solidification period, liquid and solid solder are simultaneously present. Fluidity strongly decreases as solidification progresses. Consequently, any motion imparted to the soldered joint during solidification is liable to cause cracks in the solder mass that will not be filled again and this results in an unreliable joint.

The lifting force exerted by liquid solder is the sum of the buoyancy force and the surface tension, whereby the latter is many times larger than the former. The total lifting force experienced by the component termination provided it has not been wetted amounts to approximately 10^{-3}N. The force of 10^{-3}N per termination is just sufficient to lift (partially unseat) a transistor (0,3 g) via its terminations. As soon as the terminations have been wetted, the surface tension will pull the component downwards again.

Chapter 2

WETTING OF SURFACES

Wetting is an essential prerequisite for soldering, and therefore will be
scussed from various points of view throughout several chapters. Wetting
coming wet), in this case, means that a specific interaction takes place between
e liquid solder and the solid surface of the part to be soldered. When a solid
tallic piece is immersed in a bath of liquid solder, there is of course contact
tween the piece and the liquid solder, but this does not automatically imply
tting, as a barrier may be present. This can only be seen if the piece is
thdrawn from the solder: does the solder flow off completely or not?
Wetting is possible only if the solder can come into immediate contact with the
tallic surface of the solid metal part; then sufficient attraction is ensured. Any
mly adhering contamination such as oxides on the surface to be soldered will
t as a barrier to metallic continuity and thus prevent wetting. A drop of solder
a contaminated surface behaves in the same way as an isolated drop of water
a greasy plate (Figure 2.1).

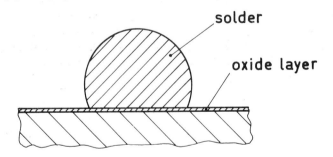

Fig. 2.1 Drop on oxidised plate; the solder does not wet.

The kind of joint in which an oxide layer is still present between the base metal
d the solder is obtained if one works at too low a temperature. Such joints are
lled cold joints. The electrical conductance of these is rather poor, because the
rrent has to pass through the more or less insulating oxide film. Adhesion is
o poor, and after solidification the solder drop can easily loosen when
bjected to mechanical load.
If the surfaces are clean and their metal atoms are thus positioned immediately
the interface, wetting takes place and the solder flows across the surface. This
uation is shown in Figure 2.2. The solder atoms are now able to come so close
the atoms of the base metal that they are attracted and will form an alloy at the

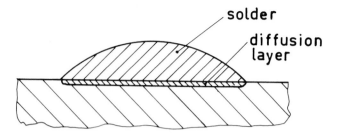

Fig. 2.2   Drop on clean plate; the solder spreads while a diffusion layer grows at the interface

interface, which ensures good electrical contact and good adhesion. The formation of alloy at the interface makes it impossible for the situation before wetting to be recovered.

2.1 SURFACE TENSIONS

The extent to which a liquid solder will spread across a surface, or flow into a gap between two or more surfaces, depends among other things on the surface tensions acting between the interfaces involved. For a good understanding of the soldering process some knowledge of these surface tensions is essential. This Chapter deals with the surface tensions in so far as they are relevant for soldering, but further discussions can be found in textbooks on physical chemistry [Adamson, Murr, Partington].

2.1.1 The Concept of Surface Tension

The surface tension of a liquid, γ_l, is a thermodynamic quantity, and is equal to the amount of work needed to enlarge (isothermally) the liquid surface area. According to this definition, the surface tension has the dimensions of energy per unit area (J/m^2). From thermodynamics it is known that a system strives to a minimum value of its free energy, and hence to a minimum surface area. A floating droplet therefore assumes the shape of a sphere, because this shape has the minimum surface area at a given volume. This tendency to reduce the surface area implies that there exists a pressure difference, ΔP, between the two sides of a curved surface:

$$\Delta P = \gamma_l \left(\frac{1}{R_1} + \frac{1}{R_2} \right),$$

(Equation 2.1)

R_1 and R_2 being the two radii of curvature. A radius is taken as positive when it lies inside the liquid (see Chapter 2.4.2). The surface tension, γ_l, is not a function of R, as long as R is much greater than the interatomic distance. Equation 2.1 is known as the Equation of Laplace.

For a sphere it is found that: $\Delta P = \dfrac{2\gamma_l}{R}$

For a droplet of tin-lead solder with a surface tension of 0,4 J/m^2 and a radius of 1 mm, the pressure in the solder in excess of the atmospheric pressure is:

$$\Delta P = \frac{2\gamma_l}{R} = \frac{2 \times 0,4}{10^{-3}} \approx 10^3 \, \text{N/m}^2 = 10^{-2} \, \text{atm.}$$

A column of liquid within a vertical capillary tube has a curved upper surface, the meniscus. When the liquid has risen above the level of the undisturbed surface, i.e., when the tube has been wetted by the liquid, the meniscus is concave.

If the radii of curvature of the meniscus are assumed to be equal to the inner radius R of the tube, the pressure difference across the meniscus is:

$$\Delta P = -\frac{2\gamma_l}{R}$$

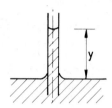

The pressure in the liquid is negative with respect to the 'air', because the radii are outside the liquid. This negative liquid pressure is the hydrostatic underpressure in the liquid, $\varrho g y$, in which ϱ is the liquid density, g is the acceleration of gravity and y the height of the column.

Hence: $$y = \frac{2\gamma_l}{\varrho g R}$$ (Equation 2.2)

For liquid solder, the capillary rise is approximately:

$$y = \frac{2 \times 0,4}{8000 \times 9,8 \times R} \approx \frac{10^{-5}}{R}$$

For a 1 mm hole, y is 2×10^{-2} m $= 20$ mm.

Equation 2.2 can not be used for an accurate measurement of γ_l because in reality the liquid surface is not a precise hemisphere and a small correction of the equation is necessary. The profile of the meniscus is identical to the profile of the sessile drop inverted.

The concept of surface tension applies not only to liquid surfaces but also to solid surfaces and liquid-solid interfaces. A solid surface cannot be changed as easily as a liquid one, but even a solid surface tries to minimise its area (ignoring the complication that the surface tension of solid materials is anisotropic). This fact is observed at high temperatures when the shape of a solid body may change without any external force being applied. An example of the influence of surface tension on solid surfaces is the sintering of a powder mass, where the driving force for the movement of the atoms finds its origin in the tendency to reduce the surface area.

In all considerations it is necessary to distinguish between three surface tensions:

γ_l – surface tension of the liquid
γ_s – surface tension of the solid
γ_{ls} – surface tension of the liquid-solid interface

The values of γ_s and γ_l should be well defined, for instance, as being valid in an atmosphere of saturated vapour of the relevant material. For metals, these circumstances are difficult to obtain. γ_s and γ_l are therefore often measured in argon, hydrogen, a vacuum, *etc.*, and for soft solders in liquid flux in contact with air. More details on measuring methods for surface tension can be found in the literature [Flint, White].

2.1.2 Equilibrium Shape of Droplets

Figure 2.3 shows the well-known situation of a liquid-solder droplet on a solid surface. When the gravity is negligible, which is the case with small droplets, the shape of the droplet is determined solely by the three surface tensions. As, with this assumption, the pressure is the same everywhere in the liquid, the curvature according to Equation 2.1 is constant along the liquid surface and the shape is therefore that of a spherical cap.

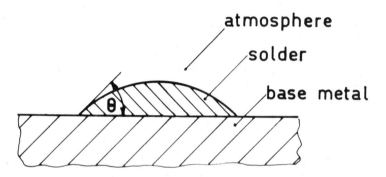

Fig. 2.3 Droplet on a flat surface. The assumption of a flat interface does not represent the ultimate equilibrium situation, but is still sufficiently accurate for considerations on soldering.

As every system tends towards minimum free energy, the areas of the interfaces and the free surfaces tend to become as small as possible. In doing so, however, they counteract one another, the reduction of one area leading to the enlargement of another. The droplet selects that shape for which the total surface free energy, $F_{surface}$, has its minimum value:

$$F_{surface} = \gamma_s \times (\textit{solid surface area}) + \gamma_{ls} \times (\textit{interfacial area}) + \gamma_l \times (\textit{liquid spherical area}).$$

From this condition can be obtained (see Appendix 2.4.1):

$$\gamma_{ls} + \gamma_l \cos \theta = \gamma_s \qquad \text{(Equation 2.3)}$$

This is known as Young's equation. The angle θ is called the contact angle. The contact angle so defined is an equilibrium value found on a perfectly smooth solid surface, with both droplet and base material consisting of homogeneous and continuous matter. The equation, first expressed in words in 1805 [Young], is

ostly obtained with the help of a force-vector diagram, in which only the
rizontal components are considered. Though this derivation is correct, it
nnot easily be understood how these 'forces' should operate on the material at
: edge of the drop. The equilibrium shape as a result of minimum surface free
ergy can, however, be understood quite readily.

It should be realised that the shape of Figure 2.3 is the result of a calculation in
ich it was assumed that gravity could be ignored and that the solid surface is
t [Brando *et al*]. In practice, the solid material will dissolve in the molten
der and the final equilibrium shape will always tend towards that of Figure 2.4,
ice this has a still lower total surface free energy. Final equilibrium is often not
ched because of the slow rate of dissolution and diffusion. In most cases the
umption that the surface is flat holds fairly well, as does Young's equation.

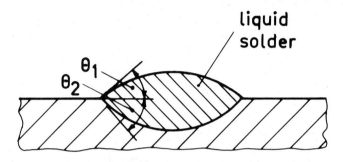

ig. 2.4   Surface tensions in equilibrium. For this case the equation is: $\gamma_s = \gamma_l \cos \theta_1 + \gamma_{ls} \cos \theta_2$.

f the gravity cannot be neglected, the shape of the liquid becomes more
mplicated: a flattened sphere cap. The contact angle θ is the same because
uation 2.3 is still valid [McNutt *et al*], as the equilibrium conditions at the
ee-phase boundary do not depend on gravity. The precise shape of a flattened
op is obtained by numerical calculation (see Section 2.2.5).

From Equation 2.3 it is clear that wetting, *i.e.*, a small contact angle θ is
omoted by small values of γ_l and γ_{ls} in combination with a relatively large value
γ_s.

The surface tensions of oxides are distinctly lower than the values for the
responding metals [Bondi]. An effective reaction of a flux with the oxide
a solid surface causes an increase of the surface tension γ_s by removal of the
ide, hence promoting wetting. Thus, as a rule it is impossible to wet the surface
a solid metal as long as it is oxidised. However, the effect of removal of the
ide film from molten solder is not so clear: a decrease of γ_l is favourable for
tting. On the one hand it is found experimentally that oxidised solder gives a
ger spread than unoxidised solder [Tabelev *et al*], but on the other hand
re is a reduction of γ_l under the influence of fluxes (see Chapter 4.3.2).

any case, the influence of γ_s in general dominates that of γ_l, because its
gnitude is much larger. The solid oxide skins on the molten solder may hamper
reading and correct flow of the solder, with the result that in soldering practice
mplete oxide removal must always be the goal.

For a discussion of the soldering process it is insufficient to take into account
ly the values of γ_s and γ_l. One has also to consider the magnitude of γ_{ls}
awakatsu *et al*]. This is, for example, demonstrated by the wetting of iron

by silver or copper [Klein Wassink]. It is known that iron is extremely w▪
wetted by copper but is poorly wetted by silver at temperatures of about 5C
above their melting points. The γ_s of iron is $\sim 1,95$ J/m^2, the γ_l of silver is 0
J/m^2 and the γ_l of copper is 1,3 J/m^2. From these values one would expect
better wetting of iron by silver than by copper. From Equation 2.3, it mu▪
therefore be concluded that here the interfacial tension makes an essenti▪
contribution to the wetting behaviour. The importance of γ_{ls} is too oft▪
underrated.

Depending on the magnitude of the surface tensions, it is possible to fir▪
values of θ between 0° and 180°, respectively, for complete wetting and for no
wetting. Of course, it is possible that $\gamma_s - \gamma_{ls} > \gamma_l$ and evidently then $\theta = 0$. ▪
this case, the liquid column in a capillary remains at $y = 2\gamma_l/\varrho g R$, b▪
nevertheless the wall of the capillary becomes completely wetted, because it
now energetically more favourable for the liquid surface area to be enlarged th▪
for the height of the column to be increased.

It is worth realising that in the wetting of metals by molten solder a conta▪
angle $\theta = 0$ is not a normal situation. This is clearly demonstrated, for instanc▪
by the experimental results for the Wetting Reference Forces in the wettin▪
balance (see Table 7.1).

2.1.3   The Origin of Surface Tension

The surface tension of a surface is determined by the interatomic bond energi▪
of the atoms. In the bulk of a liquid metal each atom has about 12 neighbou▪
and the total internal energy may be considered as a summation of the▪
interatomic bond energies. The atoms in the surface layer possess a high▪
potential energy than the bulk atoms, because they are incompletely surrounde
by the other atoms. If the surface area is enlarged, more atoms take up a positio▪
on the surface at the expense of an increasing energy. The bond energy of th▪
atoms is closely related to the heat of vaporisation; to evaporate an atom all i▪
bonds with neighbouring atoms have to be broken. To bring an atom from th▪
bulk into the surface layer, a proportion of the bonds of this atom have to b▪
broken, and thus there is a relationship between the heat of vaporisation and th▪
surface tension. The strength of the interatomic bonds is also reflected in th▪
melting point. Indeed, in general, the metals with high melting points have hig▪
surface tensions.

At the interface of two metals the atoms have two types of bonds: bonds wit▪
atoms of their own kind and bonds with atoms of the other metal. It depends o▪
the various metal-metal bond energies whether these interfacial atoms have▪
higher or a lower energy than the bulk atoms. The higher the energy of the▪
atoms at the interface, the higher the interfacial tension [see also Miedema *et al*▪

The same metal-metal bonds determine to what extent the two metals a▪
mutually soluble in the solid state. The greater the solubility of these metals, th▪
lower will be the interfacial tension between them. This can be seen in th▪
example of the wetting of iron by liquid copper or liquid silver. Iron and copp▪
are mutually soluble to about 5 (atomic) per cent, whilst iron and silver ar▪
practically insoluble in each other. The interfacial tension between iron an▪
copper is notably lower than that between iron and silver, *viz.* about 0,3 and 1,▪
J/m^2.

The aforementioned arguments apply to systems that do not form intermetallic compounds. In soldering, frequent use is made of systems in which intermetallics occur. The occurrence of these compounds means that there exists a strong affinity between the atoms involved. The great stability of such compounds is demonstrated by their high melting points in comparison with the melting points of the pure elements. The occurrence of intermetallics evidently implies that dissimilar atoms 'attract' each other more than do similar ones. If intermetallics are formed at the interface the interfacial energy should consequently be relatively low. In the case of the well known tin-lead solder alloys, wetting is promoted by the tin, which forms intermetallic compounds with the copper base metal. Pure lead is hardly ever used as a solder because it does not wet, but addition of a few per cent of tin may suffice to make a solder that can actually be applied in practice.

The spreading can be studied by melting a given amount of solder on a small plate of copper. The maximum area of spread, *i.e.*, the lowest value of the contact angle θ, is found with alloys containing about 50 per cent tin by mass, depending on the conditions [Bailey *et al*]. Incidentally, this happens to be close to the eutectic composition. On measuring γ_l of the tin-lead alloys, it is observed that addition of lead lowers γ_l. The calculation of the interfacial tension from measured values of γ_l, γ_s and θ shows that γ_{ls} becomes smaller with a higher tin content. By adding lead the value of γ_{ls} is increased, but this is overcompensated by the decrease in γ_l until about 50 per cent lead is added. Apparently, the finding that maximum spread occurs at about the eutectic composition suggests a relationship between eutectic melting and wetting behaviour. However, such a relationship does not exist.

If the solder penetrates into a gap, quite different mechanisms are involved. The change in free surface energy per unit area in this case is given by $\gamma_s - \gamma_{ls}$ and now γ_l has no influence, because the liquid surface area does not change. The maximum penetration rate of tin-lead alloys into a horizontal gap is found at 100% tin. This confirms that in fact γ_{ls} is lowest for 100% tin [Lashko *et al*]. This example clearly demonstrates that wettability tests with droplets on plates are insufficient to predict real wetting behaviour in soldering practice, where diverse geometrical circumstances are involved. Therefore, the wetting properties of a solder alloy cannot be deduced from one single test method. The viscosity of tin-lead alloys is hardly influenced at all by the mixing ratio, and therefore is not a factor in the wetting phenomenon.

2.1.4 Effect of Surface Roughness and Grooves

Suppose that the real solid surface area is larger by a factor f than the apparent geometrical area, because of the roughness of the surface. Equation 2.3 must then be modified:

$$f(\gamma_s - \gamma_{ls}) = \gamma_l \cos\nu$$

in which ν is the apparent contact angle. When the contact angle on the completely smooth surface with the same wetting properties would be θ, it is found that $\cos\nu = f\cos\theta$. This means that when θ is smaller than 90°, $\nu<\theta$ and thus the solder will spread more on a rough surface than on a smooth surface, which is in accord with experimental findings.

The influence of surface roughness, discussed in this way, is rather theoretical, and it should not be overlooked that the kind of roughness is also important. Grooves on horizontal plates act as capillaries lengthwise and the spreading will only stop when the solder has been fully consumed. Grooves that are perpendicular to the direction of spreading will act as barriers, because in every groove a position may be found where the contact angle assumes a critical value. The spreading in sidewise direction is especially hampered when the hills between the grooves have sharp edges. In such situations the spreading depends on the local profile and no general rules can be given. In practice, the spreading will no longer increase if the surface roughness is increased above 150 μm (60 Ru).

The height up to which a vertical groove in a plate is fully wetted can be determined from a modified version of Equation 2.2, in which R is replaced by R_e, an equivalent radius [Bressler]. For semi-circular grooves or triangular grooves with an apical angle of about 90°, R_e is about 2,5 times the depth of the grooves. When the grooves are sharper, R_e is smaller: at 60° apex angle, R_e is equal to the depth; at 30°, 0,35 times.

The grooves and roughness in the surface may cause the contact angle to show hysteresis. When the solder spreads, a larger contact angle value is observed than when the solder recedes: these are called the advancing and receding angle respectively. The local angle θ determines the equilibrium at the edge of the droplet, but an apparent angle, v, with respect to the average plane through the surface can be observed.

2.1.5 Equilibrium Conditions

The discussions on the surface tensions are based on the assumption that the wetting parameters do not change; in other words that the values of the surface tensions are constant. In soldering practice this is not true for several reasons:

(i) a copper surface that has been wetted by solder will never become a clean copper surface again, because a diffusion layer has been formed. So, for the spreading, the surface tensions of the interface, the liquid solder and the solid copper apply, but, for the receding, the latter is no longer valid and must be replaced by the surface tension of alloyed copper with an intermetallic layer on it;

(ii) the surface tension of the solder may alter, because during soldering, elements of the base metal dissolve in the liquid solder, thus changing the solder composition;

(iii) during soldering, the flux performs its cleaning action by which the surface (and thus the prevailing surface tensions) change. If the flux becomes exhausted or flows away, reoxidation takes place, again changing the wetting conditions;

(iv) in each soldering operation in practice considerable temperature gradients exist. The situation of thermal equilibrium, in fact, is seldom found because the soldering operation is completed in most cases before the equilibrium temperature is reached. If temperature gradients are present the liquid solder tends to flow in the direction of the highest temperature because in general at higher temperatures the surface tensions are smaller (Marangoni effect [Scriven *et al*]). Sometimes this effect can be used in practice if a long and narrow gap has to be filled with solder

Unfortunately, in many real soldering situations the temperature gradients have the wrong direction as, for instance, with plated holes which must be filled with solder.

An extreme case of change of conditions is provided by the phenomenon of dewetting: the conditions originally favour a complete wetting, but after some time they change, thus rendering the solder coating unstable.

2.2 CONTOURS OF LIQUID-SOLDER SURFACES

The following pages deal with the profiles of some surfaces relevant for soldering. The calculation of these curves is based on a combination of the Laplace equation (Equation 2.1) and the equation for hydrostatic pressure: $P = -\varrho g \Delta y$. Height and curvature are thus simply related. For simple shapes, the profile can be calculated analytically, but for more complicated situations there is no analytical solution and the calculation must be done numerically (see Appendix 2.4.2). The result of the calculation is the contour of a liquid that is in mechanical equilibrium. This contour is stable if it represents a situation of minimum energy with regard to small changes of the profile at a constant volume [Inoya *et al*, Majumdar *et al*, Pitts].

2.2.1 A Plate Dipped in Solder

When the solder wets a plate which is dipped vertically into it, the meniscus will be curved upwards against the plate. For this two-dimensional problem, a solution was given by Rayleigh before 1900. Figure 2.5 shows the profile curve known as 'elastica'; an elastically looped wire with the ends pulled apart displays this shape (Figure 2.6).

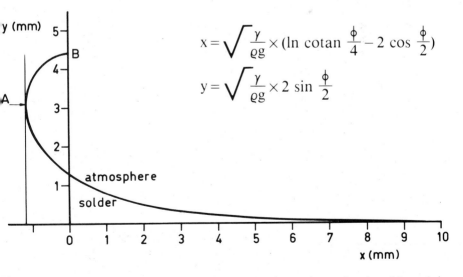

$$x = \sqrt{\frac{\gamma}{\varrho g}} \times (\ln \cotan \frac{\phi}{4} - 2 \cos \frac{\phi}{2})$$

$$y = \sqrt{\frac{\gamma}{\varrho g}} \times 2 \sin \frac{\phi}{2}$$

Fig. 2.5 The 'elastica' curve for liquid solder. The Equations for x and y as a function of the angle ϕ are shown. ϕ is the angle between the curve and the x-axis.

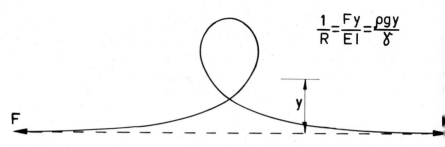

Fig. 2.6   The elastica. This curve is produced if the ends of the looped wire are pulled apart. Th mechanical stiffness of the wire, *EI*, is equivalent to the surface tension, γ, and the force, *F*, equivalent to the density of the solder, ϱg.

The parameter representation of the curve, given in Figure 2.5, shows th characteristic parameter for solder profiles, $\sqrt{\frac{\gamma}{\varrho g}}$. The specific combination of ϱ and g under the root can be easily obtained by dimensional analysis. Taking fc liquid solder $\gamma \cong 0,4$ J/m² and $\varrho = 8000$ kg/m³, one obtains $\sqrt{\frac{\gamma}{\varrho g}} = 2,2 \times 10^{-3}$m. is interesting to note that the dimensions of the contours of molten solder and c water at room temperature are almost the same, because their values of $\sqrt{\frac{\gamma}{\varrho g}}$ ar about equal.

The angle φ between the elastica and the x-axis ranges from:

$\phi = 0°$ at $x = \infty$ and $y = 0$, to
$\phi = 90°$ for $x = -1,2$ mm and $y = 3,1$ mm in point A, to
$\phi = 180°$ for $x = 0$ and $y = 4,4$ mm in point B.

(If the elastica is rotated about the x-axis, point B will coincide wit $x = -2\sqrt{\frac{\gamma}{\varrho g}} = -4,4$ mm; point A will coincide with $x = -2,5$ mm).

At $\phi = 90°$, the pressure in the solder is:

$\Delta P = -\varrho gy = -2,6 \times 10^2$ N/m² ($= 2,6 \times 10^{-3}$ atm), and the radius of curvatur $R^{90} = \frac{\gamma}{\Delta P} = -1,6$ mm (the radius is outside the solder; the superscript refers to th angle φ).

The horizontal extension of the lifted solder is about 10 mm (in practice).

If the contact angle $\theta = 0°$ and the plate is vertical, the solder rises 3,1 mm ($\phi = 90°$) (Figure 2.7a). If the plate is inclined towards the solder, φ will be greate than 90° (Figure 2.7b). The maximum height the solder can reach is 4,4 mr ($\phi = 180°$). For $\phi > 180°$, the curve is the mirror image around $x = 0$; $\phi > 180°$ i unstable.

If the contact angle, θ,, is not zero, a vertical plate will be wetted to a heigh that follows from $\phi = 90° - \theta$, (Figure 2.7c, see also Figure 2.10 for wire wit infinite radius). The profile for the region of smaller φ values remains of cours unchanged.

The area under the profile can be calculated to be $\frac{\gamma}{\varrho g} \sin \phi$. For a vertical plat

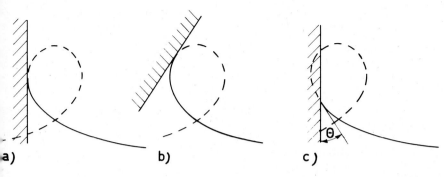

Fig. 2.7   Profiles of solder against a plate: (a) for vertical plate with θ = zero; (b) for inclined plate with θ = zero; (c) for vertical plate with a certain value of θ.

and θ = 0°, hence φ = 90°, the mass of solder per metre width is $\frac{\gamma}{g}$ kg, and so the vertical force on the plate is γ N/m.

During machine soldering of printed boards there is full contact between the board surface and the molten solder. The solder must then come away from the board, which happens via a series of metastable transition states. This may become clear from an example given in Figure 2.8. Two cases are presented in which a wetted metallic strip, typically a conductor, is lifted from a solder bath. On the left, the strip is wider than 2,4 mm; on the right, narrower. In both cases four equilibrium liquid shapes are shown, taken from the elastica of Figure 2.5. When on the left the angle φ reaches 180°, the maximum height is found. If the strip is lifted further the solder must break. On the right, the two curves meet and the solder breaks before the height of 4,4 mm is attained.

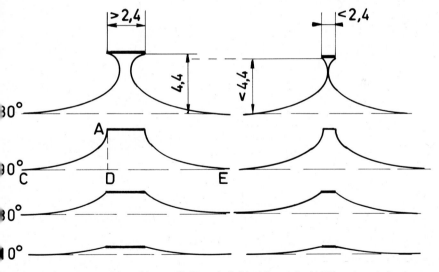

Fig. 2.8   Various stages of the solder profile if a strip is lifted from a bath. When the strip is narrower than 2,4 mm, the elastica curves meet before the complete curves have been formed. To the left the values of φ have been given at the place of contact between profile and strip.

A great part of the curve, however, is not stable but metastable, because the curved elastica is longer than the spanned horizontal distance. For instance, for φ = 90°, the curve C – A is 1,3 mm longer than the horizontal distance C – D. Hence, with a strip narrower than 1,3 mm, the unlifted horizontal liquid D – E plus the strip together are shorter than the two elasticas. With a strip narrower than 1,3 mm, the

lifted solder is metastable and can break, for instance, starting from an initiation site on the st
somewhere outside the plane of the drawing. For $\phi = 90°$ the minimum stable strip width is 1,3 mm, a
for $\phi = 180°$ it is 4,4 mm.

It is clear that the breaking of the solder is a complex phenomenon, which in a real solderi
operation will depend on specific details of the actual configuration, like conductor shape and proc
conditions. The passage through the metastable intermediate states ending in the final breaking of t
solder is important, because during these steps the volume of the soldered joints and the occurrence
bridges and other soldering defects are determined.

Attempts in the Author's laboratory to measure the breaking or to make motion pictures of it w
not satisfactory.

2.2.2 A Wire Dipped in Solder

This case is more complicated because there are now two radii of curvature
the solder surface, one on the outside of the solder rotating in the plane of t
drawing, R_1, and one inside the solder rotating in a plane perpendicular to t
plane of the drawing, R_2 (see Appendix 2.4.2). Some results from a numeric
calculation are shown in Figure 2.9, in which the line $x = 0$ represents the axis
the wire. From the Figure it can be seen that, with greater radius of the wire (
$\phi = 90°$), there is a higher rise of the solder. For an infinitely thick wire the cur
of Figure 2.5 is obtained.

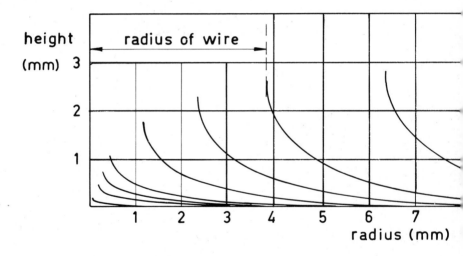

Fig. 2.9   Solder rise against wires of various diameters. The y-axis ($x = 0$) represents the axis of t
wire. The height and horizontal extension of the lifted solder decrease with the wire diameter.

If the contact angle between solder and wire is not 0°, but a certain value betwee
0° and 90°, the height of the solder against the wire is smaller (Figure 2.10).

Note: Figures 2.5 and 2.9 apply to solder which is lifted. If the solder is depressed as in the case
non-wetting the same Figures apply, but inverted. Compare also Figure 3.14.

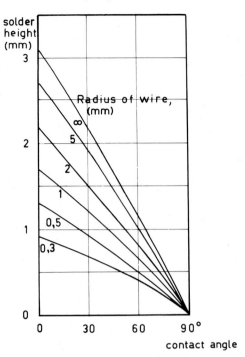

Solder rise against wires for the conditions $\gamma = 0{,}4$ J/m^2 and $\varrho = 8000$ kg/m^3. The line representing radius $= \infty$ is for the same case as given in Fig. 2.5.

,2.3 Perpendicular Plates

Consider a pair of connected plates, one vertical and one horizontal, with their ne of contact horizontal. If liquid solder is placed in the corner between the lates, which are assumed to be wetted by the solder ($\theta = 0°$), this solder will, epending on its volume, take a certain equilibrium shape in the corner Figure 2.11).

Considering first the case where the solder is placed above the horizontal plate. he maximum amount of solder that can be placed in the corner is the amount etermined by the elastica, with an area between the two plates and the solder rface of 4,8 mm^2. If more solder is added, this will flow away across the surface f the horizontal plate. For the elastica at $y = 0$ (the horizontal solder level), the ressure difference across the surface is zero, and the radius R is infinite ($\Delta P° = 0$; ie superscript refers to $\phi = 0$).

Of course, it is possible to place less solder than the amount of the elastica, roducing similar profile curves, with an angle of elevation also going from $\phi = 0°$ it $y = 0$) to $\phi = 90°$ (against the vertical plate). However, for these curves the ressure $\Delta P°$ is not zero, but has a certain negative value. Some curves are shown i the upper part of Figure 2.11, whilst the values for ΔP^{90} are indicated to lentify the curves.

In the second case, the solder is assumed to have been placed below the orizontal plate (lower part of Figure 2.11). The maximum area that is possible

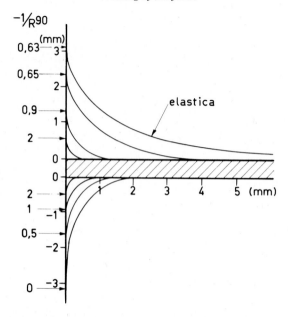

Fig. 2.11 Profile curves of solder in the corners of perpendicular plates (with their line of conta perpendicular to the paper at 0,0). Two sets of curves are shown: the upper set with solder above t horizontal plate and the lower set with solder below the horizontal plate. The curves are identified t the liquid pressure at the point of contact with the vertical plate. With one value of $\Delta P^{90} = -1/R^9$ the whole curve is completely determined.

for solder below the plate is for the curve with $-1/R^{90} = 0$. This area is 0,96 mm The maximum height of the curve relating to this maximum area is 3,1 mm, an the horizontal extension is 1,9 mm. The pressure at the indicated position at th vertical plate is just zero. The smaller curves have a negative pressure everywhe in the liquid. When more solder is added to the maximum volume this extr solder will flow down the vertical plate.

Finally, consider the case where there is solder above and below the horizont plate, with the two volumes in contact via a gap or a small hole in it. The tot volume of solder is distributed in such a way that the liquid pressures match. the horizontal plate is very thin, the maximum total cross-sectional area of th two matching curves is about 1,3 mm². Corresponding to the lower curve wit $-1/R^{90} = 0$, giving a maximum area below the plate of 0,96 mm², there is a upper curve with $-1/R^{90} \cong 0,9$ mm⁻¹. If more solder is added to the volume abov the horizontal plate it will flow down through the hole or gap and then furth down the vertical plate.

2.2.4   Fillets on a Wire

The contours of solder in the corner between plates (Figure 2.11) can b calculated analytically, but the case of axial symmetry, with a vertical wire and horizontal plate, can only be solved numerically (see Appendix 2.4.2).

Figure 2.12 shows the results of such calculations for solder in the corne between a wire with a diameter of 0,6 mm and a horizontal plate. The paramete

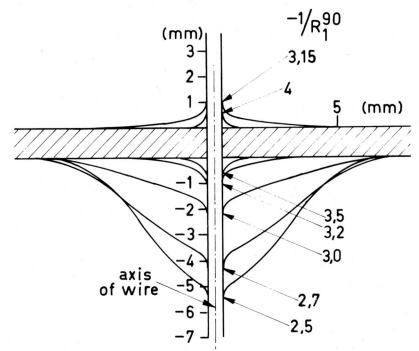

Fig. 2.12 Profile curves of solder in the corners of a vertical wire (0,6 mm) and a horizontal plate. Compare Fig. 2.11. The solder in the joint between the plate and the wire is called fillet. Note the differences in fillet sizes above and below the plate.

of the curves is the value of $-1/R_1^{90}$, indicated in the Figure (for all curves R_2^{90} = the radius of the wire = 0,3 mm).

The curves extend from $\phi = 0°$ on the horizontal plate to $\phi = 90°$ against the wire, assuming that the contact angle θ is zero.

As before, the spaces in the corners above and below the horizontal plate are first considered separately.

The solder fillet above the plate with the maximum volume (or area in the Figure) has a value of $-1/R_1^{90} = 3,15$ mm^{-1}, and a height of about 0,9 mm. It is the same contour as obtained with a wire dipped in a solder bath (Figure 2.9). The horizontal extension of this contour is infinitely large. Fillets with larger values of the parameter $-1/R_1^{90}$ rapidly become very small.

The fillets below the plate, with a parameter value larger than 3,5, are also very small, but with decreasing value of $-1/R_1^{90}$ the dimensions of these fillets grow rapidly. Between 2,5 and 3 all lower fillets have a diameter at the horizontal plate of about 14 mm. The maximum lower fillet volume (175 mm^3) is reached for $-1/R_1^{90} = 2,5$. Larger volumes are not stable and hence cannot exist in reality.

In Figure 2.12 the horizontal plane is larger than the maximum diameter of the solder contour. If this is not so, as with solder lands on a printed board, the fillets will end on the periphery of the land at an angle with the horizontal which is not zero. Only a part of the full curve will then be present.

Now consider the case where the solder fillets above and below the horizontal plate are in contact via a hole in the plate, as applies to a plated hole in a printed board. The solder fillets on both sides of the board must assume such shapes that their volumes add up to the given total volume of solder (apart from the solder in the hole). At the same time their liquid pressures must match, that is to say the difference in liquid pressures in the upper and lower fillet must correspond to the difference in height ($\Delta P = \varrho g \Delta h$). If this is so, the upper fillets will always be smaller than the lower ones.

Table 2.1 contains quantitative data for fillets on boards, calculated for board thickness of 1,6 mm and various land diameters.

Table 2.1

Fillets on Double-Sided Boards

Pressure	Land Radius	Lower Fillet				Upper Fillet				
		0,5	1	1,5	2	0,5	1	1,5	2	mm
−100	max. radius	0,5	1	1,5	1,6	0,5	1	1,05	1,05	mm
	height	0,31	0,51	0,57	0,58	0,29	0,41	0,41	0,41	mm
	volume	0,04	0,27	0,52	0,53	0,04	0,17	0,17	0,17	mm³
0 N/m²	max. radius	0,5	1	1,5	2	0,5	1	1,35	1,35	mm
	height	0,34	0,59	0,71	0,83	0,31	0,47	0,48	0,48	mm
	volume	0,045	0,40	0,71	1,80	0,05	0,24	0,31	0,31	mm³
100	max. radius	0,5	1	1,5	2	0,5	1	1,5	1,8	mm
	height	0,36	0,66	0,90	1,22	0,33	0,52	0,60	0,66	mm
	volume	0,05	0,48	1,25	4,1	0,06	0,33	0,69	1,08	mm³

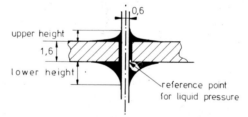

Form of the fillets around a wire on a board with a thickness of 1,6 mm. The dimensions are given in Table 2.1.

If solder is added to the fillets, the total volume will increase until the profile of the lower fillet is no longer stable and the extra solder flows down the wire. The maximum volume of the fillets is obtained when the lower fillet acquires a profile corresponding to $-1/R^{90} \cong 2,5$. Table 2.2 contains some data for maximum fillets on boards with a thickness of 1,6 mm (volume of solder in the hole not included).

Table 2.2

Maximum Sizes of Fillets

Radii of Lands	Lower Height	Upper Height	Pressure at Reference Point	Total Maximum Fillet Volume
1	0,8	0,6	266	1,0
1,5 mm	1,2 mm	0,8 mm	233 N/m²	3,5 mm³
2	1,7	0,83	193	8,9

After a wave or drag soldering process, the pressure at the underside of the board will be much smaller than the maximum values given in the Table; in many ases even negative. High, positive values for the pressure can be obtained if older preforms of a sufficient volume are applied.

From the Tables the following conclusions can be drawn:

(i)   if large fillets are desired, most of the solder is at the underside of the board, and it makes little sense to enlarge the land radii at the upperside;

(ii)   if small fillets are desired, the land radii at the underside of the board in particular should be limited.

The results in the preceding Tables were derived assuming the contact angle of e solder against the solid surfaces to be zero, *i.e.,* for the conditions of ideal etting. Similar calculations can be made for other contact angles. If the contact ngles at underside and upperside of the board are the same, the lower fillets are lways bigger than the upper ones.

On applying the solder as a preform at the upperside of the board the molten older flows downwards through the gap until matching fillets have been formed. ' in this case the wetting is not ideal, the result may be that at the upperside of e board the contact angle is the receding angle and at the underside of the board e contact angle is the advancing angle. If such a situation exists, the ratio of olumes of upper to lower fillets will be higher than given in the Table. In extreme ases, the upper height may even be greater than the lower height [Chu].

.2.5   Sessile Drops

Solder droplets having the same shape as those in Figures 2.1 to 2.3 are referred
 as 'sessile' drops. These droplets have been drawn as parts of spheres. This is
rrect provided the droplets are small. If the drop is large enough its top will be
attened owing to the effect of gravity. A numerical solution for this case was
btained in 1883 by Bashforth and Adams, who compiled extensive tables
Hartland *et al*].

In Figure 2.13 profiles are given which have been calculated by integration by

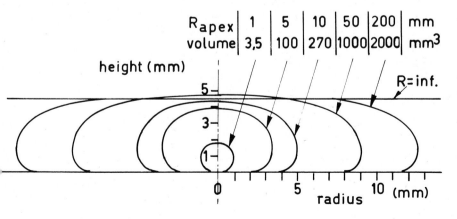

ig. 2.13   Sessile drops of molten solder on a flat surface, assuming that the contact angle is 180° (no wetting).

parts, for different values of the radii at the apex. (The volumes have also be[n]
given). When the radii at the apex are very large, the profile is the same as show[n]
in Figure 2.5, but inverted. It is interesting to note that the droplet height pass[es]
through a maximum of 4,7 mm when the apical radius is approximately 30 m[m]
with greater radii, the height falls to a value around 4,4 mm [see also Batra *et a*[l.]

The profile of the upper part of the sessile drop, inverted, is the same as t[he]
liquid profile in a wetted capillary. If the contact angle, θ, is smaller than 180[°]
only parts of the sessile drops of Figure 2.13 are present, namely the top par[t]
with φ<θ (see also Chapter 7.2.5).

For small drops, when the gravity can be neglected and the shape is a sphe[rical]
cap, the relations between the contact angle and the dimensions of the drop ca[n]
be calculated analytically (see Appendix 2.4.1).

Note: The word 'sessile' is borrowed from biology where it means 'stalkless'.

2.2.6   Drops on a Wire

A layer of liquid metal concentric around a cylinder, for instance solder on
copper wire, is unstable. The liquid solder will tend to ball together in droplet[s]
This is not dewetting, as it is in no way related to the contact angle. T[he]
formation of drops occurs because the total surface area then is lower than for
cylindrical shape, even when θ = 0. The instability depends on the dimension[s]
Thick layers on thin wires are very unstable.

If there is a drop on a wire and the gravity is ignored, the pressure inside t[he]
drop is given by:

$$\Delta P = \gamma \left(\frac{1}{R_1} + \frac{1}{R_2} \right),$$

and is the same everywhere in the drop. The profiles (unduloids) for selecte[d]
values of $\Delta P / \gamma$ can be calculated.

In Figure 2.14 some unduloids with cos θ = 1 have been drawn around a wi[re]
with a diameter D. The parameter in the Figure is a measure of the pressure insi[de]
the drop. With increasing pressure, *i.e.,* with smaller volumes, the lengths of t[he]
drops become smaller, but only until a limit of about 3,2 D is reached. Short[er]
drops thus cannot exist. If an unstable coating forms into droplets on the wir[e]
the incipient droplet already has a length of 3,2 D.

The liquid is transported from the cylindrical part of the wire to the incipie[nt]
drop, because in the drop the liquid pressure is lower than in the cylindrical laye[r]
When the drop grows in size, the pressure in the drop decreases further. The ra[te]
of droplet formation is determined by the pressure difference and the viscosit[y]
Droplets are not formed within a few seconds, unless the layers are thicker tha[n]
100 μm. When the layer is thin, the formation of drops is not likely because th[e]
flow is less easy in a thin layer and the solder must be transported over a long[er]
distance.

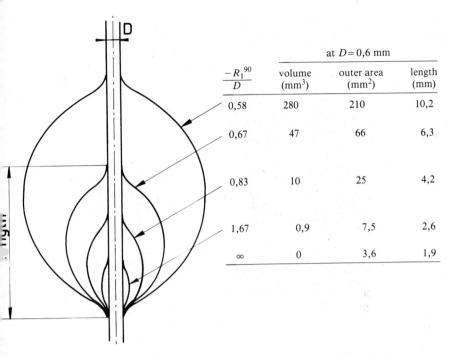

$-\dfrac{R_1{}^{90}}{D}$	at $D=0{,}6$ mm		
	volume (mm³)	outer area (mm²)	length (mm)
0,58	280	210	10,2
0,67	47	66	6,3
0,83	10	25	4,2
1,67	0,9	7,5	2,6
∞	0	3,6	1,9

Fig. 2.14 Drops on a wire, calculated ignoring the gravity. The smallest drop that can exist has a length of 3,2 *D*.

2.3 DEGREES OF WETTING

In the description of wetting, several terms are used when referring to the state of the solid surface after a soldering operation. The various states can be easily understood from an immersion test, in which molten solder covers the surface for a while before being drained off. One or more of the following appearances can then be observed:

(i) non-wetting: the surface becomes uncovered again, without any visible interaction with the solder. A copper surface retains its colour. Non-wetting occurs if the oxide film on the basis material is too thick to be removed by the flux applied, within the available time;

(ii) wetting: the molten solder is drained off, but a relatively thin layer of solder is retained, proving that metallic interaction has taken place. Perfect wetting is associated with a uniform, smooth, unbroken and adherent layer of solder to the basis material;

(iii) partial wetting: the surface has some regions showing wetting and other regions showing non-wetting. This case should not be confused with that in which a part of the solder remains fixed to its place on the surface, because it simply did not flow off sufficiently. Such a fixed layer can in most cases be peeled off. The contact angle provides evidence of real wetting at the boundaries of the wetted regions (Figure 2.15);

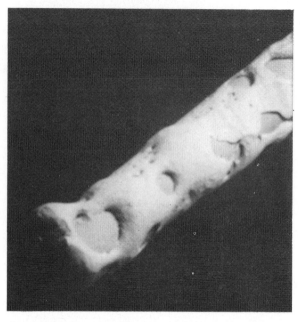

Fig. 2.15 Soldered monel lead showing partial wetting and a stuck layer of solder. Diameter of lead 0,6 mm, dipped in tin60-lead40 solder at 235°C, using activated rosin flux.

(iv) dewetting: the surface is initially wetted, but the solder then withdraws from part of the surface into droplets, while leaving a very thin layer of solder on the dewetted areas. A quantitative assessment of the degree of dewetting is often difficult, because the boundary between a wetted and a dewetted region is not sharply defined. Moreover, the dewetting is often unevenly distributed over the surface.

2.3.1 The Need for Flux

Even at the maximum solderability level of solderable metals, some flux is needed in the soldering process to produce the desired cleanliness of the surfaces to be soldered. The majority of metals, with the exception of the noble metals, show a strong tendency to form compounds with oxygen (from the atmosphere). This explains why common metals that are exposed to the air are rapidly covered with an oxide film, even at room temperature. On tin and copper a layer of about 2 nm is formed almost instantaneously. The oxides are removed by means of substances called fluxes, which are liquid at the soldering temperature and capable of reacting chemically with the oxides, and of dissolving or dispersing the reaction products.

Fluxes are applied before or during soldering and they cover both the base metal and the solder. This retards oxidation by oxygen from the atmosphere, which would otherwise occur even more strongly at soldering temperature. In areas where the oxide film has been removed, a direct metallic contact is established between solder and base metal, so that one single interface with low energy exists instead of the original two interfaces. From this point of contact the

older will spread (Figure 2.16). Upon removal of the oxide a clean metallic
surface is created beside the solder, this surface having a higher surface tension
than the previously oxidised metal.

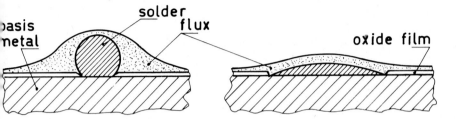

Fig. 2.16 Two stages of the spreading of a solder droplet on an oxidised base metal. Spreading
proceeds upon removal of the oxide layer under influence of the fluxing action.

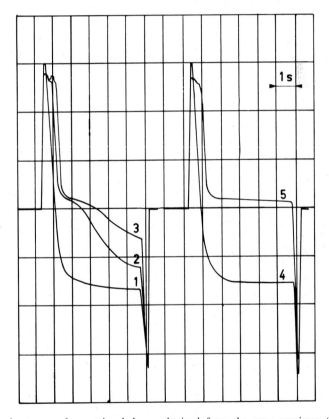

Fig. 2.17 Recorder traces of a wetting balance obtained from the same specimen (see text).
Experimental conditions were:

run	depth of immersion	application of flux
1	3 mm	yes
2	3 mm	no
3	3 mm	no
4	5 mm	yes
5	3 mm	no

The need for a flux can conveniently be demonstrated by a series of wetting experiments in a wetting balance (for an explanation of the wetting balance see Chapter 7.2.1). In Figure 2.17 wetting balance recordings are reproduced, which have been made on the same copper specimen at intervals of about one minute starting with trace 1 and ending with trace 5. The freshly presoldered surface obtained in the first dipping operation wets badly in the second run in which no flux has been applied. In runs 2 and 3, the flux that was still present at the border of the wetted zone could act again, but with decreasing power. In run 5, no flux at all was present at the border because the immersion depth was 2 mm less than in the preceding run, with poor wetting as a consequence.

Fluxless Soldering

Only if certain conditions are complied with is it possible to obtain acceptable soldering results without a flux. The conditions for this are, among other things, that at least one surface be virtually free from oxide. In practice, this means that one of the two surfaces to be joined has to be provided with a coating of a noble metal, if soldering takes place in air.

Soldering without flux is of course assisted by the complete exclusion of air during soldering, for instance by heating in a protective gas [Hartmann, Spigarelli].

A special example of fluxless soldering is ultrasonic soldering where the removal of oxides is realised by cavitation.

2.3.2 Progress of Wetting

The progress of wetting can be investigated using a wetting balance. With this apparatus the net forces of the surface tensions on the periphery of a dipped specimen can be measured as a function of time. The recorded measurements however, reflect only the 'average' wetting situation on the periphery of the specimen.

If a rectangular specimen is dipped in the solder, the conditions on the vertical edges differ from those in the middle, with the result that at first the wetting proceeds faster at the edges than in the middle. At the end of the wetting period however, the rise in the middle exceeds the rise at the edges. This can be understood qualitatively, assuming the edges to have more or less the properties of a wire, and the middle those of a large plate (*cf.,* Figures 2.5 and 2.9).

The progress of wetting has been studied with a high speed film camera directed towards the face of a flat specimen immersed vertically in a solder bath [Klein Wassink]. The most difficult problem in making films of the wetting phenomenon is to obtain good illumination, without all kinds of changing reflections during the advance of the solder. Detailed information was obtained by examining the films frame by frame on a monitor provided with a measuring graticule. The observations show that the wetting of a plate does not proceed uniformly but that the solder rises irregularly, swinging ahead step by step till the final position is reached. This effect is most pronounced with non-activated fluxes. With activated fluxes, the wetting is more regular and of course quicker.

In Figure 2.18 the positions of the three-phase boundary of solder/plate material/flux are depicted as they appear on separate film images, after ten periods, each of one second, in a wetting test with non-activated flux on a

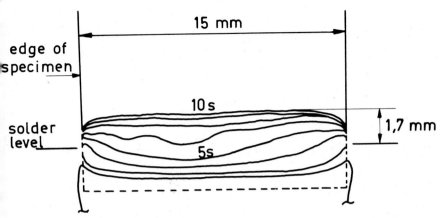

Fig. 2.18   Solder rise against a vertical copper plate dipped into solder, as observed on film images, one second apart. The boundary lines for the first two seconds are invisible because they are behind the rim (lowest line) of the depressed solder. The line for 9 seconds is the same as for 10 seconds.

strongly aged copper specimen (ageing 24 hours at 100°C: specimen badly solderable).

It can be observed that the maximum solder depression, just after the moment of immersion, and the maximum solder rise, at the end of the period, are in the middle of the plate. The final front line is curved and the maximum solder height is about 1,7 mm. The forces in the wetting balance, recorded during the film runs, reach a maximum value of about 9 mN after 10 seconds. This implies a wetting angle of 40° and a solder rise of 1,9 mm, in the case of a very wide plate (see Chapter 2.5). The value of 1,7 mm in the film experiment is less than 1,9 mm owing to the influence of the edges of the plate.

In the particular case of Figure 2.18 it takes about 4 seconds for the solder to reach the height of the solder bath level, often called the moment at which the contact angle $\theta = 90°$. The Figure shows that at the edges this moment of $\theta = 90°$ is attained earlier than in the middle and it can thus be concluded that the expression '$\theta = 90°$' is without much meaning in this complicated situation.

Note: The Marangoni effect [Scriven *et al*] can be clearly observed when the film is shown at reduced speed. Small droplets of flux on the copper and on the solder surface are in continuous and irregular motion as a result of varying surface tensions caused by the fluxing action.

Rate of Wetting

The rate of wetting in a dipping experiment is dependent on the rate of heating of the specimen and on the rate of cleaning of the surfaces by the flux.

Note the distinction between:

(i) dipping speed limit: the maximum dipping speed at which a sound solder coating is obtained (see Chapter 6.1.2);

(ii) 90° dipping speed: the dipping speed at which the solder meniscus against the specimen during dipping is just 90°.

The speeds mentioned have been measured on various specimens in a clean condition, using an activated rosin flux (0,5% Cl⁻), and are given in Table 2.3.

Table 2.3

Speeds of Wetting (mm/s) at 235°C

	Copper	Brass	Nickel Silver
dipping speed limit	>30	15	6
90° dipping speed	3	16	4,5

The conditions at which the two rates have been obtained differ as do the results. In both cases the wetting is 'forced', contrary for instance to the wetting in a wetting balance, which is 'free'. For brass and nickel silver the dipping speed limit and the 90° dipping speed are about the same, but for copper the difference is an order of magnitude. The 90° dipping speed of copper is low for thermal reasons, but when the dipping of copper occurs at a higher rate, hence with a convex solder meniscus between the solder and the easy-to-clean copper, a good bond is still obtained. Poor bonding is not obtained unless the dipping rate is above 30 mm/s.

2.3.3 Dewetting

Dewetting is the phenomenon in which the molten solder withdraws from a surface that has been previously wetted, resulting in a typical combination of dewetted regions and irregularly shaped solder droplets (Figure 2.19). If the dewetting is from copper, the surface of the dewetted copper retains the solder colour, indicating that solder is still present, or that a reaction has taken place between the copper and the solder prior to dewetting.

Fig. 2.19 Various degrees of dewetting produced on pickled copper plates containing oxide particles. Dipping times respectively: 2, 5, 10 and 20 seconds at 280°C. Plates shown are approximately actual size.

Dewetting is a practical problem encountered in soldering practice. It can affect the quality of soldered joints by reducing the size of the solder fillets on printed boards (see Figure 12.7). In other cases, the component terminations can exhibit dewetting which will also result in poor joints. Although the occurrence of dewetting can easily be observed, quantification of its effect is much more difficult, as will be shown in Chapter 7.7.2.

Despite the frequent occurrence and practical importance of the dewetting phenomenon, little has been published on the subject.

The following three causes will be discussed:

(i) dissolution of a wettable coating on a non-wettable substrate;
(ii) non-wettable spots on a wettable surface;
(iii) contamination of the solder.

2.3.3.1 DISSOLUTION OF A WETTABLE COATING ON A NON-WETTABLE SUBSTRATE

Coatings of silver and gold readily dissolve in molten tin-lead solder. When such a coating on a ceramic substrate is soldered, excellent wetting takes place initially. After some time, however, the coating completely dissolves, exposing the ceramic surface to the solder which will then withdraw.

Coatings on contaminated metallic substrates may exhibit similar behaviour. Tin, tin-lead, silver, and gold coatings dissolve in the solder, exposing the contaminated metal substrate to the solder, and this may also result in dewetting [Elliott, Williams]. This cause of dewetting can be considered as a trivial one and will not be discussed in any greater detail.

2.3.3.2 NON-WETTABLE SPOTS

A variety of non-wettable spots can promote dewetting. These may be rolled-in or brushed-in particles, spots consisting of a thick oxide or corrosion layer, intermetallic crystals grown on the outer surface, cuprous oxide particles in fire-refined copper, *etc.* [Thwaites *et al*, Davis, Anon. Ref. 14].

Figure 2.20 shows a SEM micrograph of a tin-coated copper product in which the tin-copper intermetallics have locally grown to the surface. These non-protected intermetallic compounds oxidise to such an extent that they rapidly become non-wettable (under the conditions used in soldering practice).

Many other metal combinations which produce intermetallic compounds may exhibit dewetting. In this form it has been reported for tin-coated steel plate, with the tin-iron intermetallic compound grown to the outer surface [Johannesson *et al*] and it has been seen to occur with indium (at 200°C) on gold or nickel (Figure 2.21).

Fire-refined copper sheet containing cuprous oxide particles also exhibits dewetting. These particles, with a typical size of a few micrometres, appear at the surface because their copper matrix dissolves in the liquid solder. Their presence at the surface is clearly related to dewetting, as is easily established microscopically.

On the dewetted regions a film of solder is still present in which three different features may be observed as shown diagrammatically in Figure 2.22. The solder film has a composition which can be guessed from Figures 2.23-2.25 from the ratio of tin to lead. Microsectioning establishes that this film has a thickness of only about 1 μm.

On pure copper which was properly precleaned and soldered with pure soft solder (tin60-lead40) no dewetting could be produced at all, either at high temperatures or with long contact times.

Fig. 2.20 SEM-picture of a matt tin surface of which the Cu_6Sn_5 intermetallic phase has locally grown up to the outer surface. Magnification $1200\times$.

Fig. 2.21 Dewetting of indium on nickel, caused by the growth of intermetallic compounds between the indium and the nickel. Magnification $160\times$.

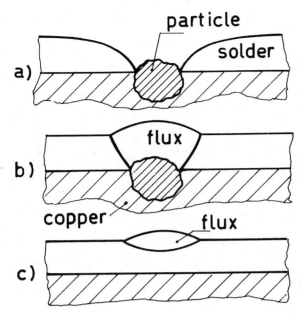

g. 2.22 Three types of hole observed in the solder layer: (a) non-wetted oxide particles surrounded solder which has solidified in the absence of flux (Fig. 2.23); (b) non-wetted oxide particles rrounded by solder which has solidified with flux droplets on the oxide particles (Fig. 2.24); (c) mples in the solder surface caused by flux droplets remaining on it during solidification (Fig. 2.25).

g. 2.23 SEM-picture of non-wetted particles in a dewetted region. Magnification $5000 \times$, viewing angle $45°$.

Fig. 2.24 SEM-picture of non-wetted oxide particle in a dewetted region (*cf.* Fig. 2.23 Magnification 5000×, viewing angle 45° (this Figure is a detail of Fig. 7.40).

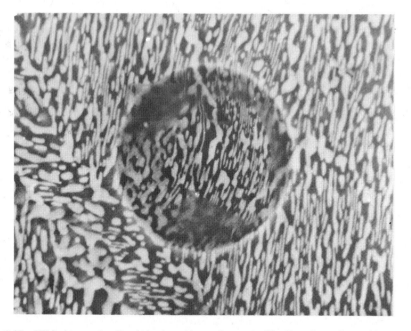

Fig. 2.25 SEM-picture of a dimple in the solder surface caused by flux. Some flux residues are still present. Magnification 5000×.

3.3.3 CONTAMINATED SOLDER

Zinc contamination of solder causes strong dewetting. Although the dewetting echanism in this instance has not been unravelled completely, a similarity is ound between this case and that discussed in the preceding paragraph. Figure 26 shows a dewetted copper plate with zinc-contaminated solder (0,3% by ass). Part of the surface (not shown) is covered by droplets with an appearance milar to that of the droplets in Figure 2.21. On the dewetted region solder is bviously present, and again many non-wetted spots are found. On the other and the surface shows features, such as that present at the top-left of the picture, sulting from broken oxide skins.

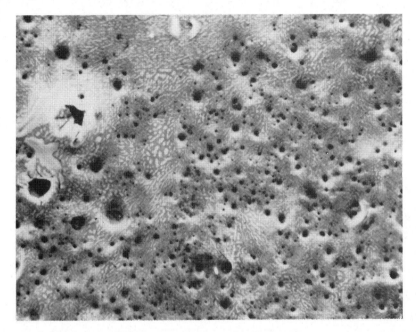

g. 2.26 SEM-picture of dewetting of solder on copper caused by a contamination of the solder ith zinc. On the dewetted surface a large number of small non-wetted places can be observed. Magnification 1250×.

3.3.4 COMPUTATIONAL MODEL OF DEWETTING CAUSED BY NON-WETTABLE SPOTS

In all the cases of dewetting of which the Author is aware, tiny, non-wettable ots scattered over the surface are the cause of the phenomenon. Based on this bservation, a simple computational model has been developed to describe ewetting. The model is based on the tendency towards minimum surface free ergy of a system, which in this case is equivalent to a minimum solder surface ea, assuming that no interaction exists between solder and non-wettable spots. In the model two configurations are compared:

(i) a wettable surface with non-wettable spots, completely covered with a thick layer of solder (Figure 2.27a);

(ii) a wettable surface with non-wettable spots, partly covered with solid
      droplets of equal shape and size, and on the other part (the dewetted region)
      covered with a very thin film of solder on the wettable surface and no solder
      on the non-wettable spots (Figure 2.27b).

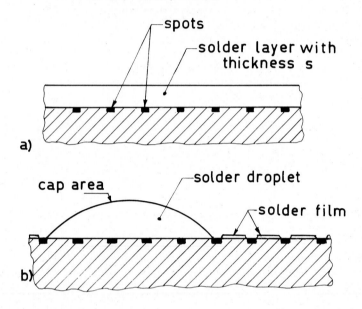

Fig. 2.27 Scheme of the model: (a) shows the wetted situation with the non-wettable spots covered
by solder; (b) shows a droplet and a dewetted region with the non-wettable spots in that region free
from solder.

In the first configuration, with the solid surface completely covered by a solder
film, the total (free) solder surface area is the sum of the area of the outer surface
and the areas of the interfaces between the solder and the non-wettable spots.
the area fraction of the non-wettable spots on the surface is f, then the sum
mentioned on a unit geometrical area of the substrate is $1 + f$. The total solder
surface area is independent of solder thickness s (which is the same as the solder
volume per unit area). The wettable part of the soldered surfaces does not enter
into the calculations, because it is completely wetted with solder (either thin or
thick) in all the cases considered.

First, consider the extreme case of dewetting, in which only the very thin solder
film is present on the wettable part of the surface (no droplets). In this case, the
total solder surface area per unit area is $1 - f$. Thus the difference in solder
surface area between the completely covered and the completely dewetted
configuration is $(1 + f) - (1 - f) = 2f$. This is the maximum difference in surface
area possible.

Now take a surface of unit area that has partly dewetted. The solder volume
has been taken up into N droplets of equal shape and size. For the shape, a spherical
cap is taken and for the size, a base area A_1 and a cap area A_2 (see Appendix
2.4.1).

The total solder surface area is now the sum of:

(i) the total surface area of the sphere caps, which is $N \times A_2$;
ii) the total surface area of the non-wettable spots under the droplets, which is $f \times N \times A_1$;
iii) the surface area of the solder on the dewetted region, which is $(1-f) \times (1 - N \times A_1)$.

The difference in solder surface area between the completely covered system with area $(1+f)$ and this sum is:

$$\Delta A = (1+f) - (N \times A_2 + f \times N \times A_1 + (1-f) \times (1 - N \times A_1)).$$

This difference is a function of the solder volume s, of the non-wettable surface fraction f, of the number of droplets N, and of the contact angle θ of the droplets (in fact the apparent contact angle, see Chapter 2.1.4).

The calculations show that at each combination of s and f there is a size of the droplets at which ΔA is positive, indicating that dewetting will occur [Klein Wassink et al]. The value of ΔA increases with the size of the droplets, implying that there exists a tendency for the droplets to grow. Moreover, thin layers (small values of s) give larger values of ΔA than thick layers at the same droplet size, but of course with fewer droplets.

Figure 2.28 presents some results for the combination $f = 0,01$ and $s = 0,01$ mm, in which ΔA is plotted versus the contact angle θ. Lines are given for the numbers of droplets: 1, 5, 10, 50 and 250 per 1000 mm² plate area. The maxima of these lines are found at $\theta = 11,5°$, also obtainable from $\cos \theta = 1 - 2f$, following from the equilibrium conditions at the edge of the droplets. The dotted lines in the figure are for the base areas of droplets of 1, 3, 10, 20 and 100 mm². These lines have their maxima at 16° (as can also be found analytically).

The differences in surface area, ΔA, as a function of the contact angle, θ, calculated under the assumption of either a constant number of droplets or a constant droplet size, show broad maxima so that there is no strong preference for a specific contact angle, or hence for a specific shape of droplet.

As can be seen in Figure 2.28, the solder surface area can be decreased by reducing the number of droplets, with a concomitant increase in their size. The droplets on a dewetted surface are still in mutual contact via the thin layer of liquid solder on the dewetted zone. Hence, the smaller droplets (with a higher liquid pressure) can disappear into the larger droplets via the thin layer of solder. This phenomenon is the same as that which occurs in grain growth.

Maximum surface area reduction is reached when all the solder on a specimen has been taken up into one single drop.

The results regarding dewetting in relation to the simple geometrical model discussed clearly demonstrate the characteristics of dewetting. With thinner solder layers and larger fractions of non-wettable spots on the solid surface, dewetting is more likely. The gain in solder surface area is virtually independent of the contact angle θ of the droplets formed. Hence, in practice, all kinds of droplet shapes can be expected. The actual appearance of a dewetted surface will therefore be determined by other factors, such as variations on the surface, influences of gravity, and temperature gradients.

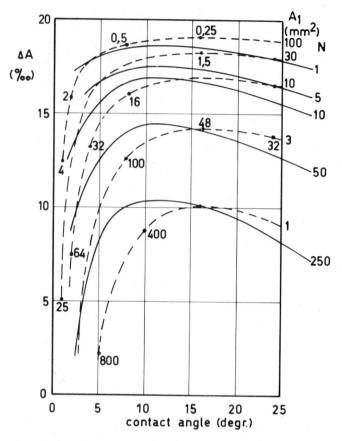

Fig. 2.28 Results of calculations for non-wettable fraction $f = 0,01$ and original solder layer thickness $s = 0,01$ mm. The difference in area upon dewetting, ΔA, is plotted *versus* the contact angle θ. The lines are for constant numbers of droplets. Dotted lines represent constant base areas of the droplets. The figures beside the lines and the values of N are the number of droplets per 1000 mm² plate area.

2.3.4 Wetting Assisted by Ultrasonic Vibrations

The removal of the oxide layer, the prerequisite of wetting, can also be effected by means other than by flux, for instance by mechanical abrasion. To obtain acceptable wetting, the abrasion must be performed with exclusion of air, otherwise the fresh surface oxidises immediately. This can be achieved by rubbing or scraping the oxide film under the surface of the molten solder.

A special application is the ultrasonic soldering technique, in which ultrasonic vibrations are applied to the solder bath in which the parts to be soldered are immersed.

2.3.4.1 PRINCIPLE

The beneficial effect of ultrasonic vibrations is due to the occurrence of cavitation. The vibrations produce forces of acceleration in the liquid by which

: liquid is locally torn apart. At 20 kHz and an amplitude of 1 μm, the peak locity is $\hat{v} = 0,13$ m/s and the peak acceleration $\hat{a} = 16000$ m/s$^2 = 1600$ g. The ess in the liquid solder at which cavitation commences depends on the number nuclei in the solder. For normal tin60-lead40 solder this stress is about 2×10^5 'm^2. At a lower stress no cavitation is generated, hence a minimum ultrasonic ergy is needed before an effect is noticed.

The stresses and the acceleration are related according to the mass to be celerated. If the energy is applied from the bottom of the solder bath as in gure 2.29, no cavitation is possible in the upper layer of the solder, because ove a certain level the inertial stresses are too low. The mass to be accelerated is ufficient. This layer thickness $h_0 \cong \dfrac{\sigma_c}{\varrho\omega^2\Delta y}$, in which σ_c is the critical stress, s the density of solder, ω is the angular velocity and Δy is the amplitude. The plitude is nearly constant provided the depth of the bath is small in mparison with a quarter wave length. For $\Delta y = 1$ μm and a frequency of 20 Iz, the value of $h_0 \cong 2$ mm. The $h_0 -$ value can be reduced by taking higher plitudes. However, at high amplitude levels the transmission drops, esumably because of the intense cavitation in the lower layers of the bath.

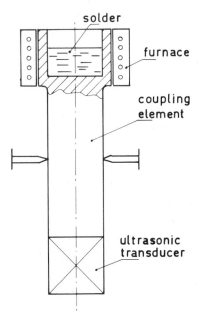

. 2.29 Ultrasonic soldering bath. The bath is heated by an electric furnace, whilst the heat lation between the bath and the transducer is realised by making the coupling element of a suitable material.

During the moments of positive stress the cavities implode, thus giving rise to cal shock waves. The implosions occur at high speed, within less than 1 μs, so at pressures up to 10^9 N/m^2 (10000 atm) are built up. In the cavity a jet stream is nerated with a speed of $\sim$500 m/s, which is generally directed towards the jacent solid surface in the fluid. This jet stream removes the oxides from the rface of the object in the bath by a kind of hammering action, inducing aining speeds of 10^4 to 10^5 per second in the solid surface.

2.3.4.2 APPLICATIONS

Despite the attractive cleaning principle provided by the cavitation, the numb
of actual applications of ultrasonic soldering is small. One reason for this is t
difficulty of guiding the ultrasonic vibrations to the desired places. This restri
the freedom of choice of shape and dimensions.

The simplest solution is a plain bath in which sequential dipping can be carri
out mostly of relatively small objects. In such a way, incidentally, electro
components can be pretinned, provided that they can endure the inter
vibration.

The ultrasonic soldering of printed boards on top of a bath or wave is r
possible, because the mass of the board is insufficient to generate cavitation at t
lower face of the board (at an acceptable amplitude and frequency of vibratio

The only important application is the soldering of aluminium parts, but th
example is outside the field of electronics [Schuster *et al*]. Once the oxide layer
removed, perfect wetting is achieved by a large number of solder alloys.

The alternative approach to using an ultrasonically agitated solder bath is
use a vibrating probe in contact with the solder. An example of such equipment
the ultrasonic soldering iron, which is a combination of a normal soldering ir
provided with an electrical heater element, and a vibration transducer. T
various aspects of equipment, power requirements, *etc.*, are not further discuss
here.

2.3.4.3 EVALUATION

The idea of tinning without the use of flux is so attractive [Fuchs] that ma
engineers are inclined to attempt it, especially when they encounter solderi
problems. As a rule it will be ineffective: ultrasonic soldering is no panacea.

As a result of the cavitation, the basis metal rapidly dissolves into the sold
bath, say ten times as fast as in a normal solder bath [Friedrich *et al*]. Therefor
relatively small baths are quickly polluted.

Finally, there is one principal objection to ultrasonic soldering. In norm
wetting without ultrasonic vibrations, the wetting result will prove by
appearance that real wetting has been achieved and that a good chance exists th
the joint is sound. After wetting obtained by ultrasonic soldering, there may st
be a strong element of doubt concerning the nature of the wetting. Wi
ultrasonic soldering one can even succeed in 'tinning' a piece of glass, but this
certainly not the type of bonding desired on metallic parts, where better joints c
be achieved by other means.

2.4 APPENDIX TO CHAPTER 2

2.4.1 Calculations for an Ideal Spherical Cap

In many calculations on solder droplets these are considered as spherical cap
Useful equations are given as follows:

(a) Basic Formulae (Figure 2.30)

R = radius of sphere
b = radius of basis area
h = height of spherical cap
A_1 = interfacial area $= \pi b^2$
A_2 = liquid surface area
A_3 = total area of plate
b = $R \sin \theta$; $h = R(1 - \cos \theta)$;

$$\tan \theta = \frac{b}{R - h} = \frac{2bh}{b^2 - h^2} \; ; \; A_2 = A_1 \cdot \frac{2}{1 + \cos \theta} = \pi(h^2 + b^2)$$

Volume of spherical cap: $V = \dfrac{1}{6}\pi h(h^2 + 3b^2)$

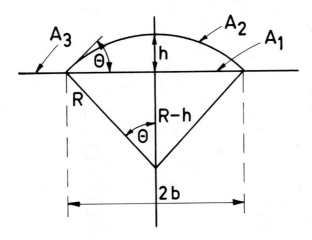

Fig. 2.30   Geometry of spherical cap.

)   Young's Equation (Equation 2.3)

The total surface free energy is given by:

$$F_{\text{total}} = \gamma_{ls}A_1 + \gamma_s(A_3 - A_1) + \gamma_l A_2$$

$$A_1 = \frac{2V}{h} - \frac{\pi h^2}{3}; \quad A_2 = \pi h^2 + \frac{2V}{h} - \frac{\pi h^2}{3}$$

the results for A_1 and A_2 are inserted in the equation for F_{total}, a function is obtained in which F_{total} depends on h.
differentiating F with respect to h gives:

$$\frac{dF}{dh} = \gamma_{ls} - \gamma_s + \gamma_l \left(\frac{R - h}{R}\right).$$

Hence: $\gamma_s - \gamma_{ls} = \gamma_l \cos \theta$ (Young's Equation)

(c)   Expression for h as a Function of V and b

The equation for the volume of a spherical cap:

$$V = \frac{1}{6}\pi\, h(h^2 + 3b^2)$$

may be rearranged to show the relation between b and h for a given volume:

$$h^3 + (3b^2)h - \frac{6V}{\pi} = 0$$

This equation has one real solution:

$$h = \left(\frac{3V}{\pi} + \sqrt{\left(\frac{3V}{\pi}\right)^2 + b^6} \right)^{1/3} + \left(\frac{3V}{\pi} - \sqrt{\left(\frac{3V}{\pi}\right)^2 + b^6} \right)^{1/3}$$

which can be written as: $h = j + k$.

(d)   Expression for θ as a Function of V and b

If the value of h is inserted in the equation:

$$\tan\theta = \frac{2bh}{b^2 - h^2},$$

it follows that:

$$\tan\theta = \frac{2b(j + k)}{3b^2 - j^2 - k^2}$$

The above formulae permit a calculation of θ when V is given and b is measured (Figure 2.31).

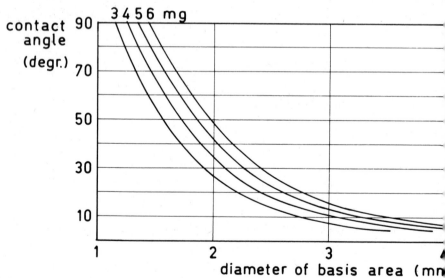

Fig. 2.31   Contact angle *versus* diameter of the basis area of spherical caps, for droplet masses of 3, 4, 5 and 6 mg. With $\varrho = 8000$ kg/m³, the volumes of the liquid droplets are respectively ⅜, ½, ⅝ and ¾ mm³. For such small droplets the actual contact angle, taking gravity into account, is only 1 to 2 degrees larger than the values taken from the graphs.

The value of b can be measured on solidified drops, assuming that the periphery of a small drop does not change its position during solidification. A calculation of θ based on the measurement of h will be less accurate, because h certainly changes during solidification. Sometimes even a shrinkage hole forms in the top of the sphere cap.

(e) Expression for the Spread Factor as a Function of θ

In spread tests a spread factor is often determined. This factor is given by the formula: $S = \dfrac{D-h}{D}$, in which D is the diameter of a sphere of the same volume as the drop:

$$D = \sqrt[3]{\frac{6V}{\pi}}$$

The relation between S and θ is:

$$S = \frac{\sqrt[3]{h^3 + 3b^2 h} - h}{\sqrt[3]{h^3 + 3b^2 h}} = 1 - \frac{1}{\sqrt[3]{1 + \dfrac{3b^2}{h^2}}} = 1 - \frac{1}{\sqrt[3]{1 + 3(\cotan \frac{\theta}{2})^2}}$$

The relation between S and θ is also shown in Figure 2.32.

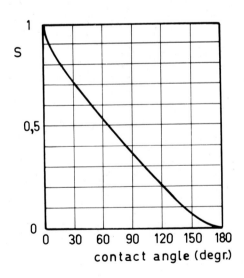

Fig. 2.32 Relation between the spread factor S and the contact angle θ for spherical cap

(f) Expression for the Base Area as a Function of V and θ

From the equations $b = R \sin \theta$ and $h = R(1 - \cos \theta)$, it follows that:

$$h = \left(\frac{1 - \cos \theta}{\sin \theta} \right) b$$

Putting h in the equation: $V = \frac{1}{6}\pi\, h(h^2 + 3b^2)$ produces:

$$V = \frac{\pi b^3}{6} \left(\frac{1 - \cos \theta}{\sin \theta} \left\{ \left(\frac{1 - \cos \theta}{\sin \theta} \right)^2 + 3 \right\} \right) =$$

$$\frac{\pi b^3}{6} \left\{ (\tan \tfrac{\theta}{2})^2 \times (3\,\mathrm{cosec}\,\theta - \tan\tfrac{\theta}{2}) \right\} \qquad \text{[Bailey } et\ al\text{]}.$$

From this, it is possible to write: $\pi b^2 = f_0 \cdot V^{2/3}$, in which f_0 is a function of θ. The relation between θ and f_0 is shown in Figure 2.33.

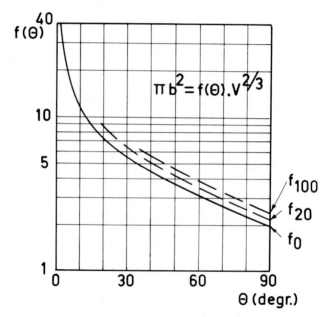

Fig. 2.33 The relation between the contact angle θ and the factor f for three volumes of a solder droplet. f_0 is for small droplets with the shape of a spherical cap, f_{20} and f_{100} are for droplets of 20 mm^3 and 100 mm^3 respectively.

When the volume of the droplet increases, the assumption of an ideally spherical cap becomes less accurate. In Figure 2.33 the values of f for $V = 20$ and 100 mm^3 are also shown. These values are obtained by a numerical calculation in which gravity is taken into account. Approximate expressions for the relation between πb^2, θ and $V^{2/3}$ have been given in the literature, but either their area of validity is not known, or they are faulty.

2.4.2   Calculations for the Liquid Solder Surface

Most of the calculations of contours of liquid solder surfaces have been made by combining Equation 2.1: $\Delta P = \gamma(\frac{1}{R_1} + \frac{1}{R_2})$ with the equation for hydrostatic pressure: $\Delta P = -\varrho g \Delta y$.

R_1 and R_2 are the radii of curvature of the surface, ϱ is the density of solder, and g is the acceleration due to gravity.

The radii are positive when they lie inside the solder, negative when they lie outside the solder (Figure 2.34). R_1 rotates always in the plane of the paper, R_2 in

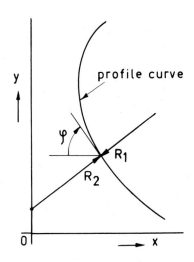

y

profile curve

φ

R_1

R_2

0

x

Fig. 2.34   Solder profile.

a plane perpendicular to it. If the liquid shape has an axis of symmetry, R_2 sweeps out a cone coaxial with this axis ($x = 0$). An added superscript, as in R_1^0, gives the value of the angle ϕ at which the quantity is measured. From Figure 2.34 it is deduced that:

$$\frac{dy}{dx} = -\tan \phi; \quad -R_1 = \frac{1}{\sin \phi} \frac{dy}{d\phi} \quad \text{and } R_2 = \frac{x}{\sin \phi}$$

(a)   Plate in the Solder

Here $R_2 = \infty$ and hence: $\Delta P = \frac{\gamma}{R_1} = \Delta P^0 - \varrho g y$

Taking the hydrostatic pressure $\Delta P^0 = 0$, at $y = 0$ ($\phi = 0$), gives: $y = \frac{\gamma}{\varrho g} \frac{\sin \phi \, d\phi}{dy}$,

which can be integrated directly. x can be integrated from: $dx = \frac{-dy}{\tan \phi}$

(b) Rotational Symmetry

From: $\Delta P = \gamma(\dfrac{1}{R_1} + \dfrac{1}{R_2}) = \Delta P^0 - \varrho g y$

it follows that: $dy = \dfrac{\sin \phi \ d\phi}{\dfrac{\sin \phi}{x} + \dfrac{\varrho g y}{\gamma} - \dfrac{\Delta P^0}{\gamma}}$

and: $\qquad dx = \dfrac{-\cos \phi \ d\phi}{\dfrac{\sin \phi}{x} + \dfrac{\varrho g y}{\gamma} - \dfrac{\Delta P^0}{\gamma}}$

These equations can be integrated by parts. For different cases there are different boundary conditions.

Two examples are given:

(i) Wire in the Solder

for $\phi = 0$, $y = 0$ at the undisturbed liquid surface, $\Delta P^0 = 0$.
for other cases in which $R_1^0 \neq \infty$, R_1^0 is the parameter and then:

$$\frac{\Delta P^0}{\gamma} = \frac{1}{R_1^0}$$

(ii) Hanging Fillet Around a Wire

for $y = 0$, $\phi = 90°$, and $x = R_2^{90}$.
R_1^{90} is the parameter (having a negative value because it is outside the liquid).
This then gives: $\dfrac{\Delta P^{90}}{\gamma} = \dfrac{1}{R_1^{90}} + \dfrac{1}{R_2^{90}}$

Chapter 3

THERMAL ASPECTS OF SOLDERING

The subject of this Chapter has been underestimated in the existing literature
n soldering, which is remarkable, as a large number of soldering defects can be
ttributed to bad thermal design. Quite often solderability or machine settings are
lamed although it is often thermal difficulties which cause the trouble.

In discussions on soldering the thermal aspects are mostly dealt with in a vague
nd qualitative way, although in fact there exists a wealth of specific knowledge
n heating matters. Unfortunately this has been insufficiently employed in
oldering practice.

This Chapter tries to bridge the gap between the science of heat and the every-
ay soldering world; it is hoped that it may initiate further contributions.

.1 SOLDERING AND HEAT

The objects to be soldered must be heated to the soldering temperature. If the
emperature difference between the heat source and the object is ΔT, the
ransport of heat will be: $\alpha A \Delta T$, in which α is the coefficient of heat transfer and
4 is the surface area through which the heat is transported. This heat will produce
 temperature rise in the object.

Hence: $\varrho c V \dfrac{\mathrm{d}T}{\mathrm{d}t} = \alpha A \Delta T$, in which ϱ = density, c = specific heat and
V = volume of the object considered.

From this can be obtained:

$$T - T_O = (T_S - T_O)(1 - \exp\frac{-t}{\tau}) \qquad \text{(Equation 3.1)}$$

n which:

T = the temperature at the time t;
T_O = starting temperature;
T_S = the temperature of the heat source;
τ = response time of the process = $\dfrac{\varrho c V}{\alpha A}$.

The equation given is sufficiently accurate to be used in approximate calculations
Mollendorf, Ammann et al].

53

The response time, τ, is the product of the heat resistance, given here as $\frac{1}{\alpha}$ and the heat capacity $C = \varrho c V$.

A more precise analysis shows that the heat resistance is the sum of transf resistances and conduction resistances.

The heat transfer coefficient, α, varies considerably with the proce conditions. It is expressed in $W/(m^2.K)$ and is:

$\alpha \cong 10$ for heat transfer by still air;
$\alpha \cong 100$ for heat transfer by moving air;
$\alpha \cong 1000$ for heat transfer by agitated liquid;
$\alpha \cong 10000$ for heat transfer by liquid metal.

The heat capacity of an object made of different materials is the sum of th heat capacities of the separate parts. For electronic components, it is always o the order of 3×10^6 J/(m^3.K), as follows from Table 3.1.

Table 3.1

Heat Capacity and Thermal Conductivity of Various Materials

Material	Heat Capacity ϱc (in 10^6 J/(m^3.K))	Thermal Conductivit λ (in W/(m.K))
copper	3,5	370
aluminium	2,4	230
alumina	4	35
iron	3,7	75
nickel silver	3,7	33
iron nickel cobalt	3,7	16
glass	2	1
solder	1,7	50
synthetic materials	~2	~0,2

The values of α and ϱc imply that thermal τ-values in soldering processes rang from 0,5 to 300 seconds.

For instance, an alumina substrate of $50 \times 50 \times 1$ mm^3 has a heat capacity o 10 J/K. If the heat transfer coefficient is 1000 W/(m^2.K), the heat resistance (o one face of 50×50 mm^2) is 0,4 K/W and hence $\tau = 4$ seconds.

3.1.1 Strategies for Heating

Two strategies can be distinguished for the heating of parts to be soldered:

(i) excess heating strategy;
(ii) asymptotic heating strategy.

In the excess heating strategy, the temperature of the heat source is much higher than the desired soldering temperature. If the heating of the parts to be soldered is not stopped at a certain moment, the ultimate temperature that will be reached is much too high and in general the components will suffer damage.

In the asymptotic heating strategy, the temperature of the heat source is at the soldering temperature (or only slightly higher) and the heating process is continued until the equilibrium state is (nearly) reached.

In processes with excess heating, the heating time is usually $t<0,5\tau$; with asymptotic heating $t>3\tau$, (Figure 3.1).

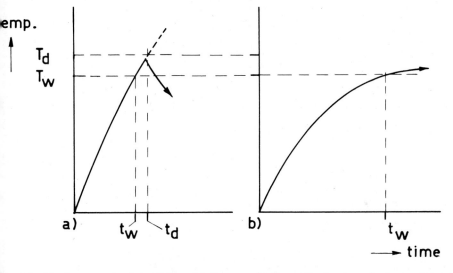

Fig. 3.1 Heating strategies for soldering: (a) the excess heating method, using a heat source at a much higher temperature than needed for melting of the solder; (b) asymptotic heating method, using a heat source at a temperature little higher than that needed for melting of the solder.

On applying the excess heating strategy, the wetting temperature of the solder, T_w, is passed at the time t_w, and the temperature at which damaging of the component occurs, T_d, at the time t_d. The time interval between t_w and t_d is available for soldering. The time intervals for the various components to be soldered in one single soldering operation must therefore overlap sufficiently to make the process possible. It is clear that the extent of the time interval $(t_d - t_w)$ is smaller when the heating curve is steeper (with the same levels of T_w and T_d).

In the case of asymptotic heating, all parts reach the temperature T_w (or slightly higher). If the parts cannot endure this temperature, the process is impossible. Overshoot, and reaching a much higher temperature than intended, cannot take place in the asymptotic strategy.

The situation is often, however, much more complicated than this, especially in the excess heating strategy. Owing to the high rate of heating, the different parts of the components have different traces of temperature versus time, this being particularly true with relatively heavy components.

3.1.2 Safe Operating Area of Soldering

In Chapter 3.3 it will be shown that for every component there appears to be an area of soldering time and soldering temperature within which an effective soldered joint can be achieved, reconciling at the same time the opposing requirements of sufficiently high temperature for soldering and sufficiently low temperature to prevent damage.

If components of varying nature are to be soldered simultaneously care must be taken to ensure that there is a liberal overlap of their respective safe operation areas. This is demonstrated by the graph of Figure 3.2 in which is plotted along the vertical axis the contact time of the printed board with the solder bath, and along the horizontal axis the temperature of the solder bath.

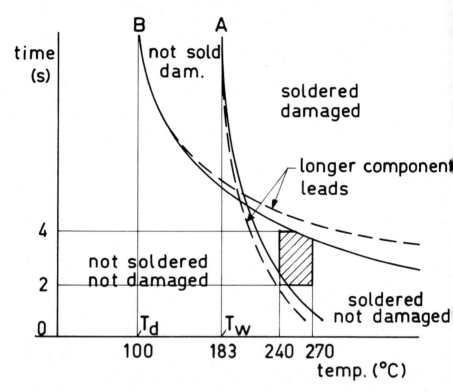

Fig. 3.2 The safe operating area for soldering (hatched area). Curve A represents the situation where a just adequate soldered joint is obtained. Curve B represents the situation where the component just suffers irreparable functional damage.

Two curves, A and B, are shown. In the region to the left of curve A the solder bath temperature is too low, so that no wetting can occur. In the region above curve B the contact time between component and solder bath is too long, causing damage to the component.

Curve A has a vertical tangent associated with the melting temperature of the solder. Curve B has a vertical tangent associated with the temperature at which the component is irreparably damaged. In Figure 3.2 this is presumed to be 100°C. The intersection of curves A and B divides the graph into four areas. Only the bottom right hand area is usable, having the correct combinations of solder bath temperature and contact time, so that the wetting occurs without damaging the component. The safe operating area is represented by the hatched region. The simplest method of locating the various components inside the safe operating area is to increase the length of the component leads, sometimes by employing elevated (stand-off) mounting of components. The increased length of component leads has the effect that the ends of component leads to be soldered ssume the desired temperature for soldering before the component body reaches emperature detrimental to the life of the component.

For increased lengths of component leads the paths of curves A and B are changed and have been shown as dashed lines. The usable time interval between A and B for a given solder bath temperature has consequently increased.

Another important parameter is the length of the component termination projecting from the conductor side of printed boards (underboard length). Up to an underboard length of approximately 2 mm, heat transfer increases markedly with increasing underboard length of termination; for underboard lengths greater han 2 mm this effect is considerably less.

In those situations in which the thermal quantities are unknown although they might yet be critical, resort must be made to testing (measuring) or calculating. Critical situations crop up repeatedly with vertically-mounted electrolytic capacitors and nearly always with partitions and brackets.

It is good engineering practice to locate the conditions well inside the safe operating area and to adapt the design of the product to this, instead of occasionally changing times and temperatures. In practice, however, such a change may not always be avoidable. If problems are of a thermal nature, the following rules apply since the curves of Figure 3.2 are roughly horizontal and vertical:

(i) if the leads are not wetted in a soldering process, it is preferable to increase the temperature of the solder bath;
(ii) if the body of a component is damaged in a soldering process, it is preferable to shorten the contact time.

n both cases, the other possible change (longer contact time or lower solder bath temperature) would have to be relatively much greater in order to obtain a properly soldered joint.

The resistance of components to damage by soldering operations is covered in Chapter 7. Components must be able to withstand a specific dip test.

3.2 HEATING OF SUPPORT PLATES

The majority of electronic components nowadays are mounted (placed and fixed) on relatively thin plates. These plates provide mechanical support for the components whereas electrical interconnection is effected by means of a conductive pattern on the plates to which the components are connected. If the components are soldered to the plates, these plates (or relevant parts of them) must be heated simultaneously with the component terminations.

3.2.1 Local Heating

Local heating of specific areas on the support plate is appropriate when components are mounted individually. This may be the case for instance in repair work by hand soldering. If a specific area on top of a support plate is heated, the heat will diffuse through the plate to the bottom, and will also flow sideways, thus heating a larger area of the plate than intended.

Two cases should be distinguished:

(i) thermally thin plates;
(ii) thermally thick plates.

3.2.1.1   THERMALLY THIN PLATES

If the thickness of the plate is smaller than $d \cong \sqrt{at}$ (in which $a =$ thermal diffusivity $= \dfrac{\lambda}{\varrho c}$ (see Table 3.1) and $t =$ heating time), the temperature at the bottom face of the plate is practically the same as on the top face. For 0,7 mm alumina, $t = \dfrac{d^2}{a} = 0,06$ seconds and, for 1,6 mm phenolic paper board $t = 25$ seconds.

This means that, with heating times longer than 0,1 s, alumina support plates of 0,7 mm thickness have no appreciable temperature gradient from one side to the other. For phenolic paper of 1,6 mm thickness, the situation is totally different and, provided the heating time is shorter than 25 s, a considerable temperature gradient exists in the plate.

To analyse local heating, consider the rate of temperature increase at the place where heat is transferred (transient situation).

The case of a dissipating cylinder is treated by Carslaw and Jaeger, from which is obtained the temperature rise at the inner radius, r (Figure 3.3a).

The case in question is somewhat different (Figure 3.3b), but it is possible to use the results of the dissipating cylinder if some assumptions are made:

(i) the flux Φ differs from Φ_r by the ratio of the cylindrical area ($2\pi rd$) to the circle area (πr^2);
(ii) the heating of the cylindrical volume ($\pi r^2 d$) must be taken into account;
(iii) the temperature distribution in the cylindrical volume is not considered.

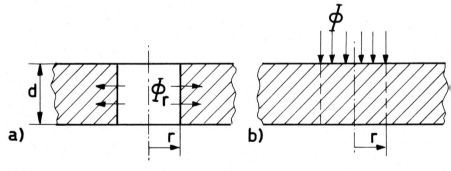

Fig. 3.3   Heating of a support plate: (a) heating by a dissipating cylinder with radius r; (b) heating by a heat flux on a circular area with a radius r.

From the calculations based on this model it is found that the temperature increase is proportional to the heat flux used.

The results for alumina are shown in Figure 3.4 where $\dfrac{\Delta T}{\Phi}$ (temperature increase over heat flux) has been plotted for three values of the radius of the heated area. For thicker support plates the temperature increase is proportionally lower.

Considering, for instance a spot with $r = 2$ mm for a plate of 0,7 mm thickness it is found that after 5 seconds a temperature rise is reached of $\Delta T = \frac{0,88}{0,7}\Phi = 1,26\Phi$. Hence with $\Phi = 100$ W/cm², $\Delta T = 126$ K. With a heated spot of $r = 1,15$ mm the temperature increase on the circumference of the spot is only 60 K after 5 seconds.

From the figure it can clearly be seen that longer heating times have almost no effect when the radius is small. A period of 10 seconds instead of 5 seconds ($r = 1,15$ mm) gives ΔT only about 17% higher.

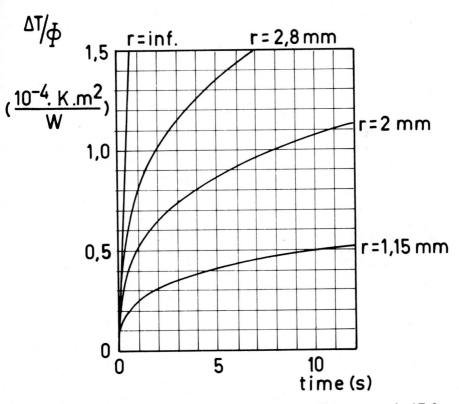

Fig. 3.4 Local heating of plates of alumina with a thickness of 1 mm. The temperature rise ΔT after a certain time is proportional to the heat flux Φ, and depends on the radius r of the heated area, as indicated in the figure.

3.2.1.2 THERMALLY THICK PLATES

If heat is supplied to a discrete area with a radius r for a short time, so that $\frac{r}{2\sqrt{at}} > 1,5$, the lateral heat flow may be neglected. For alumina, the equation is satisfied only for very short times, but for phenolic paper and other synthetic materials, with spot radii of $r = 2$ mm, the equation is satisfied until t is about 5 seconds. In these cases, the plate behaves as if it were infinitely thick and the temperature rise is independent of r:

$$\frac{\Delta T}{\Phi} = 2\sqrt{\frac{t}{\pi\lambda\varrho c}} = \frac{2}{\lambda}\sqrt{\frac{at}{\pi}}$$

For phenolic paper this is:

$$\frac{\Delta T}{\Phi} \cong 18 \times 10^{-4}\sqrt{t}$$

Heating with a directed stream of hot air at 400°C with $\alpha = 200$ W/(m^2.K) gives with $\Phi = \alpha\overline{\Delta T}_{air}$ and a desired temperature rise of the top face of the plate of 160 K:

$$\Delta T = 160 = 200\frac{(400-20)+(400-160)}{2} \times 18 \times 10^{-4}\sqrt{t}$$

This gives $t = 2$ seconds, in accordance with experiments. For longer heating times when the inequality $\frac{r}{2\sqrt{at}} > 1,5$ is no longer valid, the expression for $\frac{\Delta T}{\Phi}$ gets an additional term:

$$\frac{\Delta T}{\Phi} = \frac{2}{\lambda}\sqrt{at}\left\{\frac{1}{\sqrt{\pi}} - \text{ierfc}\frac{r}{2\sqrt{at}}\right\}^{*}$$

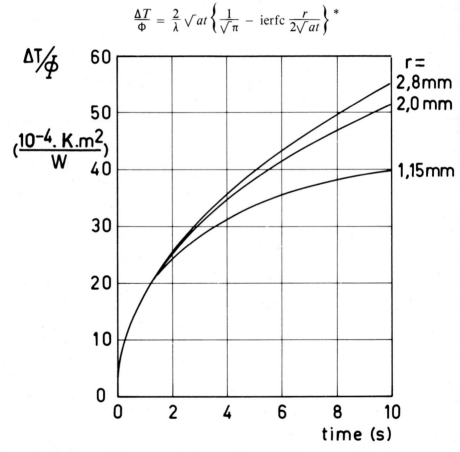

Fig. 3.5 Local heating of a thick plate of phenolic paper material. r is the radius of the heated area. The temperature rise is proportional to the heat flux Φ.

---

*The function ierfc x is related to the error function erf x by: $\text{ierfc } x = \frac{1}{\sqrt{\pi}}e^{-x^2} - x(1 - \text{erf } x)$.

This equation has been worked out for phenolic paper laminate, the result being depicted in Figure 3.5.

From Figures 3.4 and 3.5 it is seen that local heating of phenolic paper is easily possible (a well known fact in hand soldering), but that the same operation on alumina is difficult.

3.2.2 Uniform Heating by Conduction Through the Support Plate

This situation exists in cases such as:

(i) soldering of hybrid circuits;
(ii) 'reflow' soldering of boards by heating from below.

It is interesting to consider the question of how much time is needed for the topside of the support plate to reach a certain temperature if the plate is heated from below.

Consider the plate without holes, components, *etc.*, using the parameters as shown in the sketch.

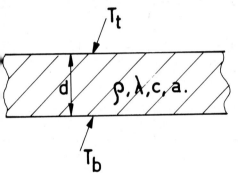

T_t and T_b are the temperature of the top and the bottom of the plate respectively
d is thickness of the plate
λ is heat conductivity
ϱ is density
c is specific heat
a is thermal diffusivity.

This case is treated in the book of Gröber *et al*, where a general graph is given from which the desired times can be derived. The times have been calculated for plates made of various materials and having various thicknesses (see Table 8.2). A heat source temperature of 240°C was chosen, the desired top temperature being 183°C.

Figure 3.6 gives the times *versus* the heat transfer coefficient, a, (in the range of 100-10000) and Figure 3.7 gives the times *versus* the thickness, d.

Both Figures can be considered as perpendicular sections through a three-dimensional diagram of time—thickness—transfer coefficient. The considerable influence of the value of the heat transfer coefficient a is apparent. In Figure 3.6 the lines for alumina and copper are almost straight, resulting from the fact that the temperature difference between the top side and the bottom side of the plate is very small (homogeneous temperature).

The heating of the plate then proceeds as given in Equation 3.1, but for thicker plates and larger values of a noteworthy deviations are observed.

For materials with lower conductivity than alumina, for instance phenolic paper, the lines in Figure 3.6 will bend. In this case, the temperature of the top

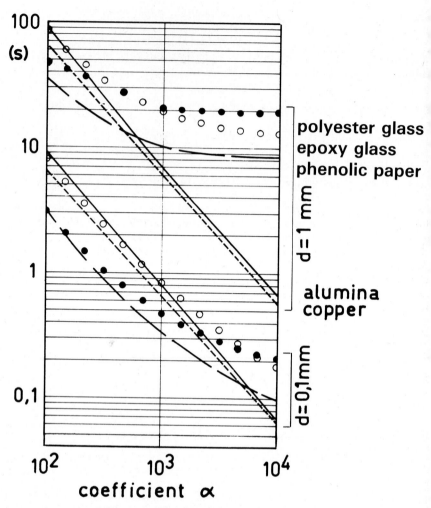

Fig. 3.6 Time to reach 183°C on the top side of a plate *versus* the heat transfer coefficient, α, at th
bottom side of the plate. Lines are shown for various materials: polyester glass, epoxy glass, phenoli
paper, alumina and copper.

face of the plate is no longer solely determined by the coefficient of heat transfer,
α, but also by the heat conductivity, λ.

For low values of α, the heating of the top face of a phenolic paper plate is
more rapid than that of a copper plate in spite of the much lower heat
conductivity. Besides heat transfer and heat conductivity, density and specific
heat also play a role.

In Figure 3.7, in which only two materials are shown, the same characteristics
can be observed as in Figure 3.6, displayed in another way.

The lines of the top and bottom faces of alumina plates for $\alpha = 100$, and also
for $\alpha = 1000$, coincide, but for $\alpha = 10000$ the difference mentioned earlier is
notable. The lines for the top face of phenolic paper are shown with the addition
of a line for $\alpha = \infty$, infinitely large.

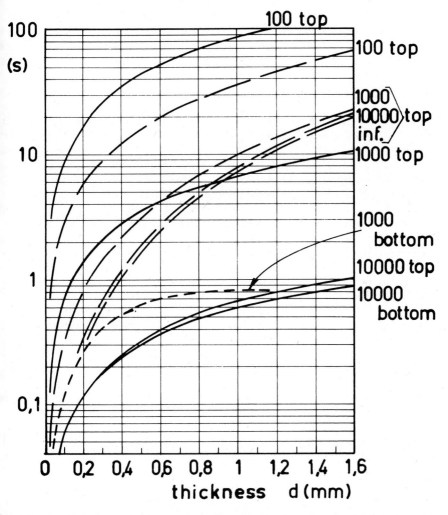

Fig. 3.7 Time to reach 183°C on bottom side and top side of a plate *versus* the thickness of the plate. The figures to the right of the figure give α at the bottom side of the plate. Full lines are for alumina, dashed lines for phenolic paper plates.

The bottom face is only present with one line for $\alpha = 1000$. For $\alpha = 10000$ the ine for the bottom face is horizontal at 0,008 s except for very small thickness <0,1 mm).

Some important conclusions can be drawn from Figures 3.6 and 3.7. For good onducting materials such as alumina, an increase of the heat transfer coefficient wers the heating time. For epoxy laminates, *etc.*, an increase of α above 1000 as only a limited effect (thickness 1 mm or more). On the other hand, it is oncluded that if for one reason or another such a material is chosen, an increase f the heating rate can not be obtained by increasing the heat transfer between the eat source and the lower face of this support plate.

Reflow Soldering

The preceding considerations are treated on a more practical basis i
Chapter 10.2 on reflow soldering methods, where various heating methods ar
discussed, such as contact with a hot plate and contact with hot oil or hot meta

Soldering of Printed Boards

In the wave and drag-soldering processes for printed boards with single-side
or double-sided conductor patterns, the lower faces of the boards are brough
into contact with a relatively large amount of solder. The supply of heat and c
solder are simultaneous. For the supply of heat, no problems at all exist for th
boards as the lower faces of these boards (together with the conductor pattern:
assume the soldering temperature within a very short time (within 0,1 s). Th
preheat treatment, which precedes the actual soldering operation, is therefore nc
carried out to obtain sufficient rate of heating of the board, but is mainl
intended to treat the flux. Moreover, the preheating serves the function o
reducing the temperature gradient from bottom to top of the board durin
soldering, thus reducing the tendency of the board to bend in the wave (se
Chapter 8.1.2).

3.3 HEATING OF COMPONENTS

The thermal aspects of the soldering of components involves two requirement
which at first sight seem diametrically opposed:

(i)   the leads of the components should be raised to a temperature high enoug
      for them to be wetted by the solder;
(ii) the temperature to which the component rises during soldering should nc
      be so high as to affect its operating characteristics.

Each component has its typical soldering range, *i.e.*, a range of values for th
solder bath temperature and for the immersion time (contact time), within whic
both of these requirements can be satisfied. There must be a good overla
between the soldering ranges of components of different types. The simple
means of ensuring this is to adjust the length of the leads [Klein Wassink].

In the next Section an electrical network will be discussed that can offer a fair
good simulation of the thermal behaviour of a component during soldering. Th
method of calculation based on this network allows the required solder bat
temperatures and contact times to be determined easily from a grapl
Conversely, the method can also be used to good advantage for designing ne
components that must be suited to a particular soldering method.

3.3.1   The Model and the Temperature—Time Diagram

The electrical network that serves as the simplest analogue for calculating tt
thermal behaviour of a component is shown in Figure 3.8. The compone:
consists of a body and a lead which is inserted through an opening in a singl
sided printed board. The thermal behaviour in cases where the lead is inserte
through a metallised hole in a double-sided board requires a more complicate
electrical analogue, which will be referred to briefly in the Section dealing wit
the validity of the model.

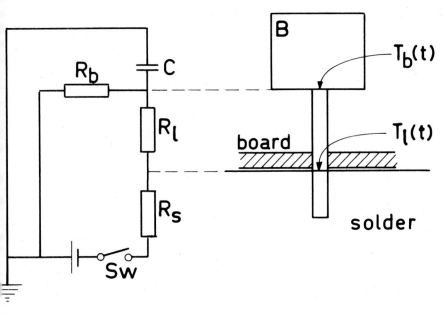

ig. 3.8 An electrical network (left) for simulating the thermal behaviour of an electronic ɔmponent (right), consisting of a body (B) with a lead, during soldering on a single-sided board. Closing the switch, Sw, corresponds to the moment of immersion in the solder bath.

Making contact with the solder bath corresponds to closing the battery switch, w, in the model. This has the effect of applying a step-function voltage to the etwork. The resultant increase in the potential at the various points in the etwork corresponds to the rise in temperature at the corresponding points in the ɔmponent. The value of the capacitance in the network corresponds to the hermal capacity of the body. For the sake of simplicity, it is assumed that no ɛmperature gradients occur in the body of the component, so that its ɛmperature is the same at all points. To calculate the behaviour of the potential ·s a function of time, it is sufficient in the case of Figure 3.8 to solve a simple ïrst-order differential equation. The model used here is therefore generally lassified as a 'first-order model'.

Solving the differential equation gives $T_l(t)$, the temperature of the lead at the .eight of the underside of the board and also $T_b(t)$, the temperature of the body, ·oth as a function of time [Verbeek].

These two temperatures must be known for an assessment of the success of the ɔldering process.

The moment at which contact between lead and solder bath starts is taken as ιe time $t = 0$. The solution for the temperature $T_b(t)$ is an equation similar to :quation 3.1.

$$T_b(t) = T_p + \left\{ \frac{T_s - T_a}{1 + (R_s + R_l)/R_b} - (T_p - T_a) \right\} \left\{ 1 - \exp \frac{-t}{RC} \right\} \quad \text{(Equation 3.2)}$$

'he resistance R is given by:

$$\frac{1}{R} = \frac{1}{R_b} + \frac{1}{R_s + R_l}$$

which is the expression for a parallel arrangement of the thermal resistances R_s and $(R_s + R_l)$.

The solution for the temperature $T_l(t)$ is:

$$T_l(t) = T_s - \frac{R_s}{R_s + R_l} \left\{ T_s - T_b(t) \right\} \qquad \text{(Equation 3.3)}$$

The significance of the symbols in these equations is:

$T_b(t)$ = temperature of the body as a function of time;
$T_l(t)$ = temperature of the lead as a function of time;
T_s = temperature of the solder bath;
T_a = temperature of the ambient air;
T_p = temperature of the body and the lead at the time $t=0$, as a result preheating;
R_s = interface resistance between solder bath and lead;
R_l = thermal resistance of the lead;
R_b = interface resistance between body and air;
C = heat capacity of the body.

It thus appears that the temperature of the lead, which is between the (high) solder bath temperature and the body temperature of the component, is derived by a simple 'potential division' in Figure 3.8. This division involves only the thermal resistances, R_s and R_l, and is independent of time. The temperature calculated from Equation 3.2 and Equation 3.3 are plotted in Figure 3.9 for component whose characteristic data are listed in Table 3.2 by way of example.

The time in Figure 3.9 is expressed in units of RC, the characteristic time

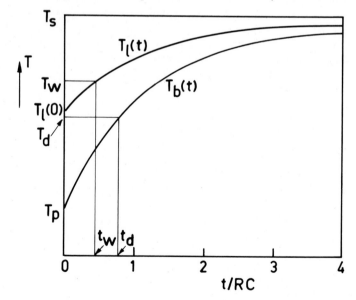

Fig. 3.9 A calculated temperature-time diagram for the soldering of an electronic component. T temperatures, $T_b(t)$ and $T_l(\cdot)$, are for the body and the lead of the component respectively. T_w is t wetting temperature of the lead; T_d is the temperature at which the component is damaged.

onstant of the component. In the model, the heat capacity of the lead is eglected so that its temperature becomes $T_l(0)$ at the same time as immersion egins.

When the damage temperature, T_d, of a component and the wetting emperature, T_w, of its lead are also known, the corresponding time durations t_d nd t_w can be derived from Figure 3.9. The contact time during soldering must be hosen between the limits represented by these quantities.

Table 3.2

Thermal Quantities of Figure 3.9 and Figure 3.10.

Temperature (°C)		Thermal Resistance (K/W)	
T_p	50	R_l	15
T_s	250	R_s	15
T_a	20	R_b	315
$T_b{}^{max}$	230 } calculated from the		
$T_l(0)$	150 } Equations 3.2 and 3.3		
T_d	145		
T_w	183 (the eutectic temperature of tin-lead)		

Note: $T_b{}^{max}$ is the maximum temperature that the body of the component would have after an nfinitely long period of time.

Figure 3.10 shows a temperature-time diagram derived from Figure 3.9 by giving

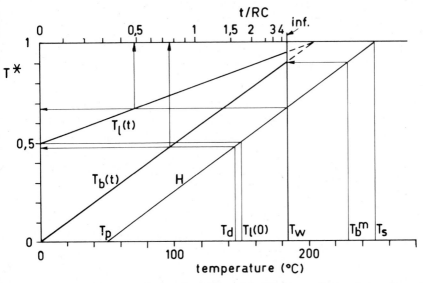

g. 3.10 The temperature-time diagram from Figure 3.9 with the coordinate axis transformed to ake the curves straight lines. H is the conversion line for transforming the temperature T (°C) into a mensionless quantity T^*. The dimensionless time axis is at the top; the unit of time is the RC onstant of the component. The temperature curves for the body and for the lead are the lines $T_b(t)$ nd $T_l(t)$; these lines are found from the calculated $T_b{}^{max}$ and $T_l(0)$. Taking $T_d = 145°C$ and $_w = 183°C$ as given data for the component and the solder, the time limits τ_d and τ_w can be read from the graph.

values to the coordinates such that the curves for $T_b(t)$ and $T_l(t)$ are straight line
Since a dimensionless quantity (T^*) is plotted instead of the temperature, th
diagram also gives a conversion line from which the temperature T correspondir
to T^* can be read, where T^* is equal to $(T - T_p)/(T_s - T_p)$.

The given linearised diagram, of course, only applies quantitatively t
components whose characteristic data (temperature and thermal resistance:
correspond to those contained in Table 3.2.

Starting with a damage temperature, T_d, of 145°C and a wetting temperature
T_w, of 183°C, it is first necessary to find the corresponding dimensionles
temperature on the vertical scale. With these and the two temperature lines th
limits τ_d and τ_w for the duration of contact are then found on the dimensionles
time axis. Each value between these limits, after multiplication by the tim
constant RC, gives an appropriate contact time for the component.

The conversion of Figure 3.9 into a graph containing only straight lines is
simple matter. From Equation 3.2 it can be deduced directly that $\left\{ T_b(t) - T_p \right.$
is proportional to $\left\{ 1 - \exp(-t/RC) \right\}$. The curves in Figure 3.9 can therefore b
transformed into straight lines by taking the scale distances along the t/RC axi
from $\left\{ 1 - \exp(-t/RC) \right\}$. In the case, frequently found in practice, wher
$R_b \gg R_s + R_l$, the proportionality factor is equal to $(T_s - T_p)$, so that T^* then goe
from 0 to 1 when t goes from 0 to ∞. If $(R_s + R_l)$ is not negligibly small compare
with R_b, then T^* at $\tau = \infty$ is somewhat less than 1. A similar approach applies fo
$T_l(t)$. The values of T_b^{max} and $T_l(0)$ can be calculated from the Equations 3.2 an
3.3. A blank graph has been appended for those readers who want to experimen
with the graphical method (Figure 3.11).

3.3.2   The Main Thermal Quantities in the Model

The dimensions of the component and the component lead must b
transformed into quantities that can be used in the model.

3.3.2.1   HEAT CAPACITY

The heat capacity, C, of a component is equal to ϱcV, where V is the volume o
the body, ϱ is its density and c its specific heat. The product, ϱc, and the therma
conductivity coefficient, λ, for various materials are given in Table 3.1. It can b
seen that the product, ϱc, has approximately the same value for various materials
so that it is not necessary to know the precise composition of the body in order t
calculate a reasonable value for the heat capacity.

3.3.2.2   THERMAL RESISTANCES

The thermal resistance, R_l, of the lead can be calculated from the relatio
$R = l/\lambda S$, where l is the soldering distance (or 'free length') of the lead and S th
area of its cross-section (Figure 3.8).

The thermal resistance of copper, aluminium and iron leads is calculated pe
millimetre of length, and with the widely used diameter of 0,6 mm it is equal t
10, 16 and 50 K/W respectively.

The thermal resistances, R_s and R_b, are interface resistances, R_s being betwee
the solder and the immersed part of the lead and R_b between the body and th
ambient air. Their values are calculated from the general formula $l/\alpha A$, where

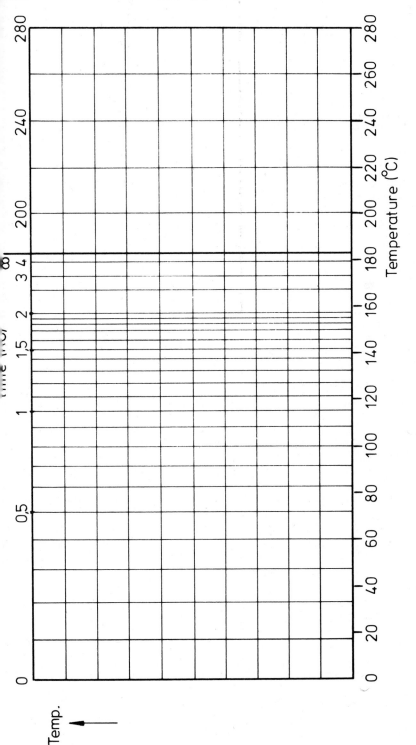

Fig. 3.11 Diagram for the graphical determination of the thermal behaviour of components with wire terminations during soldering.

is the appropriate heat-transfer coefficient and A the interface area. Uncertainti
exist regarding the thermal resistance, R_S, and these will be mentioned in t
Section on the validity of the model.

With an interface area of 10 mm², R_S can be assumed to have the order
magnitude of 10 K/W, with α taken as 10 kW/(m².K).

The value given for α is reasonably accurate for wave soldering. For dip soldering, a lower val
must be used, about 6 kW/(m².K). The thermal resistance, R_S, then has a value between 15 a
20 K/W. This means that in dip soldering the quantity R_S/R_1 is rather higher, as is reflected in t
longer contact time required. The increase in R_S affects the temperature of the body mainly throu
the increase of the time constant, RC. If the free length of the leads is not too small, however, t
body temperature after wave soldering is found to be only a few per cent higher than after
soldering (during the same time). Measurements and calculations agree completely on this point.

The interface area of the body is about 100 mm². The coefficient, α, for t
heat transfer from the body to the air is about 10 W/(m².K). The therm
resistance, R_b, thus amounts to about 10^3 K/W, a hundred times higher than R
so that it is often reasonable to allow for an infinite thermal resistance betwee
body and air.

3.3.2.3   THE DAMAGE TEMPERATURE

In the discussion of the model several references have already been made to t
damage temperature, T_d. In fact, T_d is not a fixed quantity, nor is it fixed f
each type of component. The damage temperature can best be regarded as t
temperature at which certain characteristics of the component change by mo
than a permissible percentage (see Chapter 7.4).

3.3.3   The Validity of the Model

The model described contains a number of simplifications that require som
explanation. It is assumed, for instance, that the heat capacity of the lead
negligible. This is of course admissible when the heat capacity of the lead is ver
much lower than that of the body. In general, this is the case, although exception
do exist, such as small ceramic capacitors. Because the heat capacity of the lea
differs from zero, the initial temperature, $T_1(0)$, of the lead is not produce
instantaneously on dipping. There is a delay of the order of 0,1 s. This means tha
the body temperature starts to rise rather less steeply than indicated b
Equation 3.2. A counteracting effect here is that of the heat capacity of the solde
itself round the end of the lead. The presence of the printed board has n
significant effect on the thermal behaviour, although in theory the board shoul
increase the thermal inertia. When single-sided boards are dipped, the undersid
with the conducting tracks comes into contact with the surface of the solder bat
immediately. The time to reach T_w is so short that there is no significant effect o
the thermal behaviour, as was shown in Chapter 3.2.2, and therefore the model
entirely acceptable in this respect.

For double-sided boards, where the solder penetrates the holes up to th
topside of the board, the model is still valid, though there are some reservation
In this situation, additional heat is transferred by the metallised wall of the ho
in the printed board, and the rising solder also brings its own heat with it. Th
electrical network that could be used as an analogue contains a larger number o
resistors and capacitors than the one in Figure 3.8. The behaviour of the extende
network has been calculated from computer programmes, but the results for th

ermal reliability were almost identical. It is therefore preferable to make the
lculations with the original model. Since the upperside of the printed board
w has to be wetted as well, the position for calculating the temperature of the
ad must be taken at the upperside, and not at the underside. This means that the
otential division' must be modified when Equation 3.3 is used: the heat
sistance, R_l, in Equation 3.2 has to be reduced by the correction term, $d/\lambda S$,
here d is the thickness of the board. The body heats up more quickly than the
modified model suggests.

The final factor limiting the validity of the model is the variation in the thermal
sistance, R_S. In the expression, $1/\alpha A$, for this resistance neither α nor A is
nstant. The coefficient, α, varies because of the marked variation in the
mperature at the lead/solder interface. In addition, the heat transfer is affected
 the layers of oxide and flux initially present, and also by the solvent that
aporates from the flux during soldering. The area A is not constant owing to
e rise in the solder level. Immediately after dipping, the meniscus of the solder
curved downwards; at the end, for complete wetting, the meniscus is curved
wards (Figure 3.12). With a lead of 0,6 mm diameter the difference in solder
el can be as much as 0,9 mm. The effect of this is to reduce the free length of
e lead, with full wetting, by about 1 mm (maximum), which means that the
dy is heated up rather more rapidly than the model predicts.

The overall effect of the deviations from the model is that the experimentally
served heating (and also the cooling) does not fully proceed along a simple
ponential curve. During heating (and cooling) the 'RC-time' increases, as has
en shown by a large number of experiments (see Figure 3.16).

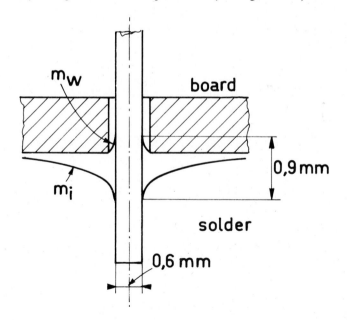

3.12 Solder 'climbing' a lead during soldering. Immediately after immersion of the lead in the
der bath the surface meniscus becomes convex (m_i). When the surface meniscus becomes concave
) the lead is fully wetted. For clarity the diameter of the hole in the printed board is shown
disproportionately large.

3.3.4　Model Calculations on Capacitors

As an example, the model in Figure 3.8 was used to calculate the therm behaviour of two very different capacitors. The data used are listed in Table 3. the free length of the leads was varied from a few mm to 10 mm. This paramete which has a considerable effect on the thermal behaviour, usually provides tl simplest means of adapting various components to the soldering process use The results of the calculations are summarised in Figure 3.13, which can I compared with Figure 3.2.

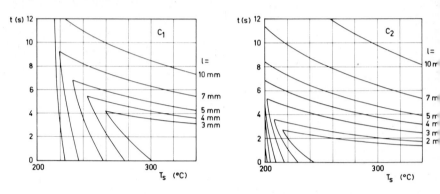

Fig. 3.13 Calculated thermal-behaviour profiles of the electrolytic capacitor, C_1, and microcapacitor, C_2 (Table 3.3). The contact time is plotted vertically, the solder-bath temperati horizontally. Beside the 'horizontal' branch of each profile the free length l is given for the lead which the curve relates.

Table 3.3

Data for Calculating the Thermal Behaviour of an Electrolytic
Capacitor (C_1) and of a Microcapacitor (C_2)

Component	C (J/K)	R_l/l (K/(W.mm))	R_S (K/W)	R_b (K/W)	T_d (°C)	T_w (°C)	$T_p =$ (°C
C_1	0,28	10	20	∞	85	183*	20
C_2	0,055	41,5	20	∞	114	183*	20

*the eutectic temperature of tin-lead solder

Complete wetting of the lead without damage to the capacitor occurs only I combinations of the contact time, t, and the solder-bath temperature, T_S, on t right of the 'vertical' branch of the appropriate profile. To the left of t 'vertical' branch the wetting is insufficient, and above the 'horizontal' branch t capacitor is damaged. The 'vertical' branches of some of the profiles of C_2 lie the left of the vertical axis ($T_S = 200$°C) for this capacitor and are therefore n shown. If both capacitors, C_1 and C_2, have to be soldered to a particular board acceptable contact time and solder-bath temperature can easily be found for bc by varying the length l.

A study has also been made of the extent to which the material of the le affects the thermal inertia, the materials compared being iron and copp (Figure 3.14). The wetting time for iron leads is about a sixth of that for copp

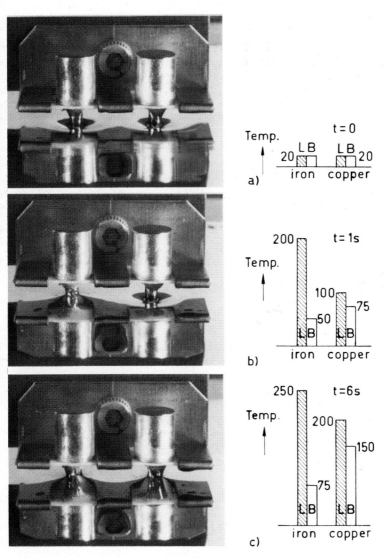

3.14 Comparison of the behaviour of iron-leads (*left* in the photographs) and copper leads (*right*). (a) At $t=0$ both leads are dipped into the solder. In both cases the meniscus is curved downwards. (b) After 1 second the iron lead is wetted (meniscus curved upwards). (c) After 6 seconds the copper lead is also wetted. The histograms give the corresponding lead temperatures, T_l, and body temperatures, T_b, in °C. L lead. B body.

...ds, under otherwise identical conditions. The temperature of a body with an ...n lead is significantly lower than that of the same body with a copper lead at all ...ating times.

It should be emphasised in passing that this superior soldering performance of ...n leads is not the only factor determining the choice of material.

3.3.5 Preheating

It is of interest to return to the question of preheating which has been
subject of some debate. Clearly, preheating will make the moment of wett
earlier. The Author's calculations, which closely resemble those made with
examples given in the previous Section, indicate that the time interval between
moment of wetting and the moment at which the body reaches the damag
temperature is independent of preheating. Thus, the moment at which dam
begins is brought forward to the same extent, so that preheating does not o
any wider a margin.

When the conditions of the soldering process are such that the lead is wet
immediately on immersion, the preheating only makes the onset of damage oc
earlier. Under these conditions the preheating therefore shortens the avail:
contact time, as demonstrated in Figure 3.15, in which lines are shown that h

Thermal resistance (K/W)	Temperature (°C)
$R_w = 25$	$T_{sol} = 240$
$R_s = 10$	$T_{wet} = 183$
$R_b = 1000$	$T_{amb} = 20$
$R \approx 34$	
$R = \dfrac{R_b(R_s + R_w)}{R_b + R_s + R_w}$	Thermal capacity C OPEN CHOICE

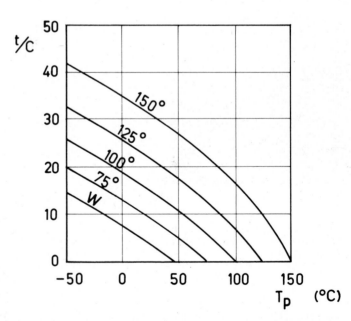

Fig. 3.15 The effect of preheating on soldering. The calculated (dimensionless) contact tim
plotted vertically, the preheating temperature T_p horizontally. W = wetting line; this gives
minimum time necessary for wetting the lead. The four other curves are 'damage' lines; the va
beside them are the temperatures at which damage occurs. The acceptable contact times lie betw
the wetting line W and the damage line.

:n calculated for the characteristic data given in the Figure. The curves give an
lication that the time-interval between wetting and damage is constant, at least
preheating temperatures lower than about 50°C, since the curves in that range
: parallel.
Finally, it should be noted that preheating is also applied for other reasons than
)se considered here, in particular to remove excess solvent from the flux and to
lit board warping during soldering.

$.6 Measurement of the Body Temperature of Components

'n connection with the work on the model for calculation, the Author has
ried out many measurements of the temperature of the body of components
ring the heating process. For this purpose, thermocouples were joined to
evant parts of the components, after which the leads of the components were
)ped in a stationary bath or in a wave of solder tin60-lead40. The thermocouple
es were of chromel-alumel having a diameter of 50 μm and were solidly
ached to the body of the component by spot welding in order to avoid contact
istances. The thermal conductances of the thermocouple wires can be ignored,
npared with that of the copper leads of the components measured, as they
ve a diameter of 0,6 mm. The leads were made perfectly solderable by a
:soldering operation. In addition, they were fluxed before each measurement
h activated colophony, which was subsequently dried with an air blower.
mponents measured comprise carbon resistors (0,33 W), flat film capacitors,
ite capacitors, micro-capacitors, *etc.*, of various sizes. During the experiments
ee parameters were varied:

i)   temperature of solder bath and solder wave;
i)   depth of immersion;
i)   soldering distance (length of lead between solder and body).

n normal soldering, the immersion time is only a few seconds, and the
ximum temperature of the body reached during the soldering period is much
ver than the ultimate temperature reached if the heating is continued. Figure 3.16
)ws a temperature-time curve of a flat foil capacitor (body length 10 mm, body
ume 280 mm³). At a solder temperature of 230°C, the ultimate temperature of
body is 202°C at an ambient temperature of 21°C. An analysis of the curve
)ws that during heating the rise in temperature is much more rapid at the
;inning than later on, compared with an exponential curve (see Equation 3.2).
e reasons underlying this phenomenon have been given in Section 3.3.3.
n Table 3.4 a number of results are given of measurements on the flat film
)acitor, also shown in Figure 3.16, and on a carbon resistor of type CR 25
33 Watt). Heating was performed by dipping.

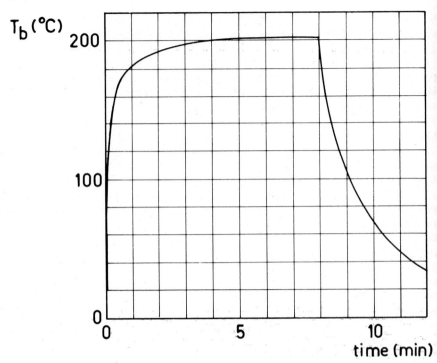

Fig. 3.16 Temperature-time curve of a flat film capacitor, showing the body temperature of component during prolonged immersion of the leads in solder at 230°C. The ultimate be temperature is 202°C.

Table 3.4

Body Temperature After 5 Seconds (°C)

Component	Temperature of Bath (°C)	Soldering Distance 4 mm Immersion Depth (mm)		Soldering Distance 2 ? Immersion Depth (m	
		2	4	2	4
Capacitor	230	115	118	129	133
	260	141	142	151	157
Resistor	230	177	176	183	186
	260	179	185	188	193

If all measurements are averaged, including those in the Table, some sim rules of thumb are obtained:

(i) increasing the depth of immersion from 2 to 3 mm gives a temperature of the body of about 1 K;

(ii) increasing the length of the lead reduces the temperature of the body about 5 K per mm extra length;

(iii) wave soldering produces a 5-10% higher body temperature than soldering;

iv) a 10% increase in solder temperature gives a corresponding increase in body temperature of about 10%.

If the measurements are repeated with the same component after it has been booled to ambient temperature again, the results are satisfactorily reproduced. However, when the same measurement is made on another component of the ame type, a considerable difference may be observed, mainly caused by the lack f definition of the correct measuring place in the body, or at the very end of the ad. The temperature difference may be as great as 10 K.

A consequence of this is that the results of the measurements have a large egree of uncertainty and hence in most cases are not preferable to those of the ather crude calculations according to the model discussed.

With small components, like carbon resistors and small ceramic capacitors, the eat capacity of the lead is not negligible compared with the heat capacity of the ody of the component. The smaller the component, the more the total thermal naracteristic of the component is determined by the lead. All very small omponents therefore behave in more or less the same manner. They seldom ause thermal problems with the soldering of the leads, because these components re soldered simultaneously with other components that possess a much greater hermal inertia. On the other hand, the highest temperature of the body of a small omponent reached in a soldering operation is much higher than that of larger nes, as is shown in Table 3.4. This can be easily appreciated.

In the measurements described, the components were analysed separately. The measurements of the body temperature of components during soldering can aturally be carried out on production boards, applying a wave soldering process. uch work is quite laborious, but in this way the effects can be obtained of the ackage density, of adjacent components, of the width of the tracks, as well as of rocess parameters such as speed of travel and preheating treatment [Kessler *et al*].

,4 THERMAL ADAPTATION

The places to be soldered must reach the wetting temperature within the short eriod of contact of the board with the solder bath. If this temperature is not ached locally, the quality of the joints will be inadequate. Various factors can npede the rise of temperature during the soldering process:

(i) thermally unfavourable components having large heat capacity, such as coil cans, ground rails, and electrolytic capacitors with too short terminations;
(ii) a pattern layout on a double-sided board having plated holes with too many outgoing conductors at the component side;
iii) the clearance between termination and hole wall of plated holes being too small.

Because the supply of heat for proper penetration of the solder into the oldered joint takes place to a large extent via the termination of the component, should be specified that the protruding length of the termination below the oard be not less than 1,0 mm, so that a sufficiently large area is in contact with e molten solder. For connections on printed boards without hole plating, this rotruding length serves also to produce a sufficiently strong soldered onnection.

3.4.1 Raised Mounting of Components

In connection with the thermal demand of the component itself, raise mounting is sometimes necessary for good penetration of the solder. Wi increased height of assembly there is an increasing thermal resistance in t direction of the component, so that more heat remains available for the solderi side.

The effect of lead length on the wetting time of leads has been extensive discussed in Chapter 3.3. The model given there makes it possible to quantify t influence of increased mounting distance of a particular component. Chapter 7.3 a measuring method is described for the thermal demand components, from which the 'specific soldering distance' can be obtained, which the height of mounting above the printed board is related.

This specific soldering distance is determined at an immersion depth of 2 m and with a bath temperature of 235°C.

In these conditions the distance then corresponds roughly to the minimu height of mounting necessary for thermal reasons, depending on the type printed board:

  (i) for printed boards without hole plating, the length of the terminatio above the printed board must be at least equal to the specific solderi distance minus the board thickness;

  (ii) for printed boards with plated holes, the length of the leads above t printed board must be at least equal to the specific soldering distance.

With a smaller length of protrusion than 2 mm on the solder side the minimu height of mounting must be increased. The requisite soldering distance depen also on the temperature of the solder, although this is not mentioned explicitly Chapter 7.3. A higher temperature of the solder provides some extra margin, the length of the leads is not shortened.

The minimum soldering distance in conditions other than the standard on can be determined by measurement or by calculation. For a quick referenc Table 3.5 gives general rules, which are applicable to copper leads with a diamet of 0,6 mm.

A known example of a large heat demand is represented by ground rails a stiffening strips to be soldered to a printed board. This unfavourable situatic can be improved considerably by punching holes in the strips, as shown Figure 3.17.

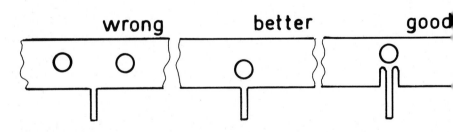

Fig. 3.17 Adaptation of metallic strips to be soldered in printed boards.

Table 3.5

Rules of Thumb Regarding Soldering Distance, s.

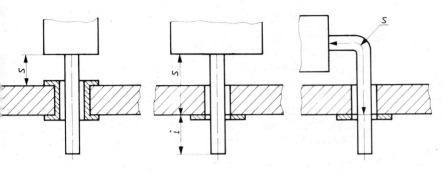

		Mounting Condition
Immersion depth at 235°C	⩾ 2 mm	s ⩾ specific soldering distance (see note 1)
	between 1 and 2 mm	s ⩾ specific soldering distance $+ 3(2 - i)$
Soldering temperature		for each 25 K bath temperature increment, a 1 mm less immersion depth is tolerable

Notes:

The soldering distance (with a view to good penetration), in the case of a wire with a diameter of 0,6 mm and depths of immersion of 2 mm and 1 mm respectively, need never exceed 3,5 mm and 6,5 mm respectively, whatever the heat capacity of the component.

Raised mounting may be necessary to prevent thermal damage to a component which is sensitive in this respect. It may also make it possible to use components which, were they to be mounted directly on the printed board, would have to be rejected. For further details on such raised mounting, reference should be made to the relevant component specification.

3.4.2   Printed Boards

Single-sided boards do not give rise to thermal problems, because the heating of the lower face of the boards is very rapid. For boards with plated holes the requirement, discussed in Chapter 7.7.2, is that the holes fill completely with solder within the contact time of 3 seconds. These 3 seconds apply at a bath temperature of 235°C, but without any preheating of the board.

To allow this requirement to be met, it is necessary to ensure a greater thermal supply to the holes and less thermal dissipation from the holes, according to whether the printed boards are thicker or contain more copper as intermediate layers in multilayer boards.

This can be achieved by making the width of the conductors in contact with the solder lands as large as possible on the solder side, and the total width of the conductors leading from these places on the component side (and in the intermediate layers if any) as small as possible (Figure 3.18). A larger space

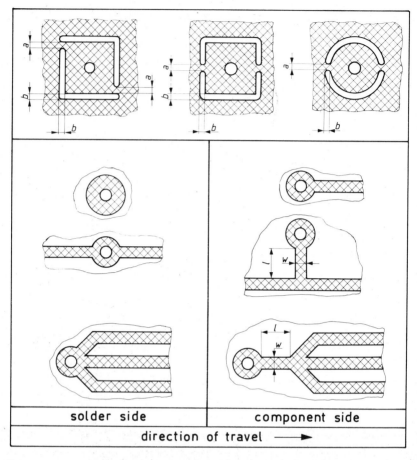

| solder side | component side |

direction of travel ➜

Fig. 3.18 Thermal adaptation of configuration on printed boards with metallised holes. Above: solder lands on component side in large copper areas. $a = 0,3$ mm; $b \geqslant 0,25$ mm. Below: configuration of solder side compared with configuration on component side. $l > 3w$.

between the wall of the hole and the termination also has a favourable effect in this respect. The maximum board thickness at which these measures can still prove advantageous is about 2 mm.

3.4.3 Plating Thickness in the Holes

The influence of the plating thickness is evident. When the solder penetrates into the hole, it brings with it its own heat, but it is cooled down by the cold metal plating, the amount of cooling depending on the plating thickness. It is easy to calculate the combined temperature, T, of the solder plus the plating, if the board material is assumed not to play a significant part.

For a hole with an internal diameter of 0,8 mm, a board thickness of 1,6 mm (hole volume 0,8 mm³), a solder temperature of 250°C and a board temperature of 25°C, the temperature T follows from:

$$0,8 \times (250 - T) \times (\varrho c)_{\text{solder}} = \text{vol}_{\text{copper}} \times (T - 25) \times (\varrho c)_{\text{copper}}$$

(for the quantity ϱc see Table 3.1)

able 3.6 gives the values of T for three plating thicknesses.

Table 3.6

Thermal Effect of Plating Thickness in the Hole

lating ickness (μm)	Cross-Sectional Area of the Plating (mm²)	Volume of the Plating (mm³)	T (°C)	Conduction of Wall Conduction of Hole
10	$2,5 \times 10^{-2}$	4×10^{-2}	229	0,37
25	$6,5 \times 10^{-2}$	10×10^{-2}	204	1
70	$19 \ \times 10^{-2}$	31×10^{-2}	150	4,6

In reality, the temperatures will be lower still for two reasons:

i) conduction of heat into the laminate material;
ii) the internal surface of the copper plated hole is often provided with a solder plating, which also has to be melted.

The area of the hole is 50×10^{-2} mm². Table 3.6 also gives the relative thermal nduction of the wall of the hole compared with the hole itself filled with solder. r a wall thickness of over 25 μm, the conduction of the wall contributes more an 50% of the total conductance.
With a greater plating thickness, greater cooling but better conduction are served. Experiments show that the optimum is about 30 μm. Figure 3.19 ustrates two plated holes.

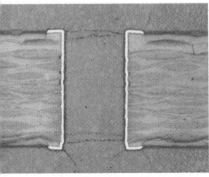

. **3.19** Plated holes in epoxy glass fibre reinforced laminate (note the glass fibres). Internal meter of the holes 0,8 mm, plating thickness 25 and 70 μm. The occurrence of an air pocket (void) in a soldered hole or joint is not exceptional (see Chapter 8.4.4).

Besides the thickness of the plating, its quality is also very important and can : investigated by metallographic methods [Bulwith] or by measuring the sistance between upper and lower solder land [Weinstock].
The heating of the walls of the holes is retarded if large solder lands are present the top side of the board, or when the lands are connected to relatively wide nductors. The effect of the land diameter will be more pronounced the smaller e plating thickness in the holes.

3.4.4   Wires in the Holes

The generally accepted opinion that wires in the holes always help to fill th
has not been confirmed experimentally. Results are dependent on the h
transfer from the bath to the hole with wire, the heat transfer in wave solder
being better than that in dip soldering.

The influence of the heat that is transported with the solder itself is a
reflected in the effect of the clearance between wire and internal wall of the h
[Tamura *et al*]. The number of joints with imperfect solder take-up decrea
when the clearance is increased up to 0,7 mm, depending of course on the therm
capacity of the body of the component. Because such faults are linked with
time that is available for heat transport, a clear effect of the time of contact w
the solder bath, and also of the temperature of the bath is to be seen. High
temperatures give fewer imperfections.

In connection with this, it should be mentioned that soldering tests on
soldering machine using test boards without components in general yield bet
results than those with components. Hence, such tests are of limited value.

Chapter 4

SOLDER ALLOYS

Solder alloys are sometimes explicitly called soft-solder alloys to distinguish them from brazing alloys. The main constituents of solders are tin and lead, but they also often contain certain amounts of other relatively low-melting metals such as bismuth, indium, antimony and silver.

TIN-LEAD SOLDERS

There is a great variety of solder alloys based on tin and lead, many of them being used in practice. For soldering in electronics, the solder with 60-62 mass % of tin and 38-40% of lead is the one most commonly used.

.1   The Use of Solders

Soft soldering is an operation in which metallic parts are joined by a molten filler metal having a melting temperature lower than 450°C. In practice, most soft-solder alloys have a melting point much lower than 450°C, that is between °C and 300°C.

The technique of soldering was already known many centuries ago [Allen, Walters]. In Roman times a tin-lead alloy was used to join leaden water pipes. This alloy, 'tertiarium', consisting of one part of tin and two parts of lead, is still used today for this purpose.

In the modern industrial era, the electronic industry produces the greatest number of soldered joints, about 10^{12} annually, but as regards volume it consumes about 40% of the world production of soft solders. The rest is used, in approximately equal quantities by the packaging industry for metal cans and by the automotive industry for engine radiators, and for engineering and building purposes.

The free-world production of tin is about 200 000 tons and of lead 4 million tons per annum. The known world resources of tin are about 10 million tons.

Use of tin:	tin plate	33%
	solder	26%
	other alloys	23%
	chemicals	7%
	other uses	11%

Use of lead:	accumulators	48%
	petrol additives	16%
	chemicals and paint	15%
	ammunition	6%
	solder	4%
	other uses	11%

The total free-world production of soft solders is thus about 2×10^5 tons year [Lea]. With a price ratio of tin to lead of 20:1 the tin content in comm solder alloys accounts for about 95% of the total solder value.

Of the very wide range of solders that can be made by alloying various meta only a limited number are used for the electrical interconnection of electro components. Of these solder alloys, the alloy of tin and lead with near-eutec composition is the one mainly used. Only if specific requirements have to fulfilled are other alloys considered.

The special position of the mentioned tin-lead alloy is due to a combination useful properties with only a few drawbacks:

(i)   because of the affinity between tin and many other metals, good wetting c be achieved with the aid of only mildly active fluxes;

(ii) the solder alloy itself has no brittle intermetallic compounds. Mechani strength values of solder joints are low, but this is the case with all so solder alloys;

(iii) the melting point (183-189°C) lies well above the maximum serv temperature of electronic equipment, but is low enough to permit the desi of components that can endure the high temperature associated with soldering process;

(iv) though the solder oxidises quite rapidly, the characteristics of the tin oxi films pose relatively few problems compared with the oxide films of so other low-melting metals.

4.1.2   Types of Solid Solder Metals

For soldering in electronics, the range of preferred types of solder alloys in and solid-wire form given in Table 4.1 suffices in most cases. The soft-sol alloys listed have been ranked according to the tin-lead ratio, which has b graded in useful steps. The specific alloys have been selected from the exist standardised alloys.

The number of compositions to be included in any standardised range i matter of personal discretion. In Table 4.1 the tin contents, besides the genera applied 100%, 60% and 0%, have been chosen as 35%, 20%, 5% and 1%. practice, however, many intermediate compositions are used.

The extremities of the selection are self-explanatory: pure tin and pure le Alloys in the vicinity of the eutectic composition, *i.e.*, the tin-lead alloys with lowest melting points, obviously have the widest field of application. Preferer is given to the alloy tin60-lead40, which is more widely used than the eutec alloy tin62-lead38.

Alloys with a higher tin content than 60%, which are consequently m expensive, find very limited application. Those with a lower tin content than eutectic alloy are often chosen mainly because of their lower cost.

Table 4.1

Selection of Soft-Solder Alloys

Uses	Properties			Comparable National Material Standards and Designations				
	Designation	Melting Point or Range °C	Density at 20°C g/cm³	France	Germany	Great Britain	Japan	USA
Solder manufacture, tinning	Sn99,95	232	7,3		Sn99,95 DIN 1704	grade T$_1$ BS 3252	Tin metal class 1A JIS H 2108	Grade AA ASTM B 339-72
Joining electronic components	SnPb40	183-189	8,5	60/40 NF C90-550	L-Sn60Pb DIN 1707	BS solder K and KP BS 219	H60S H60A JIS Z 3282	Alloy Grades 60A and 60B ANSI/ASTM B 32-76 Sn60 QQ-S-571
Step soldering, tinning of winding wire	PbSn35	183-245	9,5		L-PbSn35(Sb) DIN 1707	BS solder H BS 219	H35S H35A JIS Z 3282	Alloy Grade 35A and 35B ANSI/ASTM B 32-76 Pb65 QQ-S-571
Soldering of mechanical components	PbSn20Sb1	183-277	9,8				H20B JIS Z 3282	Alloy Grade 20C ANSI/ASTM B 32-76 Sn20 QQ-S-571
High Service Temperature	PbSn5	300-315	11,2	5/95 NF C90-550			H5S H5A JIS Z 3282	Alloy Grade 5A and 5B ANSI/ASTM B 32-76 Sn 5 QQ-S-571
Good strength at elevated temperatures	PbAg2,5Sn1	295-320	11,3	0/97/Ag3 NF C90-550	L-PbAg3 DIN 1707			Alloy Grade 1,5S ANSI/ASTM B 32-76 Ag1,5 QQ-S-571
Solder manufacture	Pb99,99	327	11,3		Pb99,99 DIN 1719	Pb99,99 BS 334 Type A	Pig lead special class JIS H 2105	Corroding lead ASTM B 29-55

Note: It is the custom, in the abbreviated designation of the composition of the solder, to mention the metal with the highest content first.
Example: solder SnPb40, PbSn50, PbSn40; mass per cent of tin 60, 50, 40 respectively.

A lower tin content increases the liquidus temperature and in general decreas‹ the wetting properties. The minimum permissible tin content depends on th specific application. Instead of PbSn20, the alloy PbSn20Sb1 is mentionec because this alloy is more readily available. In special cases, the high-lead solde: are sometimes used if afterwards a second soldering operation must be performe on the same product; for this second soldering operation, the solder SnPb40 or still lower-melting solder is used.

The properties of the solder alloys change only gradually with the ratio of th main constituents and there is seldom a need for a precise value of this ratio. Ti and lead contents therefore need not be specified to a greater accuracy than ±1 %‹

Special Alloys

Outside the range of the general purpose alloys so far mentioned, other alloy exist that are particularly suitable for meeting specific requirements; in fact th number of soft-solder alloys is very large.

The special properties of the other alloys may be associated with:

(i)   dissolution of base metals into the molten solder;
(ii) strength properties;
(iii) melting point;
(iv) specific physical properties.

4.1.3   Cored Wire

Many alloys are available as flux-cored solder wire for use with a solderin‹ iron. The alloy with 60% tin and 40% lead is the universal solder for quality wor‹ in electronics, certainly when heat-sensitive parts have to be soldered.

Alloys with less tin (available in 50, 45, 40, 35, 30, 20, 15%) are cheaper, bu‹ their liquidus temperature is higher, necessitating a higher working temperatur‹ (= bit temperature). In the cored solder wires, various fluxes are supplied; th‹ amount is about 20 volume per cent, equivalent to 3 mass per cent (see Chapte‹ 11.1). The production costs of the wires are virtually independent of th‹ composition. Because of the different densities of the alloys, the price difference‹ between wires with various compositions are smaller than would be expecte‹ from the difference in metal prices (Table 4.2).

Table 4.2

Relative Prices of Cored Solder Wire SnPb40 and PbSn40

1983	Tin	Lead	Flux	Metal SnPb40	Metal PbSn40	Making + Shaping Ø 1,2 mm	Wire with 20 Vol% of Flux SnPb40	PbSn40	
Price per kg	30	1,5		18,60	12,90	2,50	20,50	15,00	fl.
Density	7300	11300	1100	8500	9300				kg/m‹
Price ratio per kg of metal							1,44	1	
Price ratio per kg of wire							1,36	1	
Price ratio per volume of metal in the wire							1,25	1	

Note: Prices, in Dutch currency, are only indicative

ecial Alloys for Flux-cored Solder

Adding copper or silver to the solder reduces the dissolution of copper or silver m the soldering iron bit or from the workpiece.
Examples of such alloys are:

Alloy (mass %)		
	I	II
Sn	50	62
Pb	48,5	36
Cu	1,5	
Ag		2

The soft soldering of aluminium is difficult because of the oxide film on solid iminium, which cannot be easily removed. Joints on aluminium can be made th the solder alloy tin80-zinc20, but these joints corrode rapidly in (salt) water. ix-cored solder with 80,1% lead, 18% tin and 1,9% silver (working nperature 350°C) gives better results (trade name: Multicore Alu-Sol 45D) llen], see also Chapter 6.1.3.2.

.4   Health Aspects of Soft-Solder Metal

Apart from tin and lead, the solder alloys contain only relatively small amounts other heavy-metal elements. Cadmium and zinc, which may constitute a health zard because of their low vapour pressure [Kosnač *et al*], are seldom found wadays in solders used in electronics. The lead in the solder, although a tentially dangerous element, has never been reported to cause illness. Lead in : atmosphere of a soldering workshop is generally far below the maximum owable value (TLV = 0,15 mg/m^3), certainly when the workshop is ventilated, th the result that lead poisoning by inhalation does not occur [Boogaerdt *et al*].)wever, if dry solder dross is scooped from a bath the whirled lead dust may fer a hazard, so that in this case a dust mask should be worn.

Hand soldering operators who are in continuous and long term contact with : solder, and who may smoke or eat during their work, could be expected to)w detectable effects. Experiments reveal that the lead level in the blood of :h workers is equivalent to that of a control group which has no contact with der at all [Barrett *et al*, Sidhu]. Hence, there exists no danger of intoxication used by ingestion of lead during soldering. (Nevertheless, it is recommended t, after handling solder, risks should be avoided by washing hands before ing and smoking) [see also Courtney].

?   METALLURGY OF TIN-LEAD ALLOYS

A significant property of these low-melting alloys is their tendency to undergo uctural change at the operating temperature, even if this is room temperature. ie low mechanical strength values, especially the low creep strength values, are ated to this structural instability. Another characteristic of the tin-lead alloys, d of many other tin alloys, is the relatively fast solid state reaction with ments such as gold and copper, giving rise to intermetallic compounds.

4.2.1 Phase Diagram

The tin content of the alloys that are used for soldering may vary considerabl
depending on the application. Moreover, other elements may be added. With lc
contents of these other elements, their influence remains insignificant and
mostly neglected. However, the precise positions of characteristic points in t
phase diagram are then uncertain. The phase diagram presented in Figure 4.1 w
assist in understanding the behaviour of tin-lead alloys [Smithells]. In tl
diagram the temperature is plotted along the vertical axis and the compositi
along the horizontal axis.

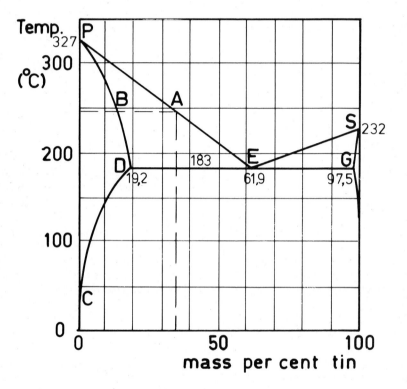

Fig. 4.1 Tin-lead phase diagram, showing the eutectic temperature of 183°C and the eutec
composition of about 62 mass % of tin.

In Figure 4.1, the compositions are specified in mass percentages, as this
always the case in soldering practice. If the composition is specified in atomic p
cent, conversion into mass per cent can be carried out as follows:

$$mass \text{ \% } tin = 100 \times \frac{atomic \text{ \% } tin}{atomic \text{ \% } tin + 1{,}746 \times (100\text{-}atomic \text{ \% } tin)}$$

Point P represents the melting point of pure lead; point S is the melting point of pure tin. Point E is the melting point of the so-called 'eutectic composition', tin62-lead38 (26 atomic % lead). In terms of temperature, this point is called the 'eutectic temperature' and is situated at 183°C. Sometimes tin63-lead37 is specified as the eutectic composition, especially in the catalogues of solder manufacturers.

Above the lines P-E-S (called the 'liquidus') in the diagram, only liquid exists. Below the line P-D-G-S (called the 'solidus') in the diagram, exclusively solid exists. In the intermediate range, solid and liquid exist together. If, for instance, the high lead-bearing alloy, lead65-tin35, cools down from the liquid state, then at approximately 245°C (point A), segregation of lead-rich crystals commences. These lead-rich crystals have absorbed in their space-lattice so many tin atoms that their composition is not 100% lead, but corresponds to point B in the diagram. As a result of the segregation of these crystals, the composition of the liquid shifts more to the tin side, while its solidifying temperature is lowered. Upon continued cooling, this shift continues, accompanied by continuing segregation of lead-rich crystals. In this process the composition of the liquid moves along the line A-E, and that of the segregating and segregated lead along the line B-D, that is to say that on continued cooling the already segregated lead-rich crystals absorb still more tin.

When the liquid has attained the composition of point E at a temperature of 183°C, it is in equilibrium not only with segregating lead-rich crystals having composition D, but also with tin-rich crystals having composition G. The composition of the liquid now ceases to shift, whereas crystallisation continues at constant temperature and composition of the liquid: the 'eutectic temperature' and the 'eutectic composition'. During this crystallisation process a closely intermixed structure is formed of very fine lead-rich crystals of composition D and tin-rich crystals of composition G. Embedded in this structure are the larger, previously segregated tin-bearing, (primary) lead-rich crystals. Thus the solidification process of lead65-tin35 solder stretches over a range of approximately 60 K. From 245°C to 183°C, the solder gradually passes through a pasty state.

A solder of eutectic composition does not have a solidifying range, but has a solidifying or melting point. Figure 4.2 shows the structure of tin60-lead40 alloy, which is close to the eutectic composition. The intermixed structure is clearly visible. The lead-rich crystals are black, the tin-rich crystals white. The oblique feature is a lead-rich primary crystal. Within this black crystal, small white spots are visible, due to secondary crystallisation of tin-rich crystals. The lead-rich crystals after solidification have a composition corresponding to point D of Figure 4.1, but at room temperature the lead-rich crystals cannot contain more tin than is given by point C, so that during cooling tin has to precipitate.

The solder structure with its large interfacial area has the tendency to coarsen and thus to change its appearance. At 100°C, the changes proceed rapidly. As a consequence of the precipitation, recrystallisation and coarsening, the mechanical and physical properties of the alloys also change. This is particularly noticeable in such properties as strength, superconductivity [Livingstone] and intensity of X-rays from standard samples used in quantitative spectroscopy [Glade et al]. The change is more noticeable with chill-cast materials than with slowly cooled specimens (Figure 4.3).

Solder Alloys

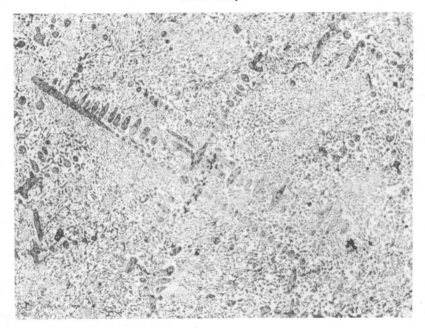

Fig. 4.2 Microstructure* of tin60-lead40 alloy (with 30 volume per cent of lead) having a near eutectic composition. The sloping feature in the figure is a primary lead crystal. Magnification 120×

In Figure 4.3, the structure of the lead65-tin35 alloy is shown immediately after solidification and after a heat treatment for different casting conditions. In Figure 4.3b, the primary crystallisation is no longer visible and the appearance has completely changed. This effect makes microscopic analysis of solder alloys rather complicated.

4.2.2 Cooling Curves

The heat dissipated on cooling and solidifying of solder offers the possibility of a simple, rapid, approximate analysis of its composition. For this purpose a quantity of the solder, for example 20 grams, is melted in a small porcelain laboratory crucible at a temperature of approximately 300°C. A thermocouple is placed in the molten solder, and the molten solder is then allowed to cool. During the cooling, the temperature is continuously recorded. Provided no solidification occurs, temperature decreases regularly, but, as soon as solidification

---

*Note: Metallographic sections of soft solders can be etched in different reagents [Eyre, Anon. Ref 27], including:

   (i) hydrochloric acid in alcohol;
  (ii) nitric acid in alcohol;
 (iii) glycerine-acetic acid;
 (iv) ammonia + hydrogen peroxide.

In many cases etching can be omitted.

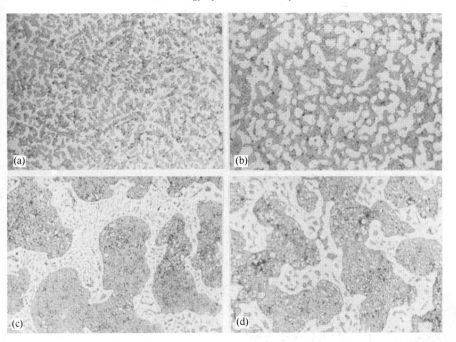

Fig. 4.3 Microstructure of lead65-tin35 alloy: (a) after solidification by rapid cooling; (b) as (a), followed by 300 hours, 155°C; (c) after solidification by slow cooling; (d) as (c), followed by 300 hours, 155°C. Magnification of the four photographs is 180×.

commences, heat is liberated, causing a slowdown in the cooling (Figure 4.4). Consequently, at incipient solidification, a break in the cooling or freezing curve is witnessed. For lead65-tin35 solder this should occur at 245°C (point A in Figure 4.1), but due to undercooling the break in the curve occurs at a somewhat lower temperature, A′.

While the cooling is taking place, the lead-rich crystals segregate continuously until the temperature drops a few degrees below the eutectic temperature, again as the result of undercooling. After a certain amount of undercooling (at point E′), the tin-rich crystals start segregating and the liberated heat causes the temperature to rise again until the eutectic temperature of 183°C is attained. This temperature is then maintained for some time until the solder has completely solidified. Thereafter cooling is resumed.

With 100% tin, the undercooling may reach several degrees below the melting point of tin (232°C) before solidification (with release of latent heat of fusion) again raises the temperature to this point; similar arguments apply to the eutectic alloy. If the alloy contains more than two constituents, the freezing process is much more complicated and interpretation of the freezing curve is correspondingly more difficult. A horizontal part of the curve a few degrees below 183°C is indicative of admixture of low-melting metal or silver to the tin-lead alloy.

Though the solidification of the solder is a rapid phenomenon, its duration is not negligible in practical soldering. It is erroneous to think that eutectic solder, which is known to have a solidifying point, solidifies more rapidly than a solder having a solidifying range.

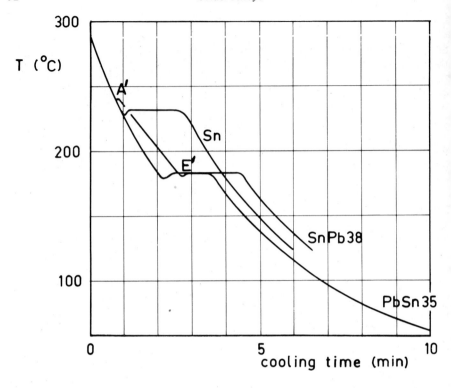

Fig. 4.4 Cooling curves of solders of different compositions. At the melting (eutectic) temperature the cooling is interrupted for a while and a horizontal part of the curve is observed. Note the undercooling at the beginning of the horizontal part of the curves.

During solidification, heat must be dissipated, including:

(i) the latent heat of fusion (approximately 5×10^4 J/kg);
(ii) the specific heat (which in this temperature range is approximately 200 J/(kg.K)).

Thus, in the solidification time of a eutectic alloy 5×10^4 J/kg must be dissipated whilst for an alloy with a solidification range of 10 K this is $(5 \times 10^4 + 10 \times 200)$ J/kg, which is only 4% more. Consequently, the solidification times for both types of alloy are not significantly different.

4.2.3 Tin Pest

Tin pest is the disintegration of metallic tin into a grey powder. This disintegration is a result of the allotropic transformation of β-tin into α-tin which is associated with an increase in volume of 26%, causing disintegrating of the material. The transformation may occur after a long incubation period at temperatures below 13°C, the rate of transformation being highest at approximately -30°C. Subjecting the material to a mechanical load (tensile stress) considerably accelerates the process. With electroplated pure tin coatings

a copper after long exposure at low temperature it is possible to encounter
transformation, but not with hot dip coating [Spergel].

Solder with 40% lead is seldom affected by tin pest provided that inoculation
with previously transformed grey tin is avoided. The transformation can be
entirely suppressed by adding 0,1% of antimony or 0,5% of bismuth to the solder
[Bornemann, Williams].

4.4   Whiskers

Pure tin, particularly electrodeposited tin, is prone to whisker generation, but
tin-lead solder having a tin content below 70% is practically exempt from this
problem (see Chapter 6.7).

4.5   Intermetallic Layers

The strong interaction between the solder, especially its tin content, and some
base metals results in the formation of intermetallic layers which grow rapidly at
high temperature [Brothers, Kay *et al*]. As the intermetallic layers are brittle, the
layers can have a detrimental effect on the mechanical properties of the soldered
joints [Zürn *et al*, Saperstein *et al*]. In other cases, the wettability is adversely
affected by the intermetallic layers.

4.5.1   TIN-GOLD INTERMETALLICS

The growth of the intermetallic layer between tin and gold is extremely rapid,
giving rise to the compounds $AuSn$, $AuSn_2$ and $AuSn_4$ (mainly $AuSn_2$, *cf.*
Chapter 4.4.4). After 300 hours at 150°C, a total layer thickness of about 40 μm
has been formed.

Gold wires can be very efficiently bonded by thermocompression-soldering, in
which the wires are pushed into a solder layer with a hot pin at a temperature
below the melting point of the solder. Later on, however, the wires are consumed
because of the formation of intermetallic layers (Figure 4.5). After about 400
hours a wire of original diameter 45 μm will have been completely consumed.

This problem can be overcome by applying copper wires, which for the sake of
bonding efficiency are gold plated (1 μm). Another approach is to use a different
solder composition, for instance a tin-lead-indium alloy [Braun].

The aforementioned growth rate is only one fifth of the rate reported for the
growth between gold wires and plated solder [Hall *et al*].

4.5.2   TIN-COPPER INTERMETALLICS

Between tin and copper, layers of Cu_3Sn (ε-phase) and Cu_6Sn_5 (η-phase) are
observed (see the copper-tin phase diagram in Figure 4.28). Figure 4.6 shows the
ε and η-phases grown on tin-plated copper. The thickness of the intermetallic
layers increases with time, following approximately $\delta = k\sqrt{t}$, in which t is the time
and k is the growth constant at the temperature considered. The growth constant
is related to the absolute temperature, T, by the equation:

$$k = k_0 \exp(-\frac{Q}{RT}),$$

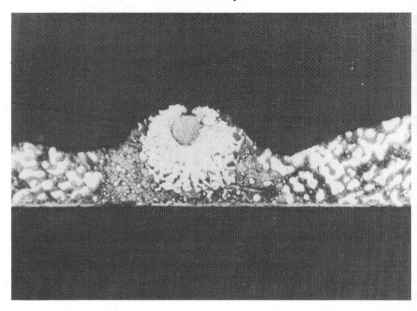

Fig. 4.5 Formation of intermetallics around a gold wire thermocompression-bonded into a layer tin-lead solder. The situation shown is present after 140 hours at 155°C, when the thickness of wire has decreased from 45 to 26 μm. Around the intermetallics the tin fraction in the solder is visi reduced. Magnification 300×.

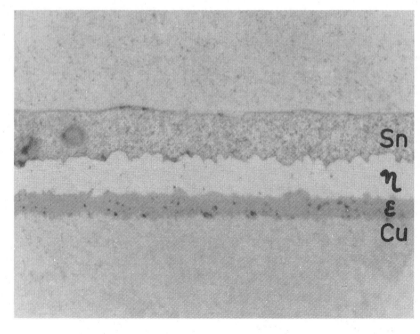

Fig. 4.6 Intermetallic layers between tin and copper after 400 hours at 170°C. Magnification 1000

where k_O is a constant, R is the gas constant and Q is the activation energy.

k_O and Q have been determined for ε-phase and η-phase under various conditions. The results vary within a factor of three depending on the following criteria: plated or fused tin, matt or bright tin, tin or solder, amount of lead in the solder [see also Kumar *et al*], condition of the base material, and the way in which the layer thickness is measured and computed. It is therefore understandable that the data in literature do not agree. The growth rate of the total layer thickness $(ε + η)$ for electrodeposited tin or tin-lead on electrolytic copper is shown in Table 4.3.

Table 4.3

Growth Constant k at 170°C in $\mathrm{nm.s}^{-\frac{1}{2}}$

Hot Dip Solder	Matt Tin	PbSn30	SnPb30	Bright Tin
5	7,7	11,2	12,0	13,7

For practical purposes, Figure 4.7 is sufficiently accurate for intermetallic layers between electrodeposited solder and copper. The indicated layer thickness is that of the grown layer, being about twice as thick as the thickness of the consumed tin. This Figure has been drawn to the equation included in the Figure, but for thin layers (1 μm) it may give times that are too long because of the often-observed knee in the curve of $δ$ *versus* $\sqrt{t}$.

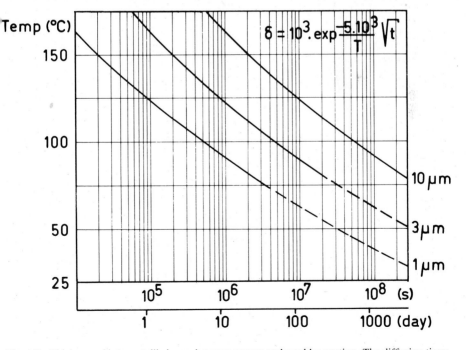

Fig. 4.7 Thickness of intermetallic layers between copper and a solder coating. The diffusion times encountered in reality can vary considerably and the data shown must be considered as average values.

The nature of the ε-phase differs from that of the η-phase, as is clear from Figure 4.8, showing fracture surfaces. The hardness values of the intermetallic

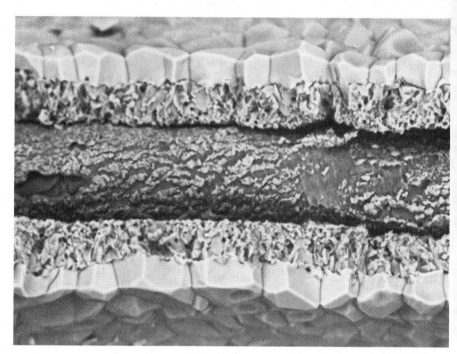

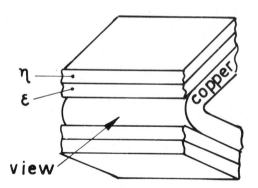

Fig. 4.8 Scanning electron micrograph of fractured intermetallic layers between copper and solder PbSn30. The solder layer, not yet consumed but still remaining on the η-phase, has been selectively removed by chemical etching, thus exposing the η-phase surface. The specimen has then been broken. Note the η-'teeth' on both sides and their perfect matching. Magnification 2500×.

layers are about 500 microhardness units. (The various sources are not in complete agreement, see Table 4.4.)

Table 4.4

Microhardness of Tin-Copper Intermetallics (kp/mm^2)

	Creydt et al	Fidos et al	Dunn	Author's Experiments
·hase	472	550	400	590
·hase	539	440	460	630

The morphology of the interface between the η-phase and the tin or tin-lead
n be relatively flat (Figure 4.8) or granular. During the growth of the layer, not
ily is there an increase in its thickness but also in the size of the grains [Schmitt-
ιomas *et al*]. Figure 4.9 shows excellent examples of grain growth of the

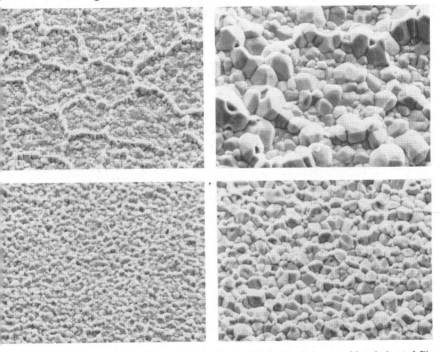

g. 4.9   Appearance of the η-intermetallic phase lying under the tin plating or solder plating (*cf.* Fig.
8). The upper photographs are of a layer under a matt tin plating, the lower ones of a layer under a
ilder (SnPb30) plating. Heat treatment of the specimens was at 135°C for 1 day (*left*) and 25 days
(*right*). Magnification of the four photographs is 1000×.

phase. In the case of the η-phase grown under a matt tin plating, a distinct
fference in the grain size is observed, which makes a thickness measurement in a
:tion rather difficult. The large crystals in the 'hexagonal' arrangement are
ing under the original grain boundaries in the tin layer. Under a solder plating
e η-phase crystals grow more uniformly.
A solder layer affects the ductility of the copper or brass on which the solder is applied. If the solder
ating is heated for 3 to 10 minutes at 300°C, the elongation at 20°C of the copper or brass is about
% higher, but if the heating is performed at a much higher temperature (400-450°C), giving a

thicker intermetallic layer, a substantial reduction of the ductility at 20°C is observed. The strength the copper or brass is not affected [Lashko *et al*].

If copper is in contact with molten solder, as already mentioned, an intermetallic layer is form but at the same time it is dissolved in the molten solder, ultimately yielding a constant layer thickne This thickness is about 8 μm for tin-lead solders in a wide range of compositions, at 400°C under sta conditions [Shoji *et al*]. The size of the intermetallic η-crystals also increases to a constant val depending on solder temperature. At 240°C with solder tin60-lead40 on brass, a final crystal size 1,5 μm is found after about 30 s [Friedrich *et al*].

4.2.5.3 WETTABILITY

If the intermetallic layers have grown to the surface, this means that a surfa layer that can melt during soldering is no longer present. This situation is oft encountered with hot-dipped wires on which the solder layer is eccentric a hence is consumed sooner in areas where the layer thickness is small. The η-lay at the surface is less wettable than the tin or tin-lead layer previously present.

The wettability of the intermetallics has undergone investigation. The materi were made by plating copper coupons with tin, followed by growing the layers evacuated glass envelopes at 170°C for a sufficiently long period of tim Gradually the tin is consumed until the outer surfaces consist of η-phase. Th η-phase is transformed to ε-phase if the treatment is continued. Figure 4.10 sho

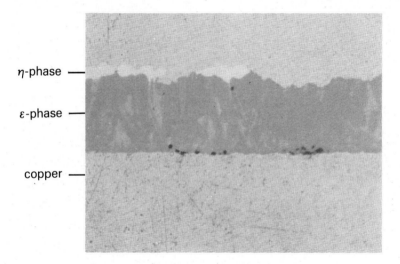

Fig. 4.10   Copper covered with tin-copper ε-phase. The structure was obtained by prolonged heati of a tin-coated copper plate. Magnification 1250×.

the situation just before η-phase has fully disappeared. Wetting balan measurements of the wettability have revealed that the ε- and η-phases are bo wettable by molten solder using a strongly activated flux. The thickness of t oxide layer, however, has a very powerful effect on the wetting times and ev 1,5 nm of oxide on the intermetallic surface reduces the wettability to a lev unacceptable in practice. With thicker oxide layers, the wetting times increa more than proportionally.

In spite of the long wetting times, the rate of wetting was sometimes quite rapid in the Autho experiments. This is a case of retarded wetting (see Figure 7.9). The specimens displayed so

wetting, especially at the rim of the immersed zone in the wetting balance. The rapid oxidation of
ermetallic compounds at the outer surface is also found for tin-nickel intermetallics (see Chapter
..5.5).

2.5.4 BARRIER LAYERS

A layer of lead between tin and copper is not effective as a barrier, but
oduces an increase in the growth rate of the η-phase (Figure 4.11). The
ermetallic tin-copper layers grow at the copper side of the lead layer, as tin is
e atom with the fastest diffusion rate through the lead. This produces a
ucture of tin/lead/η-phase/ε-phase/copper. The positive effect of lead on the
owth rate of intermetallics has also been observed with layers of AuSn$_4$ [Creydt
al].
As barriers to the growth of tin-copper intermetallics, intermediate layers of
balt and nickel are used, though their effects are not very pronounced. Iron is
ore effective [Kay *et al*] but is not used in practice because of the risk of rust
rmation.

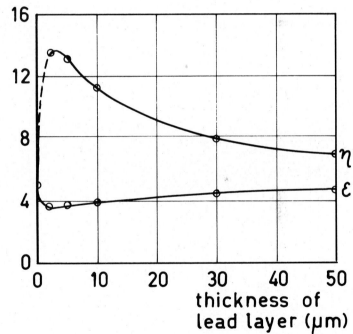

. 4.11   Thickness of the intermetallic phases of tin on copper as a function of the thickness of an
intermediate layer of lead, after heating at 180°C during 36 days.

2.5.5 TIN-NICKEL INTERMETALLICS

Nickel is often used as a barrier layer between tin and copper. Before the tin-
pper intermetallics are formed, the nickel reacts with the tin. At relatively low
nperatures, the tin-nickel layers form about as rapidly as the tin-copper layers
, but at higher temperatures their growth rate is distinctly lower [Harman]. At

Fig. 4.12 Tin-nickel intermetallics grown between 50°C and 150°C. The free intermetallic surf
was obtained by selective chemical etching of the tin layer on top of the intermetallic layer. The sn
cubes should be ignored, because they have been formed later. Magnification 1250×.

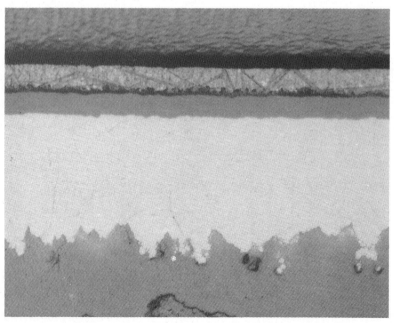

Fig. 4.13 Microsection through a tin-plated conductor on a printed board. From bottom to tc
adhesive, copper with irregular shape at adhesive side, nickel layer, tin-nickel intermetallic (1 μ
visible in Fig. 4.12 as fine particles), tin layer with plates of tin-nickel to the surface. Magnificati
1000×.

100°C, a 2 μm layer is formed in 50 days, at 170°C within 2 days. A 10 μm layer is formed at 170°C in 38 days (see Figure 4.7). The appearance of the intermetallic layers, as well as their composition, depends on the temperature at which they are formed. Figure 4.12 shows the structure of the tin-rich layer obtained below 150°C. In a metallographic section the plates are visible as needles reaching to the outer surface (Figure 4.13). With layers grown at 200°C, holding other conditions constant, plates are no longer visible. When the plates reach the outer surface, the wettability is seriously affected. It can, however, be restored by etching with hydrochloric acid, but the etched surface rapidly deteriorates again at room temperature [Harman].

The tin-nickel plates should certainly not be present in solder coated detachable contacts as in large edge connectors, if these are submitted to relative movements, for instance caused by thermal expansions. Otherwise the hard plates in the soft matrix will produce severe fretting corrosion, leading to deterioration and rapid failure of the electrical contacts. In solder coated contacts the nickel barrier layer should be omitted or only applied as a strike of about 0,1 μm or less.

4.3   PHYSICAL PROPERTIES OF TIN-LEAD ALLOYS

This Section gives a summary as far as it is relevant for soldering. Further information is to be found in handbooks on tin and lead [Price *et al*, Hofmann].

4.3.1   Elasticity

Solder has very low mechanical strength, and a measurement of the modulus of elasticity is easily influenced by the creep which occurs even at relatively low stresses. A large variation is therefore found in the data given in the literature.

The modulus of elasticity [Smithells] for lead is 16×10^3 N/mm^2 and for tin is 50×10^3 N/mm^2, making it possible to calculate a value for eutectic tin-lead solder of about 32×10^3 N/mm^2. The E-modulus depends strongly on temperature, but the low values at higher temperatures may be caused partly by the increasing contribution of creep.

4.3.2   Surface Tension

The surface tension, γ, of a liquid tin-lead alloy depends on alloy composition, as is shown in Figure 4.14 [Bircumshaw], in a way that can be understood from thermodynamics [Angal *et al*]. The temperature dependence of the surface tension of tin-lead alloys is in the order of -10^{-4} J/(m^2.K), but the data of γ and $\dfrac{d\gamma}{dT}$ show considerable spread with the conditions considered, especially the ambient atmosphere [Flint]. Most values cited for γ have been obtained in an inert atmosphere (also Figure 4.14), but these values are too high to be used for soldering conditions where a liquid flux is present [Howie *et al*, Goldman *et al*, Leinauer *et al*, Deighan, Zado].

From measurements in the Author's laboratory the conclusion can be drawn that the surface tension of tin60-lead40 solder at 250°C, in air and in the presence of flux, is close to 0,4 J/m^2. Some tentative data of the surface tension of molten solder are: 0,50 J/m^2 in air (without flux), 0,41 J/m^2 in the presence of non-activated colophony in isopropanol, and 0,38; 0,36 and 0,35 J/m^2 if activated with 0,2; 0,5 and 1% of chlorine respectively (see Chapter 5.5.3). The lowest value of 0,33 J/m² has been found using an active flux of inorganic salts in polyethylene glycol, but still lower values of γ have been reported recently [Howie *et al*, Zado].

As is shown in Figure 4.14, pure lead has a lower surface tension than the tin-lead alloys. Pure lead, however, does not wet copper because of the influence exercised by the interfacial tension between lead and copper. As tin is much more active with respect to copper, for wetting purposes it cannot be dispensed with [Klein Wassink].

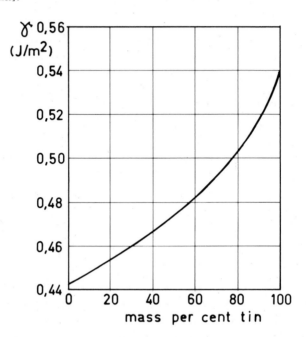

Fig. 4.14 Surface tension of tin-lead alloys, measured at 350°C in an inert atmosphere.

4.3.3 Viscosity

The viscosity values of molten solder alloys are about 2×10^{-3} Pa.s ($=$ N.s/m²)$=2$ centipoise, and are only slightly dependent on temperature [Fisher *et al*, Gebhardt *et al*, Jones *et al*, Thresh *et al*].

Table 4.5

Viscosity of Tin, Lead and Solder

Temperature °C	Tin	Eutectic Alloy	Lead	
200	-	2,2	-	
250	1,9	2,0	-	
300	1,7	1,7	-	10^{-3} Pa.s
350	1,5	1,6	2,4	
400	1,4	1,5	2,3	

3.4   Density of Tin-Lead Alloys

When tin and lead are mixed, the total volume is almost equal to the sum of the separate volumes (no contraction or expansion). This implies that to a fair degree of accuracy the density of alloys is a linear function of the volume fractions (or the specific volume a linear function of the mass fractions).

Hence: $\dfrac{1}{\varrho} = \dfrac{f_{\text{tin}}}{\varrho_{\text{tin}}} + \dfrac{f_{\text{lead}}}{\varrho_{\text{lead}}}$

in which f_{tin} = mass fraction of tin
          f_{lead} = mass fraction of lead

and ϱ, ϱ_{tin} and ϱ_{lead} are the densities of the alloy, of tin and of lead, respectively. At 20°C, $\varrho_{\text{tin}} = 7290 \text{ kg/m}^3$ and $\varrho_{\text{lead}} = 11340 \text{ kg/m}^3$, so that for solder tin60-lead40 the density is obtained from:

$\dfrac{1}{\varrho} = \dfrac{0{,}60}{7290} + \dfrac{0{,}40}{11340}$, giving $\varrho = 8500 \text{ kg/m}^3$

The relation between the density of the tin-lead alloys and the tin content is:

$$mass \ \% \ of \ tin = \frac{2041000}{\varrho} - 180$$

This relation provides a method for easy determination of the tin content of a solder alloy [Davis *et al*] (see the Appendix to this Chapter). Experimental data for the density of tin-lead alloys have been given in the literature [Fischer *et al*, Schwaneke *et al*].

When making cost comparisons between different solder types, the difference in density must be taken into account. In practice, a definite volume of solder, not a definite weight of solder, is required per soldered joint. This means, for instance, that if the price of tin per kg is 20 times that of lead, tin50-lead50 is approximately 18% less expensive per kg than eutectic solder, but about 14% less expensive per litre.

3.4.1   OTHER ELEMENTS IN THE SOLDER

When other elements besides tin and lead are present, the same calculation can be made, again based on the assumption that there is no contraction or expansion as a result of the combination.

This means: $\dfrac{1}{\varrho_{\text{alloy}}} = \dfrac{f_{\text{tin}}}{\varrho_{\text{tin}}} + \dfrac{f_{\text{lead}}}{\varrho_{\text{lead}}} + \dfrac{f_{\text{antimony}}}{\varrho_{\text{antimony}}} + \dfrac{f_{\text{bismuth}}}{\varrho_{\text{bismuth}}}$, etc.

The following densities apply at 20°C, so in the solid state [Smithells]:

antimony	–	6680 kg/m^3
bismuth	–	9800
cadmium	–	8640
tin	–	7290
lead	–	11340*

The figure given by Smithells (1976 p. 940) is incorrect.

For instance, for tin-lead-antimony alloys:

$$mass \ \% \ of \ tin = \frac{2041000}{\varrho_{alloy}} - 180 - 1{,}26 \times (mass \ \% \ of \ antimony)$$

4.3.4.2 LIQUID METALS

For liquid tin and lead, the following data are known:

Metal	Density in kg/m^3 at 1 K above the Melting Temperature	at 350°C
Tin	7000	6900
Lead	10700	10600

For eutectic solder, the density at 250°C is close to 8000 kg/m^3 and the decrease in density with increasing temperature is about 1 kg/m^3 per K.

4.3.4.3 COEFFICIENT OF THERMAL EXPANSION

The linear expansion coefficient of polycrystalline tin over the range 0-100°C is $23{,}5 \times 10^{-6}$/K, of lead is 29×10^{-6}/K, and of eutectic solder is $24{,}5 \times 10^{-6}$/K [Smithells]. The volume change from room temperature to 183°C is about 1,2% whilst the shrinkage during solidification amounts to about 4%. This can be roughly measured by pouring water into the shrinkage cavity formed when solder is allowed to cool in a solder pot. (Caution: the water could spatter dangerously when the pot is reheated). The coefficient of linear expansion of the compounds Cu_3Sn and Cu_6Sn_5 is $18{,}4 \times 10^{-6}$/K and $20{,}0 \times 10^{-6}$/K respectively, from 25°C to 100°C [Anon. Ref. 5, Reichenecker].

4.3.5 Specific Heat

Some values of the specific heat are given in Table 4.6.

Table 4.6

Some Thermal Data of Tin, Solder and Lead

Property	Tin	Solder SnPb40	Lead
Heat of fusion (J/kg)	60000	46000	24000
Specific heat at 20°C (J/(kg.K))	221	176	10
Heat required to raise the temperature of 1 cm³ of material from 20°C to 50 K in excess of melting point (J)	900	736	74

When a quantity of solder solidifies, the heat of solidification has to be dissipated. It is interesting to note that the total freezing time of different solder alloys is approximately equal. This can also be seen in Figure 4.4, where lead65 tin35 can be compared with tin62-lead38.

Thus, the time during which a soldered joint must be held steady to prevent rupture in the structure of the freezing solder is almost independent of the composition of the alloy.

4.3.6 Electrical Resistivity and Thermal Conductivity

Data are given in Table 4.7:

Table 4.7

Electrical Resistivity and Thermal Conductivity of Selected Metals

Property	Tin	Sn60-Pb40	Lead	Copper
Electrical Resistivity				
at 25°C (μOhm.m)	0,12	0,17	0,21	0,017
at 100°C (μOhm.m)	0,16	0,32	0,27	0,02
Thermal Conductivity				
at 25°C (J/(m.s.K))	65	51	35	390
at 100°C (J/(m.s.K))	63	49	34	390

The electrical resistivity of solder is approximately ten times as high as that of copper. In general, the relatively large cross-sectional area of the soldered joint renders the higher electrical resistivity of solder less significant. Depending on the shape of the joint, the treatment of the wire and the solder, the contact resistance of a soldered wire is usually between 1 and 10 mΩ [Le Penven *et al*]. The contact resistance will increase during ageing or thermal cycling [Shelepaev].

The electrical resistivity of the copper-tin intermetallic compounds Cu_3Sn and Cu_6Sn_5 at room temperature is, respectively, about 120% and 70% of the resistivity of tin60-lead40 alloy at the same temperature; at 100°C, respectively, about 70% and 50% [Reichenecker].

The thermo-EMF for tin-lead alloys against copper between 0 and 100°C is about 3 μV/K for the entire range of compositions (for tin60-lead40: 145 μV at $\Delta T = 50$ K) [Pascoe, see also Ivlev *et al*].

4.4 IMPURITIES IN TIN-LEAD SOLDERS

All solders contain small amounts of other metals [Keysselitz], either introduced by the producer of the solder or by the user, or economically impossible to remove from the metals when they are extracted from the ore.

4.4.1 Composition

Usual purchase requirements for the composition of tin60-lead40 solder are as follows:

> tin 60±0,5% by mass
> lead remainder
> antimony ≤ 0,12%
> copper   ≤ 0,05%
> bismuth ≤ 0,10%
> iron   ≤ 0,02%
> arsenic   < 0,01%
> aluminium + zinc + cadmium < 0,002%
> total of other impurities   < 0,08%

These impurity levels, being currently the lowest purchasing maxima that can be obtained at an economic price, ensure a reasonable life of the solder-bath content before the operating maxima are exceeded by the change of composition while the bath is in use. While the solder is in use in a machine, it can pick up one or more elements which may eventually impair its function. Some take-up of copper is difficult to avoid as copper is always present in the components to be soldered. During the process, the contamination increases till an equilibrium level is reached depending on the drag-out of contaminated solder, the input of copper and the replenishment of the solder consumption with pure solder. It is a matter of adjusting the process parameters to ensure that the contamination is maintained below the acceptable maximum (see Chapter 9.1.2). Contamination by other elements may be caused by accident, for instance when metallic parts plated with an unwanted metal unintentionally come into contact with the solder. As soon as the contamination level becomes too high, the solder must be completely replaced. To dilute contaminated solder with fresh and pure solder is not in general effective enough. The impurity metals affect the wetting properties of the solder mostly in a negative way, but provided the total amount of unwanted metal is below about 1% the changes in wetting time, wetting force, area of spread, *etc.*, are fairly limited [Ackroyd *et al*, Becker *et al*]. However, the wetting properties of the solder should not be regarded as the sole yardstick for the maximum acceptable impurity levels of the solder in a machine. Troubles originating from contaminated solders include bridging, webbing and oxide-skin formation [Schmitt-Thomas *et al*, MacKay].

4.4.2 Antimony

The soldering properties of solders are not sensitive to small amounts of antimony. In the purest solders a maximum of about 0,1% is tolerated, but up to an antimony content of 0,5% scarcely any detectable change in the properties for normal soldering is found. With 1% of antimony, a reduction in the area of spread of 25% is observed [Ackroyd *et al*], and also a reduced wetting speed [Lenz]. A small amount of antimony in the solder may be of advantage, as it promotes the elimination of aluminium contamination by the forming of solid AlSb intermetallic, which is taken up in the dross.

Antimony is sometimes added to the solder deliberately, because it is cheaper than tin [Langan *et al*]. About the same liquidus temperature is maintained when 2% of tin is replaced by 1% of antimony. The ternary alloy tin52-lead45-antimony3 has a melting range of 7°C, similar to that of tin60-lead40, but its liquidus point is a few degrees higher. The alloy is somewhat stronger than common tin-lead solder.

Despite its reduced wetting properties, the antimony-containing alloy is successfully applied by various users; it is commercially available under the name 'Functional Alloy' (Alpha Metals) [US Patent 3,945,556 (1976)]. For soldering on zinc and brass, antimony-containing solder is less suitable owing to the formation of brittle zinc-antimony intermetallic crystals.

4.4.3 Copper

If the copper content of solder exceeds 0,2%, difficulties start cropping up in bath soldering in the form of solder bridging (sticking) on insulation materials.

Because, in general, copper or copper-containing terminals are soldered with attending dissolution of small quantities of copper, the composition of the solder bath requires a copper check in case of difficulties. The maximum permissible copper contamination is usually specified as 0,3%. The solubility of copper in tin60-lead40 at 400° is about 2,5 mass % [Shoji *et al*], at 250°C about 0,5% and at 200°C about 0,2%. During the cooling of copper-containing solder the excess copper crystallises in the form of fine needles (dendrites) of Cu_6Sn_5 intermetallic compound, with the result that the viscosity of the solder increases progressively and the formation of bridges is promoted. Finally, the needles may impart a gritty appearance to the solid solder surface.

By pouring the contaminated solder at about 190°C through a fine-mesh stainless steel strainer, the copper content can be reduced to about 0,25%.

4.4.4 Silver and Gold

The solubility of silver in tin60-lead40 at 250°C is about 5%. A silver concentration below 2% does not cause any deterioration in soldering results, but at a higher silver content grittiness of the surface due to the intermetallics that are formed can be observed.

In liquid tin60-lead40 solder at 250°C, about 15 mass per cent of gold can be dissolved, but, as the solubility in the solid state is limited, the gold precipitates during solidification [Prince, Karnovski *et al*]. This occurs in the form of brittle, mostly plate shaped gold-tin intermetallic crystals of $AuSn_4$ (in a microsection needle shaped, see Figure 4.15).

Below 0,5% of gold in the solder no difficulties in soldering are encountered, but at a higher concentration the solder becomes slow-moving (sluggish) during cooling on account of the primary crystallisation of gold-tin plates. The shear

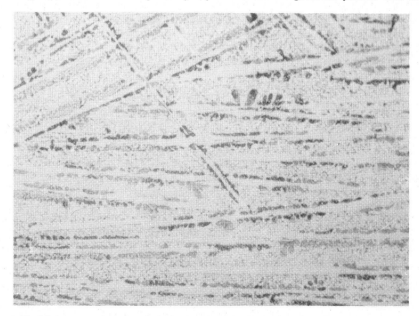

ig. 4.15 Microstructure of eutectic tin-lead solder with 10 mass per cent of gold after rapid cooling, showing intermetallic plates. This tin-lead-gold alloy is brittle. Magnification 250×.

strength of the solder is only slightly influenced by the gold, but when the gold concentration is higher than 4% [Wild] the alloyed solder will, under plastic deformation, exhibit brittle fracture. Contamination of the bath with gold occurs when gold-plated terminations are soldered, but the level at which soldering properties are influenced is not likely to be reached. A bath with 0,5% of gold should not be used for soldering, but should be sold for its gold value (with 0,1% of gold the metal value is twice as high).

4.4.5   Aluminium, Zinc and Cadmium

These metals change the oxidation behaviour of solder because they are selectively oxidised, producing strong and tough oxide skins which are not easily deformed. When the solder is stirred, as in a wave soldering machine, large quantities of dross are generated which impart a creased appearance to the solder and render flowing of the solder almost impossible. The tolerable level of these metals is therefore very low, less than 0,005%.

In normal practice, such metals should not be present in parts that are likely to come into frequent contact with the solder. Though aluminium is not wetted by solder because of its oxide layer, it still cannot be used for jigs and frames for printed boards. Repeated contact with flux and solder, combined with mechanical wear, will finally damage the oxide layer and allow the aluminium to react and dissolve. (Cast aluminium carriers are occasionally used, but these are provided with a protective coat of, for instance, 40 μm PTFE.)

4.4.6   Iron and Nickel

The rate of dissolution and the solubility of these metals at normal soldering temperatures (250°C) are so low that there is no measurable effect on the solder properties. It is common practice to make solder pots, *etc.*, of cast iron or chromium steel without difficulties being experienced. The use of unalloyed steel, however, is not recommended.

4.4.7   Bismuth

The effect on solder properties is insignificant when the contamination is below 3%. Bismuth in the solder at a concentration higher than 2% gives the solder joints a matt appearance which is beneficial for the visual inspection of joints. An example of such an alloy is tin60-lead37,6-bismuth2,4 with a liquidus temperature of 186°C. The alloy tin48,5-lead48,5-bismuth3 has a melting range from 176 to 202°C.

4.4.8   Non-Metals

Arsenic will give rise to dewetting especially on brass, a level of max. 0,03% being tolerable.

Sulphur will be present in the form of particles of SnS and PbS which impart to the solder surface a gritty appearance. It is only permissible in the parts per million range and in most cases is undetectable using common analytical techniques.

Phosphorus is sometimes applied for the deoxidation of the solder, though even at a very low concentration (0,01%) dewetting occurs.

In all requirements for solder composition, metallic contaminants are 1antified but there are no requirements available which deal quantitatively with ide content and gas content. Information on these non-metals is scarce: the tal gas content of N, O, NH_3, CO_2, *etc.* in solders is about 10 ppm and a .cuum treatment has no effect upon the spreading properties of the solder.

4.9 Elements Improving Strength

Elements are occasionally added to solder to improve its mechanical 'operties. Experiments have been carried out with alloying elements such as hium and beryllium (<0,1%) [Paschen *et al*], which increase the strength :yond the values obtainable with pure tin-lead alloys. Small quantities of llurium and cerium have been added to lead-rich solders, mainly to improve tigue strength. Compositions which have been investigated are as follows (mass) [Schmitt-Thomas *et al*]:

lloy	Tin	Silver	Tellurium	Cerium	Lead
1	1,3	0,1	0,01	-	remainder
2	1,4	-	-	0,04	remainder

ne added elements are presumably present in the form of oxide particles, which iring solidification initially act as nuclei and later inhibit grain growth. The two fects combine to produce a fine-grain structure. Similar effects have been ported for the addition of magnesium to tin-lead solders [Lashko *et al*]. About 1% of magnesium added to eutectic solder gives a greater shear strength, a finer ain structure and a marked reduction of the age softening (see Chapter 4.7.1). owever, these special alloys have not as yet been used in soldering practice.

5 OXIDATION OF LIQUID TIN-LEAD SOLDERS

Tin-lead solders oxidise quite rapidly when liquid. After skimming the oxide in from a bath of molten solder, a new oxide skin is formed immediately. The ide consists mainly of tin oxides. For the oxidation rate a distinction must be ade between static and agitated solder, as in a solder pot and a wave soldering achine respectively.

5.1 Static Solder

The oxidation rate, that is, the growth rate of the oxide layer, depends on the operties of the layer and thus on its composition and character. The oxygen ke-up behaves parabolically with time according to the equation:

$$\frac{\Delta m}{A} = k\sqrt{t},$$

which:

Δm = mass increase in kg
A = surface area in m^2
t = time in seconds
k = 'growth coefficient', $k = k_0 \exp(-B/T)$

T = absolute temperature

k_O and B are constants

For tin60-lead40: $k_O = 1{,}6 \times 10^{-2}$ kg.m^{-2}.s$^{-\frac{1}{2}}$ and $B = 4900$ K.

thus at 240°C: $k \cong 10^{-6}$ [Kurz *et al*].

The value of k for 100% tin is twice that for tin60-lead40. Addition of other elements exerts some influence [Grühl *et al*], if these elements change the nature of the oxide skin. Elements such as aluminium which produce a dense oxide film retard the oxidation rate of static solder, whereas other elements such as magnesium cause the oxidation rate to increase.

The composition of the oxide films has been studied by Auger electron spectroscopy [de Kluizenaar], see also Chapter 5.3.2. On clean tin60-lead40 solder, a complex oxide layer is formed consisting of three regions (Figure 4.16).

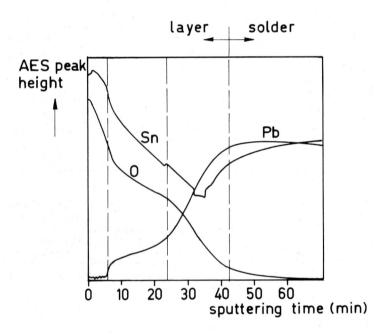

Fig. 4.16   Typical AES sputter depth profile of an oxide film on pure solder SnPb40, grown at 250°C during 15 minutes. The sputtering rate is about 0,3 nm/min.

(i)   a thin outer layer of SnO_2 of thickness about 2 nm;

(ii) a layer of SnO, mixed with finely dispersed metallic lead;

(iii) a transition layer of SnO and metallic tin and lead. The tin oxide concentration decreases with depth, whilst the tin metal concentration increases. Below this layer is the underlying solder metal.

A similar type of oxide layer is observed on solder containing copper or nickel. On solder contaminated with aluminium, zinc or phosphorus, the contaminants are oxidised preferentially, resulting in an aluminium oxide film, a zinc oxide film and a mixed phosphorus oxide-tin oxide film, respectively.

.5.2   Agitated Solder

With agitated solder the situation is different, because now not only oxide film ut also dross formation has to be coped with [Stoneman *et al*]. Dross consists of ells of solder metal enveloped by an oxide skin. Although the oxide fraction of ie dross is very small, the appearance of the dross in most cases is non-metallic. he dross may be intermixed with burned and disintegrated solder oil and flux. ross formed around a pump shaft on a bath looks different from that formed y a wave (without oil application).

Around a rotating shaft (without oil on the bath), black dross is formed ontaining yellow, blue and purple particles. Regardless of the type of solder, this ross contains 2,5-3% oxide. X-ray diffraction shows that the oxide on tin60-:ad40, formed at about 250°C, consists of SnO with less than 0,5% crystalline nO$_2$. No lead oxides are present in the films. The dross is generated because the kin forming on the solder surface is continuously sheared by the rotation of the haft. Its amount is a function of the product of diameter, D, and circumferential elocity, v, of the shaft (Figure 4.17). The dross particles range in size from less

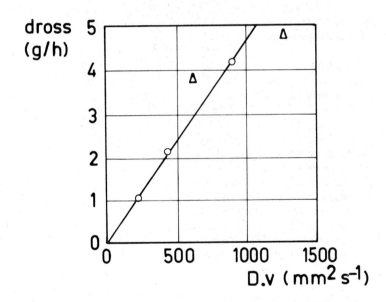

ig. 4.17   Formation of dross around a pump shaft. Circles are for 6 mm shaft, triangles for 8 mm shaft.

tan 100 μm to more than 4 mm (Figure 4.18). Because the dross around the ump shaft contains small particles of metal with a large surface area, it may :atch fire' spontaneously though not violently. When this happens a glowing one passes gradually through the whole volume of dross.

The dross formed on the surface of a bath (without oil) of a wave soldering 1achine has a grey and dull appearance, though the oxide is again SnO. The mount of oxide in this type of dross is about 1%. When such dross is ompressed, a portion of the oxide skin around the cells is broken and solder 1etal is liberated from the cells. In this way the oxide content can be raised to, for

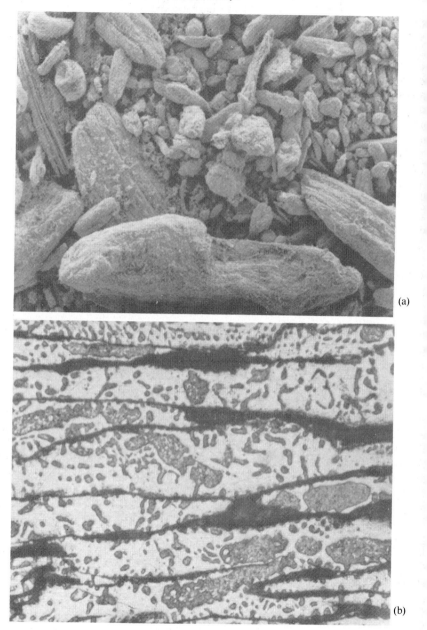

(a)

(b)

Fig. 4.18   Dross formed on solder. (a) SEM photograph of dross particles formed around a rotating shaft. Magnification 20×. (b) Section through a dross particle. Magnification 640×.

instance, 5%, which means that 80% of the encapsulated metal is reclaimed. With a 'quiet' solder wave, the oxide skin on top of the wave is almost immobile, as can be easily shown by placing a small piece of paper on top of the wave. At

e place where solder flows into the bath, turbulence cannot be completely
oided, and at this point dross is generated.
The oxide skin is continuously folded together while small quantities of solder
e enveloped. Once isolated cells have been formed, they will remain stable and
e encapsulated solder will not unite again. This enveloping action depends
ainly on the flow characteristics of the solder, determined by the solder process
rameters. The composition of the solder has only a limited effect on dross
rmation. Only if the oxide skin properties become truly different will dross
rmation be influenced. Phosphorus in the alloy gives only a slight reduction in
oss formation under otherwise equal process conditions, although the amount
oxide in the dross is much less.
Turbulences in the solder are partly generated by the pump impeller. If the channel between pump
peller and nozzle is too short, the turbulences can not be damped down before the solder reaches
· wave. When the flow of solder is forced to become laminar, the amount of dross is reduced
isiderably. This can be realised by applying a feed tube with a length to diameter ratio over 10 or by
unting partitions in the feed tube in the direction of solder flow.

5 DISSOLUTION OF BASE METALS

A piece of solid metal immersed in liquid solder will dissolve until the solubility
nit is reached. In soldering practice, this level is not normally attained because
e equilibrium concentration, determined by the dissolution of metal and drag-
it of contaminated solder, is lower.

5.1 Rate of Dissolution

The rate of dissolution depends on various factors [Bader, Berg *et al*], such as
se metal, solder composition, temperature and flow velocity of the solder,
fluencing the manner in which the dissolved metal is transported from the
erface [Shoji *et al*]. Dissolution rates are mostly expressed as the time needed
r the complete dissolution of a wire of a specified diameter, and also as the rate
removal of metal from a flat or cylindrical surface. The decrease in the
ameter of a wire in liquid solder is approximately proportional to time. For a
ven set of conditions, it can with reasonable accuracy be described as:

$$\frac{D}{t} = Ae^{-\frac{B}{T}},$$ in which T is the absolute temperature, and A and B are constants.

any metals of considerable importance as base metals in electronics have
latively high dissolution rates in tin-lead solder alloys.
In Figure 4.19 the dissolution rates of some metals in tin60-lead40 are given,
th the proviso that these data are only approximate, as the dissolving
nditions will vary from case to case. Under truly static conditions the
ssolution rate is much lower, because it is then determined by diffusion. For
pper in tin-lead solder at 400°C less than 0,05 μm/s is found [Shoji *et al*], but
atic conditions are seldom if ever found in soldering practice.
The rate of dissolution of a specific metal is lower if some of the metal is
ready present in the solder. The retardation of dissolution is especially
iportant if a thin metal coating on a non-solderable substrate has to be
idered.

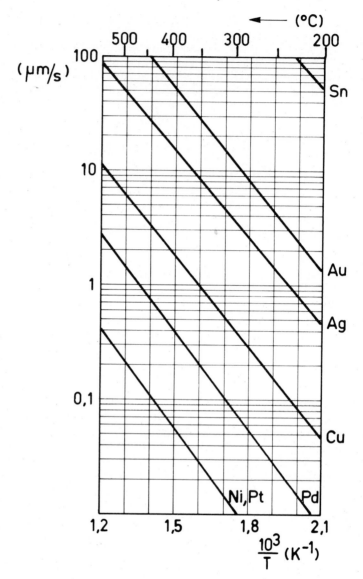

Fig. 4.19 Dissolution rates of various metals in solder as a function of temperature. The Figure was obtained by averaging a large number of data from literature and from the Author's own work.

4.6.2   Dissolution of Gold

The dissolution rate of gold in tin-containing solders is always extremely high this being due to the strong interaction between gold and tin. A solder bath will therefore take up gold when gold plated component terminations are soldered. The level at which deterioration of the properties of the joint occurs (see Chapter 4.4.4) is seldom reached because the equilibrium content is sufficiently low, as is shown by this calculation:

Suppose that gold plated terminations of diameter 0,4 mm with a plating thickness of 1 μm (5×10^{-3} mm^3 gold per lead) are soldered, and that the volume of a joint is 2 mm^3. In the beginning gold is taken up in the bath, but with increasing gold content more and more gold is also dragged out of the bath, until equilibrium concentration is reached, implying that no more gold is added to the bath. The final gold content in the bath hence will be 5×10^{-3} mm^3 of gold per mm^3 of solder, which is about 0,6 per cent. For a bath of 4 dm^3, all the gold of about 2 million terminations is required to reach a gold level of 0,6%, but if only a fraction, f_1, of the terminations are gold plated, the final gold content in the bath will be proportionally lower. The same is true if only a fraction, f_2, of the solder is taken up in the joints; this may be the case when $(1-f_2)$ of the solder is consumed by oxidation (drossing).

In Figure 4.20, the calculations are given for $f_1 = 0,1$ and $f_2 = 1$ and 0,5 respectively. It is interesting to note that for a lower value of f_2 the final level is not only lower but is also reached sooner.

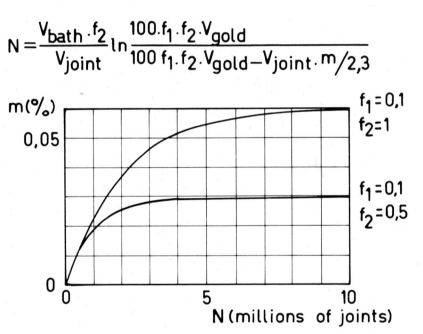

$$N = \frac{V_{bath} \cdot f_2}{V_{joint}} \ln \frac{100 \cdot f_1 \cdot f_2 \cdot V_{gold}}{100\, f_1 \cdot f_2 \cdot V_{gold} - V_{joint} \cdot m / 2,3}$$

4.20   Take-up of gold in solder baths. f_1 = fraction of leads that is gold plated, f_2 = fraction of solder that is taken up in the joints, V_{bath}, V_{joint}, V_{gold} = volumes of the bath, joint and gold per lead, respectively. m = mass per cent of gold in the bath.

The dissolution of gold into the solder is reduced by applying tin-free solders, for instance lead-indium solders [Yost]. For this reason, indium50-lead50 alloy is preferred for soldering to thin film circuits [Mulholland *et al*]. The lower dissolution rate of these alloys is obtained only at the expense of reduced wetting properties. Addition of silver to tin-lead solders also reduces the rate of dissolution of gold.

4.6.3   Dissolution of Silver

The graph of Figure 4.21 gives the time to complete dissolution of a silver w
of diameter 150 μm in various solders at various temperatures. With increas
lead content the rate of dissolution is lower. An addition of 5% silver to tin-le
solder markedly reduces the rate of dissolution of silver. If, for instance, a w
must be soldered to a silver coating of a few μm thickness on a ceramic plate
silver-containing alloy and a low soldering temperature must be used in order
prevent the complete disappearance of the coating.

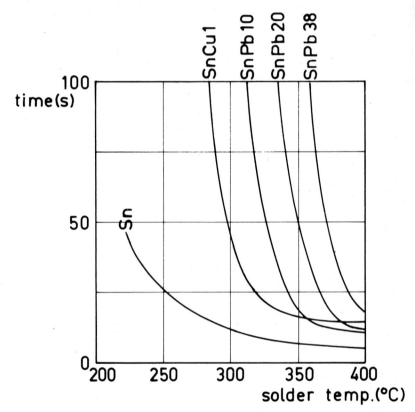

Fig. 4.21   Dissolution time of silver wires in various solders as a function of temperature. The in
wire diameter is 150 μm.

The dissolution of silver is also retarded by zinc [Offenlegungsschrift 2733
Al (1979)]. In this respect, 2% zinc is as effective as 5% silver. However,
addition of zinc enhances the formation of oxide skins on the liquid solder.

The dissolution of silver is of significance in the field of thick-film technolo
[Holmes *et al*]. The silver from the silver-palladium conductors dissolves into
molten solder during soldering, thereby giving a loss of adhesion of
conductors.

The resistance of the dissolution of the conductors is tested by dippi
substrates with conductors of about 0,5 mm width into molten solder. The ti

ceded for either a certain decrease of width (10%), or a complete scavenging of the conductor is determined. This dissolution of the conductors is usually called 'solder leaching'. However, the term 'leaching' is also (faultily) used for metallurgical effects (like diffusion) that occur after the solder has solidified and which also produce adhesion degradation [Leven].

6.4 Dissolution of Copper

Copper dissolves less than silver in tin60-lead40 solder [Howes *et al*], and it is found that addition of 1,5% copper to this solder increases the time of dissolution of thin wires at 400°C by at least a factor of 20 [Allen]. Lead-rich solder alloys are superior to tin-rich alloys [Bader]. Figure 4.22 shows the effects of the solder composition on the dissolution time of thin wires.

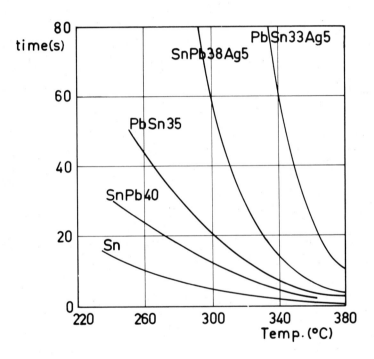

g. 4.22 Dissolution time of copper wires in solders of various compositions. The initial wire diameter is 150 μm.

Reduction of the dissolution rate is very important when fine magnet winding wires with 'solderable' enamel coating are applied [Gutbier *et al*], because to remove the coating a temperature must be chosen (∼380°C) which is much higher than normal soldering temperatures (Figure 4.23). In certain cases, the stripping of the wires can be achieved chemically, hence at low temperature [Sprengling].

When copper is soldered on a wave soldering machine at about 250°C, the dissolution rate is around 0,1 μm/s (see Figure 4.19). The copper area of termination and land is about 10 mm^2 and the copper dissolution after 3 seconds is thus 3×10^{-3} mm^3. With a solder joint volume of 2 mm^3, the final copper

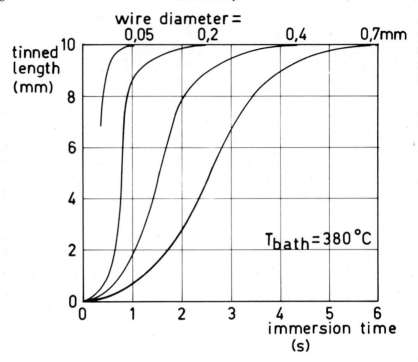

Fig. 4.23 Tinning of 'solderable' enamel-coated wires at a bath temperature of 380°C. T immersed wire is wetted starting from the free end, while the organic coat is removed mainly evaporation. (The word 'tinning' in this case actually means: covering with solder.)

content of the bath will then be about 0,15%. When the printed coppe conductors on the board are not coated with a solder resist, more copper transferred to the bath than with coated wiring, but the solder consumption then higher.

With increasing copper concentration in the bath the rate of dissolutio decreases, so that the take-up of copper is self-limiting. The final coppe concentration in most cases lies between 0,2 and 0,3%.

Copper is occasionally added to solder wire in order to reduce the dissolutio of copper bits of soldering irons. With the more widespread use of iron-plate bits, which are much less rapidly attacked by solder, this copper addition ha declining significance.

4.7   STRENGTH PROPERTIES OF SOFT SOLDERS

The mechanical strength of soft solder is low, amounting to only a few percer of that of commonly used engineering materials. Strength is particularly low a elevated temperatures (strictly speaking, room temperature is already a relativel high temperature for these alloys) and when cyclic thermal loading takes place.

Tensile tests on test bars of bulk solder or shear tests on lap joints, *etc.* therefore give only very limited information on the behaviour of the solder in real joint under actual conditions of use. In view of the great number of factor that influence the measured strength values, the figures in the literature ca hardly be compared one with another: similar values from different sources diffe

more than a factor of two. No guarantee can be given therefore that a
rticular solder alloy, which shows better creep and fatigue characteristics than
other alloy in a graph or a table in literature, also performs better in a specific
ictical combination of loads and temperatures.
By alloying tin-lead alloys with, for instance, some antimony, the strength can
increased somewhat, but it does not change significantly. In general, it can be
d that the tin-lead alloys are unsuitable for mechanical joints in which the
ess, at 20°C, lies permanently above 1 N/mm^2.
In the case of temperature-cycling the strength is only a fraction of 1 N/mm^2.
a number of temperature cycles in excess of 2000 between 20°C and 110°C,
shear strength is 0,1 N/mm^2. This means that, under these conditions, the
aximum permissible load on a wire of 0,6 mm diameter that has been soldered
er a length of 1,6 mm in a plated-through hole is approximately 0,2 N. If a
onger connection is required, mechanical loading of the solder must be
evented, for instance by forming the wire end into a hook in the solder tag.
The thickness of the intermetallic reaction layer between the solder and the
se metal affects the fracture resistance of a soldered joint. Its effect upon joint
ength depends also on the shape of the joint and on the direction of the load.
e peel strength, *e.g.*, is inversely proportional to the thickness of the reaction
er and thus a higher soldering temperature and a longer soldering exposure
e give lower peel strength values [Saperstein *et al*].

7.1   Tensile Strength and Shear Strength

The properties of solder depend strongly on the microstructure just after
lidification. The 0,2% yield strength of near-eutectic tin-lead solder varies from
to 40 N/mm^2, proportionally to the square of the grain size diameter (being
2-1,7 μm), depending on the 'casting' temperature and the solidification rate
ack *et al*]. The tin-lead alloys exhibit loss in strength and hardness values
ring storage after solidification. In some cases, an initial increase occurs for the
st few days (at room temperature), but subsequently the values decrease over a
w months to, say, 80% of the starting value [Lampe]. This age softening is
ributed to the precipitation of secondary tin from the saturated lead-rich
ase. The presence of antimony retards the precipitation and thus also the
ftening process.
The decrease in the strength values of tin-lead solders after prolonged heating
temperatures above 100°C may be 50% or even more [Hagstrom *et al*].
The shear strength of solders is normally measured using test specimens
nsisting of a plug soldered inside a ring, so that a known average gap is present
ec. Ref. 20] although in certain cases more or less simple lap joints are used.
ength values increase with decreasing gap width down to a gap of about 50 μm.
low this gap width the filling of the joint may be doubtful.
The measured stress values are influenced by the form of the test set-up [Koch
al] and the differences in elastic properties of the solder and the base metal. For
s reason push tests with ring-and-plug test-pieces give higher values than pull
ts. The difference is larger when smaller plug diameters and a higher ratio of
ig diameter to joint length are chosen [Shawki *et al*].
Results of strength tests depend on the strain rate (Table 4.8). Increasing this
e by a factor of 1000 leads to an increase in strength by a factor of 2 [Keil].

Despite the influence of the strain rate on strength, information concerning it
not always included in literature.

Table 4.8

Shear-Strength Values of Various Solders in Ring-and-Plug Joints (N/mm²)
(data obtained from ITRI [Thwaites *et al*, see also Stone *et al*])

| Alloy | | | | Temperature 20°C | | Temperature 100°C | |
| | | | | Strain Rate | Strain Rate | Strain Rate | Strain Rate |
Sn	Pb	Sb	Ag	0,05 mm/min	50 mm/min	0,05 mm/min	50 mm/min
60	40			20	39	13	34
10	90			17	36	11	16
62	36		2	28	52	12	34
40	58	2		24	43	11	25
95		5		28	55	14	29
5	93,5		1,5	18	30	12	21

(the indicated strain rate is the rate of movement of the beam of the testing machine; the solder g
between the ring and plug is between 0,005 and 0,25 mm.)

4.7.2 Creep of Solders

Solders show a slow plastic strain (creep) under low permanent stresses. Thi
means that with long-term loading the strength is much lower than with shor
term loading [Haug, Zürn *et al*]. For eutectic tin-lead solder at 20°C, the time t
failure for various shear stresses is approximately:

$$10 \text{ N/mm}^2 - 10 \text{ hours}$$
$$4 \text{ N/mm}^2 - 1000 \text{ hours}$$
$$2 \text{ N/mm}^2 - 100\ 000 \text{ hours}$$

These figures depend on the form of the test specimens and on the test conditions
The effect of temperature is shown in Figure 4.24, referring to shear load test

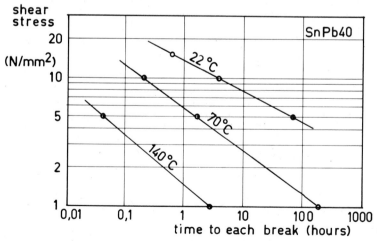

Fig. 4.24   Creep of tin60-lead40 solder at various temperatures. [Data obtained from Becker]

n copper ring-and-plug specimens with a gap of 0,1 mm, soldered with tin60-
:ad40 alloy. Similar graphs for other solder alloys have been published elsewhere
[Koch *et al*].

The creep of solders allows for stress relaxation when the strain is maintained
[Baker; Baker *et al*]. For tin60-lead40 solder the decrease of stress from 20 to 10
N/mm^2 takes about 60 minutes at 50°C, from 10 to 5 N/mm^2 about 10 hours and
from 5 to 2,5 N/mm^2 about 100 hours. The step from 5 to 2,5 N/mm^2 takes about
00, 15 and 4 hours respectively at 25°C, 75°C and 100°C.

The data given have been obtained for a more or less uniaxial stress. When the
material is constrained in another way, naturally, other results are obtained.

4.7.3   Fatigue

In solder joints, the fatigue as a rule is caused by cyclic plastic deformation as a
result of temperature changes produced by intermittent currents in the electronic
equipment. The results of such fatigue are cracked joints, which cause either a
complete interruption of the connection, or an intermittent contact producing
crackling noise. Different alloys may show quite different fatigue data even if
their compositions are similar. The fatigue cracking of joints is further influenced
by any additional permanent load on the joint, caused for instance by the weight
of a component. Figure 4.25 applies to tests on specimens made of copper wires
soldered with eutectic tin-lead solder in a steel plate. These specimens were cycled
between 30°C and 120°C with a cycle time of 3 hours, while the breakage was
observed. In Figure 4.25 lines of failure probabilities are shown. At a constant
load of 0,2 N (*i.e.*, 0,06 N/mm^2, which is quite low) 2,5% of the specimens shown
in the Figure fail after 1000 cycles.

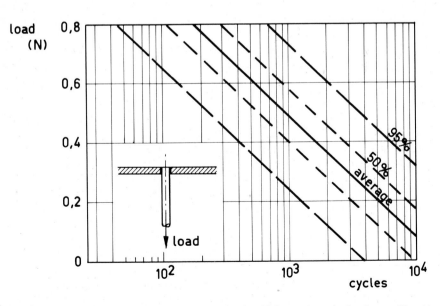

Fig. 4.25   Fatigue of eutectic solder in a construction in which a copper wire has been soldered in a
steel plate. Temperature cycles: $\Delta T = 90$ K; wire diameter = 1,0 mm; plate thickness = 1,0 mm and hole
diameter 1,2 mm.

For this low-cycle fatigue the Coffin-Tavernelli relation can be used:

$$N^{\frac{1}{2}} \times \delta = \text{constant}$$

in which N is the number of cycles and δ is the plastic strain amplitude. The constant is derived from the plastic strain in a tensile test where $N = \frac{1}{4}$. On a log-log graph paper of strain vs. number of cycles a straight line is obtained, though for fatigue tests on soldered joints the power of N is not always 0,5 but may lie between 0,3 and 0,5 [Wild]. For shear tests on eutectic tin-lead at 25°C with one cycle per 15 minutes:

$$N^{0,4} \times \delta = 0,56$$

So for 3% strain at $\frac{1}{15}$ cpm $N \approx 1900$ cycles.

The cycle time has a strong effect: with 5 cpm and 3% strain at 25°C $N \approx 16000$ cycles. At 100°C with 5 cpm and 3% strain $N \approx 3000$ cycles. The decrease in fatigue life with decreasing cycling frequency has also been found for lead95-tin5 alloy [Rathore *et al*].

The definition of the moment of failure is arbitrary: sometimes the moment of appearance of a crack is taken, in other cases a specific increase in the contact resistance, a complete breakage, *etc.*

The cracks, once initiated, follow the lead-rich portion of the eutectic structure [Dunn] and are associated with the voids that are present in the solder or that are created during deformation [Novick]. With soldered surfaces that were moderately wettable, the crack paths have the tendency to follow these surfaces, more than in cases of perfect wettability.

The sensitivity of soft solders to thermal fatigue is not only due to stresses that arise from the joint shape but also to the anisotropy of the tin crystals in the solder. Tin crystals have a tetragonal structure, which means that the thermal expansion along the principal axis of the crystals is different, the extreme values of the coefficients being $30,5 \times 10^{-6}$ and $15,5 \times 10^{-6}$/K. Lead crystals, which have a cubic structure, are consequently isotropic and their expansion coefficient is close to the maximum value of the tin crystals (29×10^{-6}/K). When the temperature is changed, the differential expansions of the tin and lead-rich phases have to be accommodated internally by elastic and plastic strains. For $\Delta T = 100$°C, the strains are $(30,5 - 15,5) \times 10^{-6} \times 100 = 0,15\%$, which is more than can be taken up elastically.

The cyclic plastic strain on a microscale produces a roughening of the original smooth solder surface, and in extreme cases ($\Delta T > 150$ K) a complete disintegration of the structure may be observed (see Figure 8.35).

The indium-lead alloys used for 'flip-chip solder' show an improved thermal-fatigue resistance over conventional tin-lead solders [Howard]. Unlike the tin-lead alloys which have a two-phase structure in a large part of the composition range, these alloys are mainly monophasic. However, the thermal expansion of polycrystalline indium is greater than that of tin, and so is the difference of the coefficients along the principal crystal axis.

4.7.4 Alloys with Higher Strength Values

As the normal tin-lead solder has a very low strength and is prone to creep and fatigue, an extensive search has been conducted to find stronger alloys which can be used as soft solder. Whilst a wide range of literature on the subject is available, it is still difficult to compare the strength data and to bring these into accordance

ith one another, because different test conditions, ageing conditions, etc.,
revail.

If tin and lead remain the main constituents of the alloys, only limited
nprovements of the properties can be achieved by adding other alloying
ements (see Chapter 4.4.9).

The main alloying elements that are used to increase the strength values are
ntimony and silver. When small amounts of these elements are added to eutectic
n-lead solder, it is found that:

(i) up to about 2% of silver improves the shear strength at room temperature
     (see Table 4.8), the creep strength at room temperature by 10%, and at
     100°C by 20%;

(ii) up to 6% antimony improves the shear, tensile and creep strength at room
     temperature [Drefahl *et al*].

It might be natural to expect better creep values from alloys with higher melting
oints, but this is not always the case [Nesse], *e.g.*, the lead-silver alloy with a
nelting point of 305°C shows poor creep characteristics.

For better creep properties, three groups of alloys are available, of which two
lloys have been included in Figure 4.26:

(i)   tin-antimony alloys with high tin content, for instance tin95-antimony5;
(ii) lead-tin-silver alloys with high lead content;
iii) tin-silver alloys with high tin content [Davies], possibly with addition of
      antimony, for instance, tin65-silver25-antimony10 [Olsen *et al*].

hough in general these alloys are superior to the tin-lead alloys, their creep
rength values are still low. If permanent loads are to be borne, all soft solders
·e quite unsuitable for transmitting the forces. Joint design should be such that
ιe permanent stress in the solder metal is practically zero.

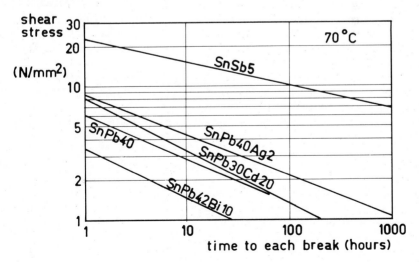

g. 4.26 Creep of some solder alloys at 70°C, measured with ring-and-plug test specimens. [Data
obtained from Becker]

The alloy lead90-cadmium9-zinc1 has a higher fatigue resistance than eutectic tin-lead solder [Denlinger *et al*], but this alloy has several technological disadvantages, such as the high melting range of 238-260°C.

4.7.5 Gap Between Soldering and Brazing

Mechanically strong connections can be obtained by employing brazing metals which are either single metals or alloys having either a melting point or a melting range above approximately 700°C.

Apart from a few gold-bearing alloys [Olsen *et al*], there are no easy-flowing metals with a melting point in the range between 350°C and 700°C. The element zinc (420°C) and magnesium (650°C) admittedly have their melting points lying within this range, but these metals are precisely the ones exhibiting a strong tendency towards oxidation. Neither do suitable alloys exist in this temperature range. One particular solder is available with a melting range between 595°C and 630°C, this being an alloy of 40% silver, 20% copper, 21% zinc and 19% cadmium. Owing to the volatile and toxic cadmium which it contains, application of this alloy is permitted only where adequate fume exhaust is provided.

Because brazing is a joining method which in general differs considerably from soft soldering, the present text will not enter into further aspects of brazing.

4.8 LOW-MELTING ALLOYS (Fusible Alloys)

By addition of certain other metals to tin and lead, eutectic alloys can be formed having still lower melting points than that of eutectic tin-lead solder (183°C) [Evans, Fasching]. The best-known ternary eutectics are those of tin, lead and cadmium with a melting point of 145°C, and of tin, lead and bismuth with a melting point of 99,5°C (Figure 4.27). Even lower lies the quaternary eutectic of tin, lead, cadmium and bismuth, at 70°C, the so-called Wood's metal. A quinary eutectic is formed by adding indium to the latter alloy. The eutectic temperature then becomes 47,2°C. Such low-melting alloys are little used as solder. They may offer advantages in those cases in which soldering operations must be performed on assemblies that have been previously subjected to soldering, where there would be a risk of the first soldering becoming damaged under the influence of the heat dissipated during the second soldering.

These low-melting alloys find some application as thermal safety fuses in the form of a soldered joint holding two electrical metal contacts together. They can also be used for the dissolution of higher melting point alloys at low temperature. The tin-lead-bismuth-indium alloy with a melting point of 58°C is most suited to this purpose; it can subsequently be washed away with hot water [Ward].

Many of the alloys do not contract on solidification; some of them even expand, especially those with a high bismuth content. This property makes them particularly suitable for 'tube bending alloy' or for matrix alloy for the temporary location of punches, dies, *etc.*

The low-melting alloys have the following disadvantages:

(i) the mechanical strength is even lower than that of tin-lead solder [Wild];

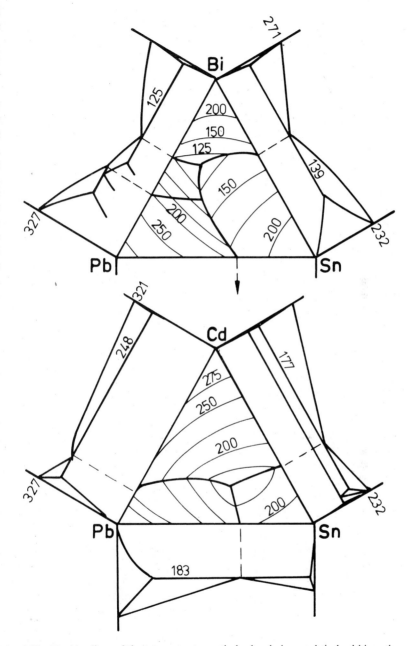

Fig. 4.27 Liquidus lines of the ternary systems: tin-lead-cadmium and tin-lead-bismuth.

i) the usual fluxes are insufficiently active to achieve good adhesion at the low melting point of the alloy. The remedy in this respect, namely to increase the temperature, defeats the original purpose of the low melting alloys. Aggressive fluxes must be used that necessitate extra rinsing operations;

126 Solder Alloys

(iii) severe oxidation occurs, both in the liquid state and in the solid state (exce for the expensive tin-indium alloys). In the case of thermal safety fuses, instance, the soldered joint must be coated with a protective age otherwise the oxide film formed will prevent the interruption of the jo after the liquidus temperature has been reached;

(iv) cadmium-containing alloys being toxic, their processing requi precautionary measures. It is to be expected that the use of cadmiu containing solder will be prohibited in the foreseeable future, or at least w be subjected to stringent restrictions.

Table 4.9 includes a number of low melting alloys obtained from vario literature sources, which are not always in agreement. There always remains so doubt as to whether the alloys mentioned have a definite melting point at t stated composition.

Table 4.9

Selection of Low Melting Alloys

Melting Point °C	Sn	Pb	Bi	In	Cd	Other Elements	Generic Name
16				24		76 Ga	
20	8					92 Ga	
25						95 Ga; 5 Zn	
29,8						100 Ga	
46,5	10,8	22,4	40,6	18	8,2		
47,2	8,3	22,6	44,7	19,1	5,3		
58	12	18	49	21			
61	16		33	51			
70	13,1	27,3	49,5		10,1		Lippowitz' al.
70-74	12,5	25	50		12,5		Wood's met
72,4			34	66			
79	17		57	26			
91,5		40,2	51,7		8,1		
93	42			44	14		
95	18,7	31,3	50				Newton's me
96	16	32	52				
96-98	25	25	50				d'Arcet's me
103,0	26		53,5		20,5		
96-110	22	28	50				Rose's meta
117	48			52			
125		43,5	56,5				
127,7				75	25		
139	43		57				
144			62		38		
145	49,8	32			18,2		
156,4				100			
170	57					43 Tl	
176	67				33		
178	62,5	36				1,5 Ag	
180	63	34	3				
183	61,9	38,1					

4.9   APPENDIX TO CHAPTER 4

4.9.1   Some Phase Diagrams Relevant to Soldering

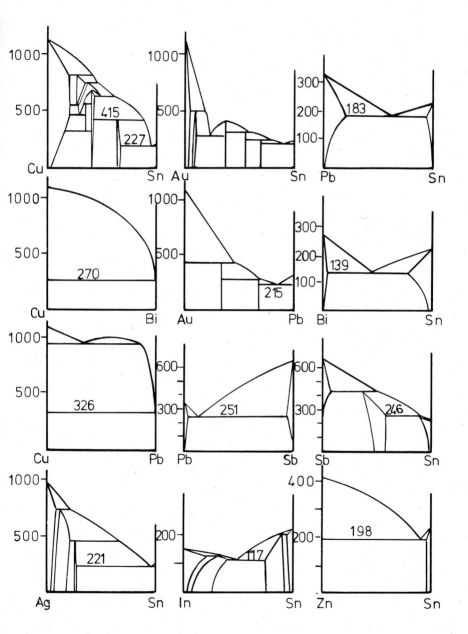

Fig. 4.28   Phase diagrams of binary systems relevant to soft soldering. The temperature, along the vertical axes, is given in °C; the concentration, along the horizontal axes, is given in mass per cent [Hansen and Smithells give concentrations in atomic percentages].

Table 4.10

Selection of Alloys with Definite Melting Points

Melting Point °C	Sn	Pb	Bi	Sb	Cd	Zn	Au	Ag	Other Elements
183	62	38							
198	91					9			
215		85					15		
221	96,5							3,5	
232	100								
248		82,6			17,4				
251		89		11					
266					82,6	17,4			
271			100						
280	20						80		
288		97,2							2,8 As
304		97,5						2,5	
318		99,5				0,5			
321					100				
327		100							
356							88	12	Ge
370							97	3	Si
420						100			

4.9.2 Methods for Determining the Solder Composition

Density

The tin content of a tin-lead alloy can be obtained from the density either using the formula given in Chapter 4.3.4 or the graph in Figure 4.30.

Cooling Curves

To evaluate the solder composition it is possible to use cooling curves of the solder. These are not discussed in detail (see Chapter 4.2.2). It will suffice to mention here that the shape of the cooling curves depends on the method of determining the curves and that it is often necessary to compare them with standard curves.

Instrumental Methods

Many methods are used [see, for instance, Skoog *et al*]:

(i) measurement with betascope (Beta Backscatter Method) [Damkjaer];
(ii) X-ray fluorescence analysis: this method is also suitable for determining possible contamination of the bath, with the exception of As, Fe and Al. With measures such as thorough homogenisation of the sample, making good calibration standards and inter-element correction, an accuracy of 5% is attained;
(iii) X-ray diffractometry, with an accuracy of about 20%;

(iv) polarography: this electrochemical method is very sensitive and accurate, though laborious [see Kolthoff *et al*];

(v) atomic absorption spectrophotometry: widely used for impurities and minor alloying additions, it gives accuracy of about 1,5% for the main constituents of the solder [Carleer *et al*].

For all these methods special equipment is needed. Radiation methods usually employ calibration standards, to which the test specimens are compared. The calibration standards of solder, however, even age at room temperature, so that systematic errors must be taken into account. A eutectic tin-lead calibration sample, for instance, could have changed so much after one year as a consequence of precipitation that X-ray diffractometry indicates 1% excess tin in the test samples.

Wet Chemical Methods

These methods are still the most reliable for soft-solder alloys. Standard methods are given by ASTM, BS, *etc*. [See also: Price and Smith.].

4.9.3 Method for Determining the Density of Solder Alloys

A suitable quantity of the alloy (about 5 cm³) is scooped out of the bath by means of a spoon. In a wave-soldering bath the solder is taken directly from the wave; in a stationary bath the oxide film must first be skimmed off and the bath stirred.

The contents of the spoon are poured into a sample tray containing a few ml of polydiol. The excess solder can be returned to the bath. In order to obtain a smooth specimen, in which contraction depression is open to the surface, the solder must be allowed to cool slowly in a place free from vibration and draught. For this purpose the tray is placed on a few strips of PTFE or cardboard and, if necessary, covered. At one end of the specimen, a hole with a diameter of 2 to 3 mm is drilled to allow suspension of the sample in a simple way during weighing, and also to give some impression of the presence of pores or flaws. The specimen is then cleaned thoroughly, first with water then with ethanol.

Then the density can be calculated from:

$$\varrho = \frac{(G_S - G_O) \times \varrho_{water}}{G_S - G_{SW} - (G_O - G_{OW})}$$

The significance of the symbols used follows from Figure 4.29. For an accurate calculation, the effect of temperature on the density of water must be taken into account, but in most cases it is accurate enough to use $\varrho = 998$ kg/m³ (valid at 22°C). Taking $\varrho = 1000$ kg/m³ systematically gives too high densities (as in the Tables of Price and Smith).

The accuracy of this method of density determination depends on the extent of the success in preparing pore-free and flaw-free specimens, which is why the sampling should be performed with the utmost care. Even then an accuracy better than 0,5% may not be expected. With this accuracy, the tin content of a solder alloy can be calculated to within about 1% of tin.

Example

G_O = 0,2159 g
G_S = 34,3938   thus, in this case $\varrho = \dfrac{(34,394 - 0,216) \times 998}{34,394 - 30,385 - 0,216 + 0,208}$
G_{SW} = 30,3854
G_{OW} = 0,2077   hence, $\varrho = 8525 \text{ kg/m}^3$
T = 22°C

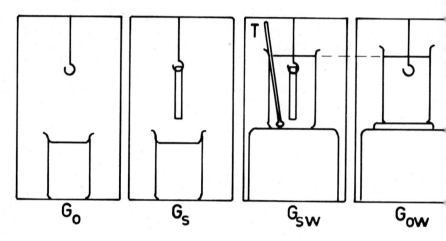

Fig. 4.29 Weighings necessary for density determination:

G_o = weight of the hook
G_s = weight of the hook + the specimen
G_{sw} = weight of the hook + the specimen immersed in water (to which one or two drops of surfa
active substance have been added)
G_{ow} = weight of the hook immersed in water (approximately to the same depth as in the previous
measurement).

4.9.4 Correcting the Tin-Lead Ratio of Solder Baths

When two different tin-lead alloys are combined, the total ma
$M_{total} = M_1 + M_2$; if alloy 1 has a tin percentage of m_1, etc., the tin percentage afte
combination will be:

$$m_{tin} = \frac{m_1 M_1 + m_2 M_2}{M_1 + M_2}$$

Usually a certain tin percentage m_{tin} will be desired, and m_1 (tin percentage in th
solder bath), m_2 (tin percentage of the added alloy) and M_1 (mass of the alloy i
the bath) will be known, whereas M_2 has to be found.

$$\text{Then: } M_2 = \frac{m_{tin} - m_1}{m_2 - m_{tin}} \times M_1$$

Example: a 10 kg bath contains 55% tin.
How much tin must be added to bring this bath up to 60%?

$M_1 = 10$; $m_1 = 55$; $m_2 = 100$ and $m_{tin} = 60$, so: $M_2 = \dfrac{60 - 55}{100 - 60} \times 10 = 1,25 \text{ kg.}$

inging the bath to eutectic composition (62% tin) requires: 1,84 kg (Figure
30). If instead of 100% tin an alloy containing 80% tin is added, about 3,9 kg is
ided to obtain 60% of tin in the bath.

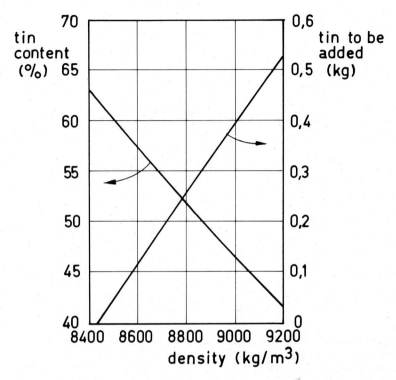

Fig. 4.30 Correction of solder baths. Two lines are shown:
in content of the solder in relation to the density of the solder at room temperature;
quantity of tin to be added per kg of existing bath, to bring the solder to eutectic composition (62%
in), in relation to the density of the solder at room temperature.

Chapter 5

FLUXES FOR SOLDERING

Soldering fluxes are used to promote wetting and thus assist the prope
formation of soldered joints.

The fluxes have three functions:

(i) chemical function: the main task of the flux is to remove tarnish films fro
surfaces and to protect the cleaned surfaces against reoxidation;
(ii) thermal function: assisting the transfer of heat from the heat source to tl
joint area;
(iii) physical function: the reaction products must be removed from the surfac
to allow the solder to come into intimate contact with the base met
surfaces.

These functions influence the surface tensions of the base metal, the solder al
the interfaces and hence have an effect upon the wetting conditions.

A considerable number of different fluxes exist. The formulation of those
current use for soft soldering is chiefly based on the results of trial and error

Fluxes consist of active agents dissolved or dispensed in a liquid. Tw
categories can be distinguished:

(i) fluxes soluble in organic liquids (e.g., resin-type fluxes);
(ii) fluxes soluble in water.

This solubility applies especially to the flux residues remaining after soldering

After the application of flux, which can be performed in several ways, tl
solvent evaporates, leaving the active agents on the surfaces. In the case of cor
solder the flux is contained in the solder wire without solvent and becom
available upon heating and melting of the solder wire.

The selection of a flux is governed by two criteria, discussed in detail
Sections 5.1 and 5.2:

(i) flux efficacy: the ability of the flux to promote solder wetting. Efficacy
closely related to chemical activity;
(ii) flux corrosivity: the ability of flux residues to affect the soldered produc
after the soldering process.

The two criteria of efficacy and corrosivity oppose each other. A highly acti flux will be corrosive as well, whereas a non-corrosive flux will have little activity, if any.

Because the majority of electronic components are highly sensitive to corrosion, the choice of fluxes is restricted to those with a limited activity. The deleterious effects of the flux residues can be avoided if the residues are washed away, but doubt always remains as to whether complete washing has been achieved.

The other approach is to inactivate the residues. In principle, this is possible because the activity should prevail at the soldering temperature, usually above 200°C, whereas if corrosion takes place it will be at a much lower temperature, normally below 70°C, the probable maximum working temperature of the electronic equipment.

Nevertheless, in all cases, the surface of electronic parts to be soldered should be relatively free from contaminants compared with the degree of cleanliness required in many non-electronic uses of soldering. The use of flux is no substitute for adequate surface preparation; flux is not a universal cleaner.

5.1 EFFICACY OF FLUXES

Flux efficacy is the ability of the flux to promote wetting of the surfaces by molten solder within a specific time. As thus defined, it comprises the ability of the flux itself to wet the surfaces to be joined, to transfer heat to them from the heat source, and to clean those surfaces chemically. The last of these properties is known as flux activity. The efficacy of a specific flux can be investigated by one of the methods used for the testing of solderability of surfaces. The maximum amount of information is obtained by those methods in which the rate of wetting is established, particularly at wetting times of a few seconds and at heating rates close to those associated with the actual soldering processes.

5.1.1 Flux Activity

During the heating of the flux its activity increases continuously, but above a certain temperature it decreases because of degradation of the active substances. As the oxidation behaviour of the solid and liquid metals are also temperature-dependent, the cleaning process and, consequently, the wetting are complicated and not easy to predict quantitatively.

Figure 5.1 shows the result of spread tests of solder on copper plates, using two fluxes with different characteristics under otherwise identical conditions.

The area of spread (0A = area of solder pellet) of the solder is plotted along the vertical axis, the time along the horizontal axis.

Flux 1 shows a rapid action, but is soon exhausted.

Flux 2 is much slower but works longer and ultimately produces a greater extent of solder flow. With a different temperature cycle, a different relation between the two fluxes may be observed.

A flux which works well at a specific temperature and time may not be satisfactory under other conditions. The degree of chemical activity of the flux must therefore be adapted to the soldering process:

(i) in a fast process fluxes are necessary that develop their activity very rapidly; they are allowed to be unstable;

(ii) in a slow process the flux must be more stable and possess a prolonged protecting capability.

The efficacy of a flux cannot be deduced solely from the amount of free acid present in the flux. Other properties of the flux also play a role.

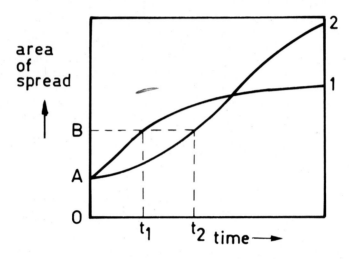

Fig. 5.1　Spread tests with two different fluxes. Though flux 2 exhibits a larger area of spread at the end, flux 1 is faster at the beginning.

5.1.2　Effect of Soldering Temperature

If the logarithm of the wetting times, t, is plotted against the reciprocal absolute temperature, T, a straight line is quite often obtained within the experimental error (Arrhenius plot), suggesting the relation:

$$t = t_0 \, e^{Q/RT},$$

in which R is the gas constant, and Q is the activation energy. This is the case for globule times (see Figure 5.2), or wetting times in a wetting balance. The value of Q is about 40000 J/mole for rosin fluxes.

Different chemicals applied as fluxes produce a wide range of activation energies, as do different solder alloys [Shipley]. The activation energies of ionic amine hydrohalide activators in colophony fluxes show no correlation with the wetting rate produced [Weinberger *et al*].

The relatively low energies of activation that are often found indicate that the process of wetting is not purely chemically determined.

The effect of temperature on flux behaviour can be investigated using techniques such as differential thermal analysis and thermo-gravimetric analysis [Goldman, Hill *et al*, Rubin *et al*]. Figure 5.3 shows an example of a combination of the two techniques, though without explanation of the effects.

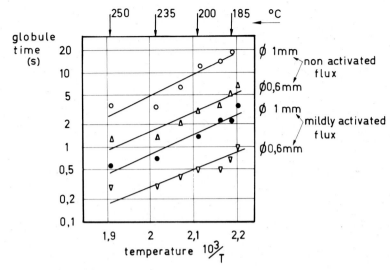

Fig. 5.2   Globule test times as a function of temperature, showing the thermal effect of wire diameter and the chemical effect of the activity of the flux. Note that the experimental points for the highest temperature (*viz.* 250°C) deviate from the general trend. [Data obtained from Ten Duis]

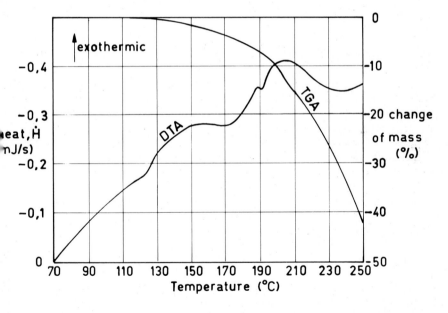

Fig. 5.3   DTA (differential thermal analysis) and TGA (thermo-gravimetric analysis) of a rosin flux, *viz.*, flux b of Chapter 5.5.5. The flux was dried at 100°C for 30 minutes before the analyses. The horizontal is the nominal temperature and the heating time (TGA 10 K/min). The vertical is the heat of reaction and the decrease in weight of the specimen. Starting mass of specimen is about 1 mg.

5.1.3   Protective Capability of Flux

In spreading tests, only the cleaning action of the flux is considered. However the flux should also protect the surfaces against reoxidation, for instance at the place where the boards leave a solder wave, to prevent the formation of bridge and icicles. The constituents of the flux that clean the surfaces of components printed board and solder metal at initiation of the soldering operation may not b suited to this protective task in the end phase of the soldering process. If a flux i perfectly suited to pretinning, it may still not meet the requirements for machine soldering (see also Figure 7.28).

5.1.4   Protective Atmospheres

The main task of fluxes is to clean the surfaces, chiefly by removing oxide (tarnish) layers. It might be thought that reducing gases could be used for thi purpose. However, the temperatures and times permissible in making the soldered joints are insufficient for successful reduction of oxide to metal. On the other hand, gases could be used to fulfil the protective task of fluxes. Yet, even for this purpose gases are seldom applied in soft soldering, because an effective shielding is hard to realise and is therefore expensive. In this respect it can b noted that the Vapour Phase Soldering Method makes use of an inert gas, thu providing complete exclusion of air.

5.2   CORROSIVITY OF FLUXES

Corrosion by flux residues is the unwanted chemical attack by these residues o the soldered product during its lifetime. The residues originate from flu vapours, heated flux, and non-heated flux and their effect may range from a mer discoloration to a complete destruction of the functioning of the product. Closel connected to corrosion is the question of reduction of surface resistance under th influence of the flux residues. The prediction of failure by corrosion or a unacceptable decrease in surface resistance is hard to give, and no generall accepted test methods are available. Different methods are often applied i combination in order to increase the reliability of the predictions [Studnick *et a* Dunn *et al*].

The test methods can be divided into two groups:

(i) tests on the flux itself, neglecting the influence of the soldering operation o it;

(ii) tests on boards after soldering, in which all processing treatments of th product under test are taken into account.

5.2.1   Tests on the Flux

The translation of the test results into corrosion reality is quite difficult becaus the flux is assessed in the non-heated condition. These test methods are therefor mainly suited to incoming inspection purposes [see also Spec. Ref. 18], and t give information on the effect of spilt flux.

5.2.1.1 HALIDE CONTENT OF FLUX

Though many activators causing corrosion do not contain any halide at all, the halide content of the flux is still considered to be an important figure. It can be measured by a potentiometric titration method using a silver nitrate solution. Halide content is expressed as a mass percentage with respect to the flux without solvent (% of solids content), because the solvent is evaporated before reaching soldering temperature and is not present in the flux residue.

Free halides in soldering fluxes can be detected at the level of about 0,07% and higher, by performing a simple spot test using silver chromate impregnated paper [Spec. Ref. 11, Sabo].

5.2.1.2 ACID VALUE OF FLUXES

The acid value (acid number) of a rosin flux is the number of milligrams of potassium hydroxide required to neutralise the free acids in 1 gram of the solid components of the flux under the test conditions. The value is determined by titrating a solution of the rosin in alcohol with a standard solution of potassium or sodium hydroxide using phenolphthalein as indicator. The determination of the acid value is a simple way of investigating whether any organic acids have been added to the flux, and once the type of acid is known the quantity in the flux can be calculated.

Table 5.1 gives the acid values of different types of rosin and Table 5.12 gives the acid values of a number of acids.

Table 5.1

Acid Value of Rosins

Rosin	Acid Value
Abietic acid	185
Gum rosin	168
Wood rosin	163
Hydrogenated rosin	160
Dehydrogenated rosin	154
Polymerised rosin	144
Dimerised rosin	140

Fluxes with the same acid value can differ widely in activity and corrosivity. The acid value is a quantity quite unrelated to the pH value, most rosin fluxes having a pH of between 3,5 and 5 at room temperature [Dunn *et al*].

5.2.1.3 RESISTIVITY OF WATER EXTRACT OF THE FLUX IN WATER

The resistivity shows to what extent ions that cause conduction in water are present in the flux.

In this test, 50 mg of the flux solids to be tested are boiled for 1 minute in 50 ml of water with an initial resistivity of 0,5 MΩcm minimum. After cooling, the resistivity of the aqueous extract must be at least 100 kΩcm.

This requirement effectively restricts the presence of halogen-containing activators in a rosin flux to an amount of more than 0,2% by mass (of halogen expressed as Cl⁻ with respect to the rosin). The results of the extract measurements are expressed either as resistivity in Ωcm or as specific conductance in S/cm (see Chapter 5.7.3).

A water extract of oxidised colophony without any added activator also shows an appreciable conductivity, and can sometimes fall below 100 kΩcm. Disproportioned rosins display a higher resistivity than normal rosins.

5.2.1.4 COPPER MIRROR TEST FOR DIRECT CORROSIVE ATTACK

A very thin layer of copper (about 80 nm thickness) is exposed to flux residues.

0,05 ml of flux solution is pipetted onto freshly vapour-deposited copper on glass, the copper having a transmission factor of 10% for light of 0,5 μm. After 24 hours' conditioning in a dust-free room at 23°C and a relative humidity of 50%, the copper must be free from visual sign of attack and penetration of the copper layer at any point.

Some characteristics of this test are:

(i) despite the clearly expressed pass/fail criteria, the test is somewhat subjective as it is based on visual assessment [Spec. Ref. 11];

(ii) the test results are strongly influenced by the flux solvent and by the formulation of the activators. When, for instance, dimethylammonium chloride is dispersed in small droplets, these may float upwards, thus imparting to the flux in contact with the mirror a different composition from the average composition;

(iii) for preparing the specimens, special vapour deposition apparatus, *etc.*, is needed or mirrors can be purchased from specialised manufacturers (about $1,5 per piece);

(iv) the deposited layers should be free of oxidation before the beginning of the test, because oxidised copper is attacked even by an alcohol solution of colophony WW. The specimens should therefore be reasonably fresh. Their shelf life is not longer than a few months, unless they are carefully sealed under nitrogen.

Highly activated fluxes do not pass this test, but for the fluxes with less than 1% of halide no relationship exists between the resistance to copper mirror corrosion and the individual flux halide concentration [Dunn *et al*].

5.2.1.5 DEGRADATION OF MECHANICAL STRENGTH OF WIRES

Corrosion can be quantitatively assessed by monitoring the strength degradation of thin wires or strips under the influence of flux residues and humidity. Such a method is naturally very time-consuming.

5.2.2 Tests on Soldered Printed Boards

The tests will provide evidence for the reliability of the product. As corrosion is greatly enhanced by moisture, damp conditions are often applied in these tests.

5.2.2.1 CLIMATIC TESTS OF BEHAVIOUR OF FLUX RESIDUES

In most cases, these tests are carried out on special comb test patterns which are handled in the same way as production boards. As it is impossible to ensure that all the flux was exposed to the soldering temperature during the soldering process, a test must also be performed on test boards with flux but without soldering. If the soldering process is followed by a cleaning procedure, the cleaned boards should be tested in the same way.

Choice of test depends on the specifications for the end-product. For normal environmental conditions, the damp heat steady state test is used [Spec. Ref. 5]. The temperature and relative humidity during the test must be maintained at $40\pm2°C$ and $93^{+2}_{-3}\%$ respectively. The duration of the test is as required by the relevant specification: 4, 10, 21 or 56 days. If, during the use of the end-product, condensation of water can occur on the printed boards, then another test should be incorporated in the test programme, namely temperature cycling between $25\pm2°C$ and $65\pm2°C$ at high humidity, $93\pm3\%$, in a 24 hour cycle. The number of 24 hour cycles should be 10 unless otherwise specified.

During the climatic tests half of the comb patterns should be at a bias voltage. For most comb patterns, the space between the pattern lines is in the range 0,3-0,75 mm and for these a bias voltage of 100 V DC is used. The same voltage can also be used for measurements of insulation resistance. Here, the voltage drop across a current-limiting resistor of 100 kΩ, put in series with the test pattern, is measured. In this way measuring can take place during the climatic test without disturbing the test array, because the series resistors are mounted on a panel outside the test chamber. Depending on the requirements and the specification for the end-product, the measuring requirements must be fulfilled during and after the test. However, in most cases, only the test requirement after a recovery period is given.

After the climatic tests and insulation resistance measurements, the comb pattern lines should be visually inspected for evidence of corrosion products, using a magnification of $10\times$. Inspection must be made along all pattern line edges. Corrosion products will be recognisable by their colour deviation from the normal colour of the flux residues; they may also have a dendritic or bleeding appearance.

Corrosion will reduce the section of the conductors on a board and hence can also be assessed by measuring the change of resistance of these conductors. For this measurement a specially designed board is used with a long conductor, having a width of about 100 μm, following a meandering course between the fingers of two combs (as shown in Figure 5.4). The bias voltage is applied between the two combs which have been interconnected and the long conductor between the combs. While the test pattern is in the humidity chamber, the resistance of the long conductor is measured at time intervals. The same test board can also be used for the measurement of surface resistance.

5.2.2.2 SURFACE RESISTANCE OF SOLDERED BOARD

The surface resistance of a soldered board is very important because it may affect the electronic functioning of the circuit on the board, especially in areas where high impedances are present. It may also give an indication of the possibility of corrosion caused by ionic transport across the surface.

In a resistance measurement, use is made of a printed test pattern on a piece of board under relevant test conditions. The IEC method [Spec. Ref. 2] applies a ring and disc pattern that is submitted to a 'Damp Heat Steady State' test of

4 days' duration. The resistance measurement is taken after 1 minute at 500 Volts.

Besides this pattern many others are used, for instance the 'comb' pattern type having arrays of uniformly spaced copper or solder-plated copper conductors such as shown in Figure 5.4 [Jol, see also Spec. Ref. 9]. The surface resistivit value is given as resistance in $M\Omega$ per unit square. Each comb pattern has its ow multiplication factor for calculating the surface resistivity, R_S, from the measure resistance, R:

$$R_S = \frac{l}{w} \times R, \text{ in which}$$

l = effective length of the electrodes, and
w = effective distance between the electrodes.

Comparison of different test patterns is, however, only possible if these pattern have approximately the same shape and dimensions. In fact, no preference exist for a certain design; they are all suitable if creepage distances are not too small

After application of flux to a test comb on epoxy board material, the data o Table 5.2 were obtained.

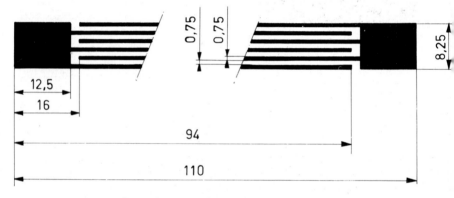

Fig. 5.4 Comb pattern with multiplication factor of 500.

Table 5.2

Surface Resistivity

		Pure Rosin	Activated Rosi
After application of flux and soldering		42×10^6	44×10^6
During Damp Heat Test (Test Ca, IEC 68-2-3):			
after	7 days	4×10^6	$0,5 \times 10^6$
	21 days	3×10^6	$0,3 \times 10^6$
	56 days	3×10^6	$0,3 \times 10^6$
After 56 days, followed by 4 days of conditioning at 25°C and 65% relative humidity		45×10^6	8×10^6
		$M\Omega$ resistance per unit square	

The results of the resistance measurements are assessed from two points of ew:

(i) the decrease of the resistance in the damp condition;
ii) the recovery of the resistance after the damp test.

Under the damp conditions of relative humidity above 80% absorbed water ims of several molecular layers are always present on the insulating material, ith the result that even in the absence of ionic residues a reduced surface sistance is found. A film of pure water, having a thickness of 10 nm and a ecific resistance the same as the bulk resistance of pure water (see Chapter 7.3.1), has a surface resistance of 17×10^6 MΩ per unit square. If ions from the mosphere or from the flux residues are present, as is always the case in practice, wer resistance values are measured, giving rise to larger ionic transport. These ns, however, may be inhomogeneously distributed so that the reduction of the erall resistance of a test board may originate from only a few regions having a latively low resistance. The presence of such bad spots also explains the large read found in the surface resistance of test boards of the same batch. Bad spots ive as a consequence that the ionic transport is localised there.

The ionic transport across the insulation between conductors produces metal owth over the insulation, which creates short circuiting sooner or later, pending on the flux residues on the board and the environmental conditions igure 5.5). This conductive anodic filament growth (CAF growth) becomes iportant with closely spaced conductors, high applied voltages and humid ivironment. The growth is mostly from cathode to anode but under certain rcumstances it may occur from the other side or both.

It may also take place in the inside of the printed boards along the glass inforcing fibres between adjacent, oppositely biased plated holes [Mitchell *et*].

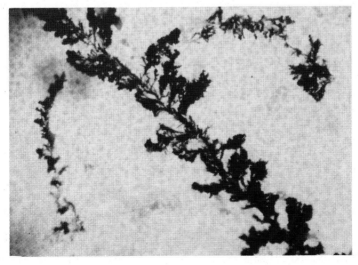

g. 5.5 A conductive filament grown on the board surface between two conductors, during a steady te climatic test under a bias voltage. The filament shows a typical ferny appearance. The nductors are just outside the field of the photograph: the anode at the top side and the cathode at the bottom. Magnification 180×.

The filament growth can easily be observed under a (40×) microscope, when a drop of wate
applied to the board surface between two neighbouring conductors which have been connected t
voltage of 20 volts. If after short circuiting the bias voltage is maintained the current will destroy
filament, but growth will continue without interruption at the same place or elsewhere.

The lifetime of flux-treated printed circuitry can be estimated by measuring t
insulation resistance under accelerated conditions. For this purpose seve
specimens with fine-line comb patterns are subjected to environments of 80
relative humidity and temperatures of 55, 70 and 85°C. The times are determin
that it takes for at least 50% of the test circuits to fail (*i.e.*, develop an elect
short or show a definite sudden drop in insulation resistance of more than
order of magnitude). The expected lifetime at room temperature (and 80% RH)
obtained by extrapolation, assuming an Arrhenius relation.

Surface resistances are in general high. With such high resistance values t
measurements are rather difficult to reproduce because unexpected effects m
occur. To avoid effects of polarisation, it is possible in principle to measure wi
alternating current, but even at low frequencies the capacitive component of t
current will be much larger (100×) than the reactive component, so that
sophisticated measuring apparatus is necessary.

Finally, it has been noted that the bulk resistance of most laminate materials
so high that conduction through the bulk can be ignored, as long as close
spaced holes are absent. A suitable laminate should be selected for the tests.

Silver Migration

Migration under the influence of an electrical (DC) potential in combinati
with moisture, as shown in Figure 5.5, occurs with several meta
[DerMarderosian]. It is most pronounced with silver in which case the migratic
may extend along the surface for many millimetres, and tends to follow pat
through fibrous materials along the fibre surfaces [Kohman *et al*]. Silv
migration is also known on thick film circuits where silver-palladium conducto
are used [Naguib *et al*], or on silver plated ceramic components.

Such migration is likely because the silver oxide, easily formed electrolyticall
has a relatively high solubility in water, which in humid environments is alwa
present on the surfaces considered, including glass and ceramics.

The migration of other metals such as copper, tin and lead, being much slow
than that of silver, is often more significant in electronics, because silver can t
avoided in many critical constructions, whereas the other metals cannot.

5.3   SURFACE CONTAMINANTS

The main contaminants to be removed by the flux are the reaction products
the base metals with air: oxides, hydroxides and sulphides.

5.3.1   Copper Oxides

The thin oxide layer important for soldering, which grows on copper
atmospheric conditions, consists of Cu_2O, the thermodynamically stable oxid
(Early literature sources that mention CuO are obsolete. This type of oxide
present only under conditions where black scaling occurs.) The nature of the lay
is investigated by electron diffraction analysis, Auger spectroscopy [Tissier *et al*
potentiodynamic electrochemical reduction [Ambrose *et al*], *etc*.

The growth of the oxide layer on copper at room temperature proceeds arabolically for about 100 hours [Krishnamoorthy *et al*], but for longer times a near growth is observed (Figure 5.6).

A layer of 10 nm is formed in about 90 days, the same layer thickness being ound at 105°C after 16 hours. Such a layer has 5×10^{-8} mole Cu_2O/cm^2. The rowth of the oxide layers is influenced by the condition of the surface just before ie oxide forming treatment starts. Table 5.3 gives the concentration of a number f elements on the copper surface after various pickling treatments, as obtained y Auger electron spectroscopy in the Author's laboratory.

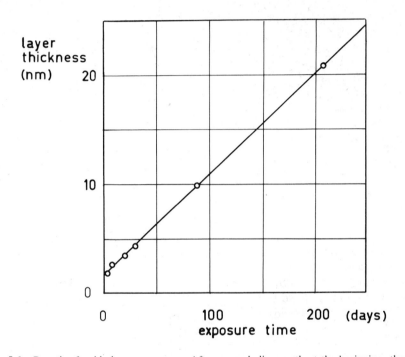

g. 5.6 Growth of oxide layer on copper. After a parabolic growth at the beginning, the layer thickness increases linearly with time.

Table 5.3

Surface Contaminant Concentration on Pickled Copper

ckling Method	Atomic Concentration of Element							
	S	Cl	C	Ca	N	O	Cr	Cu
arting material	0,2	8	28	0,6	0,6	26	1,4	55
$_2O_2/H_2SO_4$; demineralised water	0,3	14,9	9,4		0,7	18,5		55,6
$_2O_2/H_2SO_4$; tap water	0,7	3,7	17,4	2,8	1,7	19,3		54
uCl$_2$; HCl; demineralised water	0,9	14,7	26,1			12,3		43,8
rO$_3/H_2SO_4$; tap water; demineralised water	2,6	10,1	14,3	0,3	0,4	23,3	4,4	44,7
rO$_3/H_2SO_4$; HCl; demineralised water	0,9	12,3	20,6		0,8	15,1	1,5	48,8

From Table 5.3 it can be seen that in all cases a considerable amount of chlorine is present on the surface, irrespective of the presence of chlorine in the pickling acid. If from a washing and rinsing treatment some salt or acid residue remain, this may change the given figures by a factor of 10 and will render the oxidation non-reproducible. The result is a changing degree of oxidation of specimens that are supposed to be homogeneous. This is certainly one of the sources of non-reproducibility inherent in soldering and solderability testing.

5.3.1.1 DAMP HEAT TREATMENTS

Damp heat treatment causes the growth of a thick oxide film of a different nature. Slight contamination with inorganic salts enhances this growth, while slight contamination with organic material and pre-ageing in air diminish the growth rate of the film.

It is not evident whether this reduced oxide growth, when samples are pre-aged in air, is caused by a transition in the natural oxide film or by adsorption of organics from the air. The nature of the oxide films grown in damp heat is not completely clear. They are partly hydrated, but with X-ray diffraction only Cu_2O is found. With the potentioscanning method an extremely high reduction potential is found, much higher than that of Cu_2O.

Relatively thin layers of this type of surface film severely impair solderability, to a much greater extent than does thermally grown Cu_2O.

5.3.1.2 CHROMATE FILMS

As-delivered copper sheet materials for printed board manufacture have a corrosion-resistant surface film with a thickness of a few nanometres, consisting of either a copper chromate or a copper chromate-phosphate mixture. Pickling of a copper surface in a CrO_3-H_2SO_4 aqueous solution leaves behind a chromate film. If it has been formed under unfavourable conditions, a chromate film can strongly influence the solderability, as is sometimes the case in the actual soldering of a printed board. This type of film can be removed by HCl (dilute 1:10) but some minutes are needed for complete removal.

Copper chromate films and copper benzotriazole films are effective corrosion inhibitors. If applied in the appropriate way, solderability is to a large extent unimpaired. If very thick layers are formed, which can easily happen, poorly solderable or even non-solderable surfaces are the result.

5.3.2 Tin Oxides

Two oxides of tin are known, SnO and SnO_2. In the oxidation of tin in air below 200°C both play a part [Britton], although SnO is the main one [Britton et al]. The tin-oxide layers are transparent to light, thus producing only a slight discoloration. Above 200°C the thickness increases and interference colours become visible.

The same is true for tin as for copper: the differences in cleaning treatment produce considerable variations in the properties and growth rate of the tin-oxide layers that are subsequently formed. Tin-oxide layers grow more slowly than copper-oxide layers. Both are of p-type with cation vacancies, but the SnO layer is more dense.

˙resh layers have a thickness of about 1,5 nm [Evans] and grow approximately arithmically with time: at room temperature 2 nm after a week, 3 nm after a ar and only 6 nm after 20 years (1 nm = 10 Å).

At about 200°C, the growth rate is approximately twice the rate at 100°C. At)°C after 24 hours, a layer of 30 nm is formed on the tin coating on copper ˙es [Fidos *et al*]. Both water and water vapour enhance the growth of the layer ısiderably [Britton *et al*], as is shown in the next Table for tin in boiling water.

Table 5.4

Thickness of Oxide Layers on Tin in Boiling Water

Minutes	*Thickness (nm)*
5	2
30	2,5
60	3,5
240	4,5

˙e effect of lead (in solid solution in the tin) on the oxidation rate of tin can be ˛lected. Antimony and bismuth assist oxidation, whilst phosphorus, zinc and ˙ium retard growth [Boggs *et al*] in accordance with Hauffe's valency rules. The surface of tin-lead alloys is enriched with lead, but the tin in the alloy ıdises preferentially [Frankenthal *et al*, Nelson *et al*, Okamoto *et al*], so that for ˙der alloys the main oxide is also SnO (see also Chapter 4.5.1).

˙.3　Sulphides

˛ulphides in general play a minor role because the sulphur content of air is low: ˙mally $(1-20) \times 10^{-9}$. On tin-lead, the interaction of H_2S and SO_2 is negligible at ıcentrations and humidities likely to exist in practice [Tompkins], even in ˙luted atmospheres. Only on silver is the formation of sulphides well known, ˙ing a black discoloration of the surface. Silver scarcely oxidises at all at room ˙nperature.

˙rtificial sulphurisation is recommended for the preparation of series of specimens with ˙oducible levels of surface contamination [Spec. Ref. 18], but it is an open question to what extent ı sulphide layers are representative of tarnish (oxide) layers on aged surfaces [MacKay *et al*].

CHEMICAL FUNCTION OF FLUXES

˙part from trivial contaminations such as grease, the surfaces are covered with ˙nish layers that must be removed by the flux. The base materials are mainly ˙pper and tin-lead coatings, but may also include nickel, brass, iron, nickel iron ˙ nickel silver. After the appropriate chemical reaction of the flux with the ˙nish layers, the reaction products have to be dissolved in the flux, which must ˙ capable of transporting the reaction products away from the borderline ˙ween base metal and solder. The contaminated flux must still be easily ˙placed by the advancing solder, so the viscosity characteristics of the flux are ˙ important.

˙he fluxing action is a thermally activated process. At a higher temperature a higher rate of wetting is observed, as shown in Section 5.1.2. It is, however, v⟨ difficult to obtain really adequate information about the processes by measuri⟨ wetting times or wetting rates as a function of temperature. The data for wetting test are always the combined result of heat transfer and chemical action a more or less transient situation. The temperature normally stated is not t actual reaction temperature but the maximum temperature reached.

It is noticeable that chlorine plays an important role in many fluxes, be⟨ present in the main constituents of the flux or in the activators commonly us⟨

A comprehensive theory on the chemical and physical actions of the flux d⟨ not exist. Many factors controlling the fluxing action are not yet fu⟨ understood, because basic studies in this field are scarce and certainly ⟨ conclusive [Onoshi *et al*, Rubin *et al*].

5.4.1 Flux Reactions with Metal Oxides

Most fluxes have only a limited dissolving capability for metal oxides as t⟨ compounds used in chemical analysis to convert oxides to soluble compoun⟨ *e.g.*, alkali metal carbonates and sulphates, are seldom found in fluxes; neith⟨ are sulphuric acid, nitric acid, nitrates or chlorates. They all lack suffici⟨ efficacy.

Cuprous compounds in general are unstable and easily yield cupric compou⟨ and metallic copper. The reaction: $Cu_2O \rightarrow CuO + Cu$ has a positive reaction-f⟨ energy ($\Delta G \approx 20000$ J/mole), but the reaction product, Cu, will dissolve in t⟨ liquid solder or react elsewhere, thus compensating for the ΔG and enabling t⟨ reaction $2Cu^+ \rightarrow Cu^{++} + Cu_{solder}$ to occur. Cuprous oxide (Cu_2O) is easily remov⟨ by dilute acids, with the exception of nitric acid:

$$Cu_2O + 2HCl \rightarrow CuCl_2 + Cu + H_2O$$
or: $$Cu_2O + H_2SO_4 \rightarrow CuSO_4 + Cu + H_2O$$

$CuCl_2$ is very deliquescent and is soluble in water, methyl alcohol and et⟨ alcohol. The reactions are in fact more complicated than given; for instance, ⟨ oxygen in the air also has a role to play.

The reaction with the chloride of an activator (such as discussed in Chap⟨ 5.5.3) may be assumed to be the same as that with HCl in which 2 atoms ⟨ chlorine react with 1 mole of oxide.

Consider the application of an activated flux with 0,2% Cl^- on solids. Af⟨ drying, the flux quantity will be about 0,3 mg/cm^2, which means that ab⟨ 2×10^{-8} gram-ion Cl^- per cm^2 is present. This can react with 10^{-8} mole of oxi⟨ which is considerably less than the amount that corresponds to an oxide thickn⟨ of 10 nm; hence it is concluded that stoichiometrically the activator cannot do t⟨ work by itself. The acids of the colophony have also a cleaning capability ⟨ copper tarnish, albeit not a very effective one. On the other hand, not all ⟨ chlorine in the activator of activated fluxes reacts during the dwell period at h⟨ temperature, which is too short for complete decomposition of the activator.

The effect of the chlorine will presumably also be related to the formation ⟨ complex compounds with copper. $CuCl_2$ in water gives a number of compl⟨ reaction products. With increasing dilution are observed:

$CuCl_4^{--}$, $[CuCl_3(H_2O)]^-$, $CuCl_2(H_2O)$, $[CuCl(H_2O)_3]^+$ and $[Cu(H_2O)_4]^{++}$.

urthermore, the complex acids, H_2CuCl_3 and $HCuCl_2$, are known, and amines ch as $Cu(NH_3)_4Cl_2$. Aniline hydrochloride ($C_6H_5 . NH_2 . HCl$) reacts with copper form the blue product, $Cu[C_6H_5NH_3]_2Cl_4$, insoluble in water [Onoshi *et al*], d $CuCl_2$.

The effect of an activator on the wetting rate on clean copper is given in Figure .11. The effect on heavily oxidised copper (aged 16 hours at 120°C, and hence r soldering practice unsolderable) is shown in Figure 5.7, where a number of etting balance recordings are reproduced from which the marked influence of e activator content can be observed. The wetting rate increases rapidly with tivator concentration until about 1% of Cl^-, and then levels off, so that above % of Cl^- no substantial increase is apparent [Weinberger *et al*].

Stearic acid dissolves copper oxide [Batra *et al*] giving the green copper earate, though the reaction rate is low. In contact with solder, the copper in the earate will be reduced and the metallic copper will dissolve in the solder, while n (or lead) stearate is formed. Benzoic acid works similarly.

Hydrazine is known to reduce oxides at elevated temperature:

$$N_2H_4 + 2Cu_2O \rightarrow 4Cu + 2H_2O + N_2.$$

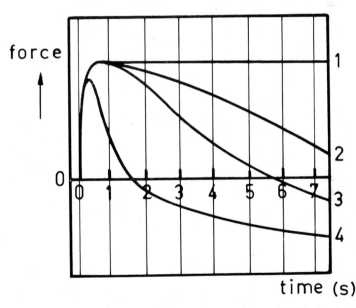

ig. 5.7 Force-time traces from a wetting balance (test temperature 235°C), showing the effect of activator added to the flux (*cf*. Fig. 5.11). Material: heavily oxidised copper (16 h at 120°C).

Curve	% Solids	Activator (%Cl^- on solids)
1	25	-
2	25	0,2 (DEA HCl)
3	25	0,5 (DMA HCl)
4	40	1 (DMA HCl)

The reaction: $Sn + 2Cu_2O \rightarrow SnO_2 + 4Cu$, which is expected thermodynamically, lisplaces the oxygen from the tarnish layer on the base metal surfaces to another lace where it is unlikely to hamper the flow of the solder. The same reasoning

applies for $CuCl_2$, which can also react with tin or with lead: the metallic copp
from these reactions will dissolve into the solder.

5.4.1.1 FLUXING ACTION OF ZINC CHLORIDE

The fluxing action of the salts zinc chloride and ammonium chloride is base
on the fact that hydrochloric acid is evolved in the presence of water, convertii
the metallic oxides to chlorides. These chlorides form low melting and solub
compounds with the salts, which are easily displaced from the metal surface t
the molten solder.

Zinc chloride has a melting point of 283°C. It is a hygroscopic salt easi
soluble in water, alcohols and polyethylene glycols but not very readily soluble i
glycerol. It raises the boiling point of water-hydrochloric acid mixtures to 250°C
When the salt is applied completely dry, it has no fluxing action below its meltir
point. In the presence of water, it will hydrolyse according to the followir
reactions:

$$ZnCl_2 + H_2O \rightarrow ZnO + 2HCl$$
and $$ZnCl_2 + H_2O \rightarrow Zn(OH)Cl + HCl$$

The hydrochloric acid acts on the metal oxides according to:

$$MeO + 2HCl \rightarrow MeCl_2 + H_2O.$$

Ammonium chloride has a melting point of approximately 520°C (at hig
pressure) but sublimates completely at a temperature of 340°C. It is readil
soluble in water and glycerol but has a limited solubility in alcohols an
polyethylene glycols. It acts on the metal oxides according to:

$$NH_4Cl \rightarrow NH_3 + HCl$$
$$MeO + 2HCl \rightarrow MeCl_2 + H_2O$$

The metal chlorides form low melting soluble compounds or eutectics with th
ammonium chloride and the zinc chloride (Table 5.5).

Table 5.5

Melting Points of Selected Compounds and Salt Mixtures

Compound or Salt Mixture	Melting Point (°C)
$ZnCl_2NH_4Cl$	249
$ZnCl_2 - NH_4Cl$ (13% NH_4Cl)	232
$ZnCl_2 - NH_4Cl$ (28% NH_4Cl)	180
$ZnCl_2 - SnCl_2$ (77% $SnCl_2$)	171
$ZnCl_2 - FeCl_3$ (70% $FeCl_3$)	214
$FeCl_3 - NH_4Cl$ (15% NH_4Cl)	220
$CuCl_26NH_4Cl$	140

The zinc chloride-ammonium chloride mixtures have a greater fluxing actio
than either salt alone, ammonium chloride being the most reactive constituer

3atra *et al*]. The salts formed during the reaction are again very easily dissolved
 the zinc-ammonium chloride flux. When the inorganic fluxes are used in the
)wer soldering temperature range, *e.g.*, 150-250°C, vehicles like glycerol and
olyethylene glycols are used in the flux in order to reduce the viscosity, to keep
ie reactive components in contact with the metal surface, and to transport the
:action products from the metal surfaces.

The addition of halide acids such as hydrochloric greatly speeds up the cleaning
ction of the flux at lower temperatures but will on the other hand attack all
ietal parts which come into contact with the wet flux or its vapours.

.4.1.2   HALOS

As regards zinc chloride and ammonium chloride or mixtures of the two,
lectrochemical reactions are often mentioned in the literature [Batra *et al*].
.elated to this is halo-formation [Latin], where around a drop of molten solder
n a flat surface with flux present a region is visible having a blue colour. This
)loured area is due to the formation of a tin layer or tin-copper intermetallic
iyer, the tin being transported through the flux and deposited electrochemically.
[o lead is deposited.

These halos can not only be made with ammonium chloride-zinc chloride
luxes, but also (much more slowly!) with urea or with pure dimethylammonium
hloride; they can also be obtained below the melting point of the tin. It is
ecessary to exclude the migration of the tin across the surface because the tin can
lso pass over deep grooves. It is not known precisely how important this
lectrochemical transport is for the action of a flux in practice. It may be that it is
)o slow.

Halos have also been observed in other systems such as tin-indium on copper,
aused by condensation of metal vapour [Lea]. In this case, the halo consists of a
in-indium region close to the tin-indium droplet surrounded by an indium-rich
egion.

.4.2   Ice Shell Theory

Tin oxide is more difficult to reduce than copper oxide. The layer thickness,
.owever, is usually smaller. Another fact is important here too. Under the tin
xide layer metallic tin or tin-lead is present which will interact with the liquid
older as soon as a hole has been formed in the oxide layer. This oxide layer is
ubsequently attacked from both sides. If the tin or tin-lead below the oxide layer
; liquid or becomes liquid, the oxide layer is broken by mechanical
hydrodynamic) forces. This 'ice shell' theory is sustained by many examples
/here soldering is easy as long as, under the oxide layer, some metallic tin (not
ntermetallic tin-copper) is still present.

In these cases the flux need only penetrate the oxide layer and form holes or
hannels. This is presumably the main reason for the increase of wetting rate
Thwaites] and of the area of spread [MacKay] with larger coating thicknesses up
) about 20 μm [Budrys *et al*].

.4.3   Other Layers

Apart from tarnish layers, the surfaces may be covered with a protective

coating or with other more or less adhering substances. Colophony fluxes are
water-soluble fluxes display a marked difference in behaviour towards grea?
substances. In Figure 5.8 two curves from a wetting balance are shown for copp$
plates covered with a very thin layer of silicone grease, to be compared with tl
curves without grease.

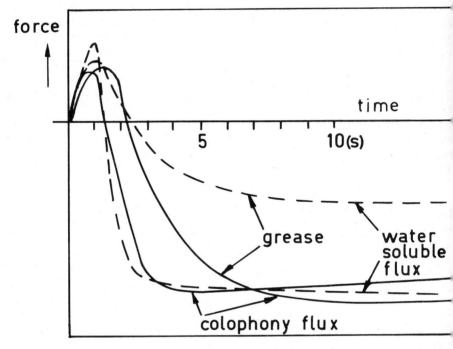

Fig. 5.8   Effect of silicone grease on force-time traces of a wetting balance. Four traces are shown f$
two types of flux, with and without grease on the specimen.

The initiation of wetting is retarded by the grease to a degree that is near
equal for both fluxes, but in due time colophony flux can remove (dissolve) tl
grease, producing even a slightly larger maximum wetting force.

5.5 FLUXES SOLUBLE IN ORGANIC LIQUIDS

Most of the fluxes soluble in organic liquids are based on colophony.

Except when used as the filling in flux-cored solder wire, solid colophony
difficult to apply as a flux and hence is dissolved in a thinner, generally
combination of aliphatic alcohols. Other compounds are often added [US Pater
4,194,931 (1978)], such as:

(i) activators (organic compounds which contain chloride or bromide, mon$
     and dicarboxylic acids, hydroxyl substituted poly-basic acids, *etc.*);
(ii) foaming agents (non-ionic surface active agents);
(iii) stabiliser solvent (alkanol amines).

Colophony fluxes are applied in electronics because colophony possesses a combination of favourable properties:

(i)   as a solid: it is non-reactive;
(ii) as a liquid: it wets tarnished metal surfaces, has a sufficiently low viscosity to remove reaction products and is reasonably stable at the soldering temperature;
iii) after soldering: it may remain on the board as a layer having good insulating properties.

The so-called activators are added because the colophony has only a low efficacy and hence a limited cleaning capability. By doing so, the activity at the soldering temperature is considerably enhanced and, though the corrosivity is slightly increased, for the most part the advantages of the use of colophony are retained. The activators left after the soldering process remain within the solid colophony from which they cannot easily escape. When cold and locked within the solid colophony residue, their corrosive tendency is inhibited to a degree dependent on their exact chemical nature.

The fluxes based on colophony or special resins can be divided as follows:

		non-activated fluxes (R)	
resin fluxes	colophony fluxes or rosin fluxes	activated fluxes (RMA and RA)	halide activated fluxes
			non-halide activated fluxes
	other resin fluxes		

Three designations are used:

(i)   R   = rosin flux with only pure colophony in a proper solvent;
(ii) RMA = rosin, mildly activated;
(iii) RA   = rosin, activated (not to be used for electronic soldering without an appropriate cleaning treatment).

The designations R, RMA and RA offer only a very rough classification as the boundaries of the groups are not sharply defined. They derive from a USA Federal Specification [Spec. Ref. 17].

The so-called SA fluxes (SA = synthesised activity), which are soluble in fluorocarbon solvent blends, were introduced recently [Turnbull]. These fluxes, containing organic derivates of sulphur and phosphorus bearing acids and reaction products with substituted amines, possess a high fluxing activity, but their residues are so corrosive that washing is mandatory. As these residues remain liquid after soldering, washing is relatively easy, whereas no solid (white) residues are retained.

5.1 Colophony

Colophony (rosin) [Enos *et al*] is a natural product and its composition depends on where the particular raw material originates. The components of rosin and related products can be investigated using chromatography [Hasson]: each source of raw material has its own 'fingerprint' [Brus *et al*].

The rosin used for solder flux (gum rosin) is obtained from pine sap tappe from various species of pine tree; this sap (oleo-resin) is separated in a distillatio process into the liquid turpentine ($C_{10}H_{16}$) and the solid colophony. Rosin consist for the most part of a mixture of several isomeric resin acids, having three ring and differing mainly in the position of the double bonds and the attached alk group. The major component is abietic acid (sylvic acid), $C_{19}H_{29}COOH$ (se Figure 5.9), with a melting point of 172°C. Pimaric acids are also present, mainl in the European types, and dehydro-, dihydro-, tetrahydro-abietic acids ma occur as well.

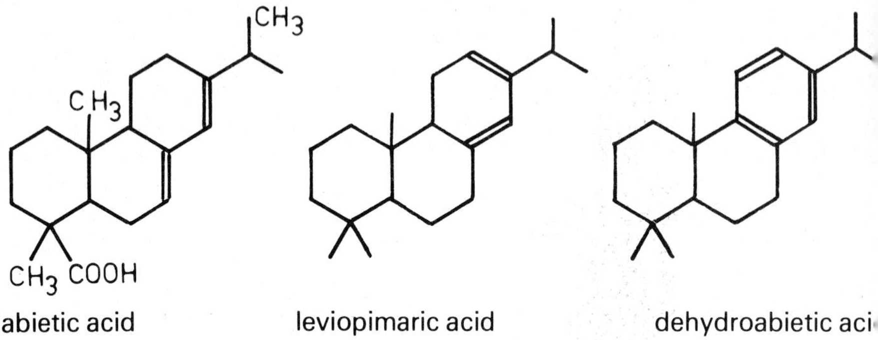

abietic acid   leviopimaric acid   dehydroabietic aci

Fig. 5.9   Some resins acids.

The colophony is sensitive to oxidation, which influences the solubility certain solvents such as kerosene. The solubility in alcohol and acetone remain but the activity decreases. The solid material should therefore be stored as lum instead of as powder, as this takes up some mass per cent of oxygen from the a within a few days. Oxidation turns the resin a brown colour.

Some of the acids in the rosin can crystallise, especially under the influence small amounts of hydrochloric or sulphuric acid. A solution of colophony (flu should not flocculate at room temperature in a week, nor in a refrigerator at 3° in a month. If 1% concentrated hydrochloric acid is added, no flocculation m be observed within 24 hours at 5°C. A flocculated or crystallised solution can restored by heating and will then normally remain stable again for some week The resin acids can be changed by various reactions, including among others

(i) hydrogenation, by which hydrogen is taken up to saturate double bond giving a greater resistance to oxidation and discoloration;

(ii) disproportionation, by which an equilibrium mixture is obtained whic dehydrogenates to form mostly dehydro-abietic acid. The reactions rend the rosin washable with organic solvents. Disproportionated colophon brings about a larger solder spread than the unchanged colophony, but th is annulled by too much chlorine in the activator;

(iii) polymerisation, by which larger molecules are formed while the −COO group remains, giving a higher melting point and a harder rosin.

The colour of the rosin depends on the purity and the state of oxidation, an can be compared with standard colour samples. A number of types exis indicated by letters. For instance, 'WW' (water-white) refers to an ASTM-designation (Test D 509-55).

The main physical and chemical characteristics of rosin (Class A., Type II, Grade WW. Spec. LLL-R-626) are:

Composition: isomers of $C_{19}H_{29}COOH$	90%
Density at room temperature	1,07-1,09
at 210°C	0,93
Softening point, °C., minimum (ring and ball)	70
Viscosity at 110°C	15 Ns/m^2 (150 Poise)
Refractive index at 20°C	1,5453
Insoluble matter in toluene, maximum (mass per cent)	0,05
Acid number, minimum	160
Saponification number, minimum	166

The curve of electrical resistivity *versus* temperature is shown in Figure 5.10.

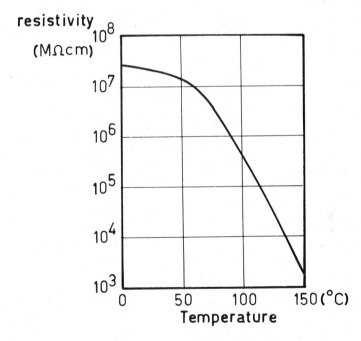

Fig. 5.10 Electrical resistivity of colophony *versus* temperature. The curve was obtained using a conductivity cell with gauze electrodes of 1 cm^2, 1 cm apart (cell constant 0,2).

The most important application of colophony is in the production of synthetic rubber. It is also applied in the paper industry, for painting ink, adhesives, *etc.* Only a low percentage of the world production is used for solder fluxes.

There are two institutes which deal specifically with the study of colophony and related products:

— Institut du Pin, Bordeaux, France
— Naval Stores Institute, Savannah, Georgia, USA

Synthetic Resin

Colophony is a natural product. The possibility of using a substitute would be interesting for various reasons:

(i) the properties of natural products depend on the place of origin and the harvest year; a synthetic resin could offer a more constant and better defined quality;

(ii) owing to the decreasing world production of colophony, shortages may arise in the supply of colophony for fluxes; a synthetic resin could be supplied with more reliability and possibly at lower cost;

(iii) synthetic resins could have superior properties compared with colophony

A recent example of a substitute is the fluxing compound in Xersin flux (Multicore), *viz.* the ester pentaerythritol-tetrabenzoate (= Pentoate). Xersin can be supplied in cored solder wire, as a liquid flux or as a protective coat [Rubin]. The compound produces less fuming during the soldering process than standard colophony flux and moreover gives little or no spattering when used as flux core solder. Its residues are paler than those of colophony and are more easily penetrated by test pins.

5.5.2   Non-Activated Rosin Fluxes

Pure colophony exhibits merely a weak cleaning action because it has only one – COOH group in its large molecule. Consequently, only very thin tarnish layers can be removed and the use of pure colophony is therefore limited to material that wet easily. The flux residues possess a very high electrical resistivity and give no detectable long-term corrosion effects; they exhibit no fungus growth. The flux is for this reason sometimes called a 'protective' flux.

For some applications, where no corrosion risk whatsoever can be tolerated, these non-activated rosin fluxes are required, for instance with very thin magnet wires. In these cases, the highest requirements must be set for the solderability of the parts to be soldered.

An example of non-activated rosin flux is one of the test fluxes of the IEC [Spec. Ref. 1], containing colophony (25 mass per cent) in 2-propanol (isopropanol) or ethanol (ethyl alcohol) (75 mass per cent).

5.5.3   Activated Rosin Fluxes

Activators are mainly organic acids or organic salts that are chemically active at the soldering temperature [Zado]. The name 'activator' is, strictly speaking, not correct, because the activator does not activate the colophony, but is acting directly. The major purpose of adding activators is to extend the capability of the flux to remove more oxide film than pure colophony can [MacKay *et al*].

5.5.3.1   ORGANIC SALTS DEA HCl AND DMA HCl

These salts are frequently used, not only in colophony fluxes but also in water soluble fluxes, because they are more effective than added acids.

Table 5.6

Organic Salts used in Fluxes

Abbreviation	Name	Formula	Molecular Weight	Melting Point °C
DMA HCl	dimethylammonium chloride	$(CH_3)_2\,NH.HCl$	81,6	170
DEA HCl	diethylammonium chloride	$(CH_3.CH_2)_2\,NH.HCl$	109,6	223,5

These salts are very hygroscopic and are readily soluble in alcohols: at 20°C, more than 40 g DMA HCl dissolves in 100 g isopropanol. They are not soluble in colophony and, while the solvent is (either completely or partly) evaporated, the salts are dispersed in the flux. In certain circumstances the salts may even become segregated on top of the flux layer.

At or slightly below the soldering temperature, the activators decompose, yielding hydrochloric acid. Both the activity and the corrosivity depend on the amount of activator added to the flux.

It is customary to express the amount of activator as mass per cent of chlorine on Cl^- on the colophony content, because the activator to colophony ratio determines the activity and the subsequent corrosivity. A mildly activated flux contains some tenths of a per cent of activator. The activated test flux of IEC 68-2-20 [Spec. Ref. 1] contains 75 mass per cent of thinner (*e.g.*, isopropanol) and 25 mass per cent of colophony to which chloride (0,5% Cl^-) is added in the form of DEA HCl (0,39 g DEA HCl per 25 g colophony).

In Figure 5.11 the wetting times are shown measured in a wetting balance (time

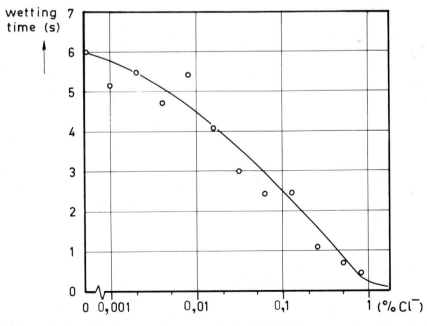

Fig. 5.11   Wetting of clean copper with varying chlorine (DMA HCl) content in the test flux. Testing temperature 235°C.

to 90° average wetting angle) as a function of the content of DMA HCl of the
flux. Tests have been carried out on copper plates of $30 \times 30 \times 0,5$ mm^3, etched in
hydrochloric acid, solder bath temperature 235°C.

From the results shown in Figure 5.11 it is seen that for readily solderable
material such as cleaned copper some activation is still helpful in increasing the
wetting rate; even with about 0,25% of halide the improvement can be attained.
The same conclusions are valid for additions of DEA HCl. In soldering practice
more halide may be necessary as the oxide layers are potentially thicker and the
flux could possibly be diluted by organic material coats.

Besides the organic salts, DEA HCl and DMA HCl, others may be applied
containing hydrazine, amine or pyridinium groups along with the halide
(chloride or bromide).

Note: Some of these chemicals necessitate the observance of stringent health precautions.

5.5.3.2 ORGANIC ACIDS

A second group of agents added to fluxes are organic acids: mono-basic acids,
di-basic acids, *etc.*, several of which are found in commercially available fluxes,
see Table 5.12 in Appendix to this Chapter. A colophony flux with these acids
added retains its character after soldering. To attain the same efficacy as DMA
HCl or DEA HCl activated fluxes, the organic fluxes require a much larger
addition of acid, see Table 5.7.

Table 5.7

Two Fluxes Exhibiting About the Same Efficacy
with Respect to Relatively Clean Copper

DEA HCl-Activated	*Sebacic Acid-Activated*
75 g isopropanol	75 g isopropanol
25 g colophony	25 g colophony
0,2% Cl$^-$ (of 25 g) =	1,7 g sebacic acid
0,05 g Cl$^-$ = 0,15 g DEA HCl	
(= $1,4 \times 10^{-3}$ mole Cl$^-$/100 g flux)	(= $8,5 \times 10^{-3}$ mole acid/100 g flux)

From the mono-basic acids, those having an odd number of carbon atoms are
rarely used. The acids with few carbon atoms (<10), are too corrosive and too
volatile (low boiling point) and moreover have an offensive odour. The reaction
of the higher acids (with for instance 16 or 18 C-atoms) is comparable to that of
colophony: the activity increases at higher temperatures.

Stearic acid does not dissolve in alcohol, but it does in toluene or alcohol-
toluene mixtures. As stearic acid and the colophony are not readily miscible, the
acid segregates. The reaction of stearic acid with tin produces a stearate film with
the fatty-acid chains upwards giving a low surface tension. The flux on the
surface retracts into small droplets producing a dull appearance on the tin surface
after solidification. The effect depends on the chain length. A shorter chain
length produces less effect because the chains are disorientated. Acids with longer
chain length are less soluble.

The di-basic acids possess more activity in the same volume than colophony or
the mono-basic acids. Hence the thickness of the flux layer can be reduced.

The reaction products of the acids dissolve only with difficulty in many agents, ut dissolve well in colophony (and glycerine). Even with quite a large amount of i-basic acids added, lack of cleaning efficacy may still be encountered, so that ften DMA HCl or DEA HCl is added also.

Succinic acid is very effective, but its vapours are extremely irritating to the hroat.

Because the higher di-basic acids do not easily decompose or evaporate, the ctivity of these acids is maintained during the entire soldering process and thus is ill present when the joints are formed, so helping to prevent the formation of ridges and icicles (see also Figure 7.28).

Many organic acids decompose while heated, producing water. The anhydrides ormed, and the water-vapour bubbles, render the flux less effective. Such acids re: fumaric, tartaric, tartronic, glutamic, isomalic, phthalic, and citric acid. The wer di-basic acids, and acids such as acrylic, methacrylic and crotonic vaporate before they can perform their job. Early escape is also the case with enzoic acid and salicylic acid, which sublimate. Though salicylic acid as such is ather active chemically, its reaction products are but slightly soluble.

Levulinic acid produces a green reaction product on copper. Lactic acid issolved in water is very effective in dissolving tin oxide but the acid is hardly oluble in colophony. Oleic acid is less active than stearic acid with the same umber of C-atoms and one $-COOH$ group; it oxidises rapidly. Anisic acid annot be used on account of medical restrictions: it must not be allowed to come ito contact with the skin.

.5.4 Strength of Flux-Residue Layer

The layer retained after soldering with a rosin flux will more or less cover the etal surfaces. This insulating layer will impair the establishment of electrical ontact by test pins during the measuring and adjustment stages following the oldering operation.

The rosin layer is more difficult to penetrate by the test pins if the time elapsed ince the preceding soldering operation is longer [Anon. Ref. 8] because the rosin ardens by oxidation.

.5.5 Examples of Rosin Fluxes Used in Practice

Two mildly activated fluxes are described which can remain on the printed oard after soldering.

.5.5.1 FLUX FOR PROFESSIONAL BOARDS

his flux is used specifically for professional board assemblies, for instance in lecommunications, where there is the highest demand for surface resistance and w corrosivity even after a long period of use. The test results given in Table 5.2 ere obtained with this type of flux.

The flux is composed of:
(i) polymerised rosin
(ii) organic acid (4% of di-basic acid on flux solids)
iii) activator (0,25% of halide on flux solids)
iv) solvent (isopropanol).

he solids content at delivery is 40 mass per cent and the density 0,880-0,890 g/ml.

The flux has excellent foaming properties and should be applied in a rather thick layer (approximately 15-20 μm when dried) in order to compensate for the low content of activating agents. The flux residues can be left on the board.

5.5.5.2 FLUX FOR CONSUMER BOARDS

With less stringent requirements for corrosion risk (*e.g.*, for consumer products) a more activated flux can be selected.

The flux is composed of:

(i) gum rosin (colophony WW)
(ii) organic acids (15% di-basic acids on flux solids)
(iii) activator (0,5% halide on flux solids)
(iv) solvent (isopropanol).

The solids content at delivery is 17 mass per cent and the density 0,825 g/ml. The flux has good foaming properties and can be applied in a thin layer (approximately 3-5 μm when dried). The flux residues are not sticky; they can be left on the board and possess excellent insulation properties.

5.6 WATER-SOLUBLE FLUXES

'Water-soluble' means that the flux residues can be dissolved in water, and does not imply that the flux formulation has to contain water because other solvents such as alcohols or glycols can be used.

Water-soluble (or aqueous) fluxes are usually formulated to provide high fluxing activity [Cassidy *et al*]. The flux residues are more corrosive and conductive than those of the resin fluxes and must nearly always be removed completely [van der Molen].

Because of their high fluxing activity, these fluxes are often seen as a panacea for the soldering of assemblies where the minimum wettability requirements for resin-based fluxes are not met or where difficulties arise in automatic test equipment because of the high insulating resistance of resin flux residues at the measuring points.

This approach can be disastrous with regard to the long-term reliability of the assembly when the parameters and conditions are not properly chosen. The type of flux, the finish, the type of board material, the components, the mounting method and the cleaning system must be fully compatible.

5.6.1 Composition of Water-Soluble Fluxes

Water-soluble fluxes are usually composed of:

(i) a chemically reactive compound for surface cleaning (activator);
(ii) a wetting agent to promote spreading of the flux components over the surfaces;
(iii) a solvent like alcohol or water to provide an even distribution of the flux components;
(iv) substances like glycols or a water-soluble polymer material to keep the activator in close contact with the metal surface for heat transfer, and to avoid reoxidation.

According to the type of activator, the water-soluble fluxes can be divided into
e classes given in Table 5.8.

Table 5.8

Water-Soluble Fluxes

		Examples
organic	salts	halide-containing salts such as: aniline hydrochloride glutamic acid hydrochloride dimethylammonium chloride
	acids	lactic acid glutamic acid amino-acids
	amines	urea triethanolamine
inorganic	salts	zinc chloride ammonium chloride – zinc chloride mixtures hydrazine hydrochloride
	acids	hydrochloric acid orthophosphoric acid

Though the chemicals mentioned could be dissolved in water, other solvents
re more often used, for two reasons:

(i)   the heat of evaporation and the specific heat of water are much higher than
      those of common organic solvents as shown in Table 5.9. The boiling point
      is also higher.

(ii) as water has the tendency to spatter, other solvents with higher boiling
      points prove preferable [Thwaites]. Examples are: ethylene glycol (*i.e.*, 1.2
      ethanediol, BP 198°C) or polyethylene glycol (BP >200°C, depending on
      degree of polymerisation).

Table 5.9

Some Thermal Properties of the Solvents Water and Isopropanol

	Heat of Evaporation	*Heat Needed to Raise 1 cm³ from Room Temperature to Boiling Point*	*Total Heat Demand per cm³ of Solvent*
	(J/cm³)	*(J)*	*(J)*
ater	2260	340	2600
sopropanol	550	40	590

Because washing always occurs, the choice of activity is not so limited as wit rosin fluxes, which generally remain on the soldered board. In water-solubl fluxes, therefore, a higher activity is acceptable. On the other hand, it is know that with the same acidity (at room temperature) a water-soluble flux at th soldering temperature has a notably lower cleaning capability than an activate rosin flux.

Non-ionic and non-acidic fluxes based on a polyoxyethylene-polyoxypropylene derivative trimethylpropane have been formulated. These fluxes do not contain solvents and possess a hig thermal stability, so that they may be used under reflow conditions at temperatures as high as 350° [Schuessler].

5.6.2   Fluxes with Inorganic Salts

These fluxes are based on inorganic salts such as zinc chloride, ammoniu chloride, hydrazine halides and inorganic acids like hydrochloric acid. The zir chloride and ammonium chloride fluxes have the widest effective temperatu range of the soft-soldering fluxes (150-450°C) and are generally used for no electrical soldering.

The greatest drawback of the zinc-ammonium chloride fluxes is that, throug hydrolysis and decomposition at soldering temperature, reaction products such zinc oxychloride are formed which are not soluble in cold water and which ca only be removed in dilute acids followed by hot water. Any inorganic halide sa residue left after the cleaning procedure will cause severe corrosion.

The hydrazine halides form a group of inorganic salts, but they behave li organic salts through their rapid decomposition at soldering temperatur Hydrazine dihydrochloride and dihydrobromide are among the most acti fluxing substances known. Because the hydrazine compounds are suspected have carcinogenic properties they are no longer used for flux manufacture.

5.6.3   Fluxes with Organic Salts

These fluxes are based on organic hydrohalides such as the amir hydrohalides, *e.g.*, DMA HCl, cyclo hexylamine hydrochloride and anilir hydrochloride; and on the hydrohalides of organic acids such as glutamic aci hydrochloride, this being more active than the neutral amine salts. Both typ leave corrosive residues when not properly cleaned. The amine hydrohalides a generally very readily soluble in alcohols, so that water in the flux can be avoidec When water is used as a solvent and the flux is rapidly heated, spattering wi occur due to violent evolution of steam. The alcohols will boil gently over a wic range of temperatures.

Fluxes with organic halides usually contain vehicles such as glycerol an polyethylene glycol; and non-ionic surface-active agents such as nonylphen polyoxyethylene, in order to retain the active and volatile decompositio products long enough at the soldering site to clean and protect the metal surfac at the soldering temperature. When properly chosen, these vehicles assist at later stage in the water-removal of ionic residues from the soldered products.

Some of these vehicles, *e.g.*, the polyethylene glycols, although being no ionic, can degrade the insulation resistance of epoxy board material [Brou Turnbull, Zado]. This occurs by penetration into the adhesive layer, renderin the surface hydrophilic and thus susceptible to electrical leakage at hig humidities.

The non-ionic organic halides which have recently been applied in rosin fluxes o not have sufficient activity to be used in water-soluble fluxes.

6.4　Fluxes with Organic Acids

These fluxes are based on water-soluble organic acids like lactic acid, melonic :id, citric acid and levulinic acid and are usually combined with vehicles such as ycerol, sorbitol or polyethylene glycol, dissolved in alcohol or alcohol-water ixtures. Organic acid fluxes are used when the presence of any halide is ohibited.

Lactic acid is one of the most efficient organic acids in fluxing action. One rawback is that it will always contain water and therefore thorough predrying of ie flux is necessary in order to avoid spattering.

Compared with halide-containing fluxes, organic acid fluxes have the ollowing disadvantages:

(i)　as the fluxing action is rather weak, use is restricted to easily solderable metals such as gold, silver, copper, tin and solder-coated surfaces;

(ii)　organic acids decompose at rather low temperatures, and should therefore generally be used only in the lower solder temperature range (180-260°C) in order to avoid the formation of compounds which are not soluble in water (decarboxylation);

iii)　to compensate for the weak fluxing action, rather high concentrations of the acid have to be used.

On the other hand, they have the advantage that the flux residues need not be ashed immediately after the soldering operation and can be left on the products or some time without the risk of severe corrosion.

6.5　Fluxes with Organic Halides and Organic Acids

These are based on a combination of the organic halides and the organic acids, iis combination of the two types of activator having a much greater fluxing :tivity than the sum of the two. The activators are usually applied in high oncentrations in alcohols or alcohol-water mixtures with low water content. The uxing activity in the lower temperature range (180-260°C) can be likened to iose of the inorganic fluxes. At higher temperatures, the fluxes still promote ood wetting, but the removal of the corrosive flux residues is strongly obstructed y the thermal decomposition products of the organic compounds. The soldered roducts should be washed with water immediately after soldering to obtain ompimple removal of all flux residues, and thus avoid any further corrosive tack.

6.6　Fluxes with Amines and Amides

These fluxes are based on amines and amides such as triethanolamine, ianidine and urea. The fluxing activity is generally low and this type is only used or special purposes like the soldering of silver and zinc. Flux residues are orrosive to various metals and should be removed completely.

5.6.7   Examples of Water-Soluble Fluxes

Most fluxes are trade secrets of which the compositions are not published. On
specific flux used for the wave soldering of boards with plated holes and whic
contains organic acid is IBM flux WSF-200 [see also Auslegeschrift 19 53 21
(1977)]. Composition is given in mass per cent as follows:

0,8%	dimethylammonium chloride;
5%	tartaric acid
24%	methanol, technical grade
12%	isopropanol (99%)
14%	ethylene glycol mono-butyl ether
44%	polyethylene glycol (E 400)

The polyethylene glycol in the flux has a similar function to that of colophony i
other fluxes. This particular flux can be applied in foam form.

An example of a halide-free foamable flux containing organic acids is the flu
with the following composition [Offenlegungsschrift 2 108 542]

54%	sorbitol (70%)
2,7%	guanidine carbonate
2,1%	citric acid
2,7%	adipic acid
38,5%	ethanol (96%)

A hot water rinse should be used for effective cleaning of the soldered products a
soon as possible after soldering.

5.7   WASHING OF SOLDERED PRODUCTS

Washing or cleaning of printed boards serves to remove the flux residue
which were left after soldering. The need for washing is closely related to th
choice of flux (see Chapter 9.1.2), and depending on the situation, the flu
residues may remain on the board or must be removed:

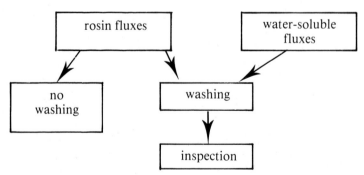

When badly solderable components are used, highly activated fluxes must b
applied and consequently washing is needed. Though washing of the residues c
rosin fluxes is often carried out, the general preference should be to leave rosi
fluxes on the soldered boards, and if washing is mandatory, to use water-solub
fluxes.

Water-soluble fluxes are washed with water, as this is the cheapest solvent, 1ough drying is difficult and expensive. The rosin fluxes are washed with 1lvents that must be capable of removing both the polar and the non-polar :sidues from the boards. The ease of washing of colophony increases in the rder: oxidised-, normal-, polymerised-, and finally disproportionated 1lophony. From experience it is known that a large amount of flux is washed .way more easily than a small amount, which apparently loses the greater part of s solubility by oxidation.

The removal rate of particulate soil depends on the nature and particle size:

soil \ particle size	large	small	
insoluble	fast	slow	removal
soluble	slow	fast	rate

`he part of the residue that is insoluble soil should be removed by agitation or crubbing, by selecting another (for instance a more polar) solvent, by changing 1e washing procedure, *etc*.

Water has the advantage of having strong bonds but on the other hand it also auses agglomeration (balling-up) of soil. Fluorocarbon type defluxing solvents ossess low attractive forces but have a good non-polar solubility.

The cleaned boards must subsequently be provided with a protective coating, or conversely, if a rotective coating is required, prior washing is essential. This coating, often called conformal coating, as the purpose of resisting, or at least minimising the performance degradation caused by hostile 1vironmental influences such as humidity. Because there is no single coating that provides perfect rotection, many coating types are available, *e.g.*, acrylics, polyurethanes, epoxies, silicones and olyimides, which may be applied in various ways [Waryold]. The application of a conformal coating important for boards with very fine conductive patterns, which are sensitive to dust particles, and 1 which harmful effects of reduction of surface resistance, voltage breakdown and migration are rst observed.

Disadvantages of Washing

The main objections to washing are the costs of investment and control:

(i) washing equipment is needed (moreover, the most expensive part of the washing is the drying!);

(ii) the mix of components must be suited to washing and mounted so that no capillaries are present between the body of the components and the boards, and in insulated stranded wires and coils where the flux residues will be held;

iii) the boards must be suited to washing. In general, boards with plain holes create difficulties;

(iv) some washing fluids are expensive;

(v) for certain washing fluids, measures must be taken to conform with environmental and safety requirements.

. comprehensive treatment of washing costs is beyond the scope of this book [see .eller, Osterman].

Advantages of Washing
  (i) washed boards appear attractive;
 (ii) washed boards can be inserted more easily into racks than boards with solder residues on their edges;
(iii) measuring pins of testing equipment can make good electrical contact at low contact force, and these pins remain more clean;
 (iv) the joints can be more easily inspected and repaired;
  (v) the major reason for washing soldered boards is that it is a specific requirement of customers, especially for high quality professional equipment [see for instance Military Specification, Spec. Ref. 10].

5.7.1 Washing of Boards Soldered with Rosin Fluxes

The cleaning solvents for rosin containing fluxes that are typically used are fluorocarbons, such as 1,1,2-trichlorotrifluoro-ethane (TCTFE), mixed for instance with ethanol or isopropanol. Their characteristics are:

  ● chemical inertness to substrate materials (though some metals such as A and Zn are attacked when no stabiliser is present);
  ● non-flammability;
  ● low toxicity;
  ● high liquid density (about 1500 kg/m^3).

Defluxing solvents of a proprietary nature frequently used are the Freon (Du Pont) series (TMS, TF, T-E 35) and the Arklone (ICI) series (grades K, L & F) [Clementson *et al*]. Similar fluorocarbons are supplied by other companies such as Union Carbide, Hoechst, *etc*.

The equipment in which washing takes place resembles a degreasing installation: the products are introduced from above and are immersed in the cleaning solvent or solvents. A further discussion of washing with organic solvents (differences between the solvents, equipment, washing procedures, washing efficiency, *etc.*) is not included in this book.

Residues of fluxes containing organic acids are more difficult to remove completely than plain rosin fluxes. Especially at high soldering temperatures (>250°C) the organic acids tend to decompose, yielding so-called 'white residues' that are insoluble in the solvent blends.

Rosin, which is a non-polar material, will not dissolve in water. However, it can be water-washed if it is saponified by suitably selected agents. The rosin soap is removed by relatively large amounts of water; the activators, of course, dissolve easily in the water. The success of water-washing of rosin lies in the completeness of the saponification reaction: if incomplete, rosin residues or cleaning agent residues will remain.

5.7.2 Washing of Boards Soldered with Water-Soluble Fluxes

In small scale production the washing of boards with water can be achieved in a large domestic dishwasher. For larger quantities special machines have been developed in which the boards to be washed are continuously transported through the various stages of spraying, washing, rinsing and drying (Figure 5.12).

g. 5.12 An aqueous cleaning and drying system. The machine shown, the Aquapak 526 from ectrovert, provides the possibility of automated in-line cleaning. (By courtesy of Electrovert, Canada.)

resistivity meter can be used in the final rinse tank to monitor the performance the automated cleaning system and to indicate when out-of-tolerance nditions occur [Woodgate]. The final rinse water should be blown off the ards as completely as possible so that no water drops remain which would herwise locally deposit their residual salts on the board upon drying. Generally, rge quantities of water are needed, the purification of the water constituting an sential part of the total costs of the washing treatment [see also Scharf].

7.3   Testing Cleanliness of Boards

Once washing has been decided upon, problems with measuring and onitoring the cleanliness of the washed products arise. A judgement of the ashing efficiency can be obtained by measuring the surface insulation resistance ter washing (see Chapter 5.2.2) or by repeated rigorous washing treatment of a st specimen under known conditions followed by measuring the take-up of ionic ntaminants in the test washing liquid [Kenyon, see also Spec. Ref. 9]. For this irpose a number of methods and equipments are available [Duyck]. The result the measurement is often expressed as an equivalent amount of NaCl on the ard. A common limit which gives 100% failures at 75°C/95% RH within hours is approximately 10 μg NaCl/cm^2 of board [Wargodz].

The testing methods for cleanliness chiefly measure the quantity of ions maining on a particular area of the board, or on the entire board. Corrosion, wever, is dependent on the local concentration of the ionic contaminants. ence, the value of the tests relies on the assumption of a homogeneous stribution of the ionic residues.

5.7.3.1   SPECIFIC RESISTANCE OF RINSE WATER

In a dilute solution such as the rinse water the ionic agents, including the weak
acids, are fully dissociated. The conductance of such a solution is the
proportional to the number of ions present, because each separate ion has its own
equivalent conductance.
Hence: Conductance = Σ (equivalent conductance × concentration).

$$K = \Sigma(\Lambda \times C)$$

in which K is given in $\Omega^{-1}m^{-1}$ or Sm^{-1}, Λ is given in $\Omega^{-1}m^2$ and C is given in mol
equivalent per m^3.

Instead of the conductance, K, the specific resistance, K^{-1}, can be used. The unit
then is Ωm, in practice mostly Ωcm or $M\Omega cm$.
   As for acids, the proton constitutes the major contribution to the conductance
all acids contribute about the same conductance per mole equivalent (= mol
weight/valency). Further, the salts NaCl, KCl and $CuSO_4$ are also about the same
(see Figure 5.13 with insert). Carefully deionised water shows a specific resistance

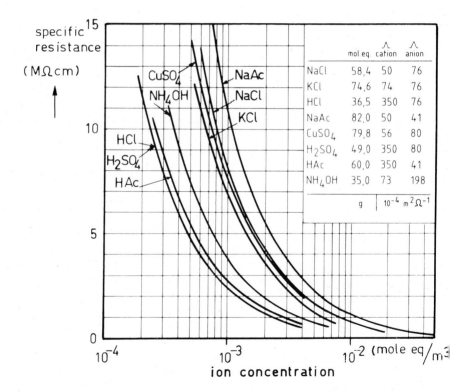

Fig. 5.13   The specific resistance of water with amounts of ionic agents. The equivalent conductance
of the various ions at 25°C (in $10^{-4}\Omega^{-1}m^2$) is given in the insert.

f about 17 MΩcm at 25°C, caused by the H^+ and OH^- ions. If 50 μg NaCl is
aken up in 100 ml of water, the specific resistance is about 1 MΩcm. 50 μg NaCl
₁ 100 ml of water = 0,3 mass ppm of Cl^-.

ote: The data given in literature tend to be confusing as they often do not indicate the amount of
nse water or the total surface area of the board used. Moreover, the units are frequently wrongly
xpressed.

.7.3.2   IONOGRAPH

An example of a commercial unit is the Ionograph (trade-mark of Alpha
Metals). This apparatus utilises dynamic conductivity monitoring (DCM) of the
rinse solution which extracts the ions from the surfaces under test [Brous,
Rickabaugh]. The rinse solution is continuously pumped through a recirculating
oop (Figure 5.14). It passes through a specimen tank, a conductivity cell and an
on-exchange column to remove the ions from the solution. The integral of
conductivity versus time provides a measure of the quantity of ions present on the
urfaces tested. The reading can be simply calibrated with a known amount of
odium chloride injected into the specimen tank. The ionograph is provided with
built-in recorder and electronic integrator for rapid and quantitative operation.

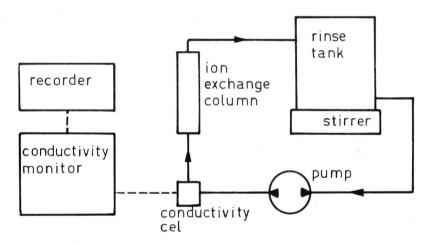

Fig. 5.14   System for dynamic conductivity monitoring of rinse solution.

.8   ENVIRONMENTAL ASPECTS OF FLUXES

In general, the common fluxes for soft soldering present no health hazard if an
fficient exhaust system has been installed (see Chapter 9.1.3).

.8.1   Colophony

Fumes of colophony may cause respiratory disease (asthma) to some people
whether or not they habitually work with fluxes [Burge *et al* – 1]. The proportion
f people in an ordinary local population that exhibit asthmatic reactions to
olophony fumes is in the order of 1%. The symptoms lead to an initial diagnosis

of bronchitis: cough, sputum, chest pain and breathlessness make their firs appearance after a prior period of symptomless exposure to the solder flu fumes. This period can range from a month to 25 years, the median being 6 years People already suffering from asthma or chronic bronchitis are more vulnerabl and may develop difficulties within a few days, and hence should not work i departments carrying out a lot of soft soldering.

If colophony decomposes in the soldering process, the products will contai aldehyde compounds (formaldehyde, acetaldehyde, acroleine, *etc.*). Th Threshold Limit Value for these compounds is very low: 0,1 mg/m^3 (calculated a formaldehyde). However, the resin acid content of the fumes, rather than th decomposition products, causes the occupational asthma [Burge *et al* – 2]. Th effect of fumes can of course be greatly reduced by providing proper ventilatio or fume extraction in the work room [see also Rubin, Courtney].

5.8.2 Solvents

The Threshold Limit Values (maximum concentrations in which it is permitte to work for 40 hours a week) for some solvents are given in Table 5.10.

Table 5.10

Threshold Limit Values of Three Solvents

Solvent	TLV	
	ppm	*mg/m^3*
methanol	200	360
isopropanol	400	980
ethylene glycol*	100	260

To remain below the TLV, an exhaust on a soldering machine is necessar depending on the size of the machine. A small soldering machine consumes abou 1 litre of solvent per day, whilst a large one may consume more than 10 litre This solvent is applied to the boards by the fluxing unit (as flux) and is evaporate in the preheating stage of the process. Some solvent also evaporates from the flu unit.

5.8.3 Activators

Activators form a very diverse group of chemicals. As some of the materia involved are highly toxic [see Sax], it is fortunate that activators are presen mostly in a limited amount. However, some chemicals having an excellen potential as activators must be disregarded for reasons of health precautions Among these are α and β naphthylamine and the hydrazine compounds becaus of their carcinogenic properties. Many amines cause dermatitis. Hydroxylamin hydrochloride (bromide) is also dangerous.

---

*now under consideration.

.9 STANDARDISATION OF FLUXES

Various national standards for flux exist, and work on an international (ISO) tandard is in progress. The national standards give groups of fluxes and testing 1ethods for several characteristics, but specific flux compositions are not 1corporated unlike the case of solders in standards for solder alloys).

Table 5.11 contains a survey of the existing standards and compares the main :st methods they incorporate. Flux efficacy is nearly always assessed by an area f spread test. This may be a good method for fluxes in general, outside the field f electronics; for soldering in electronics, however, long heating times are not sually tolerable, hence the wetting achieved within a few seconds is important. or this reason, tests for the wetting rate are more appropriate. This approach is 1ly found at present in the French Standard.

It has been the experience within the Author's company that some of the so-alled safe fluxes passing tests applicable for the physical and chemical properties ave failed in surface insulation resistance tests on boards in a humid nvironment. Since the electrical behaviour of flux and its residues on boards is in ict of greater importance than the specific properties of the flux in 'before use' ondition, the test methods to investigate the flux residue properties are the more nportant ones for assessing the suitability of the flux.

In the relevant standards for flux-cored solder, specific tests (apart from those 1entioned in Table 5.11) exist for:

(i) flux content in solder wire
(ii) spattering during melting of solder wire.

.10 APPENDIX

Table 5.12 gives a list of organic acids, many of which are used in soldering luxes, see Chapter 5.5.3.2 [see also Rubin *et al*].

Table 5.11

Testing Methods for Fluxes

Country	Document	Year	Title of Document	\	\	\	\	Main Tests							
				1	2	3	4	5	6	7	8	9	10	11	12
France	NF C 90-550	1980	Alloys and Fluxes for Soft Soldering (With Guide)		+	+	+								
Germany	DIN 8511/2	1967	Fluxes for Soft Soldering Heavy Metals		see DIN 8516		+								
	DIN 8516	1967	Soft Solders with Flux Cores on Resin Basis. Composition, Technical Conditions of Delivery, Testing	+											
	DIN 8527/1	1970	Fluxes for Soft Soldering Heavy Metals, Testing	+								+	+		
Japan	JIS Z3197	1976	Testing Methods for Resin Type Soldering Flux	+		+	+	+	+	+		+	+	+	
UK	BS 5625	1980	Specification of Purchasing Requirements and Methods of Test for Fluxes for Soft Soldering	+			+	+	+	+			+		
	BS 441	1979	Specification of Purchasing Requirements for Flux-cored and Solid Soft-Solder Wire	see BS5625		+		+			+				
USA	MIL-F-14256D	1975	Flux, Soldering, Liquid (Rosin Base)	+				+	+			+			+
	QQ-S-571E	1972	Solder, Tin Alloy; Tin-lead Alloy; and Lead Alloy	+				+	+						+
	IPC-S-815A	1980	Standard Specification Proposal—General Requirements for Soldering Electronic Connections	+				+	+			+		+	

1 Spread Test
2 Rate-of-Wetting Test
3 Acid Value
4 Halide Content

5 Resistivity of Water Extract
6 Copper Mirror Test
7 Degradation of Wires
8 Bulk Insulation Test

9 Surface Insulation Resistance Test
10 Visual Inspection after Climatic Exposure
11 Removability
12 Dryness

Table 5.12

Some Properties of Organic Acids Relevant to Soldering Fluxes

Formula	Chemical Nomenclature		Molecular Weight	Melting Point (°C)	Boiling Point (°C)	Acid Value
	Monobasic Acid	*Mono-carboxylic Acids*				
COOH	formic acid	methanoic acid	46	8	101	
H₃-COOH	acetic acid	ethanoic acid	60	17	118,5	
H₃-(CH₂)₁-COOH	propionic acid	propanoic acid	74	−21	141	
2	butyric acid	butanoic acid	88	−6	164	
3	valeric acid	pentanoic acid	102	−34	186	
4	caproic acid	hexanoic acid	116	−4	205	
5	enanthic acid	heptanoic acid	130	−10	233	
6	caprylic acid	octanoic acid	144	16	239	
7	pelargonic acid	nonanoic acid	158	12	253	
8	capric acid	decanoic acid	172	31	286	326
10	lauric acid	dodecanoic acid	200	44		280
12	myristic acid	tetradecanoic acid	228	54		246
14	palmitic acid	hexadecanoic acid	256	63	>300	219
16	stearic acid	octadecanoic acid	284	70		197
18	arachic acid	eicosanoic acid	312	76		179
20	behenic acid	docosanoic acid	340	80		165
	Di-basic Acids	*Di-carboxylic Acids*				
OOC-COOH	oxalic acid	ethanedioic acid	90	189 d	157 s	
OOC-(CH₂)₁-COOH	malonic acid	propanedioic acid	104	135	140 d	1079
2	succinic acid	butanedioic acid	118	182	235 s	951
3	glutaric acid	pentanedioic acid	132	97,5		850
4	adipic acid	hexanedioic acid	146	153		768
5	pimelic acid	heptanedioic acid	160	106	>300	701
6	suberic acid	octanedioic acid	174	140		645
7	azelaic acid	nonanedioic acid	188	106		597
8	sebacic acid	decanedioic acid	202	134		555
OOC-CH = CH-COOH {	fumaric acid	trans-butenedioic acid	116	286	>300	967
{	maleic acid	cis-butenedioic acid	116	130		967
OOC-CHOH-CHOH-COOH	tartaric acid	2,3 dihydroxybutanedioic acid	150	173	d	748
H₃-CO-CH₂-CH₂-COOH	levulinic acid	4-oxo-pentanoic acid	116	37	245 d	483
H₃-CHOH-COOH	lactic acid	2-hydroxy propanoic acid	90	25	d	623
H₂ = CH-COOH	acrylic acid	propenoic acid	72	12	141	778
⬡—COOH	benzoic acid	benzenecarboxylic acid	122	122	s	460
⬡—COOH / OH	salicylic acid	2-hydroxy benzoic acid	138	159	211 s	406
H₃-O-⬡—COOH	anisic acid	4-methoxy benzoic acid	152	185	275	369
OOC-(CH₂COOH)₂-COOH	citric acid	2-hydroxy propane tricarboxylic acid	192	153	d	

Chapter 6

SOLDERABLE MATERIALS

The wettability of materials intended for processing by machine soldering mu
be in accord with the soldering process employed. Only then will a solderir
result of good quality and reproducibility be possible.

In the electronics industry the requirement of wettability is of considerab
importance in view of the fact that in general only weakly-activated fluxes a
allowed to be used. Moreover, soldering temperature must be kept low, ar
soldering time short.

Many materials, *e.g.*, copper and nickel-iron, present no soldering problems
the surfaces are freshly made, but the wettability of the materials must also l
sufficient after storage.

For the materials to be joined to meet the aforementioned requirements, tl
presence of one or more surface coatings (consisting of materials that promo
wetting) is required. The most important of such coating materials are tin and tl
tin-lead alloys. If the surface of the soldered product has to satisfy addition.
requirements such as high electrical conductivity, then coatings of silver or gol
can be applied. The various solderable materials can be shown diagrammaticall

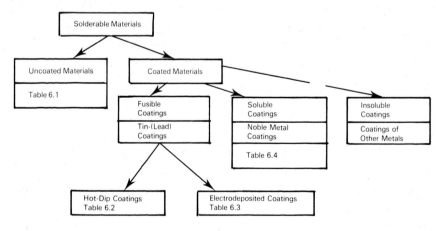

6.1 UNCOATED MATERIALS

Uncoated materials are used in electronics for many different purposes, ar
the question of their selection embodies various aspects [see Harper]. In Table 6

ommon metals and alloys are arranged in order of their ability to be wetted by
molten solder. The left hand column contains materials that can be soldered in
common soldering processes using non-activated or mildly activated fluxes.
rogressing towards the right, greater flux activity is needed to achieve wetting.
he metals in the right hand column cannot be soldered at all.

Table 6.1

Wettability of Uncoated Materials by Tin-Lead Solder

Good	Fair	Moderate	Difficult	Practically Impossible
old	bronze	kovar	aluminium bronze	chromium
n-lead	brass	nickel-iron	alloyed steel	magnesium
n	monel	nickel	aluminium	molybdenum
lver	nickel silver	steel		tungsten
alladium				beryllium
opper		zinc		

mild flux ————————————————————→ aggressive flux

Even if soft soldering of a material is possible from the point of view of
etting, it is not always feasible in a production process in which the flux activity,
mperature and soldering time are limited. In the mass-soldering processes, in
hich a large number of components are soldered simultaneously, the
olderability of all parts must be more or less the same. Many uncoated materials
re unsuitable in this respect, though they are solderable if considered separately.
uch materials, *e.g.*, phosphor-bronze, brass and nickel silver, are often used as
oated materials for mass-soldering applications.

.1.1   Uncoated Copper

Uncoated copper is used for conductors on printed boards, mainly of the
ngle-sided type. In the production of the board material, electrolytic copper
heet is bonded to the laminate base material under high pressure and at elevated
mperature. The surface of the copper on the boards undergoes a number of
eatments, ending with pickling. The starting materials have a reasonably
mooth surface, but pickled materials have a rough surface structure, which is
ifferent for each pickling method (Figure 6.1) [see also Lore]. With equal oxide
lm thicknesses, the soldering flux will have to remove more copper oxide from
uch a rough surface than from a flat surface. A surface treated with $CuCl_2$ shows
ery fine features with a shape having a larger surface area than obtained by
tching in many other agents. It is not surprising that the wettability of this type
f surface deteriorates rapidly. However, it is not known precisely how the shape
f the surface structure influences the rate of deterioration. The freshly pickled
opper is immediately covered with a Cu_2O film with a thickness of about 2,5 nm
hen exposed to air. Thereafter the growth rate is small. The thickness of the
urface films directly affecting wettability is 1-10 nm so there must be an
wareness of the fact that slight and easily overlooked differences in the
reatment of solderable surfaces can degrade their wettability. Oxide layers can,
oreover, produce solder-adhesion failures [Kumar *et al*].

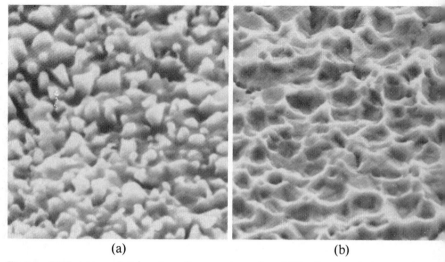

(a)   (b)

Fig 6.1 SEM-pictures of the surface of copper sheet after pickling in two solutions: (a) in CuC (Magnification 10000×, viewing angle 45°); (b) in $CrO_3 - H_2SO_4$ (Magnification 2500×, viewin angle 45°). (By courtesy of E. E. de Kluizenaar.)

6.1.2   Brass, Bronze, Nickel Silver, etc.

These materials which are applied for many products are mostly used in th coated condition. They can be soldered uncoated for only a few days afte cleaning. During storage the wettability decreases to an extent that makes the practically useless for machine soldering.

The varying wettability of these materials finds expression in their differer 'dipping speed limit', as defined in German literature (*Grenztauchgeschwindig keit*). This is the maximum speed at which the material can be dipped into th solder, yet still obtaining a smooth and continuous coating of solder. At a highe dipping speed the coating is no longer continuous; a certain fraction of th surface area is then either not wetted or poorly wetted. The precise evaluation o this fraction is somewhat subjective, just as with the evaluation of dewetting (se Chapter 7.7.2); nevertheless, a definite speed limit can be obtained (Figure 6.2) Under the conditions of Figure 6.2 the following dipping speed limits were found

flux	copper	brass	nickel silver
1	>30	4	1,3
2	>30	15	6 mm/s

The dipping speed limit is influenced by the heat conduction of the material the limit thus decreasing with increasing thickness of the plate. The impurities i the solder bath are also important: 0,1% of zinc or 0,5% of antimony can reduc the dipping speed limit to about 50% of the value with clean solder [Lenz] During normal storage the dipping speed limit decreases to some 20% of it

iginal (maximum) value; under more severe conditions the ultimate values will
lower still [Lenz *et al*].

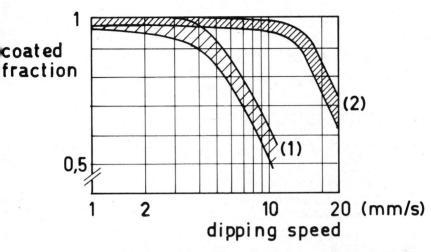

Fig. 6.2   Coated fraction of the surface of cleaned brass plates dipped at various speeds. Two fluxes
re applied: (1) Non-activated colophony flux; (2) Activated colophony flux with 0,5% of chloride
(MA HCl). The speed of withdrawal is the same as the dipping speed. Plate thickness 0,3 mm; solder
bath temperature 235°C.

1.3   Poorly Wettable Metals

Some metals can be soldered only if special measures are taken [Mohler], the
oldering methods in most of these cases differing considerably from those used
or the easy-to-solder materials commonly employed in electronics. Hand
oldering methods find frequent application. For the soldering of these metals,
ery active fluxes are always used, containing inorganic acids and salts (see
hapter 5.6), of which the residues must be thoroughly washed away. Along with
the active fluxes a relatively high soldering temperature is usually applied (high
ith respect to the melting point of the solder), because at higher temperature the
ctivity of the fluxes increases. The lack of wettability of the materials discussed
an, of course, be overcome by applying an appropriate plating, for instance
ectrodeposited copper. The applied layer must be sufficiently thick to prevent
omplete dissolution of the layer during soldering, because otherwise severe
ewetting would take place.

Soft soldering is only in rare cases the appropriate joining technique for these
etals with poor wettability. Since the soldering and cleaning operations are
umbersome and the joint strength is often low compared with the strength of the
oined parts, other joining techniques such as brazing, welding, mechanical
tachment or adhesives must also be considered.

1.3.1   STAINLESS STEEL

Alloyed steels (*e.g.*, stainless steel) can be soft soldered using strong acid fluxes
nd a relatively high heating temperature [Nishihata]. Generally, tin-rich solder
loys are applied.

6.1.3.2 ALUMINIUM

The soldering of aluminium is often studied, as it would be of great value t have an acceptable method for soft soldering this metal and its alloys. Th demand is not new, for even as early as 1923 a prize was awarded for the be solution to the problem [Bauer]. The main conclusion of the contest was that had not succeeded in providing a satisfactory answer to the question of the mo suitable solder for aluminium. Since then, more than 400 patents have bee issued on the subject and recently a review of methods for soldering aluminiu has been published [Anon. Ref. 13].

The problem of soldering aluminium is twofold:

(i) to obtain wetting of the aluminium despite the tenacious aluminium oxid film;
(ii) to produce soldered joints which do not corrode rapidly.

Fluxes for Aluminium

To remove the oxide film, highly reactive fluxes are needed, mostly containi inorganic salts, for instance mixtures of chlorides and fluorides of zinc, tin (IV potassium and ammonium. The resistance of the soldered joints to corrosi attack in brine solution is improved if 1 to 2 mass per cent of silver halide is add to the flux [Europ. Patent Appl. 0 001 677 Al (1978)]. Fluxes of the salts of heav metals react with aluminium so that the heavy metals are reduced to the metall state, whilst the corresponding salts of aluminium are formed. Zinc salts particular are applied for this purpose. The metallic zinc thus formed assists the wetting process, and it can be found at a later stage at the interface betwee the solder and the aluminium [Schwaneke *et al*]. The zinc may even produ intergranular penetration when applied in larger quantities. Apart from th inorganic fluxes, organic fluxes of numerous compositions are used, for instanc those containing diethylamine or triethylamine. Fluoroborates, particularly c zinc, are also often used. Instead of, or to assist, the very active fluxes, ultrason cavitation is sometimes applied for the removal of the aluminium oxide.

Solder Alloys for Aluminium

Many binary alloys are applied for the soldering of aluminium, for instanc tin-lead, tin-zinc, lead-bismuth and zinc-cadmium alloys, all in a variety c compositions. Ternary and higher alloys are also used, such as lead-rich alloy with cadmium, antimony and silver. Adding silver to the alloys improves the resistance to corrosion. An example of such alloys is 'Alu-Sol D' with 80,1% c lead, 18% of tin and 1,9% of silver [Patent Spec. 1 478 644 (1974)].

Tin-lead alloys, commonly used in soldering, give disappointing results o aluminium. The solder becomes cathodic with respect to the aluminium, with th effect that the interface corrodes, often without visible corrosion of the joine parts. The corrosion in humid atmosphere, usually tested in a salt spray tes causes the parts to fall apart within a short time. The addition of some silver, zir or cadmium improves this poor corrosion resistance.

Finally, it is emphasised again that the wettability of aluminium, irrespective c the choice of solder alloy and flux, is very much poorer than that of the easy-tc solder metals commonly used for soldering in electronics. Aluminium has bee iown to be 'unsolderable' for such a long time that alternative bonding methods ave been developed, such as using adhesives which adhere well to the oxide film.

2 COATED MATERIALS

Materials, whether metallic or not, may be coated for several reasons, such as:

(i) decorative;
(ii) protective, against environment and humidity;
(iii) functional, producing improved characteristics of wear, reflection, insulation, electrical contact and wettability.

2.1 Solderable Coatings

Many coating systems are used for the purpose of attaining good solderability Rothschild], but generally speaking tin-lead coatings are the most satisfactory on range of substrate materials [MacKay]. For wettability, the interfaces between ie various layers in the coating as well as the outer surface are important. A tin-ad top coating will melt and mix with the molten solder so that it is no longer istinguishable in a cross-section. A top coating of silver or gold will dissolve in ie molten solder, thus exposing the originally buried layers. The properties of iese layers then determine whether or not the wetting will be stable (see Chapter 3.3 on dewetting). During ageing, the outer surface will be influenced by teraction with atmospheric oxygen and other gases, while within the coating ffusion effects play a part. The precise effects of gases such as H_2S and SO_2 are implicated and not well understood. The wettability of electrodeposited atings after interaction with these gases can be determined in a wetting balance ee Chapter 7.2.1): the ultimate wetting forces decrease in most cases, but in ime instances a distinct increase is observed [Bogenschütz *et al*, part 6].

Electrodeposited coatings are generally porous, the degree of porosity epending on coating thickness and the surface condition of the substrate. orosity in noble metal coatings results in accelerated corrosion of less noble asis metals (or undercoating), whereas pores in coatings of tin-lead alloy on ipper or copper alloys are not so harmful.

2.2 Production Techniques for Coated Discrete Parts and Coated Stock Iaterial

Products having a readily solderable coating can be obtained employing one of ie following two methods:

(i) the material, in strip or wire stock form, is coated before the shaping of the products;
(ii) the products are manufactured first and coated later.

The advantages of the former method are:

(i) a much smaller variation in the coating thickness of electrodeposited coatings is obtained;

(ii) if desired, the shaped products can remain partially attached to the sto‹ strip, thereby ensuring that the cut edges are coated at the same time a‹ assisting the mechanisation of assembly procedures;

(iii) the coating can be applied selectively, *i.e.*, only in those areas of strip ‹ wire that will form part of the product [Anon. Ref. 16];

(iv) the cost is often lower.

A disadvantage of shaping the products from precoated material is that the c edges are not coated, and may therefore exhibit poor wettability. Whether or n uncoated cut edges are acceptable is then dependent on the application of tˈ products. The fraction of the total soldering area comprised of cut edges n conforming to wettability requirements must be minimised, and should n‹ exceed 25%.

Table 6.2 constitutes a review of coating processes, their capabilities for tˈ coating of discrete products, strip stock and wire stock, and the properties of tˈ coatings.

6.3 ELECTRODEPOSITED TIN AND TIN-LEAD

Coatings of tin and tin-lead alloys are very readily solderable if they are applied the correct way and on a suitable substrate. In transit and storage under conditio‹ that are not too humid, wettability is maintained for a considerable time. Coatin‹ for severe corrosion conditions are not discussed here [Spec. Ref. 19]. F‹ wettability after long-term storage a solder coating is superior to a tin coatiˈ [Bader *et al*]. Consequently, these coatings are preferred if the surface need n‹ meet other requirements. In essence, electrodeposited tin-lead coatings have tˈ same properties as layers produced by melting and crystallisation [Riedel], but tˈ electrodeposited layers may contain contaminants originating from the platiˈ baths. In general, retention of wettability of electrodeposited layers is improved they are subjected to a brief melting process [Bernier, Bud]. Tin coatinˈ produced by autocatalytic deposition sometimes help preserve wettability, but tˈ results obtained by this procedure are variable [Molenaar *et al*].

6.3.1 Intermediate Layers

Often an intermediate layer, also called an undercoating, is applied between tˈ base material and the top coating, four reasons for which are given as follow‹

6.3.1.1 ADHESION

An intermediate layer improves the adhesion between the base material and tˈ top coating. Either copper or nickel may be used for this purpose.

6.3.1.2 BARRIER AGAINST INTERMETALLICS

With tin or tin alloys on copper (or on a copper alloy) an intermetallic layˈ grows in the course of time (see Chapter 4.2.5). A barrier layer of nickel w decrease the growth rate of the tin-copper intermetallics, though a comple‹ suppression of growth is not achieved. Tin or tin-lead coatings with a thickness ‹ at least 3 μm on a substrate of nickel ensure sufficient wettability, even after loˈ

Table 6.2

Coating Methods for Solderability

Coating Process	Shape to be Coated	Capabilities and Limitations of Coating Process	Coating Thickness Feasibility	Coating Thickness Variation Thickness	Solderability after Storage for Correctly Selected Coating System
ytic	discrete product	all metals (Sn, Pb-Sn, Ag, Au, Cu, Ni); in barrel or by racking dependent on shape and size of product; risk of deformation of products; internal surfaces of hollow products difficult to coat.	unlimited	rather large (usually at least 100%)	good
	strip and wire stock	all metals; more than one coating in a single process (example: Ni and Pb-Sn on brass); selective coating of strip possible; coating on both sides of strip possible; different coating thickness on either side of strip possible.	unlimited	small (approx. 15%)	
mal	discrete product	low-melting metals only (Sn, Pb-Sn); *dip-coating*: risk of clustering (sticking) of products; risk of drop formation on products; *barrel-coating*: relatively low-cost; risk of deformation of product and of contamination of surface; *roller-coating*: one side only; also feasible on web-stock	limited	large (drop-formation)	good to poor, dependent on coating thickness
	strip and wire stock	low-melting metals only; undercoat cannot be applied in same process as topcoat; risk of tin or lead-tin drops, stripes and discoloration; *dip-coating*: both sides of strip; *roller-coating*: one side only; also feasible on web-stock; *flow-melting*: for web-stock only; *wire*: always eccentric coatings	limited; *strip*: wiping: 1-2 μm blasting: >10 μm draining: >15 μm rolling: >5 μm	large; (smaller in case of roller-coating)	good to poor, dependent on coating thickness
	wire	fusing of electrodeposited tin-lead coating	5 μm	small	good
ing	strip stock	all metals; selective coating possible; coating on top of strip (overlay) or inlaid in strip (stripe); possibility of applying various kinds of coating on one and the same strip;	>10 μm	small	good to poor, dependent on cleanliness of surface
ical	discrete product	thin coatings only;	limited; tin: max. 1-2 μm gold: max. 0,05-0,1 μm	small	poor, not suitable for machine soldering

storage. The same holds for 3 μm tin or tin-lead, over a nickel layer with thickness of at least 5 μm on a substrate of copper or tin-copper alloy.

6.3.1.3 BARRIER AGAINST ZINC DIFFUSION

The barrier layer is useful if brass is coated with tin or tin-lead alloy, and applied in order to prevent the diffusion of zinc to the external surface. The diffusion of zinc in the solderable coating can occur rapidly [Britton *et al*] impairing the wettability. Nickel or copper is generally used for this purpose. A undercoat with a thickness of 1 μm of nickel or 2 μm of copper inhibits zin diffusion sufficiently. In general, copper is preferred because difficulties with wetting and dewetting are less likely to be experienced.

To be effective, the barrier layer must be dense and free from pores. The coating, including the barrier layer, must be so ductile that no cracks are formed if the base metal is deformed, for instance by bending.

6.3.1.4 CORROSION RESISTANCE

A copper or nickel undercoating improves the resistance of steel to mildly corrosive environments.

6.3.2 Thickness of Coating

Products provided with a fresh uniform tin or tin-lead coating of 1 to 2 μm thickness are readily wettable. Owing to oxidation and growth of the intermetallic layer between coating and underlying material, however, wettability decreases with time. Especially with thin tin and tin-lead coatings on copper or copper alloys, when exposed to temperatures over 100°C, the formation of copper-tin compounds having relatively poor soldering properties must be anticipated.

Table 6.3 gives a condensed description of the most widely used tin and tin-lead coated materials, showing compatible combinations of base materials and coatings, and specifying minimum thicknesses (*i.e.*, local minimum thicknesses).

If this specification is complied with, good wettability is assured, even after the coating has been subjected to the ageing associated with storage for a duration of approximately one year under normal atmospheric conditions. If longer storage is expected, a greater thickness is required.

The thickness of coating depends on the place on the product under consideration. At edges and on protruding points the thickness may easily be three times the average value, whereas in corners and especially in holes it will be much less. Coating thicknesses obtained in batch processes show a large spread on products of one batch as well as differences between average values of various batches. Wire and strip products which are coated in continuous and in-line processes have a more uniform and reproducible coating thickness than the products coated batch-wise.

6.3.3 Conductors on Printed Boards

Conductors on printed boards usually consist of copper with or without a tin-lead plating. In the subtractive process for producing the conductor pattern, a etch resist is applied on the areas to be preserved. For uncoated copper this resi

Table 6.3

pes and Thicknesses of Under Coatings for Electrodeposited Tin or Tin-Lead
Alloy on Various Basis Materials

Basis Material	Under-Coating, if any	Minimum Thickness (μm)	
		Under Coating	Top Coating
pper	none	-	5
pper-tin (tin bronze)	none	-	5
pper-zinc (brass) or	copper or	2	5
pper-nickel-zinc (nickel silver)	nickel	1	3
ckel-iron or	copper or	3	5
n-nickel-cobalt (fernico) or n-nickel-cobalt (kovar)	nickel	3	3
	copper or	2	5
eel	nickel or	1	3
	none	-	3
ckel or pper-nickel (monel)	none	-	4

. 6.3 Undercutting of conductor. The degree of undercutting can be found by metallographic
ioning. The top layer in the photograph is solder, whilst the three layers underneath are copper
layers applied in various steps of the board manufacture. Solder layer thickness is 25 μm.

an organic lacquer [see Coombs]. On boards with a tin-lead coating, the
ating is used as the etch resist. The thickness of the electrodeposited layer is
nerally between 12,5 and 25 μm, and should not be less than 7,5 μm. Resistance
the etching fluid is produced by the conversion of tin-lead on the surface to
soluble compounds such as tin oxide, lead sulphate and lead chromate.
To restore wettability these insoluble materials must be removed, for instance

by etching in hydrochloric acid. Another approach is to fuse the top coating w:
the insolubles on it, using an active flux (see Chapter 6.4.3).

After etching, the plating will overhang the conductors (Figure 6.3), thus givi
the possibility of creating slivers of solder that can break off and cause sh
circuiting. Fusing has the effect of eliminating this risk, as has the application
a conformal coating (see Chapter 8.3.5).

6.3.4   Electroplating of Wire

Solder-coated wire is used in the machine fabrication of components. T
solder-coated leads, however, have a certain disadvantage, namely the buildi
up of solder on machine parts, caused by rubbing. This material transfer can, i
the most part, be overcome by applying a harder metal on the outer surface. W
this in mind, copper wires are produced, coated with a 4 μm layer of lead70-tin
alloy and a 1 μm top layer of tin95-lead5. After deposition of the top layer, i
wire is drawn through a finishing die, mainly intended to give the wire a brig
shiny appearance (Figure 6.4). Such wires with a concentric coating have excell
ageing properties. Upon ageing, an intermetallic layer develops, which uses
the tin of the lead70-tin30 part of the coat; but the tin at the outside is or
affected at a very late stage in the ageing process. The wires are (and rema
better, the more tin is left on the outer surface (Figure 6.5). Af
electrodeposition, the solder layer can also be melted to obtain a more coher
surface structure. The necessary heating can be achieved by passing an elect
current through the wire. The coating remains concentric if the wire is guid
vertically while heated, and if the heating period is short.

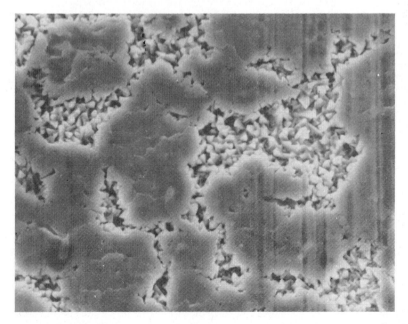

Fig. 6.4   SEM picture of outer surface of solder coated wire after polishing with a die. Af
deposition of the tin top coating on the lead70-tin30 layer, the surface has a gritty appearance, a p
of it being still present on the picture shown. Magnification 2500×.

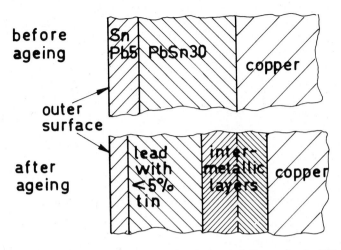

Fig. 6.5   The layer structure of electroplated wires, before and after ageing for 72 hours at 155°C.

6.3.5   Electroplating Techniques

In any electroplating process developed to produce a wettable surface, special emphasis must be placed on the cleanliness of the surface of the basis material. During soldering the coating may dissolve in the solder, and depending on the (local) thickness of the coating the underlying surface is then exposed. If this surface is contaminated, dewetting will result (see Chapter 2.3.3). The number of steps in the electroplating process, including all types of intermediate rinsing treatments, is considerable [Missel]. A full description and execution of them does not in itself guarantee adequate quality. A high level of skill by the persons employed in the work is indispensable.

The electroplating stages will not be discussed here in detail [see Price] and only a very brief summary follows:

6.3.5.1   DEGREASING (CLEANING)

Degreasing is necessary before the subsequent etching treatments, otherwise the etching will be irregular. It is achieved either with trichlorethylene followed by electrolytic degreasing, or by electrolytic degreasing alone. The electrolytic degreasing liquid may contain various ingredients such as silicates, phosphates, caustic soda and surface active agents. The product is generally connected to the negative pole where the degreasing action of the hot liquid is assisted by the violent, hydrogen evolution. Mechanical treatments such as tumbling, brushing or polishing render the surfaces difficult to clean and thus result in poor wetting [Thwaites *et al*].

6.3.5.2   ACTIVATION OF THE SURFACE BY PICKLING

Pickling solutions are based on ammonium or sodium persulphate or on chromic, sulphuric, nitric or fluoroboric acid [see also Lore]. The concentrations

and process times must be adapted to the conditions of the surfaces to be pickle(
When the pickling agents contain oxidising substances such as chromic or nitr
acid, it becomes necessary to deactivate the surface afterwards with dilu†
solutions of hydrochloric, sulphuric or fluoroboric acid.

The adhesion of electrodeposited layers varies with the degree of removal (
the oxide layers on the substrate material. A very thin intermediate layer with
thickness below 0,2 μm of silver or gold is sometimes applied to improve th
adhesion of subsequent layers. Such a thin layer, a 'flash' or 'strike', is n(
usually mentioned in the specification.

6.3.5.3   APPLICATION OF A BARRIER LAYER

A barrier layer of copper or nickel is sometimes applied, as in the case of zin(
containing alloys. This should form one step of a continuous process, especiall
when the barrier layer is of nickel.

6.3.5.4   APPLICATION OF TIN-LEAD COATINGS

Tin-lead alloys are usually deposited from fluoroborate solutions of which th
plating deposition times are currently reduced by adding agents that perm
greater current densities [Kohl]. Bright tin is deposited from acid sulphate batł
[Bellinger *et al*]; matt tin is deposited from fluoroborate or alkaline stanna†
electrolyte [Long].

Tin and tin-lead have the tendency, during electrodeposition, to grow out ȧ
laminar (plate-shaped) or acicular (needle-shaped) crystals. To obtain a unifor¤
electroplated layer, special agents (inhibitors) are added to the plating bath ȧ
order to decrease the rate of growth of the crystals already present, whil
enhancing the creation of new nuclei [Korpiun]. The inhibitors are organȧ
compounds such as peptone, which may become entrapped in the electroplate
layers, and exert some influence on the wettability of these layers. The mass (
the entrapped compounds is small (say 0,05%), but in terms of volume it ⁚
relatively large and it can cause a lower density of the coating (10%) as a result (
holes in the deposit.

Any metallic impurities in the plating bath deposited with the tin-lead ma²
produce deleterious effects on the wettability [Cavanaugh *et al*]. A small amour
of copper, especially, produces electrodeposited layers with poor solderin
quality. Owing to the low redox potential of copper compared with tin, muc
more copper is found in the layer than is present in the bath, the ratio of copp(
to tin-lead sometimes increasing by a factor of twenty. The copper in the platiṇ
bath also causes oxidation of the tin(II) to tin(IV), giving dark-coloured deposi†
and passivation of the anodes.

The composition of electrodeposited tin-lead coatings generally differs fro¤
the intended value; for instance a nominal eutectic layer may contain betwee
55% and 70% of tin with liquidus temperatures of the coating of 200°C aṇ
195°C respectively.

6.3.5.5   INTERMEDIATE RINSING TREATMENTS

Rinsing treatments are difficult to prescribe precisely, but they exert
considerable influence on the properties of the coatings produced. This ⁚

articularly the case with the final rinse of the copper before a tin-lead coating is pplied. Contamination of the copper underneath the solder coating will cause ewetting during fusion of the coating or during soldering. In this respect, ilphate ions are suspect [Williams, Roberts, Anon. Ref. 14].

4   FUSED OR HOT-DIPPED COATINGS OF SOLDER

Hot dipping is a general technique to produce a coating of tin or solder on etallic products [Thwaites]. It is used for many kinds of small products, for rip and plate, for wire, for printed boards, *etc*, and special machines have been eveloped for the in-line tinning of badly solderable components, *e.g.*, DIL ickages [Rahn *et al*].

A solder coating obtained by hot dipping on a clean basis material is perfectly •lderable and retains its wettability during a long period of time under relatively vere storage conditions. In this respect, hot-dipped layers are superior to ectroplated layers, because wetting of the basis metal has already taken place iring the dipping treatment. Moreover, the layers are usually much thicker than ectrodeposited layers, and have fewer pores if any.

If brass products are dipped, it is unavoidable that some zinc will dissolve in e molten solder. Consequently, the coating will contain a quantity of zinc which ill affect the solderability.

Coatings similar to those obtained by hot dipping can be achieved by fusing an ectrodeposited tin or tin-lead layer. This operation is also known as flow-elting, solder reflowing, flow-brightening and oil-flowing.

4.1   Hot-Dipped Copper Wire

Hot-dipped copper wire is produced by conveying a cleaned copper wire rough a bath of molten solder (Figure 6.6). At the point where the wire leaves

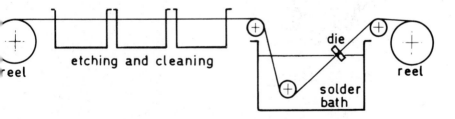

Fig. 6.6   Schematic drawing of facility for hot tinning of copper wire.

e solder bath, it is guided through a sizing die to remove excess solder and to oduce a diameter within given tolerances. Owing to dissolution of copper in the lder of the bath, the solder coating on the wire will contain about 2% of •pper. The main difficulty with those types of coated wires is the lack of lderability on part of the wire periphery after ageing, caused by eccentric •ating of the wire [Ochs, Dhaussy *et al*]. On the thinly coated areas the tin-•pper intermetallics soon grow to the surface, thus rendering them difficult to et [Fidos *et al*], whilst the thickly coated part of the periphery remains easily wettable. The soldering defects caused by these wires show an erratic incidence also reflected in the complex statistical distribution of globule tests on such wire [Lenz].

A considerable amount of work has been done to overcome this eccentricity problem by applying vertical pull-out of the wire from the solder bath, or b using sizing dies of a special shape [Friedrich *et al*]. The simple solution c increasing the average thickness of the tin coating is not acceptable, not on because it uses too much expensive tin, but also because it does not guarantee tha the minimum thickness will be increased.

The thickness of the solder layer on the copper wire can be measured usin X-ray absorption in the solder layer [Zimmerman]. Figure 6.7 shows X-ra equipment, provided with a transport mechanism for the wire, which makes possible to measure the distribution of the thickness along the length of the wir and around the perimeter.

This measurement is based on the absorption of fluorescent CuKα radiation from the copper wi by the solder layer. The CuKα radiation is generated by an incident beam of MoKα radiation. It h been shown both mathematically and experimentally that the logarithm of the measured radiatic intensity is inversely proportional to the layer thickness. Once the relationship of intensity and lay thickness is known, the measurements can be easily performed.

Fig. 6.7 X-ray equipment with an automatic transport mechanism for solder-coated copper wire The wire can be transported from one reel to another past the X-ray window. Moreover, th mechanism, including the reels, can rotate around the axis of the wire in front of the window. (B courtesy of J. Hooyer)

6.4.2 Hot Tinning of Small Parts

In the hot-tinning processes the separate parts are covered with a layer of liqu tin or solder [Anon. Ref. 17]. The problem then is to keep the parts loose whi the liquid solidifies and to avoid sticking and entangling.

By the nature of the processes the coating thickness is not uniform and can range from below 1 μm to above 100 μm depending on the shape of the products [Thwaites]. The average thickness is about 10 μm, but it can vary from 3 to 14 μm, measured on different parts of the same batch. The spread is likely to be such that 75% of the batch falls within ±20% of the mean thickness.

Before the actual dipping operation, the parts are fluxed in a very active flux of the zinc-ammonium chloride type to which hydrochloric acid may also have been added.

Two processes exist for the hot tinning of small parts.

6.4.2.1　DIP COATING

The parts, contained in a wire-mesh basket, are immersed in liquid tin or tin-lead solder. After having been coated, the parts can be spun in a centrifuge to remove excess tin or solder metal. The parts are then separated, for instance using a machine with a rotating paddle wheel, and from the separator they are fed into a water-quench tank.

6.4.2.2　HOT BARREL TINNING

In this process the parts are coated in a rotating container with a hexagonal or octagonal shape, to which the predetermined amount of solder is added (Heck-process). The container is heated to about 300°C. After a few minutes of tumbling, when the parts show a uniform appearance, indicating that the whole surface has been coated, the load is transferred either to a separator or directly to a water-quench tank.

6.4.3　Fused Coatings on Printed Boards; Levelling

A melted and subsequently solidified coating of tin-lead on printed boards can be produced either by fusing a previously electrodeposited tin-lead layer or by hot dipping the board in molten solder. The purpose of these operations is to obtain a uniform coating on the conductors having lasting wettability [Bud, Moore]. The fusing operation does in fact give an indication of the wettability of the base metal. Thus a fused coating with no non-wetted or dewetted areas will remain solderable for an appreciable time, depending on its thickness and uniformity.

A distinction is made between 'thick fused' and 'thin fused' coatings, above and below a thickness of 5 μm [Langan]. In most cases, the boards have no intermediate layer between the copper and the solder plating, so the presence and the growth of tin-copper intermetallics are important. The molten solder on the conductors assumes the equilibrium shape at the prevailing conditions [Golachev et al]. On fusing, the cross-section of an electrodeposited coating on a conductor therefore changes to a circle segment with the same area, apart from the small amounts of solder on the sides of the conductor. This circle segment has a height of 1,5 times the original thickness of the coating. If the coating is melted a second time, it will not alter its shape again. The fused coating is therefore a better basis for a lacquer (solder resist) than the original electroplating, as the latter causes serious wrinkling of the coat during soldering (see Figure 8.31). It should be noted, however, than an unchanged shape of the coating after soldering does not imply unchanged adhesion between solder and coating, as the solder will 'dewet' from the coating while maintaining contact.

The consequence of the equilibrium shape assumed by the solder during fusing is a reduced thickness of the solder at the corners between the board surfaces and the walls of the holes [Elliott *et al*, Anon. Ref. 22]. This is the weakest point in fused coatings (Figure 6.8). The wettability of the thin places becomes inadequate soon after the fusing operation. In wave soldering, the corners at the solder side of the boards do not present any problems, but the solder may not pass the upper corners with the result that the upper solder lands are not wetted. In many cases the solder joints thus achieved are sufficiently reliable and it is a matter of agreement on quality criteria as to whether such joints are acceptable (see Chapter 12.4.2).

Fig. 6.8 Fused coating in a metallised hole, showing the small layer thickness at the corner. Magnification 150×.

A remedy for the problem is to choose a larger overall thickness, presuming that this goal is also reached at and near the corners. The fusing conditions too can be selected to retain as much solder as possible at the critical areas.

6.4.3.1   SOLDER FUSING

Fusing methods for electrodeposited tin-lead layers are:

(i)   a hot liquid at about 220°C, sprayed with some force onto the board, melts the tin-lead and removes most of it. A layer of solder metal of 1 to 2 μm thickness is left on the board, the wettability of which is variable and often poor after storage. This fusing method is called the hydrosqueegee method;

(ii)   the board is passed across a wave of hot liquid to melt the plating (see Chapter 10.2.2), or the board is immersed in hot liquid (see Chapter 10.5.2) or in a condensing vapour (see Chapter 10.5.3). The hot liquid provides an acceptable rate of heat transfer, while overheating is excluded [Down]. The vapour phase fusion eliminates the need for fluxing and post-cleaning treatment [Spigarelli];

(iii)   the board is heated by infra-red radiation in a conveyorised system to melt the plating [McMillan, Kurilkin], the infra-red system having the virtue of being clean. The maximum temperature which the board will reach is not precisely predictable and will vary according to the conditions of board and environment (see Chapter 10.3.2). When the board is heated with scattered radiation from two sides its periphery will reach a higher temperature than its central area. The greatest overheating (*e.g.*, 35 K) is observed at the leading edge of the board [Kudryavtsev *et al*];

(iv)   the boards are heated while they are conveyed through a system applying hot air to them (see Chapter 12.5.1).

The overhang resulting from etching is removed by the fusing and a better pattern definition is obtained. Fused coatings have a bright and smooth appearance, and provide a good basis for a protective coat, if desired.

6.4.3.2   HOT AIR LEVELLING

In the hot air levelling process the fluxed boards are dipped edgewise vertically into a solder bath at about 220°C, and withdrawn after a predetermined dwell time (Figure 6.9). During the relatively rapid withdrawal the boards are exposed to strong blasts of hot air from flat nozzles, the so-called air knives, at both sides, to remove excess solder and to clear the holes [US Patent 3 865 298 (1973)]. The result is a thin but bright and uniform layer of solder on the conductors [Elliott *et al*, Schoenthaler].

The thickness of the coating is determined by the operating parameters such as speed of withdrawal, air temperature and air flow rate. On the surface the thickness can range from 2 to 25 μm, and in the hole, halfway between the faces of the board, from 5 to 75 μm. In general, the coating exhibits excellent ageing properties, except for a small portion at the corners of the holes, where the thickness of the coating may be less than 1 μm.

During operation the solder is blown out of the holes and will of course be spattered around. The operator must spend a significant amount of time cleaning the machine to ensure that the operation gives a consistent layer thickness. On the other hand, a continuous and careful examination of the levelled products is essential in order to maintain the necessary working conditions, so avoiding the production of solder layers that are too thin (having insufficient wettability after

Fig. 6.9　The Electrovert Levelair, a hot air levelling system with fully-protected operational area
(By courtesy of Electrovert, Canada.)

ageing), or too thick (forming heavy deposits at the bottom of the holes and the lowermost areas of the conductors) [DeBrita]. Washing of the board immediately after levelling is mandatory, because a highly active and corrosive flux is used in the levelling process.

6.4.3.3　ROLLER COATING

In this method the fluxed boards are guided horizontally between two rotating rollers, as in a clothes mangle. The lower roller is partly submerged in a solder bath and is intended to transport solder to the lower face of the boards to be coated.

Some problems inherent in this method are:

　(i)　the maintenance of a smooth and unbroken solder coating on the roller;
　(ii)　the avoidance of oxides and flux residues on the roller;
　(iii)　production of non-coated areas on the boards, resulting from thickness variations;
　(iv)　the occurrence of thickness variations in the coating, especially a very large thickness at the trailing edge of the boards (*e.g.*, on board 4 μm on trailing edge 100 μm).

6.5　COATINGS OF NOBLE METALS AND NICKEL

In addition to tin or solder coatings, silver or gold coatings are used for attaining wettability. Only in rare cases are other metals applied. The use of silver r gold coatings is, however, confined to cases where their use is absolutely ecessary for reasons other than wettability.

Table 6.4 gives the thicknesses of the electrodeposited layers usually applied.

Table 6.4

ypes and Thickness of Undercoatings for Electrodeposited Layers of Noble Metals on Various Basis Materials

oating ʳaterial	Basis Material	Undercoat, if any	Minimum Thickness (µm)	
			Undercoat	Top Coat
lver	copper or copper alloys	nickel	1	0,5
	copper or copper-tin alloys (bronze)	-	-	1
	copper-zinc alloys (brass) or	copper or	2	1
	copper-nickel-zinc alloys (nickel silver)	nickel	1	0,5
old	copper or copper-tin alloys (bronze)	-	-	0,5
		nickel	1	0,2
	copper-zinc alloys (brass) or	copper or	2	0,5
	copper-nickel-zinc alloys (nickel silver)	nickel	1	0,2
	nickel-iron or	copper or	2	0,5
	nickel-iron-cobalt alloy (kovar)	nickel	0,5	0,2
	nickel	-	-	0,2

he cleanliness of the underlying metal is of extreme importance, as silver and old are usually applied as thin coatings which dissolve very rapidly in solder. If ιe underlying metal has not been adequately cleaned prior to the lectrodeposition of silver or gold, or if the underlying metal has oxidised prior to ιe application of silver or gold or between processes, then the coated surface will ⁄et well in soldering but will dewet after dissolution of the top layer into the ιolten solder.

.5.1 Silver Coatings

Electrodeposited silver coatings are employed if, in addition to the solderability equirement, the coatings have to meet requirements of electrical conductivity or lectrical contact. The wettability of fresh silver coatings on a suitable substrate is ₀ood, but it deteriorates rapidly when sulphides form on the silver. Nickel is a ●etter substrate than copper for silver coatings, especially at temperatures of 00°C and higher.

Attack of silver plated surfaces by the atmosphere can be prevented by:

(i) effective packaging in sealed polyethylene bags. The sealed products can be stored in dry air for several months without losing their wettability. Paper or cardboard may be unsuitable because they sometimes contain sulphur;

(ii) application of an organic top coating, for instance a resin or a water-displacing liquid;

(iii) passivation of the silver surface by application of chromate coatings. I
should be noted, however, that as passivation reduces the wettability
compromise has to be effected between the degree of passivation and th
degree of wettability required;

(iv) passivation by applying a monolayer of mercaptan [Patentschrift DB.
1116216 (1962)].

The effect of an undercoating is clearly demonstrated by a test in which silve
plated copper sheets are exposed to air at 155°C for a duration of 16 hours. Silve
coatings having a thickness of approximately 1μm (without an undercoating
show strong discolouration. This is associated with a marked deterioration i
wettability. A silver coating of the same thickness applied to an electrodeposite
nickel coating of approximately 1 μm displays no discolouration during the sam
treatment, and also retains its wettability (Figure 6.10). A similar situation i
obtained if 5μm silver is applied directly to the copper.

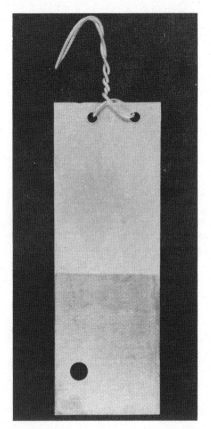

Fig. 6.10   The effect of a nickel barrier layer on the degradation of a silver coating of 1μm o
copper, during exposure to air at 155°C for 16 hours. The lower part of the plate has no barrie
plating, the upper has 1μm nickel between the basis metal and the silver coating. Plate is shown a
about actual size.

5.2 Gold Coatings

Electrolytically deposited coatings of gold or gold alloys are employed only in pplications where the special qualities of gold justify the cost. Well known roperties of gold in this context are its excellent performance as electrical ntact material and its good solderability [Ainsworth]. However, because of its gh cost, many other material combinations are considered for contact urposes, including tin and tin-lead [Nicotera, Evans, Whitley].

As a rule, very thin gold coatings are employed, although coatings having a ickness below 1 µm are always found to be porous. In particular, when very in gold coatings (thinner than 0,5 µm) are subjected to prolonged storage at mperatures above 100°C in air, soldering problems are to be expected, because oxidation of the underlying metal.

Gold is often used as a top coating over an undercoat of copper or nickel in rder to improve the reliability of the contact resistance upon heating [Antler, eel *et al*]. An advantage of nickel as undercoat is that it permits the employment thinner gold coatings than when using copper as undercoat. In a 16 hours' eam test, the wettability of a gold coating of 0,2 µm thickness on nickel proved ual to that of a gold coating of 0,5 µm thickness on copper.

The wettability of gold coatings to which specific alloying elements have been lded for the purpose of greater hardness or higher gloss is always inferior to that coatings of pure gold. However, the influence of different additions varies arkedly, *e.g.*, an addition of 1% nickel or cobalt causes a notable decrease in ettability, whereas 25% of silver scarcely changes the wettability, even if the loy is aged.

rittleness of Joints Caused by Gold

Gold plating is frequently mentioned in connection with brittle soldered joints. he objection to gold is based mainly on poor bulk material properties [Wild] or results with extremely thick layers of gold [Harding *et al*]. Reports on common ldered joints on printed boards whose failure is actually attributable to gold are arce. With smaller joint sizes, like those between micropackages and alumina bstrates on printed boards, cracks and failures caused by gold are, however, ore likely [Agniel *et al*]. The gold concentration at which the mechanical roperties of the solder begin to degrade is about 3%. Hence, care should be ken that this concentration is not reached at any point. Above 1% of gold the lder appearance can change if the cooling velocity is low. With normal plating icknesses, below 2 µm, in general the mechanical problems do not exist if fficient solder is applied [Walker *et al*], as can be understood from the lculations contained in Chapter 4.6.2.

With certain shapes the gold concentration may become more than 3%, and en brittleness can be expected due to the formation of the tin-gold compounds scussed in Chapter 4.4.4.

An example of gold plating presenting difficulties is shown in Figure 6.11, in hich copper wires are soldered to gold conductors on a thin film circuit. In this se, the wires can be easily soldered, provided that the soldering is accomplished ickly enough. Afterwards, however, reaction zones of tin-gold intermetallics e formed around the fillets with many holes caused by the Kirkendall Effect esulting from unequal diffusion rates of the different metals in the alloy).

Fig. 6.11 Copper wires soldered to gold layers on glass after a heating treatment at 150°C for 3⁣ hours. Around the solder the gold layer has been transformed into tin-gold intermetallics, having⁣ large number of holes. Magnification 10×.

Gold plated Kovar (iron-nickel-cobalt alloy) has a low resistance to stre⁣ corrosion cracking when subjected to solder fluxes [Dunn *et al*]. A deposit ⁣ nickel on the Kovar prior to gold plating minimises this effect [Weirick].

6.5.3 Palladium Coatings

Palladium is not as readily wettable as gold, and its rate of dissolution int⁣ solder is much slower. It does not produce very brittle joints because, unlike th⁣ tin-gold intermetallic which is rapidly distributed throughout the solder, the ti⁣ palladium forms a thin layer at the solder-palladium interface. Palladium is use⁣ for contact purposes, as is gold, for instance on end connectors [Bogenschütz ⁣ *al*], and is sometimes provided with a flash of gold.

A palladium coating is occasionally used to improve the wettability of nicke⁣ iron.

6.5.4 Nickel Coatings

Bright nickel cannot be activated enough to become sufficiently wettabl⁣ hence the rather less attractive appearance of matt nickel must be accepted. Ma⁣ nickel, however, can only be used for a short period after its preparation.

Tin-nickel, usually applied because of its wear resistance, is relatively easi⁣ wettable, even after storage, if covered with a gold flash of 0,1 μm [Rothschild⁣

The wettability of nickel and all nickel alloys, especially after ageing, is mu⁣ lower than that of solder-coated materials. The use of nickel and tin-nick⁣ coatings is therefore mainly restricted to intermediate layers.

6 PROTECTIVE COATINGS FOR RETAINING WETTABILITY OF OARDS

Protective coats are applied in order to preserve the wettability of printed oards during storage. Without protection, the wettability of boards will eteriorate too much, especially with unplated copper conductors. The protective oat will in most cases reduce the wettability only slightly, but in the long term the ettability is better retained, as is illustrated in Figure 6.12.

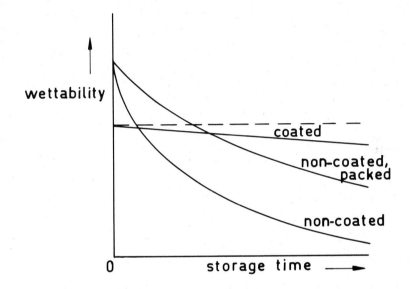

ig. 6.12 Qualitative effects of storage time on the wettability of printed boards in coated, non-coated and packed condition.

.6.1 Packaging

Fairly good protection against aggressive external environments is obtained if e boards are sealed in polyethylene bags together with silica gel (though in fact olyethylene is not gas-tight). Regardless of which method of sealing is applied, e preservation of wettability is good [Spec. Ref. 14]. Best results are obtained ith commercially available laminated bags of polyethylene-aluminium-olyester; nevertheless the wettability of the enclosed surfaces will still decrease owly. Sealing of such bags does not provide protection against oxidation during ng term storage exceeding two years.

.6.2 Organic Coatings of Resin Type

Many proprietary organic coatings exist. As these coats must not obstruct etting and the flow of the solder to the soldering areas, they must either dissolve to or mix with the flux to a sufficient extent.

Coats are applied by roller coating or by dipping in a dilute solution. The ickness of a dried coat should be between 0,5 μm and 3 μm, optimal thickness

being just above 0,5 μm. This thickness offers adequate protection again
fingerprints without hindering the action of the flux. Coating thickness can I
determined by weighing a metallic test plate before and after coating, provid
that the density of the dried solids of the coating solution is known.

Copper-clad printed boards are coated with a preservative based on modifi
colophony containing a filmformer such as acrylate or epoxy. The filmform
prevents the colophony from crumbling, which would cause contamination of t
tooling such as punches and dies. These coats are usually intended only as
protection against fingerprints and do not prevent oxidation of the underlyi
copper. Wettability retention of printed boards coated with similar preservativ
is at most six months under normal storage conditions. On printed boards wi
plated holes, use of a filmformer in the colophony is less desirable because t
filmformer present in the holes unduly retards the filling of these with solder.

Printed boards provided with a tin-lead coat are not coated with any organ
preservative.

6.6.3 Benzotriazole and Benzimidazole on Copper

Benzotriazole and benzimidazole are effective organic reagents for the contr
of undesirable surface reactions on copper and its alloys in various environment
They cause a reduction in wettability, but to an extent controllable by t
conditions under which they are applied. Benzotriazole treatment has be
proposed as a method of producing controlled degradation of wettability in ord
to compare different solderability test methods [McCarthy *et al*].

The structures of benzotriazole ($C_6H_5N_3$) and benzimidazole ($C_7H_6N_2$) a
shown in Figure 6.13. In practice, benzotriazole is used more often tha
benzimidazole.

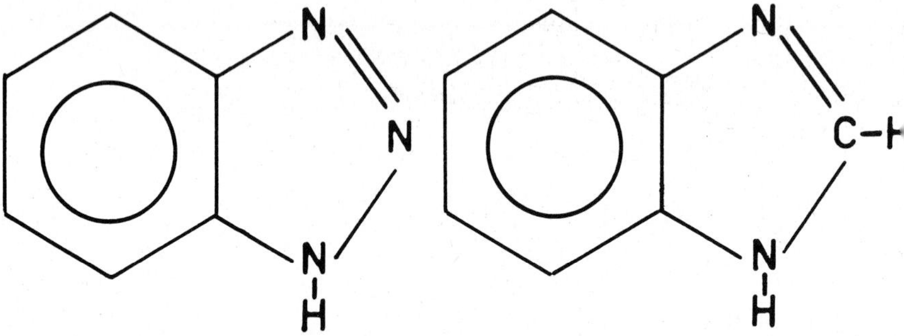

Fig. 6.13 Structure of 1,2,3-benzotriazole (*left*) and of 1,3-benzodiazole (benzimidazole, *right*).

Benzotriazole is generally applied to copper surfaces by immersion in a dilu
aqueous solution (typically 0,1% by mass) for one to three minutes. In this way
chemical layer is formed by adsorption on the copper surface with a thickness
2 to 10 nm, depending on the conditions used. This has been measured b
ellipsometry [Hobbins *et al*] and by AES sputter depth profiling [Author's work
The adsorbed layer formed is a Cu(I)-benzotriazole compound, which can b
oxidised in air to a Cu(II)-benzotriazole compound. This has been measured b
microspectrofluorimetry [Siedle *et al*] and by ESCA [Chadwick *et al*].

The wetting balance can be successfully employed to study the effectiveness of e adsorbed layer in preserving wettability over a period of time. From such vestigations benzimidazole is reported to be superior to benzotriazole Venger].

7   TIN WHISKERS

Whiskers are hairlike crystals which grow, apparently spontaneously, from the rface of solid matter [Jostan, Britton]; they are also known as 'proper hiskers' or 'spontaneous whiskers' [see also Price pp 106-117].

Progressive miniaturisation in the electronic engineering fields is being creasingly harassed by whiskers, which may cause flash over, short circuits, dible noise, *etc.* (Figure 6.14).

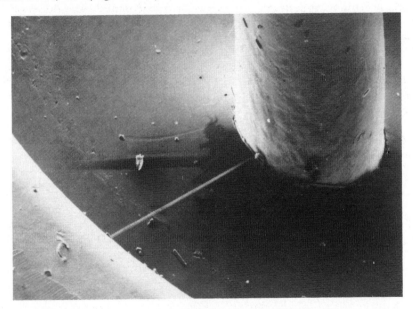

g. 6.14 SEM photograph of a whisker grown between a tin-plated lead of a transistor and the etallic capsule of the transistor, giving a short circuit. Magnification 80×. (By courtesy of PTI, Hilversum.)

Although difficulties arising from whisker growth do not often occur, the tendant damage sometimes assumes dramatic forms. Whiskers may grow on all nds of metallic parts used in electronics, not only on circuitry but also inside the ackages of semiconductors [Dunn]. Once such growth occurs, little can be done her than to clean the equipment with a brush and a small vacuum cleaner and place the relevant components by an improved version. In this sphere more an anywhere else, prevention is better than cure.

7.1   Properties

As regards dimensions, whisker diameters are in the order of magnitude of icrometres whereas, on the other hand, whisker length may sometimes assume

values of many millimetres. The current-carrying capacity of these whiskers c
be some tens of milli-amperes.

Whiskers grow on a multitude of metals and alloys but most commonly on ti
cadmium, antimony, indium and zinc. They appear less frequently on lead, irc
silver, gold, nickel and palladium. In general, the phenomenon occurs on ratl
soft and ductile materials, especially those having a low melting point. Howev
with lead, whisker growth has seldom been found.

Tin whiskers grow at a speed of 0,001 to 0,3 nm/s (0,1 nm/s being equivale
to 3 mm/year). Under certain conditions the growth rate can increase by a fact
of 100 or more.

They grow mainly from a layer applied by electrodeposition, in which there
always a certain amount of stress. Rather than remain under stress in the coatir
the atoms move into hair-thin crystals with a relatively large surface area [Furu
et al]. Because of their (typically) single-crystalline nature the whiskers for t
greater part are completely straight, having a constant cross-section along th
length.

Once the process of growth has started, the whisker grows 'from below' a
the supply of material comes from such a large region that no decrease in t
layer thickness can be observed at the base of the whisker. The growth directi
may sometimes change abruptly, resulting in bends in the whiskers.

These crystals can grow out of various metals applied to a variety of substrat
but a bright tin electrodeposited coating on steel or brass is particularly sensitiv
Under certain conditions such coatings of tin on steel may be covered with
'beard' of whiskers within a few days or a week (Figure 6.15).

Fig. 6.15 Whiskers grown from a tin coating on steel. The whiskers shown have a length of ab
0,5 mm. Besides the real whiskers, other growths are visible, at the base of the hairlike whisk
(S shape, right below), at the edge of a scratch (right middle) or even at random. Magnification 180

6.7.2 Influencing Factors

Shape, structure, size, number, rate of growth, direction of growth, initiation time, *etc.*, are not accurately predictable, although at times a certain regularity is found; in such cases some control of growth can be achieved. Conditions that enhance generation include anything causing stress in the layer out of which the whiskers grow. On the other hand, stress relief in the form of a 'post-plating baking treatment' can be used to prevent their formation [Jafri].

6.7.2.1 TOP COAT

As a general rule, materials employed in electronic engineering are, for improvement of solderability or other reasons, provided with either an electrodeposited or a hot-dipped coating. Electroplated coatings often have rather high internal stresses, unlike hot-dipped coatings which are more or less stress-free. Moreover, if the material of the outer or top coat is dissimilar to that of the substrate, stresses are likely to arise due to lattice mismatch. As a result of the prevailing stresses electrodeposited coatings particularly tend to exhibit whisker growth, the rate of which is dependent on the coating thickness: the thinner the coating, the greater the whisker growth.

Electrodeposits of a thickness of approximately 1 μm are found to manifest a very profuse whisker growth. Few data are available on still thinner coatings, so that it is not certain if the growth rate at approximately 1 μm coating thickness is really maximal. Whisker formation has, however, been observed on thin, vacuum-deposited tin coatings of 350 nm [Tu].

The composition of the electrodeposited coating is also of importance. Certain additions, for instance brighteners (to the tin bath), promote whisker growth [Zakraysek], whereas others such as cobalt, antimony or lead have a retarding effect [Metzger *et al*].

Deposits consisting of alloys exhibit far less whisker formation than single-component deposits. Tin-lead coatings, whether or not of eutectic composition, are practically free from this problem [Diehl]. Even 1% of lead in the top coating has been found to reduce their growth substantially [Arnold]. Tin-lead is easy to apply as a top coat and has a reasonable appearance, very good solderability and a low cost. Tin-nickel, on the other hand, which is sometimes recommended as a whisker-free top coat, is finding little or no application on account of its less favourable wetting properties.

Although the occurrence of whiskers on tin in the bulk state is rather rare, the risk of whisker formation must be taken into account, especially if the material is subjected to mechanical load. This is equally valid for many other bulk metals.

6.7.2.2 SUBSTRATE

Whiskers appear to grow the most rapidly of all on a brass substrate and less rapidly on copper, nickel or steel. However, the findings reported are not in absolute agreement, which leads to the conclusion that it is not only the composition of the substrate which plays a role, but also the influences exercised on layer texture and residual stresses by the mechanical and thermal history for instance.

6.7.2.3 UNDERCOAT

For the purpose of repressing whisker growth, certain undercoats ar occasionally applied between the substrate and the top coating, if such coats hav not already been provided to maintain solderability. As undercoat material, golc silver, copper and nickel are often effective, especially on substrates of brass o steel, although they cannot always be relied upon. Just as with the substrat material, the influence exercised by the undercoats has failed to be establishe conclusively. Various impurities seem to have a part to play, and certainly th plating parameters have a certain influence. Lattice matching is only partiall responsible for the effect of an undercoat so that other, still unknown, factor and properties must also be involved.

As, for reasons of cost, gold and silver cannot be applied on a large scale copper and nickel are particularly recommended, nickel in fact being the mor commonly used. An electrodeposited undercoat must have a minimum thicknes of 3 μm to be effective.

6.7.2.4 TEMPERATURE AND TEMPERATURE GRADIENT

Increase of temperature increases the mobility of atoms and thereby the growtl rate of whiskers. On the other hand, raising the temperature has a stress-relievin effect, thus counteracting whisker growth. If temperature is increased beyond certain point, the annealing mechanism predominates so that each metal exhibit maximal whisker growth at a very specific temperature. For tin this temperatur is between 60 and 70°C and, unfortunately, this is close to the workin temperature of most equipment. Besides the temperature itself, local temperatur differences exert some influence as they result in differential expansions whicl create stresses.

6.7.2.5 ATMOSPHERE

A humid and hot atmosphere in general promotes whisker growth. Indeed, it i believed that atmospheric oxygen may aid the process. On the other hand nicke whiskers have also been observed to appear in a vacuum [Poole *et al*].

6.7.2.6 MECHANICAL LOAD

Whisker growth rate is almost directly proportional to the compression stres exerted on the material. It is possible, by applying pressure, to accelerate whiske growth to a degree perceptible to the naked eye. As it is, whisker growth can be provoked by subjecting allergic materials to compressive stress, for example b clamping them in a vice: after a lapse of only a few hours whiskers develoj immediately adjacent to the area of clamping ('squeeze' whiskers). On thi account, in load-carrying applications, tin coatings must be avoided.

Clamped connections, such as in bolted constructions, are rather sensitive anc tin whiskers can occur even if the top coat is of hot-dipped tin-lead. An example of this is the whisker formation on soldered edge connectors under the pressure o contact springs. The occurrence is, however, very rare, and because the distance to be bridged in this case are relatively large a limited amount of whisker growtt is not necessarily cause for rejection of the part.

Metalworking operations may also generate severe whisker growth, notably at the cut edges of stampings.

6.7.3 Rules for Prevention of Whiskers

Universally effective preventatives are not available, but a good general rule is that all kinds of stresses should be avoided. Tin plated steel or brass should not be used in, or close to, electronic circuits. If the use of tin is unavoidable, the following precautions should be taken:

(i) use large coating thicknesses, preferably exceeding 10 μm;
(ii) apply hot-dipped layers instead of electroplating;
(iii) subject an electrodeposited coating to flow melting;
(iv) alloy with lead;
(v) consider the usefulness of undercoats.

If these possibilities are borne in mind at the design stage, the unpleasant results of whisker growth will not manifest themselves later, *e.g.*, after delivery to the customer.

6.7.4 Other Types of Whiskers

The so-called proper whiskers, as discussed in the preceding paragraphs, grow from their base. Several other types of whiskers exist, grown by various mechanisms from a suitable liquid or gas environment. As growth may proceed from all sides, the shape of the produced growths is often more complicated than that of the (usually) straight proper whiskers, having a constant cross-section. The various types of whiskers may give electrical trouble in equipments: metallic whiskers may cause short circuiting; non-metallic whiskers may produce insulating or badly conductive dust, *e.g.*, on the contacts of switches or relays (Figure 6.16). Filaments, grown under the influence of a DC potential in a humid environment are discussed in Chapter 5.2.2.2.

Fig. 6.16 Silver sulphide (Ag_2S) whiskers grown on a silver relay contact by take up of sulphur from the atmosphere of the room in which the relay was stored for a few years (without being used). No elements except silver could be detected in the bulk material of the contact, using energy

Chapter 7

ASSESSMENT OF SOLDERABILITY

When a mass soldering process is applied to an electronic assembly many ifferent components have to be soldered simultaneously, the success of the oldering operation depending on several factors, such as the joint shape, the ayout of the conductor pattern, the process parameters and the materials used.

In this Chapter on assessment of solderability, only the matter of the materials o be soldered will be considered. In the soldering process the terminations of the lectronic components, and the soldering lands and conductors on the support lates (typically printed boards), must be covered and wetted with solder to form he soldered joints. To enable the soldering to be performed in one single peration, within a limited time and temperature, the wettabilities of the various netals must be matched. Even if all materials have been selected according to ccepted standards still no guarantee exists that the soldering operation will be uccessful, because the physical and chemical condition of the surfaces at the time f soldering must also meet specific requirements.

.1 SOLDERING AND SOLDERABILITY

The ability of a material to be wetted with solder is closely related to the solderability', a complex property, to be defined later in the text (Chapter 7.1.1). This solderability depends partly on the inherent character of the material oncerned, partly on the degree of cleanliness of the surfaces after the fabrication f the components, and also on the ageing by environmental attack during torage.

In order to ensure an adequate level of solderability, especially after ageing, ertain measures must be taken. One approach is to introduce standards which he parts to be soldered must satisfy. Such standards may cover:

(i) recommended metallic coatings, including requirements for minimum layer thicknesses;
(ii) thermal requirements for components and boards;
(iii) measuring methods and requirements for solderability of component terminations, connecting parts and printed boards, including ageing treatments and sampling methods.

During the last decade the existence of such standards has contributed to a onsiderable improvement in solderability, particularly of component erminations and connecting parts.

203

The first Philips standard for solderability in 1959 recognised 5 classes of wettability, reflecting the situation at that time when machine soldering was not yet widespread. The requirement for the top class was a wetting time of 2 seconds, measured by the globule method. At the time of writing, only one class remains, and the everyday testing practice is that the majority of the components are wetted well within 1 second, with an even milder flux than that used in 1959.

In another approach, systematic specification and testing of solderability are not carried out, the risk of poor solderability being covered by the use of very strong fluxes. These active fluxes incur the risk of corrosion of the soldered assembly, necessitating thorough cleaning followed by cleanliness-testing procedures.

In a third approach the components having insufficient solderability are presoldered in a separate operation, for which special soldering machines are commercially available (sometimes presoldering is assisted by ultrasonic cavitation).

7.1.1 Solderability

The solderability of component terminations is a property defining the total suitability for industrial soldering. It has three aspects:

  (i) thermal demand: the thermal characteristics of the components to be soldered must allow heating of the solder joint area to the desired temperature within the time available for the soldering operation;
 (ii) wettability: the surface must allow wetting by molten solder within the time available for the soldering operation and without subsequent dewetting;
(iii) resistance to soldering heat: the soldering heat and the thermal stresses associated with it must not affect the function of the components beyond a specified limit.

Good solderability results in good wetting, which means the formation of a uniform, smooth, unbroken, adherent coat of solder on the base metal, without the use of highly active fluxes and without impairing the function of the parts soldered. With poor solderability, poor wetting, *i.e.*, non-wetting, partial wetting, or dewetting are observed.

7.1.2 Wetting Time and Testing Temperature

In a wettability test, time elapses between the moment the solid material (for instance a component termination) first makes contact with the molten solder and the moment the solid surface is wetted. This time is called the wetting time (or the soldering time, although this expression is also used as a time parameter in soldering processes where it relates to dwell time (see Chapter 9.1.1)). What is meant by 'wetted' is a matter of definition, but in practice any conveniently recognisable degree of wetting may be specified. The following Sections on testing methods will give further information on this matter.

The wetting time is the combined result of the thermal demand of the pieces to be heated and the wettability of the surfaces. The test temperature is the temperature of the solder just prior to the moment of contact with the pieces to be soldered, and hence is often the same as the bath temperature. The rea

mperature of the surfaces to be wetted is in nearly all cases lower than this
sting temperature; it is not constant but shows considerable variation.

2　METHODS OF TESTING SOLDERABILITY

Two basically different groups of test methods exist:

(i) measurement of non-equilibrium situations, investigating the rate of
wetting, *etc.*;
ii) measurement of the final result of the wetting process, investigating the
final degree of wetting achieved.

soldering practice, the process times are usually so short that the equilibrium
uation is far from being reached. For this reason the wettability measurements
the first group are often closer to reality than those of the second group. Quite
number of test methods for solderability have been developed [Wallis,
ickson, Long], partly as a result of the complex character of the property
lderability, and also on account of independent developments arising from
rious (personal) points of view.
In the field of solderability tests, qualitative (visual) assessment still plays an
portant part, especially in the edge dip tests for wetting and dewetting. On the
her hand, the wetting balance, for example, constitutes a method for
sessment based on quantitative information, but here also operator skill is
quired, to notice peculiarities which would otherwise be missed.
The main test methods are featured in the diagram shown in Figure 7.1.

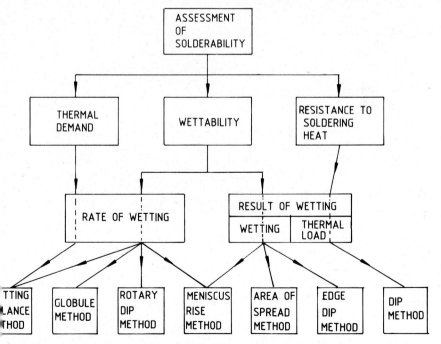

7.1　Diagram showing test methods for solderability; the various methods are dealt with in
separate sections.

The meniscus-rise method occupies an intermediate position between the tv principal groups, depending on the specific measurement procedure used.

Determination of thermal demand, as carried out using the wetting balance, an extreme example of a non-equilibrium experiment. The resistance to solderi heat, the other extreme in the diagram, is assessed by measuring the permane effects of the thermal loading of the components after this loading has ceased

7.2.1 Wetting Balance Method

This is the most versatile solderability test method, suited to the quantitativ investigation of the solderability of specimens of any shape. Normall component terminations are tested, but the method can also be employed fc other purposes such as testing of copper clad laminates, thick film substrat [Pantanelli], fluxes [Jellison *et al*] and organic coats [Wenger]. The method ca into general use after its development at Philips, Eindhoven [ten Duis *et al* though it had been applied before [Earle]. Commercial machines are availab (see for instance Figure 7.2).

Fig. 7.2   Wetting balance (without recorder). The apparatus shown is the Multicore universal teste which, after simple interchange of the arm, can also be used for globule or edge dip tests. (By courtes of Multicore Solders, UK.)

7.2.1.1 PRINCIPLE OF THE WETTING BALANCE

The specimen is suspended from a sensitive balance (typically a spring system and immersed edgewise to a predetermined depth in molten solder at a controlle temperature. The resultant of the vertical forces of buoyancy and surface tensio cting upon the immersed specimen is detected by a transducer and converted into a signal which is continuously recorded as a function of time on a high-speed chart recorder. The trace may be compared with that derived from a perfectly-wetted specimen of the same nature and dimensions. A block diagram of an arrangement suitable for the test is shown in Figure 7.3.

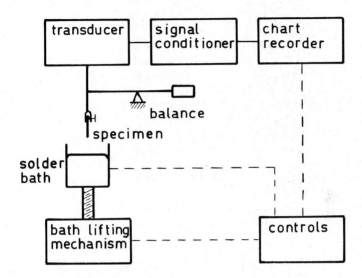

Fig. 7.3 Block diagram of wetting balance.

When the specimen has been immersed to the specified depth in the molten solder, it is held in this position for a given time and then withdrawn by lowering the solder bath. The significant part of the recorder trace of force versus time is obtained when the specimen is held stationary in the immersed position.

In Figure 7.4 five stages in the testing of a readily wettable specimen are shown:

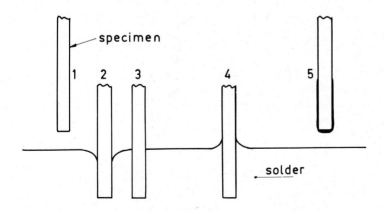

Fig. 7.4 Five situations of a readily wettable specimen in a wetting balance (see text).

(i)   just before the moment of immersion;
(ii) immediately after the moment of immersion, when the meniscus is sti
      curved downwards, resulting in an upward force;
(iii) when the wetting has reached the point where the vertical force from th
      surface tension is zero, at which point the only force acting on the specime
      is the buoyancy;
(iv) when the meniscus is curved upwards, resulting in a downward force fro
      the surface tension;
(v)   when the specimen has been withdrawn.

The trace of the resulting force on the specimen appears as a solid line i
Figure 7.5, from which it can be seen that in this case the upward force ha
changed to a downward force within one second. For various degrees c
wettability different traces are obtained, three such traces for lower degrees c
wettability being shown in Figure 7.5.

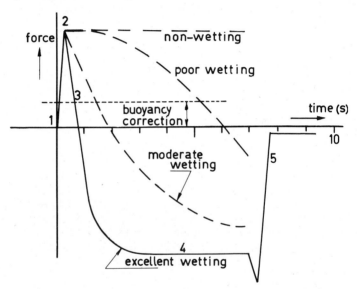

Fig. 7.5   Recorder traces of forces exerted on a specimen during the test period in a wetting balanc
The figures beside the solid curve correspond to the situations shown in Fig. 7.4.

The recorder traces give the result of the net forces of the surface tensions o
the periphery of the specimen. If a non-circular section is tested, the wettin
conditions will not be the same everywhere along the periphery (see Chapte
2.3.2), but the measured forces are still unambiguous.

7.2.1.2   PRESENTATION OF RESULTS

Traces like those in Figure 7.5 are obtained with a chart recorder, but it
equally possible to operate the wetting balance without a recorder. The varyin
forces, measured during the testing period, then have to be processed in anothe
way, for instance with a microcomputer. The apparatus in Figure 7.2 has suc
facilities and can print out relevant data after each test [see also Lin *et al*

owever, a chart recorder does offer certain advantages. The full traces of the
etting process are available and, if necessary, unexpected and uncommon
:haviour can be better evaluated and understood. In this connection, it is good
actice in non-routine testing to observe the wetting process using a stereoscopic
icroscope.

Because the forces during wetting may change rather rapidly, a chart recorder
ith a short response time is essential. Such recorders are expensive. The response
ne of the writing device of the recorder influences the test results [Allen *et al*]
ıd should be less than 0,3 s. However, the chart speed is not critical as long as
actions of a second can be easily measured. A chart speed of 10 mm/s is suitable
ıd permits easy reading of the times.

ɔrm of Chart Recorder Trace

The trace may be recorded in two forms, the only difference being the polarity
˙ the force readings.

In Figure 7.6 upward forces (non-wetting) are shown as positive and downward
ɔrces (wetting) as negative.

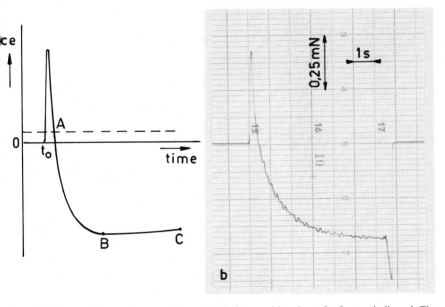

g. 7.6   (a) Drawing of recorder trace in a wetting balance, with points of reference indicated. The
ɔtted line represents the buoyancy offset caused by the immersion of part of the specimen. The force
lue at the end of the testing period (C) is slightly lower than the maximum value (B). (b) An original
ace obtained from a solder plated nickel-iron transistor lead having a diameter of 0,48 mm. The
aximum force value is found at the end of the immersion period, points B and C in fact coinciding.

˙oints of Significance

Since one of the virtues of this test method is that the entire wetting process is
xamined, it is appropriate to use the whole force-time curve. Some points on
ıese curves are especially important:

(i)   Point t_o is the time at which the solder surface and the specimen first make
      contact (indicated by deviation of the trace from the zero force line);

(ii) Point A is reached at the moment when the force acting on the specimen
      equal to the calculated buoyancy. All forces are measured with respect
      the horizontal line through point A;

(iii) Point B is the maximum value of the resultant downward force attain
      during the specified immersion period;

(iv) Point C is the point at the end of the specified immersion period. Points
      and B may have the same force value on the same specimen, as is display
      in Figure 7.6 b.

The time interval between t_o and A is the time for the initiation of wetting, and
called the wetting time. In the test requirements a maximum value is given for t
time. This time interval is of course relevant only to the early part of the wetti
process. Point A in fact defines two aspects, a precise place on the recorded tra
and a precise place on the specimen (assuming circular cross-section).

Beyond point A the wetting progresses, and the maximum force value at
(indicating the degree of wetting achieved) must exceed a specified minimu
value within a certain time. How this minimum value may be specified will
discussed under 'Reference Wetting Force'. After the maximum force value, B
attained, the meniscus may remain steady and the force value show no chan
However, this stability may be disturbed by reactions between the specimen a
the molten solder, leading to dissolution of the specimen surface by the solder
the formation of a layer of reaction product at the interface. In addition, residu
flux may be evaporated, or may decompose and migrate over the surface of t
solder bath. These effects may lead to a lowering of the measured force such th
the value at the end of the test period, C, is less than the value recorded at B.

In the case of material coated with a thick hot-dipped layer of solder, anoth
cause of decrease of force value is observed, namely melting and flowing down
the coating from above the wetted zone. Loss of flux weight or of coating weig
is inevitable, but is no proof of reduced wetting. The change imposes a limitati
on the value of the test method, because it cannot immediately be distinguish
from reduction of wettability. The stability of the wetting during the last part
the immersion period can be expressed as the ratio: force at C/force at B.

Buoyancy

The buoyancy of the specimen can be calculated as the product of t
immersed volume and the density of the molten solder displaced by the specim
(Figure 7.7). At the specified test temperature of 235°C, the value of 8000 kg/

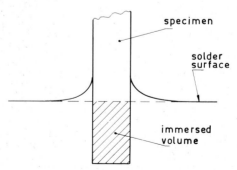

Fig. 7.7   The immersed volume is the volume below the undisturbed solder surface, ignoring t
curvatures of the meniscus.

used for the density of molten solder with 60% tin and 40% lead. With the immersed volume, v, expressed in mm³, this gives for the buoyancy force: 08v (mN).

?ference Wetting Force

The degree of wetting achieved, as given by the force value at point B, only ovides quantitative information if it can be compared with some specifiable est' value. In testing practice, component terminations of a known design (in spect of material, plating, protective coat and thermal demand) are usually ing tested and the measurements are intended to investigate the surface nditions of the particular batch of components. In this case, the forces are mpared with the best wetting value that the material having the given shape and der the conditions of the measurements is capable of showing. This best value, e Reference Wetting Force, of these component terminations can be obtained th a separate series of measurements:

A specimen is taken from the sample to be tested and is presoldered using tivated flux. This presoldering can be carried out on the wetting balance under e same conditions as are used for the wetting test. The procedure of fluxing and esoldering is repeated on the same specimen till the maximum force reading es not increase further. This maximum force reading is called the Reference etting Force. There is usually no need to measure more than one specimen. The peated soldering tends to decrease any difference between specimens.

In Figure 7.8 a number of traces are shown from which is obtained a Reference etting Force of 0,67 mN. If the procedure of dipping is continued, a decrease in e maximum values of the curves can be expected. In practice, there is no

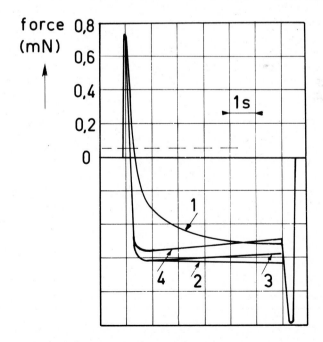

7.8 Recorder traces giving the Reference Wetting Force. The maximum force value is obtained from the second and/or the third run. The fourth run produces a lower force value.

problem at all in deciding if a sufficient number of presoldering cycles have bee
carried out.

If this procedure is applied to materials that are inherently difficult to wet wi
solder, even the measured Reference Force so obtained represents an inadequa
degree of wetting. In such cases the specimens certainly fail the requirements f
the time A-t_o.

Theoretical Wetting Force

It is sometimes necessary to investigate the general suitability of a certa
material or plating for soldering. In this event, the Reference Wetting Force ca
be compared with the Theoretical Wetting Force, obtained by calculation und
the assumptions of an appropriate surface-tension constant and perfect wettin
($\theta = 0$). The Theoretical Wetting Force can be calculated from the formula:

$$\text{Force} = \gamma_l\, p\, \cos\theta$$

(measured from the line through point A)
in which: γ_l = surface tension of solder in contact with flux
and p = periphery of specimen.

This formula is only appropriate if the cross-section of the specimen in th
vicinity of the meniscus is constant through the length of the specimen.
With p in mm, a value for $\gamma_l = 0,4$ J/m^2 at 235°C, and $\theta = 0$,
one obtains

$$F_{th} = 0,4\, p \text{ (mN)}.$$

Table 7.1 shows a series of measurements on the Reference Wetting Forces a
the calculated Theoretical Wetting Forces.

Table 7.1

Reference Wetting Forces and Theoretical Wetting Forces

	Copper Wire	Solder Plated Copper Wire	Gold Plated Copper Wire	Iron Wire	Nickel Wire	Aluminiur Wire
Diameter (mm)	0,6	0,56	0,6	0,6	0,5	0,56
Reference Wetting Force (mN)	0,66	0,65	0,65	neg.	0,46	non-wettin
Theoretical Wetting Force (mN)	0,75	0,70	0,75	0,75	0,63	0,70
Ratio $\dfrac{\text{measured}}{\text{theoretical}}$	0,88	0,92	0,86	neg.	0,73	-

From Table 7.1 it is evident that choosing a specified fraction of the Measure
Reference Wetting Force as one of the test criteria places the acceptable degree
wetting at a realistic level. Suppose that it is necessary to measure whether nick

ires on a certain component are in good condition. For this, a comparison must
e made with the value of 0,46 mN, obtained on the same material and geometry.
'o decide if nickel is a suitable material for wires to be soldered is a different
iatter.

.2.1.3   SOME REPRESENTATIVE FORCE-TIME CURVES

In the examples of Figure 7.9, the part of the curve representing forces acting
pwards on the specimen, *i.e.*, in the non-wetting state, are shown as positive;
orces acting downwards, *i.e.*, wetting, are shown as negative. The horizontal line
epresents the condition at the start of the test cycle, having cancelled the weight
f the specimen. The dotted line represents the buoyancy off-set, from which the
vetting forces are measured. There is always some electrical and mechanical noise
n the recorded traces, but in a good equipment this will be less than the
quivalent of 4×10^{-5} N. Hence, one small wire having a diameter of 0,3 mm will
ive a wetting force which is about 10 times as large as the maximum allowable
oise. In general, the noise in the curves presents no problems [see also Wallis].

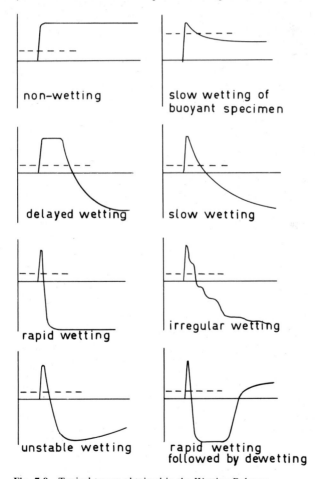

Fig. 7.9   Typical traces obtained in the Wetting Balance.

7.2.1.4   TESTING PRACTICE WITH THE WETTING BALANCE

Specimens

The specimen may be of any shape, but in order to simplify the interpretation of the curve and the calculation of forces, it is preferable for the immersed portion of the specimen to be of uniform cross-section and to be capable of being wetted by solder around its entire perimeter. To reduce errors in calculation, the specimen should be immersed with the surfaces to be tested within an angle $\pm 15°$ from the vertical.

The test can be applied to such specimens as multilayer chip capacitors or samples of printed board having large areas not wettable by solder. However such areas may produce distortion of the force-time curve.

Testing Conditions

It is important that a standard procedure for fluxing the specimens be used, so that the trace is not disturbed by the effects of solvent evaporation or dripping of flux during the course of the test. The test equipment must conform to certain requirements if reproducible and quantitative results are to be obtained. These requirements apply to: sensitivity of balance and recorder system, speed of mechanisms, dimensions of solder bath, temperature control of solder bath, zero setting, response times, chart speed, and electrical and mechanical noise.

Testing Requirements

A complete specification for wettability may require that several points on the force-time curve exhibit particular values. The following requirements may be specified for component terminations to be assembled by a mass soldering process, if tested at 235°C:

(i) time for the initiation of wetting (A-t_o) less than 2 seconds if non-activated test flux is applied;

(ii) degree of wetting achieved more than 50% of the Reference Wetting Force after a specified time of 3s;

(iii) stability of wetting $= \dfrac{\text{force at C}}{\text{force at B}}$ exceeding 75%, after 5s.

> Note: This requirement is not valid in the case of materials provided with thick layers that can melt away.

If the traces are always taken with the same recorder setting, the evaluation is simplified. Use can then be made of a transparent auxiliary graph laid over the trace.

7.2.1.5   INTERPRETATION OF THE FORCE-TIME TRACES IN TERMS OF A TIME CONSTANT

The slope of the recorder trace often, but not always, shows a continuous change between the moment of maximum upward force and the moment of maximum downward force. It is worthwhile investigating whether a time constant can be attributed to the obtained curves.

It was shown [Jellison *et al*] that the logarithm of the reduced force values of

e trace (beginning at point A in Figure 7.6) plotted versus time in many cases hibits a constant slope. This means that in the expression:

$$\ln \frac{F_m - F_t}{F_m} = -\frac{t}{\tau} \text{ , in which}$$

F_t = force at time t
F_m = maximum force
t = time,
τ is a constant (= time constant).

In fact, it is not necessary here to use the zero reference of point A, as is dicated in Figure 7.10, where τ is obtained graphically by drawing the tangent the curve at any point.

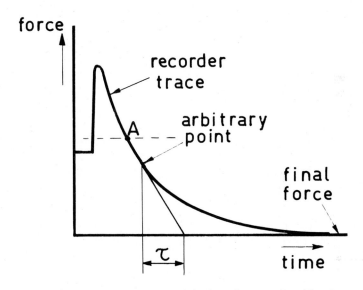

. **7.10** Determination of the time constant of the force-time trace by taking the tangent to the ce. With an ideal exponential curve the value of τ is independent of the position chosen on the curve.

On the other hand, this provides an excellent way to see if the assumed model is rrect. The evaluation of traces obtained in practice shows that many traces do ey the model, but also many traces do not, following from the observation that is not always constant.

Relatively small deviations from an ideal exponential curve may be treated by lculating a line of best fit [Allen]. Large deviations, however, make the validity the model questionable. Such large deviations are quite frequently observed on rmal specimens. The logarithmic evaluation is therefore unsuitable as a general ethod to be applied to all traces obtained in testing practice.

te: Even if it is possible to attribute a perfect response time to the relevant part of the curve, one st be aware that the single figure τ does not represent 'the' wettability; delay, for instance, is not en into account (see Figure 7.9, delayed wetting).

7.2.1.6   ONE FIGURE FOR WETTABILITY FROM THE WETTING BALANCE TRACE

It is normal to investigate whether the parts under test satisfy a number
requirements. If the method is used, however, for investigating coatings, fluxe
etc., it may be desired to obtain one single figure from the trace in order to I
able to rank the results [Schouten]. In such cases a combination of certain aspec
of the wetting curve may serve the purpose; the choice is more or less arbitra
and, depending on the specific purpose, many possibilities exist. For instance,
combination can be made of the time $(A - t_o)$, the wetting rate at point A and t
wetting achieved after 3 seconds (Figure 7.11).

The three values can be combined as follows:

$$t_w = \sqrt{\frac{t_1 \times t_2 \times RWF}{F_3}}$$, to give a quantity expressed in seconds.

The figure obtained in this way, as with other similar figures, contains le
information than the curve itself and should only be used for ranking purpose
For testing practice, the comparison of the curve with separate requiremen
remains the most satisfactory method.

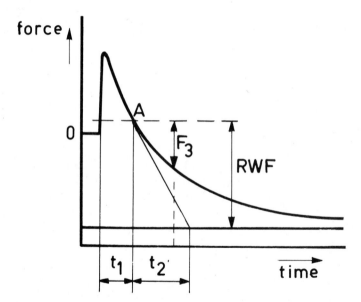

Fig. 7.11   One figure for the wettability can be obtained by combining some aspects of the force-tir
curve. t_1 = time for the initiation of wetting, t_2 = a time as a measure for the rate of wettir
F_3 = the force value reached after 3 seconds, RWF = Reference Wetting Force.

7.2.1.7   SCANNING MODE

In the standard mode of testing (discussed in 7.2.1.1 to 7.2.1.6) a rate c
immersion is chosen much higher than the wetting rate of the solder in order t
study the wettability of a particular part of the specimen. In this standard mod
the rate of immersion is about 20 mm/s, and could be much higher were it not fc

e consequent production of unwanted waves in the solder bath. In the standard ode the relevant part of the recorder trace of force versus time is obtained when e specimen is held stationary in the immersed position. The scanning mode is otally different: the rate of immersion and withdrawal is much lower than in the andard mode, in order to study the homogeneity of wettability of an extended egion of the surface of the specimen. The relevant part of the curve of force ersus time is obtained while the specimen is moving at a constant speed, which is the order of 1 mm/s.

Presentation of Results of the Scanning Mode

The traces shown in Figure 7.12 depict upward forces as positive. During the nmersion and withdrawal period, the buoyancy of the specimen changes radually [Hartmann, Becker]. A perfectly homogeneous specimen will produce raight lines parallel to the buoyancy lines: wetted specimens below the buoyancy ne, non-wetted above. The part of the curve t_o to B can (with necessary lterations) be compared with t_o to B in Figure 7.6.

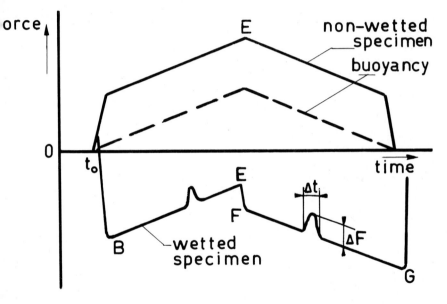

g. 7.12 Force-time traces of a wetting balance working in the scanning mode. The parts B-E and -G of the trace are relevant. Deviations from the straight line indicate bad spots on the specimen.

Points of Significance

(i) Time t_o is the time at which the solder surface and the specimen first make contact, as indicated by movement of the trace from the zero force line;

ii) point B is the beginning of the steady state during immersion, in which the wetting proceeds at a constant rate equal to the rate of immersion;

iii) point E is the end of the immersion period, where the direction of the bath movement is reversed;

   (iv) point F is the beginning of the steady state during withdrawal, in which the draining-off proceeds at a constant rate equal to the rate of withdrawal;

   (v) point G is the moment when the specimen loses contact with the solder bath.

Test Requirements

The homogeneity of the wettability is reflected in the interruptions of the partial traces B-E and F-G; the part F-G is particularly suitable for judgement. The requirements for homogeneity can be expressed in terms of the following parameters:

  (i) the number of bad spots on the specimen that can be detected from the recorder trace;

  (ii) the time intervals, Δt_i, of the interruptions in seconds being a measure of the extent of the detected bad spots;

 (iii) the force drops, ΔF_i, of the interruptions as a fraction of the Reference Wetting Force being a measure of the seriousness of the detected bad spots.

Note: The scanning mode has so far been used only for laboratory purposes, not for routine testing.

7.2.1.8   OTHER MODES

If an immersion rate is selected between very fast (20 mm/s) and very slow (1 mm/s), curves of force versus time are again obtained from which the wettability of the specimens can be assessed [Peth]. Every change of the dipping speed produces separate curves having their own peculiarities, making the interpretation of such curves difficult. In testing practice, it is extremely important to use one single immersion speed giving curves that can be easily compared and well understood in their quantitative evaluation. The standard mode with the high immersion speed conveniently satisfies these requirements.

7.2.1.9   THE TESTING OF VERY SMALL COMPONENTS

In the standard mode of testing the immersion depth is commonly 2 mm. During wetting the solder rises about 1 mm above the solder level, so that about 3 mm of the length of the termination comes in contact with the solder. This immersion procedure cannot be used with a very small component, simply because the aforementioned 3 mm length is not available on the component termination. For such components, like multilayer chip capacitors, the wetting balance can still be used appropriately provided the metallisation to be wetted is present around the entire periphery of the component termination. With the length of the component vertically, the test can be carried out with an immersion depth of almost zero (in fact 0,01 mm). Then the specimen, just touching the solder surface, will be wetted and the force can be recorded (Figure 7.13). Because the shape and heat transfer conditions are different from those of the standard mode, the trace of force versus time that is obtained must be evaluated in a different way. A large number of multilayer chip capacitors have been tested in this way, whilst the results were compared with soldering of these components in practice.

Related to the termination pads on chip components, satisfactory soldering is achieved if the following test requirements are fulfilled:

(i) time t_1 not exceeding 0,5s;
(ii) wetting force after 3s being more than 25% of that obtained on an optimally wetted reference specimen of identical shape.

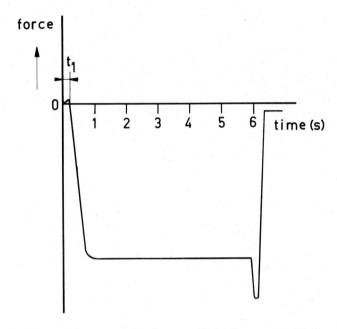

Fig. 7.13 Recorded trace of force versus time for a wettable small component. The immersion depth has been adjusted to 0,01 mm, so that there is scarcely any buoyancy off-setting of the trace.

The requirement for the force reading of chip components after 3 seconds is lower than that of component leads (see Chapter 7.2.1.4), expressing the fact that the wettability of the chip metallisation is poor compared with that of common leads. Moreover, the height of the metallisation may not be adequate for a sufficiently large solder rise. This lower requirement for the degree of wetting is acceptable because the geometry of the components and the capillary spaces between components and solder lands favour the formation of satisfactory joints.

Note: If the metallisation dissolves rapidly in the solder, this may become visible in the trace, being shown by a decreased force reading at the end of the testing period. To detect this it may be necessary to employ a longer immersion time than usual.

7.2.2 Globule Method

This is the longest established method, originally developed at Philips, Eindhoven, to measure the wetting times of component leads having circular cross-section [ten Duis]. It has since been extended to rectangular cross-sections and to plated holes [Becker]. As a technique for which commercial machines are available, it has been standardised internationally by IEC [Spec. Ref. 1].

Figure 7.14 illustrates a globule test machine.

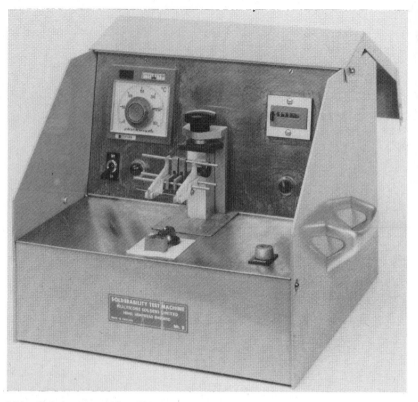

Fig. 7.14 Globule test machine. The wire to be tested is clamped and, by pushing a button, lowered into testing position while activating a clock. The clock is stopped by releasing the butt⋅ when wetting is obtained.

7.2.2.1 PRINCIPLE

The method makes use of a droplet or globule of molten solder positioned ⊂ an iron pin in a heated block (Figure 7.15a). A fluxed test wire is lower⋅ horizontally into the solder globule, bisecting it (Figure 7.15b). The globu⋅ remains bisected as long as the wire is not wetted. When the wetting gradual⋅ increases, the two parts of the globule meet and the closure of the globule th⋅ proceeds abruptly; this is easily recognisable (Figure 7.15c). The end situation ⋅ the test is shown in Figure 7.16, with the clamping device and test wire (a resist⋅ termination) in the lowermost position and with the globule closed around t⋅ wire. The time between the moment of bisecting and of closing of the globul⋅ often called the globule time, is the measured wetting time at the given te⋅ temperature. The precise start of the measuring period depends on t⋅ construction of the machine. It is the moment at which the wire makes conta⋅ either with the apex of the globule or with the iron pin. The time difference ⋅ about 0,2s is usually not considered. The contact angle between the halves of t⋅ globule and the wire decreases during the testing period. The rejoining of t⋅ solder around the test wire will occur when the contact angle, θ, reaches abou⋅ 90°. This can be understood considering that there is no room for two halves ⋅ the globule against the wire when θ is considerably smaller. The precise value ⋅

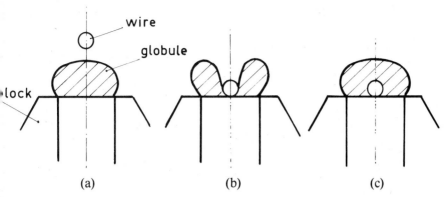

Fig. 7.15   Three positions of a globule solderability test: (a) just before the commencement of the testing period; (b) during the measuring period; (c) at or after the end of the measuring period.

Fig. 7.16   Detail of globule block (see Fig. 7.14). For clarity, in the photograph a globule has been selected of 200 mg instead of 125 mg.

The angle, θ, at which the globule will close depends on the wire diameter and the globule size (see also Figure 7.17) [*cf.* Roberts].

The wire is cold just before the test and is heated during the test time. The thermal response of the globule block is therefore very important, as it influences the measuring results. The precise dimensions and materials of the block, and thus its thermal capacity, are in consequence prescribed in the IEC Standard mentioned earlier.

The thermal demand of the wire influences the globule times: thick wires give longer times than thin wires. (Figure 5.2 shows results obtained with copper wires of two diameters). This thermal effect can be partly compensated for if globule of different volumes are applied.

Finally, it is observed that a bisected globule is unstable: the larger part will grow at the expense of the smaller part if a gap exists below the wire connecting both parts of the globule. Within the usual test times this tendency does not affect the results.

7.2.2.2 PELLET MASS

A heavier pellet, having a larger volume, will produce shorter soldering time for two reasons:

(i) more heat capacity of the globule;
(ii) more solder available to cover the wire.

Above a certain amount of solder on the pin of the globule block, even an unsolderable wire will be covered with solder. Figure 7.17 shows the diameter of an unsolderable wire which is just covered by a globule as a function of the globule mass. This curve does not pass through the origin of the graph.

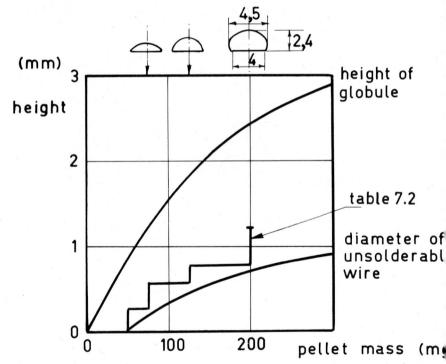

Fig. 7.17 Effect of pellet mass of a globule on the height of the molten globule and on the diameter of a non-solderable wire around which the globule will just close. Also three shapes of globules are shown for pellets of three masses. Diameter of the iron pin is 4 mm.

The Figure also shows the height of the globule in undisturbed condition versus its mass. For testing practice, specific pellet masses are standardised [Spec. Ref. 1] as given in Table 7.2, and Figure 7.17.

Table 7.2

Pellet Masses

Wire Diameter (mm)	Pellet Mass (mg)
0,25	50
0,25-0,54	75
0,55-0,74	125
0,75-1,2	200

7.2.2.3   TEST TEMPERATURE

A standard globule temperature of 235°C is used [Spec. Ref. 1]. The temperature of the globule can easily be measured with a very thin coaxial thermocouple placed in the globule, a couple with an outer diameter of, for instance, 250 μm being suitable.

The thermocouple mounted in the globule apparatus measures the temperature of the globule block, and the output of the couple is fed to the control unit of the heater element. The temperature measured, however, is not the precise temperature of the globule, as the thermocouple is placed at some distance from it. Moreover, delay times exist between the moment of temperature change of the top of the globule block, the reaction of the control unit and the arrival of additional heat at the globule.

Figure 7.18 shows the temperature of a globule during a warming-up period, followed by a cooling period on the Multicore Machine MK III. When the globule

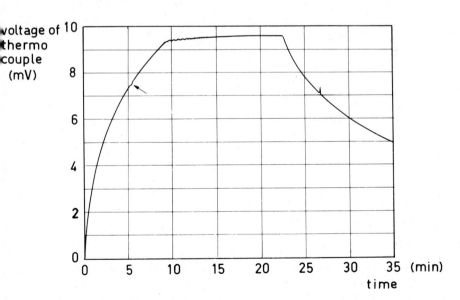

Fig. 7.18   Curve of temperature versus time of a globule on a globule block. Solderability tests are possible about 15 minutes after switching on. The temperature variations after 15 minutes are well within the required limits. (The couple was brought into position during a preceding run.)

reaches 230°C, the control unit starts switching. It is a further 10 minutes or s
before the 'final' globule temperature is reached. From then on, the variations i
the globule temperature caused by the switching remain within ±1°C. During th
heating period, before the switching starts, the power consumption is about 9
Watts. After switching has begun, the lengths of the off/on periods are 5/2.
seconds. Gradually this ratio changes until in the stationary state a ratio o
7,5/10,5 is obtained (that is 42% off). This implies a power consumption o
about 50 Watts. It is interesting to note the discontinuities in the heating an
cooling parts of the curve caused by the melting and the solidification of th
globule. In the heating curve, the 'point' (arrow) is at 183°C, whilst due t
undercooling the discontinuity in the cooling curve is some degrees lower.

The reaction time between the moment of heat demand and the switching 'on
of the element is about 3 seconds, which is longer than most testing times. In thi
respect, it should be mentioned that an intended coordination between th
switching state of the control unit and the beginning of the globule test has neve
been practised.

The variations in the globule temperature, as visible for instance in Figure 7.18
have of course the same period as the off-on switchings of the heating element
They are, however, out of phase: the element switches 'on' at about the momen
the temperature of the globule is at its maximum. This is further evidence of th
fact that a 'thermal delay' exists in the apparatus.

7.2.2.4   THERMAL RESPONSE OF THE GLOBULE BLOCK

Not only is the temperature of the globule important, but also the quantity o
heat which can be produced during the few seconds of the test. As the hea
content of the globule is insufficient for the test, the thermal response of th
block on which the globule is positioned plays an important role. All parameter
of the globule block that influence its thermal behaviour will therefore als
influence the results of the solderability tests.

Figure 7.19 shows the temperature increase of a copper wire measured whil
the wire was resting in the globule. The wire was provided with a thermocoupl
fitting in an axial hole in the wire, which had been machined by spark erosion, th
hole diameter being about 280 μm (see sketch in Figure 7.19). The temperatur
differences between the outer surface of the wire and the centre of the wire ar
very small and are consequently ignored.

The wire was placed on the globule block with the tip of the thermocoupl
(inside the wire) in the centre of the 200 mg globule and a temperature-time trac
was recorded. Three more traces were recorded in which the tip was 5, 10 an
15 mm from the centre of the globule. From preliminary tests, it became clea
that wires with a low level of wettability give slower heating, and therefore th
wires were carefully pretinned after which the globule times were about 1 second.

In the line '0 mm' an irregularity is present: after the closure of the globule a
extra increase in temperature is noticed, resulting from the increased hea
contact. At a distance from the globule, this effect is no longer visible. After 1
seconds a more or less stable situation is reached, while heat is still flowing int
the wire. The temperature gradient in the wire at that time is about 30°C/10 mr
and thus the heat flow is:

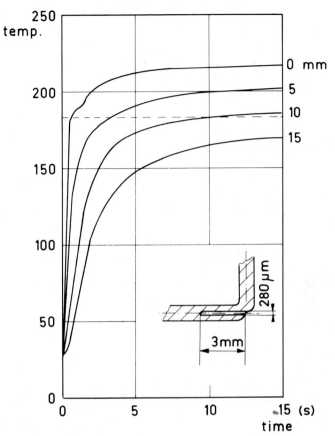

Fig. 7.19　The temperature-time curves of a copper wire positioned in the globule. The parameters beside the curves are the distances of the measuring point from the centre of the globule (4 mm diameter pin). Wire diameter is 1 mm.

$$Q = \lambda A \frac{\Delta T}{\Delta l} \text{ , in which}$$

T = temperature,
λ = heat conductivity,
A = area of cross-section of wire,
l = length,

$$Q = 370 \times \pi \times (0{,}5 \times 10^{-3})^2 \times \frac{30}{10 \times 10^{-3}} = 0{,}87 \text{ Watt.}$$

Twice this value must be transferred from the globule block via the globule into the wire. The areas of the iron pin in the block and the part of the wire immersed in the solder globule are about equal: $4\pi \times 10^{-6} \text{ m}^2$. The temperature of the wire after 15 seconds is approximately 217°C in the centre of the globule. The heat transfer from the block (assumed to be at 235°C) to the wire is given by:

Q = $\alpha A \Delta T$, in which
T = temperature,
α = overall heat transfer coefficient,
A = area through which heat is transferred.
$2 \times 0{,}87 = \alpha \times 2^2 \times \pi \times 10^{-6} \times (235\text{-}217)$
hence $\alpha = 7700$ W/m²K.

This is quite a high value considering that two interfaces (block-solder-wire) are involved.

Tests for the Globule Block

The first test is based on the method just described, in which a value for α is in fact measured.

A simpler method is based on the melting rate of solder wire. In this test a small glass pipe is clamped vertically above the iron pin of the globule block with its end about 5 mm from the pin. A length of solid solder wire of tin60-lead40 alloy with a diameter of 1,2 mm is straightened by rolling it between two flat planes. A piece of this straightened wire of 60 mm length is fed through the glass-pipe until it contacts the globule and thus starts melting. At this moment the time measurement begins. While subsequently being fed by gravity, a length of 50 mm of this wire (about 0,5 grams) needs about 12 seconds to melt. The last 10 mm of the wire are not considered because of the risk of jamming.

With this amount of solder fed into a 200 mg globule, all the solder usually remains on the block and does not drip off. The method involving the glass pipe has the considerable advantage that the test is very easy to perform.

7.2.2.5   GLOBULE METHOD FOR TESTING PLATED HOLES

The globule method has been extended for the testing of plated holes [Brit. Pat 1414792 (1972), Anon. Ref. 1, Becker]. To conduct a test, the complete board under test is placed in position with a specific hole above the globule (Figure 7.20).

Subsequently, the globule is brought into contact with the lower side of the plated hole. The time is measured which is needed to fill the hole up to the topside of the board. Before the solder cools and solidifies, the hole can be emptied with a sucking device so that the board need not be discarded but can still be used later on in production.

As can be seen in Figure 7.20, the globule is pressed between the board and the globule block, the clearance normally being 0,9 mm (see Figure 7.21).

The liquid pressure in the globule is given by:

$$P = \gamma \left(\frac{1}{R_1} + \frac{1}{R_2} \right) \cong \frac{\gamma}{R_1}$$

The hole in the board is just filled with solder to the top if:

$$- \frac{2\gamma \cos \theta}{r} + g \varrho d \cong \frac{\gamma}{R_1}$$

Taking $r = 0{,}5$ mm and $d = 1{,}6$ mm gives $\theta = 120°$. This implies that the globule

ethod in fact tests whether the advancing wetting angle in the hole is less than about 120°.

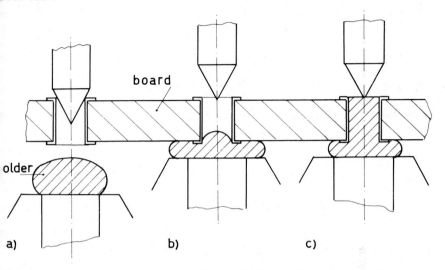

Fig. 7.20 Three stages of a test for plated holes: (a) The board is brought into position using the needle; (b) Contact with the solder; (c) End of test when the solder contacts the needle.

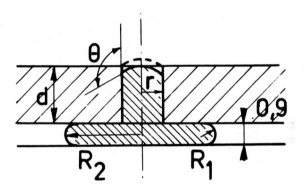

Fig. 7.21 Geometry of the plated hole filled with solder.

From Figure 7.21 it is also clear that some uncertainty exists about what is meant by 'filling of the hole to the top'. The use of the contact needle at the level of the top face of the board plating clears this ambiguity. The precise test requirements that should be applied are not discussed here.

.2.2.6   GLOBULE METHOD FOR NON-CIRCULAR SECTIONS

On the globule test apparatus specimens with a non-circular cross-section can also be measured. This may be important for soldering tags and flat component leads, in particular IC pins. For small and closely spaced leads, such as those on dual in-line packages, the usual dimensions of the globule block are too large to allow for the measurements; an adapted globule block and a smaller globule are then needed [Becker]. In addition, special holding devices must be used for these specimens.

The edges of the cross-section around which the solder must flow may be rounded or sharp; even burrs from the punching operation may be present. The specimens should be positioned flat on the globule block, with the burrs down. Edge conditions influence the spread of the solder around the specimen, possibly affecting the reproducibility of the test.

In soldering by means of wave or drag machines the leads are soldered in the direction parallel to their longitudinal axis. Certainly for those applications the wettability of the non-circular sections is preferably assessed with a wetting balance, in which the wetting also proceeds lengthwise.

7.2.2.7 THE USE OF A TIMING NEEDLE

The globule time is recorded by a timing clock, which begins to operate at about the moment when the globule block and the test specimen make contact. The clock is stopped, either by the operator or automatically, when the solder reaches a specific position. The contact needle can be placed in the centre of the hole, as in Figure 7.20, or the needle can be adjusted a small distance above the solder land.

For wires, the needle is positioned above the wire specimen. The needle recording may produce erroneous results in three ways:

(i) Flux residues remaining on the needle may prevent the clock from stopping or may cause the clock to stop too late (good cleaning is difficult);
(ii) splashes of solder sometimes stop the timing at zero or nearly zero time;
(iii) solder flows round one side of the wire further than the other and may touch the needle before it has united with the other part of the globule.

The timing needle of the 'Sincotron' testing machine has a special feature. As soon as the solder makes contact with the needle the clock stops and the spring loaded needle is released from its measuring position. The contact time of the needle with solder and flux is therefore very short and the contamination of the needle point will be limited.

7.2.3 Rotary Dip Method

This method is intended for testing the wettability of flat surfaces, such as printed board materials. It was developed at the International Tin Research Institute [Thwaites] and the apparatus commercially available is called the TRI-Moore* tester (Figure 7.22). The method has been standardised in IEC 68-2-20 [Spec. Ref. 1] and by IPC [Spec. Ref. 8].

7.2.3.1 PRINCIPLE

The specimen under test follows a circular path about a horizontal axis over a bath of molten solder (Figure 7.23). The time of contact between the specimen and the solder bath can be varied in three ways: by changing the length of the

---

*Moore is the name of the designers.

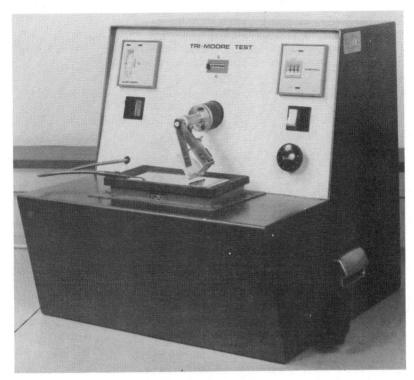

Fig. 7.22 Rotary dip test apparatus. The specimen is conveyed across the solder bath; the contact time is recorded by a timer.

Fig. 7.23 Detail of rotary dip apparatus, clarifying the principle of the method. The specimen rotates around the axis and just makes contact with the solder in its movement from right to left.

arm, by changing the speed of rotation or by interrupting the rotating movement while the specimen is in contact with the bath.

After the dipping treatment the specimen is inspected visually to assess its wettability. The nominal time of contact is measured with a timing needle that follows the same circular path as the specimen and the tip of which is at the same radius as the centre of the lower face of the specimen. The needle is not wetted by the solder and touches the solder at a place not disturbed by the specimen.

Contact Angle θ in Plated Holes

Below the underside of the specimen at a distance i below the solder surface, the liquid pressure is $\varrho g i$ (ϱ and g being the density of the solder and the acceleration of gravity). If the solder penetrates the hole (radius r) just to the topside of the board (thickness d), the liquid pressure is $\varrho g(i-d)$. This pressure equals the pressure caused by the surface tension, γ, so that:

$$\varrho g(i\text{-}d) = \frac{-2\gamma \cos \theta}{r}$$

For the contact angle $\theta = 90°$ the trivial result $i = d$ can be obtained. For $i = 0$, when the board is just touching the solder surface, and with $d = 1,6$ and $r = 0,5$ mm, the holes are filled to the top when $\theta < 85°$. The rotary dip test thus measures whether the contact angle in the holes is less than about $90°$.

7.2.3.2   DWELL-TIME VARIATIONS

As the radius of rotation differs from the ends to the middle of the specimen, the dwell-time varies over the specimen, the ends having longer dwell-times than the middle. Apart from the length of the specimen, the dwell-time depends on the depth of immersion, the length (radius) of the rotating arm and in particular on the surface condition of the specimen.

As an example, consider the region of the specimen near the leading edge, assuming that at the moment of entry into the solder non-wetting exists, whilst at the exit from the solder full wetting is achieved. Hence, at entry the solder is depressed and on exit the solder is lifted, as shown in Figures 7.24a and b. The shape of the solder meniscus while depressed or lifted is that of the elastica, as discussed in Chapter 2.2.1.

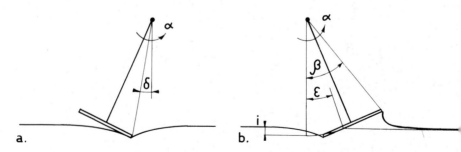

Fig. 7.24 Disturbance of the liquid solder surface by interaction with the specimen. The specimen moves from left to right. In b the specimen is assumed to be completely wetted.

Figure 7.24 shows that the total arc traversed by the region near the leading dge is $\delta + \beta$, whilst the angle traversed by the timing needle is 2ε. The relative ontact times (in this example $\frac{\delta + \beta}{2\varepsilon}$) for a variety of conditions are given in igure 7.25 (see Appendix to this Section).

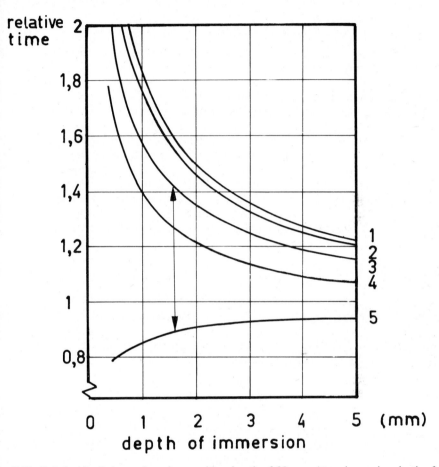

ig. 7.25 Relative dwell times of specimens with a length of 25 mm. At an immersion depth of 1,6 mm, the uncertainty of dwell time is considerable, depending on wetting conditions.

curve 1: tail of specimen, contact angle at exit 0°;
curve 2: head of specimen, contact angle at exit 0°;
curve 3: middle of specimen, contact angle at exit 0°;
curve 4: middle of specimen, contact angle at exit 90°;
curve 5: middle of specimen, contact angle at exit 180°;
all curves: contact angle at entrance 180°.

From Figure 7.25 it is evident that the deviation from the needle time can be onsiderable. For the middle part of the specimen (curves 3-4-5), at an immersion epth of 1,6 mm, a non-wetting specimen has a contact time of about 0,9 times ie needle time, whereas a specimen on which θ goes from 180° to 0° during ipping the contact time will be about 1,4 times the needle time. Even this is not the maximum time which can occur. If, also at entry, the contact angle $\theta = 0°$ there will be a relative contact time of 1,93 (not indicated in the Figure). Th variation in the real contact times implies that bad boards are tested at shorte contact times than good boards, with the result that the discrimination i increased. This may be acceptable (or sometimes even attractive) in go/no g tests, but it makes quantitative comparison with other test methods difficult.

Improvement of the Testing Procedure

To minimise the uncertainty in establishing the contact time, two measures ar obvious [Klein Wassink]:

(i) choosing a higher depth of immersion;
(ii) interrupting the circular movement of the specimen.

At an immersion depth of more than 3 mm (board thickness of 1 mm), specia precautions must be taken to prevent the solder from flooding the topside of th board. Such precautions are relatively easy to achieve. Keeping the specime stationary for a certain period of time while it is in contact with the solder i explicitly prohibited in some standardised test procedures [Spec. Ref. 1 and 8] The equipment that is commercially available in fact has a time delay switc which permits the specimen to stop on its circular path, but this stopping devic does not work satisfactorily.

7.2.3.3 TESTING PROCEDURE

Test procedure implies specimen preparation, application of flux, predrying o flux, mounting of specimen, *etc.* By selecting increments of the contact time (needle times), the contact time can be found in which a definite wetting i achieved according to specified requirements. In go/no go tests a fixed needl time is used, for instance 2 seconds.

7.2.3.4 DISTRIBUTION OF WETTABILITY FIGURES OF PLATED HOLES

This distribution can be found by measuring the holes separately with th globule tester for plated holes, described in Section 7.2.2.5. The distribution ca also be found using the rotary dip method if specimens of the batch to be teste are brought into contact with the solder for different time periods, each on shorter than the time needed to fill all the holes. After each pass over the solde the fraction of holes filled with solder is counted and thus the relation betwee the fraction of holes filled and the dwell time is obtained.

The distribution, obtained with the globule method and the rotary dip metho differ considerably because these methods employ different heat transfer, tim measurement, liquid pressure and other parameters.

Figure 7.26 contains results of rotary dip measurements from 15 specimens cu from the same board, each specimen having 88 holes. The circles represen globule measurements on a sixteenth specimen. Despite the much greater numbe of holes tested by the rotary dip method, the spread of results is larger, becaus each point is obtained by an individual measurement, whilst for the globul method the times for the separate holes have been ranked (see Section 7.5) Figure 7.26 shows that the average wetting time (50% value) for both methods i

bout the same, but that the rotary dip method has higher time values for the
igher rank measurements.

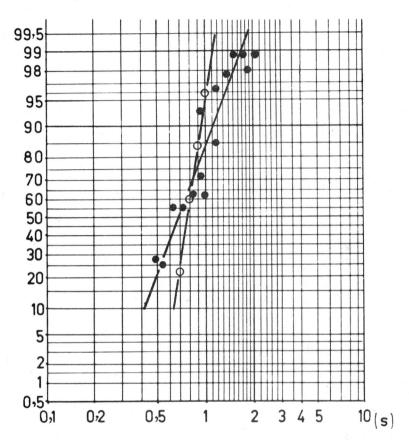

g. 7.26 Cumulative plot of globule measurements (○) and rotary dip measurements (●) on aged
plated holes. The two methods give different distribution curves.

.2.3.5 APPENDIX

Calculation of Relative Dwell times in the Rotary Dip Method

In the calculation the vertical displacement of the spot under observation on the specimen, together
with the angle of elevation of the specimen, is compared with the profile curve of the elastica. From
his are obtained the relative angles of rotation during which the specimen is in contact with the
older.
Angles of rotation, α, are measured with respect to the vertical.

R = radius of rotation
i = depth of immersion
L = length of the specimen
ϕ = angle of elevation of the meniscus

The vertical displacement of the specimen is measured from the undisturbed solder surface;

in the middle $: y = R(1 - \cos \alpha) - i$ (1)

at the lowest edge $: y = R(1 - \cos \alpha) - i - \dfrac{L}{2} \sin \alpha$ (2)

at the highest edge $: y = R(1 - \cos \alpha) - i + \dfrac{L}{2} \sin \alpha$ (3)

The vertical displacement of the elastica is:

$$y = 4{,}4 \, \sin\frac{\phi}{2}(\text{mm})$$ (4)

The relations between α and ϕ are

for $\theta = 0°$ (solder lifted) $: \alpha + \phi = 180°$
$\theta = 90°$ (solder lifted) $: \alpha + \phi = \ 90°$
$\theta = 180°$ (solder depressed) $: \alpha + \phi = \ \ 0°$

The solution of the problem is found if y and α satisfy Equations (1), (2) or (3) together with Equation (4) for the appropriate value of $\alpha + \phi$.

7.2.4 Meniscus Rise Method

When a piece of wire is dipped vertically into molten solder, the meniscus will climb up if the wire surface is wetted. In the meniscus rise method this solder rise is measured at a predetermined time after the moment of dipping while the specimen is held stationary in the solder. The measuring apparatus is called a meniscometer (Figure 7.27). From the height of the solder rise against a wire it is possible to derive the contact angle, θ, for instance using the graphs of Figure 2.10 and assuming a value for the surface tension γ.

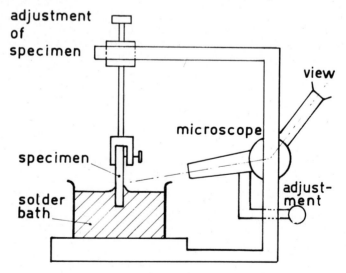

Fig. 7.27 Meniscometer. The rise of the solder against the specimen is measured using a microscope

The relationship between the height of the solder rise, y, and the contact angle, θ, for non-circular shapes is complicated; y varies along the periphery of the specimen. This relation can be given in graphs, for instance obtained experimentally.

The value of θ obtained after a specified time is a certain measure of the wettability of the specimen. The following categories of soldering quality, determined after a dipping time of 4 seconds, have been proposed [Mayhew *et al*]:

$$0° < \theta < 10° \text{ perfect}$$
$$10° < \theta < 20° \text{ excellent}$$
$$20° < \theta < 30° \text{ very good}$$
$$30° < \theta < 40° \text{ good}$$
$$40° < \theta < 55° \text{ adequate}$$
$$55° < \theta < 70° \text{ poor}$$
$$70° < \theta \qquad \text{ very poor}$$

The same classification (combining $0 < \theta \leqslant 30°$ to very good) is also used after a dipping time of 3 seconds [Spec. Ref. 18].

These contact angles are at or close to the contact angle at wetting equilibrium, and hence are comparable to the degree of wetting as found in the wetting balance.

For practical soldering, the time of 3 or 4 seconds is too long and should be nearer 1 second. In this case, however, use of the meniscometer is difficult, because of the reaction time of the operator and also because the measurement of θ becomes inaccurate at larger θ values.

In this connection the main test criteria of other testing methods are summarised for comparison as follows:

wetting balance $-$ time at which $\theta = 90°$;
globule method for wire $-$ time at which $\theta = $ about $90°$;
globule method for plated holes $-$ time at which $\theta = $ about $120°$;
rotary dip method for plated holes $-$ time at which $\theta = $ about $90°$.

These testing conditions being such that the solder is still spreading at the moment of measurement, the contact angles mentioned are advancing angles, which are always somewhat larger than the static angles.

Any classification of solderability based on meniscometry does not provide a sharp dividing line between 'pass' and 'don't pass' in practice. Though a certain angle can be selected (*e.g.*, $55°$), it remains a rather arbitrary choice, based on the individual's appreciation of the contact angle in a more or less equilibrium situation.

The meniscometer is occasionally used along with the wetting balance, thus providing a mutual reference because both the rise of the solder and the force on the specimen are a function of the surface tension, γ, and the wetting angle, θ [Barranger, Flot *et al*]. Though such a combination of testing methods is undoubtedly of theoretical interest, it is not necessary for solderability testing in practice.

7.2.5   Area-of-Spread Method

This method is frequently used in the laboratory, as well as in production in order to obtain an easy and quick impression of the wettability of the base metal by the solder alloy concerned. The technique is also often applied for the determination of flux efficacy using a known base metal/solder combination, for instance brass and tin60 – lead40 alloy. A certain amount of solder alloy is melted on a base metal plate of about 25×25 mm^2 in the presence of flux, and the spreading of the solder is assessed qualitatively or quantitatively [Thwaites]. The plate is usually heated by lowering it onto a solder bath. A base-metal strip heated by passage of an electric current may also be used [Bailey *et al*].

For base metal/solder combinations that wet very easily the test method gives only qualitative information, as the area of spread is then sensitive to the specific experimental conditions. For instance, an equilibrium state of wetting is not always achieved, because, apart from real wetting, surface migration may play a part; the test duration is then a very important parameter.

If the wetting intrinsically is not so good, the solder will assume the shape of a spherical cap, the dimensions of which can be measured precisely. In certain cases, the area-of-spread method is the only realistic possibility for a quantitative assessment of wettability. This is for instance true with small soldering lands on thick film circuits.

The result of the spread test is often expressed as a spread factor, S, [Pessel]. Assuming D to be the diameter of a hypothetical sphere made of the amount of solder under test, and h the measured height of the solder droplet after spreading, the spread factor, S, is obtained thus:

$$S = \frac{D-h}{D} \times 100\%.$$

This spread factor, S, is related to the contact angle, θ, as discussed in Chapter 2.4.1 (Figure 2.32).

The measurement of h introduces an irreproducibility problem: h changes during solidification and a shrinkage hole or depression may develop precisely at the place to be measured. It is more accurate to measure the diameter of the base area of the droplet under a microscope, as the diameter will not change during solidification of the solder. Then the value of θ can be calculated or obtained graphically. The relationship between θ and the diameter of the base area of 3, 4, 5 and 6 mg pellet masses is shown in Figure 2.31.

Dip Variant

A variant of the area-of-spread test is a method involving a specially shaped specimen made of plate material [Krell]. The specimen is provided with a bulge as in an Erichsen deep draw test. In the wettability test, the bulged specimen is lowered horizontally, onto a solder bath with the bulge downwards, until it just makes contact with the solder surface. Upon wetting, the solder climbs up to the plate after which the area of spread can be determined.

The dip variant method may be used for comparing different fluxes, as it provides information on two aspects of the flux under test:

(i) the area of spread is related to the capability of the flux to clean the surfaces at the beginning of the wetting process;
(ii) the height of the drop of solder hanging in the bulge after removal of the specimen from the bath is related to the protective capability of the flux during and at the end of the wetting process (see Chapter 5.1.3). With a good flux small drop heights are produced, but in bad cases long sharp spikes of solder remain (Figure 7.28).

The correct procedures and the requirements for these tests of the flux have not yet been worked out quantitatively. Suitable dimensions of the specimens are: plate 50×50 mm², thickness 0,25 mm; diameter of bulge in the plate 35 mm, depth of bulge 8 mm.

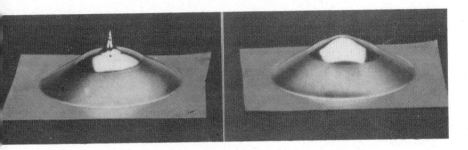

Fig. 7.28   Specimens used in a dipping experiment, shown inverted. The bulges were each provided with a flux and were predried as usual before dipping. Dipping speed 2,5 mm/s; speed of withdrawal 25 mm/s; immersion depth 0,1 mm; dwell time 2 s; solder temperature 250°C. Left: simple chloride activated rosin flux, *viz.* the activated IEC test flux (see Chapter 5.5.3). Right: a commercial rosin based flux used in soldering machines, *viz.* Fry's R8f. (By courtesy of J. de Lignie, Eindhoven.)

7.2.6   Edge Dip Method

This is the simplest of all wettability tests to perform. The specimen is partly dipped vertically and edgewise into molten solder and then withdrawn, after which the quality of the coating is assessed visually. The difficulty of the test lies in this assessment.

The dipping can in principle be done by hand, but an automatic dipping device affords more control of dipping conditions.

Figure 7.29 illustrates a versatile apparatus that serves the purpose well.

The edge dip method makes it possible to measure the dipping speed limit [Lenz *et al*, Fornara *et al*]. This is the maximum immersion rate at which complete wetting with molten solder is achieved. An apparatus to measure this 'critical immersion rate' must be adjustable between about 0,5 mm/s and 40 mm/s. The test is intended for strip or sheet made of copper or its alloys.

Fig. 7.29 Dipping apparatus, allowing independent adjustment of solder bath temperature (4), speed of immersion (3), duration of immersion (5), and speed of withdrawal (6). Solder bath (1) and control cabinet (2) can be installed separately. (By courtesy of J. Holst, Eindhoven.)

A simple but effective apparatus for dip testing is depicted in Figure 7.30, drawing which is present in many US Standard Documents [for instance, see Spec. Ref. 8 and 12].

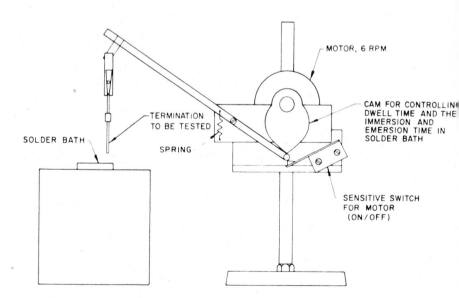

Fig. 7.30 Simple apparatus for dip testing applying testing conditions that can only be varied with difficulty (cf Figure 7.29).

Dewetting

The edge dip method is perfectly appropriate for testing the occurrence of permanent wetting or dewetting. The test time is usually chosen as 5±1 seconds at a temperature of 260±5°C; the speed of immersion and withdrawal is 25±2,5 mm/s [Test Ta Method 1, Spec. Ref. 1]. The specimen should be allowed to cool in air after withdrawal, without forced ventilation, because the development of dewetting takes some time.

7.3   THERMAL DEMAND

In the soldering process the joints must be formed within a few seconds. Dwell times of 2 to 4 seconds (after preheating to 80°C) are common, and within these short times the terminations of the components to be soldered must reach a sufficiently high temperature (say > 200°C). The thermal properties of the components and printed boards depend on their design.

7.3.1   Concepts

'Thermal demand' is a property of the components to be soldered, indicating the effort required to heat the terminations to the desired temperature.
Linked with this are three other concepts:

(i)   thermal soldering time;
(ii) soldering distance;
(iii) specific soldering distance.

'Thermal soldering time' is the time required to establish wetting under ideal surface conditions, for instance with freshly pretinned surfaces. It largely depends on what specific part of the termination is being considered. For instance, for a component with wire terminations the thermal soldering time depends on the distance from the body: at the end of relatively long terminations short thermal soldering times are found; close to the component body longer soldering times are found.
'Soldering distance' equals the length of the component termination between the point at which the termination exits from the component body and the point at which the termination intersects the solder surface, ignoring positive or negative meniscus (Figure 7.31).

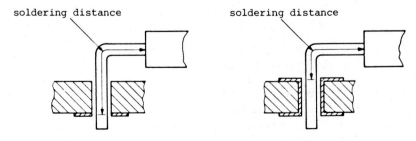

Fig. 7.31   The 'soldering distance' shown for two cases: a single-sided board (left) and a double-sided board with plated hole (right).

A soldering distance associated with a thermal soldering time of 2 seconds (in test under specified conditions) is called the 'specific soldering distance' and, such, is a property of the component. From this specific soldering distance derived the minimum soldering distance to be chosen in production, and hen the method of mounting of components, depending on the shape of th assembled board.

In solderability tests the thermal demand may influence the test results. T avoid these influences the tests should be carried out beyond a minimum distanc from the component body. This minimum distance, w, must be greater than th specific soldering distance, s,

$$w = s + 8(\lambda_t/\lambda_{Cu}) \sqrt{(A/\pi)}$$

where A is the cross-sectional area of the termination, λ_t is the therma conductivity of the material of the termination and λ_{Cu} is the thermal conductivi of copper. If λ_t is not known, it can be assumed to be equal to that of copper. I the case of circular sections, the formula means that the soldering distance in wettability test shall be at least s plus four extra diameters.

The distance w is in most cases less than 10 mm, and therefore, if wettabilit time measurements are made more than 10 mm from the component body thermal demand would usually have a negligible influence on the result. At an point closer to the component body than the distance w, the wettability can on be assessed by first detaching the termination from the body. This provide information regarding the surface quality at that point of the termination, but offers no assurance that the component can be soldered at that point, either i testing or in production.

7.3.2 Determination of Specific Soldering Distance

The specific soldering distance of components is measured by observing th thermal soldering time as a function of the soldering distance, using th stationary mode of the wetting balance. To ensure that the heat input conditio are constant, the immersion depth must be the same for all tests. The variation i soldering distance is obtained by taking a number of components and cuttir their terminations to leave different lengths attached to the component bodies

After cutting to the required range of lengths, the terminations are thorough pretinned by immersion, first in activated flux and then in molten solder, an allowed to cool. Their soldering time is then measured and plotted as a functic of the soldering distance (= termination length minus immersion depth), and th specific soldering distance determined from the graph.

In this measurement a situation is sought in which the thermal demand limi the soldering time. In such situations, irregularities in wetting are often observe for instance a stepwise progress as shown in Figure 7.32. The soldering time mu not be read from the recorder trace itself but from its higher envelope curve.

Information on the required mounting distance can also be obtained from test board provided with components at various mounting distances. Howeve the assessment is laborious. At a large mounting distance, the joints at the topsi of the board are visible, but then no problems are envisaged. At a small mounting distance, the joints are masked by the component bodies and sectio must be made to assess the result (Figure 7.33).

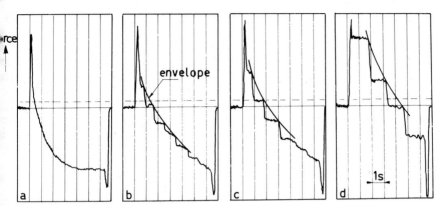

. 7.32 Measurement of thermal demand. The recorder traces a to d are derived from four ~asurements carried out on an electrolytic capacitor, case size 6 (having soldered copper terminations with a diameter of 0,8 mm, anode side), with different termination lengths.

ce a: termination length 7 mm, thermal soldering time 0,4 s;
ce b: termination length 6 mm, thermal soldering time 1,5 s;
ce c: termination length 5 mm, thermal soldering time 1,8 s;
ce d: termination length 4 mm, thermal soldering time 4,2 s.

. 7.33 Test boards with 5 groups of electrolytic capacitors, mounted on strips of different cknesses to obtain a varying soldering distance. The components were held in position during dering by 5 plates on top, which have been removed before making the photograph. Length of the board is 160 mm.

If only the wettability of component leads must be assessed, without interference of thermal mand of the component, the following simplified procedure can be applied to determine the nimum distance from the body which should be kept free in the test: (i) pretin leads of components be tested; (ii) cut one lead and record its wetting balance trace; (iii) measure leads which are still nnected to the component body with decreasing lead lengths until a definite deviation from the first ce is observed. The minimum length at which the thermal demand of the component no longer ays a role is then known.

7.4 RESISTANCE TO SOLDERING HEAT

During the soldering process the terminations of the components must reach high temperature in order to be wetted. The precise temperature that the body of the components will reach depends on the specific situation. The temperature of the component body may become the same as that of the termination when soldering occurs slowly in a near-equilibrium process, or lower when soldering performed quickly in an excess heating method.

In some cases, the body may even become hotter than the termination, for instance when heating by radiation. The design of the component also exerts major influence, as would be expected.

Figure 7.34 shows the effect of two wave-soldering operations on the cumulative capacitance distribution of a particular polystyrene film capacitor mounted in the usual way on a printed board, revealing that capacitance change strongly depends on the actual soldering operation applied.

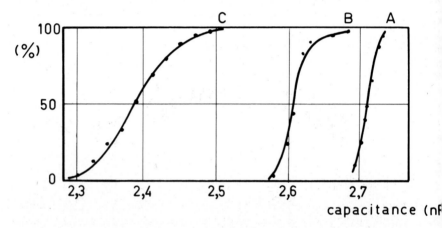

Fig. 7.34 Effect of two wave-soldering operations on the cumulative distribution of capacitance values of a certain capacitor. Curve A is before soldering (all Cs within ± 1%), curve B is for seconds at 260°C, curve C for 5 seconds at 235°C.

It has been shown (see Chapter 3) that, by varying the lengths of component leads, a satisfactory match can often be obtained between the temperature reached at the soldering position and inside the component body, during soldering processes such as wave soldering.

In considerations of heat, the concept 'damaging temperature' is used, this being the temperature inside the body of the component at which certain characteristics of the component change by more than a permissible figure. The application determines the magnitude of this figure, so that implicitly various damaging temperatures can be distinguished. The change that actually occurs depends, however, not only on the maximum temperature reached but also on the time for which this temperature prevails. One can imagine that 10 seconds 100°C inside the component body would be a more severe treatment than a cycle of 3 seconds at 125°C composed of rapid heating followed by rapid cooling. Hardly any knowledge exists on the influence of these temperature-time relations on the characteristics of the component. Most components, including electrolytic pacitors (without applied voltage) can endure 100°C for more than 10 minutes. e damage temperature of carbon resistors lies above 150°C, of various types of m capacitor below 100°C.

In test Tb of IEC 68-2-20 [Spec. Ref. 1], the resistance to soldering heat is ted by dipping the terminations of the components in a solder bath (260°C) for or 10 seconds, with a distance between the body of the component and the rface of the solder of 2 mm and with a screen placed in between. Similar tests ist elsewhere. The dipping for 10 seconds is intended to be the general test for ofessional components, whereas the shorter test is the alternative for mponents that cannot withstand the 10 seconds' test, but which nevertheless rform well in practice, especially in consumer products. The duration of the it is to be stated in the relevant specification.

The soldering temperature may occasionally be higher than the test nperature of 260°C, but in general this presents no difficulties regarding the fferent heating times.

The test for the resistance to soldering heat is typically a non-equilibrium test, oviding data for the soldering processes for standard printed boards with holes. ie heating is 'asymptotic' for the leads, but 'excess' for the component body ee Chapter 3.1.1). Tests for components with soldering pads, like multilayer ip capacitors, have not yet been fully established.

In view of the preceding arguments it is clear that a simple test for the sistance to soldering heat has only a limited value, and is thus only applicable in rtain cases. For printed boards the ability to withstand a specified thermal ock without delamination is tested by floating a specimen on a solder bath at 0°C [Spec. Ref. 4].

5 STATISTICAL EVALUATION OF THE MEASUREMENTS

The wetting times measured by any test method always exhibit a relatively large riation and it is quite common for the largest value of a series of measurements be more than twice as large as the smallest one. Therefore, it is necessary to test r more than one specimen in order to obtain a reliable test result. In the current t procedures, only a limited number of specimens can be tested for reasons of st.

5.1 Distribution

When a large number of specimens from the same batch are tested, it is found at the measured times show a distribution which is not a normal (Gauss) stribution. This is demonstrated in Figure 7.35, giving a histogram of a number globule measurements showing a tail at higher time values.

The distribution of Figure 7.35 can be normalised by choosing a logarithmic ne scale. Tests reveal that, in many cases, solderability data conform quite well such a logarithmic normal distribution. In practice, a cumulative plot of the easurements usually offers more insight than a histogram.

A cumulative distribution function of wetting times is obtained when the action of specimens with measured times below a certain value is plotted against is value. A cumulative logarithmic normal distribution function can nveniently be plotted on logarithmic probability paper (see Figure 7.36), where gives a straight line. In order to do this, the measured data are ranked (ordered

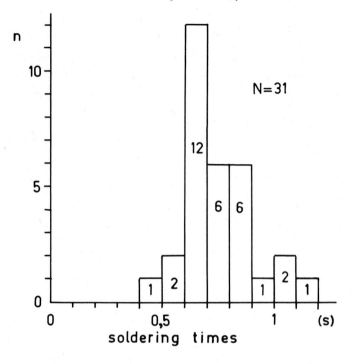

Fig. 7.35 Histogram of soldering times measured on a globule machine.

in a sequence of increasing value) and the rank value is plotted versus the measured wetting time.

For a total number of specimens, N, the rank value of the Jth specimen is not precisely J/N, but differs somewhat from this and is about $J/N+1$. With only one specimen tested, one would certainly not put the 'rank' at $1/1 = 100\%$ but intuitively at 50%, *etc*. The series of test results from Figure 7.35 is given in Table 7.3. The rank value 46,9 in the Table is, for instance, obtained from:

$$\frac{1+2+12}{31+1} = 0,469$$

Table 7.3

Ranking of Test Results

Time, s	Number of Specimens	Rank %
0,5	1	3,1
0,5-0,6	2	9,4
0,6-0,7	12	46,9
0,7-0,8	6	65,6
0,8-0,9	6	84,4
0,9-1,0	1	87,5
1,0-1,1	2	93,8
1,1-1,2	1	96,9

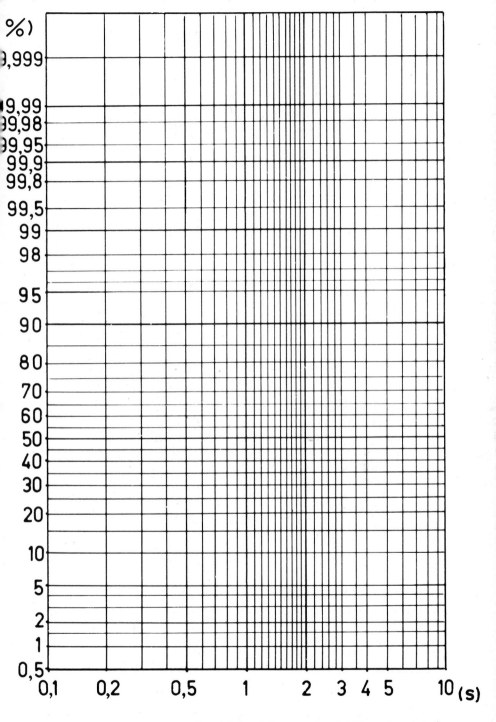

Fig. 7.36 Logarithmic probability paper. The vertical scale is a normal probability scale, only being offset from the middle. The horizontal scale is logarithmic.

The values given have been plotted in Figure 7.37 and a straight line on the paper is, in fact, obtained, showing that these test results conform to the logarithmic normal distribution.

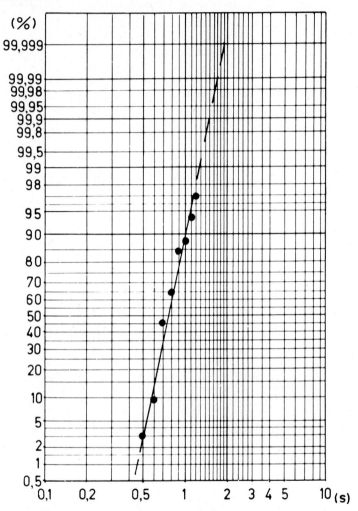

Fig. 7.37   Log-normal plot of the data from Fig. 7.35 and Table 7.3.

The calculations can be kept simple by selecting a suitable number of test specimens, for instance 24 or 49. In general, not all the measured points are plotted and the work both of measuring and plotting is considerably simplified when the test figures are grouped together at judiciously chosen intervals. The plotting of the measured values provides an easy way of obtaining insight into the total sample of terminations measured. Curves of different batches can be compared and give more information than a comparison of the actual measured values.

Occasionally the measured times do not represent a 'simple' distribution, but consist of two (or more) populations; in some cases, the origin of such double populations can be traced, but more often this is not so.

⁵.2   Extrapolation

When the measured test figures confirm a certain distribution and a plot like ﬁgure 7.37 is obtained, one might imagine that this line could be extrapolated to ﬁther values; in this way, for instance, a time could be obtained where less than 1 100 000 specimens will fail [Becker]. This obtained time, by its nature, is a ﬆtistical quantity to which a confidence interval has to be attributed, putting an ﬞper and a lower limit on it. However, even when it is clear that the measured ﬆtting times fit well into a logarithmic normal distribution over a considerable ﬞrt of the range, there is still absolutely no certainty that the tail end of the ﬞtual distribution will stretch out so far beyond the highest measured points. The ﬄarithmic normal distribution of wettability figures is nothing more than an ﬞperimental observation and so far has no theoretical background which could ﬞnstitute a reasonable basis for such extrapolation.

Thus extrapolation of the curves cannot be recommended because these ﬀtrapolated figures have no real meaning as far as real wetting times and real obabilities of failure are concerned. To use the level 99,99% as a figure of merit ײַr monitoring the wettability is possible, but may produce considerable nfusion in evaluation. On the other hand, it cannot be denied that the steepness ﬁ the curve is of major importance, and one is deprived of this indicator when ﬞly the maximum value of the measurements is considered.

When the same figures are plotted (why not?) on so-called extreme value obability paper [Gumbel], a straight line may again be obtained, but the ﬀtrapolated values differ considerably from those of the log-normal ﬀtrapolation. A plot according to a Weibull distribution [Weibull] may also give straight line over the experimental range, with different extrapolation.

For tests on which the largest value is not larger than twice the lowest value it is ﬞt absolutely necessary to use a logarithmic time scale, as a linear scale will give ﬄ significantly different result provided extrapolation is avoided.

6   ACCELERATED AGEING TREATMENTS

The wettability of a surface decreases with time. This effect is due to so-called ﬞtural ageing. As components and boards are usually stored before assembling ﬞd soldering, natural ageing constitutes a pervasive problem. During the storage ﬞriod, the degree of ageing should not be allowed to exceed a specific level. The ﬞeriod which is mostly taken into account is one year, but in specific cases even ﬞree years' storage is encountered (Figure 7.38).

⁶.1   Ageing Parameters

The ageing parameters are:

(i)   the nature of the materials;
ii)   the nature of the environment;
ﬁi)   the nature of the ageing mechanism;
v)   the duration of the ageing time.

Various factors may produce the ageing effect: oxidation of the outer surface,

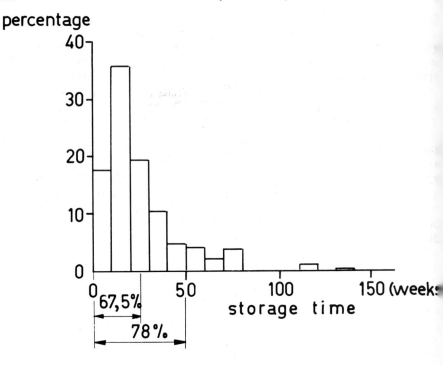

Fig. 7.38   Histogram of age of boards at the time of soldering.

reaction with sulphur or other elements, the formation of reaction layers betwee
the base metal and the coating metal.

In practice, the environmental atmosphere is not precisely known, an
certainly is not always the same. Therefore, natural ageing is irreproducible an
very difficult to predict. Still, for production practice, there must be some idea c
how wettability will degrade during storage and, for that, artificial, also calle
'accelerated', ageing treatments are needed to produce a specific ageir
simulating the effect of a certain period of natural ageing in an undefine
atmosphere. Even when such accelerated ageing treatment has been established i
official standards, this does not mean that the matching of artificial and natur;
ageing is more reliable. From one case to another large deviations a
encountered [MacKay].

7.6.2   Ageing Methods

The lack of satisfaction as regards accelerated ageing treatments has led to th
evolution of quite a large number of methods [Ackroyd] laid down in nation;
and international standards [Spec. Ref. 1, 4a and 5]:

(i)   simple steam test for 1 or 4 hours (*e.g.*, in IEC Publ. 68-2-20 Test T
Soldering);
(ii)   modified steam test for 80 minutes (*e.g.*, in IEC Publ. 326-2A Part 2: Tes
methods);

iii) damp heat, steady state test, 40°C, RH 93% for 4, 10, 21 or 56 days (*e.g.*, in IEC Publ. 68-2-3 Test Ca: Damp heat, steady state);

(iv) dry heat test at 155°C in air for 2, 16, 72 or 96 hours (*e.g.*, in IEC Publ. 68-2-2 Tests B: Dry heat);

(v) cyclic damp heat test with cycle of 25-55°C in 3 hours after which 55°C during 9 hours and cooling to 25°C in RH 95%; number of cycles 1, 2 or 6 (*e.g.*, in IEC Publ. 68-2-30 Test Db: Damp heat, cyclic (12 + 12-hour cycle)).

Two groups of methods can be distinguished:

7.6.2.1   AGEING OF THE OUTER SURFACE

This is mainly an oxidation in humid atmosphere performed with a steam test or a damp heat test. In the modified steam methods, extra gas (oxygen, sulphur dioxide, *etc.*) is added.

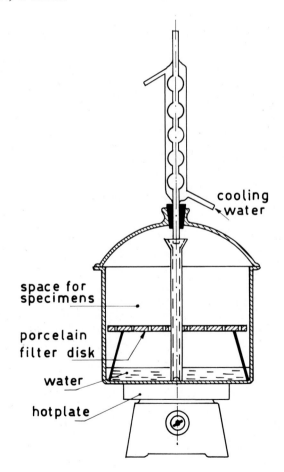

Fig. 7.39 Example of a glass steam chamber with reflux condenser, for performing simple steam ageing tests of electronic components. Diameter of the steam chamber is about 220 mm.

The steam test has been included in IEC 68-2-20 (1 and 4 hours).

The choice of 1 or 4 hours depends on the degree of severity desired. The one hour exposure is mainly intended for components which are expected to be used soon after the moment of testing or after a short period of storage under good conditions. For components which are likely to undergo prolonged storage, or which may be subjected to other treatments, the 4 hours' ageing is more suitable.

The apparatus has a significant influence upon the ageing results obtained. This is the case because the temperature and steam pressure in the beaker are rather inhomogeneous and are influenced by the set-up of the beaker. Moreover, the water may become polluted by substances washed off the treated components. The vessel should consequently be cleaned regularly.

Figure 7.39 shows a simple steam apparatus. Extra gas, if desired, can be added using a small diameter tube fed from above through the condenser into the water.

The steam apparatus as shown in Figure 7.39 gives a more homogeneous ageing result than that suggested in IEC 68-2-20 [Spec. Ref. 1], consisting of a common beaker with a round bottom flask placed on top of it as a condenser.

7.6.2.2   AGEING BY GROWTH OF AN INTERMETALLIC DIFFUSION LAYER

In this method, the coating metal is consumed by reaction with the base metal, rendering the surface difficult to wet if the diffusion layer grows to the surface. Of course, oxidation of the surface is still an important factor. Such ageing treatment, typically conducted at high temperature in a dry, hot environment, is only a valid accelerated ageing test if the assumption is warranted that wettability will be affected by intermetallics. This is the case with eccentrically tinned wires where in certain areas on the wires the tin layer is so thin that it will in the long run be consumed even at room temperature [Lenz]. Another case is constituted by plated wires that must be subjected to high temperatures before they are finally soldered. It is possible to obtain the testing time at 155°C, which is the common dry heat test temperature, from growth rate data. For copper tin layers, the layer thickness is roughly given by

$$x(\mu m) = 8.10^{-3} \sqrt{t} \qquad (t \text{ in seconds})$$

Hence, after 16 hours (at 155°C) $x = 2\mu m$.

One year storage at room temperature produces a layer thickness of about 0,3 μm, and the 16 hours' test which is often advocated is too severe for simulating the one year storage of these eccentric wire coatings. The test of 1 hour or 4 hours (at 155°C) is closer to reality, as has also been proved by experiment [Ochs].

Note: The 16 hours' dry heat test is sometimes applied to test the susceptibility to scaling of electrodeposited layers.

The two groups of methods thus have different applications as may also become clear from the following scheme.

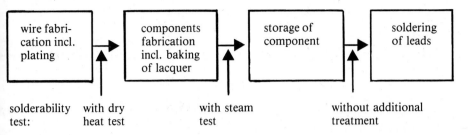

| wire fabri-
cation incl.
plating | components
fabrication
incl. baking
of lacquer | storage of
component | soldering
of leads |

| solderability
test: | with dry
heat test | with steam
test | without additional
treatment |

7.6.3 Special Cases

A special case is constituted by non-passivated silver which is exposed to an atmosphere containing some sulphur (always present in air), and which rapidly forms a sulphur compound that is not removed by, for instance, normal activated colophony fluxes. In air the wettability becomes practically zero, a property which will not be revealed by a steam test.

Another example is where protective coats which carry out their protective function excellently may not be resistant to steam at 100°C. If this is the case, the ageing protective capability is not tested, but the coat is simply ruined [van der Leest *et al*].

7.7 TESTING IN PRACTICE

Good wettability is an essential feature of the soldering system, as discussed in Chapter 1. Systematic testing of the wettability of components and boards is not only necessary to find out if a particular batch of components or boards satisfies the required standards, but will also give useful information concerning the trends of the wettability.

For the measurement of the wettability of component leads the globule tester is the most widely used machine, although the use of the wetting balance is rapidly gaining ground. In the future, the globule method will presumably only be used for cheap in-house testing, whilst the wetting balance will be employed for general testing, certainly when disputes should be avoided.

The wetting times obtained with the globule method and with the wetting-balance method display a slight difference, the wetting times with the latter tending to be 30% to 50% longer than the globule times, but having a smaller variation [Warwick, Becker *et al*]. For laminate materials and printed boards, the rotary dip tester can be used. The wetting times with this and the times obtained in a wave-soldering test show a one-to-one relationship [Thwaites].

7.7.1 Conditions and Procedures

In order to obtain comparable results, conditions and procedures for the solderability tests must be well defined. This applies to:

(i)   testing temperature (temperature of solder during test);
(ii) composition of solder metal;
(iii) composition of flux used in testing and method of application of the flux;
(iv) ageing condition of specimens;
(v)   characteristics of test equipment.

7.7.1.1 TESTING TEMPERATURE

In soldering processes, the soldering temperature is usually between 240 and 270°C, and solderability tests must aim at assessing the suitability of components in this temperature region. Generally, a test temperature of 235±2°C is selected, on the safe side of 240°C, the lowest soldering temperature used in practice.

Lowering the test temperature will produce longer wetting times, but will moreover increase the differences between good and bad specimens, thus increasing the discrimination power of the test [see Becker *et al*].

As dewetting is likely to occur at high soldering temperatures, the dewetting susceptibility is assessed after dipping at 260°C (5 seconds). This temperature is also selected for testing the resistance to soldering heat (10 or 5 seconds). It is important to use as few different test temperatures as possible. Two temperatures (235° and 260°C) actually suffice.

In soldering processes at a lower temperature than already mentioned, for instance reflow soldering with vapour phase heating (215°C, see Chapter 10.5.3), the temperature may in fact be below the melting point of the plating on the component terminations (*e.g.*, tin) or of conductors on the printed board (*e.g.*, lead rich tin-lead alloy). In this case a wettability test at 235°C, above the melting point, provides incorrect information for the process concerned.

7.7.1.2 COMPOSITION OF SOLDER METAL

In the tests no differences are observed between the alloy tin60-lead40 and the eutectic alloy. Normally, for all tests the former alloy is used, with a required composition of [Spec. Ref. 1]:

tin	59-61% by mass
antimony	< 0,5%
copper	< 0,1%
arsenic	< 0,05%
iron	< 0,02%
lead	remainder

The solder should not contain impurities such as aluminium, zinc or cadmium 'in amounts which will adversely affect the properties'. Solder commonly used for high quality soldering meets the stated requirements.

7.7.1.3 COMPOSITION OF FLUX USED IN TESTING

The composition of the fluxes for testing should be as simple as possible. The test flux need not necessarily be a flux used in actual soldering practice, because the other test conditions are also not identical to real soldering conditions.

It is often a matter of dispute as to how close the chemical activity of the test flux should be to the activity of the production fluxes. Testing with very weak fluxes (maintaining the same required maximum wetting times!) produces an extra safety for the wettability, but this safety can also be incorporated in other ways.

An activated test flux produces shorter wetting times, with less relative spread. In principle, any test flux could be used if the 'translation factor' to practice were known.

In order to obtain a real feeling for the meaning of the test results, one should if possible always work with the same composition of test flux. On this point, however, it appears to be difficult to achieve agreement between different companies and countries. As a result, a variety of fluxes for testing have been standardised; fortunately these are all colophony fluxes. IEC 68-2-20 approved the following fluxes based on colophony (25% mass) in solvent (75% mass) as shown in Table 7.4. The solvent may be either 2-propanol (isopropanol) or ethyl alcohol.

There is no technical need for more than one test flux. Within the Author's company one single test flux (with 0,2% Cl) has been applied for all wettability tests for many years. (The non-activated flux is in general inappropriate for uncoated materials, see Figure 5.11.)

Table 7.4

Fluxes used for Solderability Testing in IEC 68-2-20

Flux	Activated with Diethylammonium Chloride	For Components		For Laminates and Boards
		Wettability of Wire and Tag Terminations	*Resistance to Soldering Heat*	
1	none	used	used when a humidity test must be performed afterwards	used*
2	0,2% chlorine	not used	not used	used*
3	0,5% chlorine	used when non-activated flux is inappropriate	used	used*

* as required by the relevant specification.

7.1.4   METHOD OF APPLICATION OF FLUX

The method of application of the flux influences the amount of flux present at the moment of test and should therefore be prescribed in the test procedure. Usually the specimen is immersed in the flux, but brushing is also practised.

For Wetting Balance testing or dip testing the following procedure can be employed:

After mounting the specimen in a suitable holder, the whole of the surface to be tested is immersed in flux at room temperature. Excess flux is immediately drained off by standing the specimen vertically on clean filter paper for 1 to 5 seconds. The specimen is then suspended vertically with its lower edge 20±5 mm above the solder for 30±15 seconds, to allow most of the flux solvent to evaporate, before initiating the test cycle. (During this drying period the solder surface can be skimmed to remove oxides, and the suspension and chart recorder trace adjusted to the desired zero position.)

For printed boards with plated holes to be tested the following procedure is appropriate:

The test specimen is dipped vertically into the flux and moved to and fro so th
the flux penetrates the holes, with a dwell time at maximum depth of 3 s. The te
specimen is then withdrawn vertically at a rate of about 5 mm/s. Holes still fill
with flux after being withdrawn must be cleared again (for instance by tappi
the test specimen).

The specimens are placed in a suitable holder with their test faces upwards,
an angle of 60±15° in respect of the horizontal plane, and so arranged that tl
specimens do not affect one another (at least 10 mm apart). The holder with the
specimens is placed in a clean oven at 75±5°C for 15 minutes and allowed to co
to room temperature, after which the wetting tests are carried out.

The drying treatment for boards is performed much more thoroughly than f
component leads, because on testing wet boards trapped flux can easily invalida
the test or cause splattering of solder. Drying could be effectively achieved wi
air blowing but the oven is a practical and satisfactory solution. When after 1
minutes the boards are removed from the oven, they have not yet reached 75°C
but are still warming up.

Note: Care must be taken in the correct application of the flux and the drying of the specimer
Sloppy practice is too often observed.

7.7.2 Visual Assessments

Visual assessment is practised in three cases after a dip test, to verify:

  (i) the degree of wetting of surfaces;
 (ii) the wetting of plated holes;
(iii) the dewetting of surfaces.

It is good testing practice to examine the specimens visually during and after eac
solderability test.

7.7.2.1 95% COATING

After an edge dip test, a minimum of 95% coating is frequently required
which intends to express the fact that the surface should be almost completel
covered. The adoption of the percentage of 95 in various standards suggests tha
a quantitative assessment is possible, which, however, is very difficult and ofte
even impossible.

One way is to compare the specimens with standard samples or with drawing
showing various percentages of pinholes [Spec. Ref. 12]. In practice, this methoc
based on a general impression, is however, subjective and the results ar
inconsistent.

A semi-quantitative method for measuring the percentage of defect area
proposed by the following procedure [Spec. Ref. 13]: To every defect on th
surface a diameter is attributed, namely either 0,125 mm (0,005 in) or 0,25 mr
(0,010 in) or 0,5 mm (0,020 in), so that every defect belongs to one of thre
groups. The numbers of defects in the three groups, N_A, N_B, N_C, respectively, ar
counted and the total area of defects is obtained from:

$$(N_A + 4N_B + 16N_C) \times 0,0123 \text{ mm}^2$$

This area must be related to the total area measured. The Author has no personal experience of this measuring method; it is seldom used.

Note: The assessment of solderability based on a 95% coating dates from a time when no quantitative methods were available. In fact, it has been rendered obsolete for all common (leaded) components.

7.7.2.2   PLATED HOLES

Plated holes are usually assessed after a rotary dip operation, Tables 7.5 and 7.6 giving the criteria for this assessment. The temperature of the solder bath is 235°C and the nominal contact time is adjusted to 3 seconds.

Table 7.5

Boards with Plated Holes, Solder Side

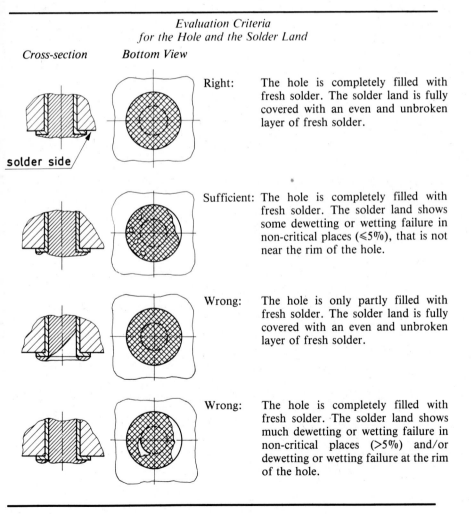

Evaluation Criteria
for the Hole and the Solder Land

Cross-section   *Bottom View*

Right: The hole is completely filled with fresh solder. The solder land is fully covered with an even and unbroken layer of fresh solder.

solder side

Sufficient: The hole is completely filled with fresh solder. The solder land shows some dewetting or wetting failure in non-critical places (≤5%), that is not near the rim of the hole.

Wrong: The hole is only partly filled with fresh solder. The solder land is fully covered with an even and unbroken layer of fresh solder.

Wrong: The hole is completely filled with fresh solder. The solder land shows much dewetting or wetting failure in non-critical places (>5%) and/or dewetting or wetting failure at the rim of the hole.

Table 7.6

Boards With Plated Holes, Component Side Soldered from Solder Side

---

Evaluation Criteria
for the Hole and the Surface of the Solder

7.6.1 Without Solder Lands and/or Conductors on Component Side

Cross-section

Right: The hole is completely filled with fresh solder where plated-through. The surface of the solder has a concave meniscus.

Wrong: The hole is only partly filled with fresh solder. The surface of the solder has a convex meniscus.

7.6.2 With Solder Lands and/or Conductors on Component Side

Right: The hole is completely filled with fresh solder up to the rim of the hole. The surface of the solder has a concave meniscus.

Wrong: The hole is only partly filled with fresh solder. The surface of the solder has a convex meniscus.

Notes regarding the evaluation of plated holes:

(i) Some or all of the solder accumulating in the hole during the test may flow out again before solidifying. If this has happened, then the area of the hole wall thus exposed must be covered with an even and unbroken layer of fresh solder. The tendency of the solder to flow out of the hole increases with the ratio of hole diameter to board thickness and is already clearly perceptible where this ratio is 1:1.

(ii) Craters are prone to render the solderability of the specimen difficult to evaluate. They chiefly occur during soldering as a result of process faults during the manufacture of the boards (for instance incomplete through-plating of the hole wall) or of inadequate drying prior to soldering. Holes affected by craters must not be involved in the evaluation of solderability.

(iii) In the case of printed boards without lands on the component side, suppliers do not usually guarantee the plating inside the hole beyond 80% of the board thickness from the solder side (Table 7.6.1).

(iv) Whether or not the solder reaches the upper rim of the hole in a copper-covered board can be tested by rubbing the solder land with fine abrasive paper (for instance number 600). The solder near the rim should be just visible. In the case of tin-lead covered boards, the presence of solder up to the rim of the hole is generally revealed by a visible zone of fusion on the solder land (Table 7.6.2).

7.2.3 DEWETTING

Determination of the degree of dewetting is difficult. Usually the percentage of the surface area that is dewetted is taken as the degree of dewetting, whilst the area with the droplets on it is considered as being 'wetted'. In this manner of counting, 100% dewetting does not exist.

The boundary between a wetted and a dewetted region rarely appears to be sharp when studied under a higher magnification (Figure 7.40). This is a strong

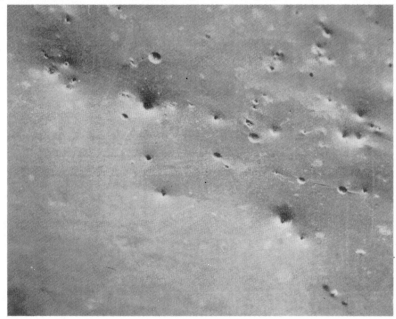

Fig. 7.40   Boundary between a droplet and a dewetted region under a magnification of 320×. The boundary goes from top-left to bottom-right. Dewetting in this case is caused by small copper oxide particles in the copper plate.

obstacle in carrying out quantitative measurements. Nevertheless, with experience, acceptable figures can be produced, using a line analysis method, although the work is very laborious. Visual estimates show a lot of spread for different persons and strongly deviate from the measured values (Tables 7.7). Even repeated estimates by one and the same person after a few days produce different results.

It is not easy to establish good criteria for rejection of tested parts based on the dewetting observed. Often a level of 95% coverage is desired, whilst the small defects such as pores and small unwetted patches do not necessarily warrant rejection, provided that they are evenly distributed. Because the precise measurements are tedious and time-consuming, the assessment is mostly made by comparison with examples (photographs, as in Figure 2.19), leading to a more or less subjective decision.

One could adopt the point of view that correct material choice and good processing will exclude dewetting, so that, if dewetting is present, something is wrong, in principle implying rejection. In reality, however, very small defects are not fully avoidable and then it is a matter of dispute as to when the unacceptable level is reached. In any case, action should be taken when dewetting is observed, such action including thorough inspection of the processes and perhaps further tests.

Table 7.7

Comparison of Estimated and Measured Dewetting

Specimen	Dewetted Percentage Estimated by Person							Average	Measur
	A	B	C	D	E	F	G		
1	20	20	25	20	20	15	5	17,7	16
2	30	25	20	15	25	20	15	21,2	32
3	40	40	50	60	55	50	40	47,9	42
4	45	40	50	30	55	30	50	42,9	34
5	50	50	75	80	80	70	70	67,9	44
6	60	40	40	40	50	80	10	45,5	35
7	40	40	40	50	40	40	30	39,8	27
8	30	25	30	45	40	40	20	32,7	26

7.7.2.4 VERY SMALL COMPONENTS

The quantitative testing methods for wettability will fail with very small components, because the area of their terminations to be wetted with solder is too small for the existing measuring methods.

The components in question are discussed in greater detail in Chapter 8.2, and include:

(i) leadless components: chip capacitors (under certain conditions the wetting balance can be used, see Chapter 7.2.1.9), chip resistors, having metallisation only on the end faces and not on the side faces, and chip carriers having concave soldering lands;

(ii) components with very small leads: SOT-23 and SO packages, on the leads of which different regions can be distinguished (sides, bottom, bent part, end faces), and components with a very large number of terminations.

The assessment of wettability of all these components has not yet been worked out, let alone standardised. For the time being one relies on dipping or immersing the components in molten solder for a few seconds, followed by a visual inspection under a stereoscopic microscope with a magnification of 10 to 20 times.

It can be anticipated that procedures and requirements, now being selected ad hoc, will be adopted in relevant standards such as IEC 68-2-20. Perhaps new testing methods will be developed.

.7.3 Testing Requirements for Component Leads

In some standards only the methods for carrying out the solderability tests are ₅tablished, leaving the requirements to be agreed between vendor and customer. ₅his is the case in IEC Publ. 68-2-20 [Spec. Ref. 1], in which two points of great ₘportance are not discussed and hence should be covered by the relevant ₚecification, *viz.* the method and severity of ageing and the level of quality ₅surance gained by the use of the test. The statement often found: 'solderability ₅cording to IEC 68-2-20' is without meaning if the points mentioned are ₒmitted.

The parameters of most soldering processes are situated within the safe area of ₚeration (see Chapter 3.1.2), signifying that process times are from 2-4 seconds ₙd soldering temperature is from 240-270°C (usually below 260°C). The ₅olderability tests should be performed taking into account the boundaries of this ₅rea, the consequences being that:

(i) the wetting times must be in the range of a few seconds;
(ii) the thermal demand must be such that a soldering temperature of 240°C is adequate;
iii) the resistance to soldering heat must be satisfactory up to a soldering temperature of 270°C.

.7.3.1 WETTING TIMES

The majority of the solder coated components will pass a 1 second ₑquirement, if a non-activated flux is used at 235°C. In globule testing one often ₑquires a maximum time of 2 seconds for the wetting of solder coated ₒmponent terminations, for instance measured on ten specimens.

In practical wetting balance testing, a maximum wetting time of 2 seconds is ₑnerally a good requirement (with mildly activated flux 1 second).

.7.3.2 DEGREE OF WETTING

The requirements for the degree of wetting in the wetting balance have been ₅iscussed in Chapter 7.2.1. In most cases, 50% of the Reference Wetting Force ₐfter 3 seconds is a suitable requirement for aged specimens using non-activated ₑst flux at 235°C (with mildly activated flux two-thirds).

Note: Specifying shorter wetting times and higher degrees of wetting than given here is nearly always ₙnecessary regarding common soldering process conditions [see Spec. Ref. 16, but note 260°C].

For dip tests for wettability (235°C, 2s) the 95% clause is applied.

.7.3.3 PERMANENT WETTING

Permanent wetting is tested by visual inspection after a dip test. A 95% coat is ₅sually required for component leads, *etc.*, after 260°C for 5 seconds. The ₘaximum 5% pores and unwetted patches must be evenly distributed and hence ₘay not be concentrated in a particular zone.

For round wires, an additional requirement is valid: a break in the coating shall ₙot cover more than 10% of the circumference. Cut edges are excluded from the ₑvaluation.

Table 7.8

Test Methods for Solderability and Related Matters as Included in a Number of Standards

	Document Number	Year	Title of Document	Methods								Tests			Ageing Treatments — Terminations			Ageing Treatments — Boards			
				1	2	3	4	5	6	7	8	9	10	11	12	13	14	15	16	17	18
IEC	Publication 68-2-20	1979	Basic environmental testing procedures, Part 2: Tests, Test T: Soldering,			+		+				+			+	+	+				
	Publ. 326-2 and 326-2A	1976-1980	Printed boards, Part 2: Test methods						+					+				+	+	+	
France	NFC 90-550	1977	Alloys and fluxes for soft soldering				+														
	NFC 93-713 and suppl.	1974-1978	Components for electronic equipment, Printed wiring boards						+	+								+	+		
Germany	DIN-IEC 68 Part 2-20*	1980	Basic environmental testing procedures, Part 2: Tests, Test T: Soldering			+		+				+			+	+	+				
	DIN 32506 Part 1-4	1980	Testing of solderability		+	+	+		+	+	+	+									
Great Britain	BS 2011: Part 2.1 T	1981	Basic environmental testing procedures, Part 2.1 Tests, Test		+																

Country	Standard	Year	Description	1	2	3	4	5	6	7	8	9	10	11	12	13	14	15	16	17	18
Japan	JIS C 5053	1974	Solderability testing methods for electronic components													+	+	+		+	+
Sweden	Mekanresultat 77006	1978	Solderability testing of component leads													+					
	IVF-Resultat 73633	1973	Solderability testing of printed circuit boards											+							
USA	ANSI/EIA RS-178B	1973	Solderability test standard	+																	
	ANSI/EIA RS-319A	1970	Solderability of printed wiring boards		+																
	ANSI/EIA RS-186-9E	1978	Standard test methods for passive electronic component parts, method 9: Solderability				+														
	IPC-S-801	1970	Edge dip solderability test for printed wiring boards		+																
	IPC-S-804 (Draft)	1980	Solderability test method for printed wiring boards			+															
	IPC-S-805 (Draft)	1983	Solderability tests for component leads and terminations					+			+			+							
	MIL-STD-202E	1973	Test methods for electronic and electrical component parts										+		+	+					
	MIL-STD-883B	1977	Test methods and procedures for microelectronics							+		+				+					

---

* DIN-IEC 68 Part 2-20 is the German translation without alterations of IEC Publication 68-2-20.
** An English version is not available.

1 Area of Spread
2 Edge Dip
3 Globule, Plated Holes
4 Globule, Terminations
5 Meniscus Rise
6 Rotary Dip
7 Wetting Balance, Scanning
8 Wetting Balance, Stationary
9 Thermal Demand
10 Resistance of Components to Soldering Heat
11 Ability of Boards to withstand a Thermal Shock
12 Damp Heat, Steady State
13 Dry Heat
14 Steam
15 Damp Heat, Cyclic
16 Damp Heat, Steady State
17 Steam
18 Steam Oxygen

Chapter 8

JOINTS ON PRINTED BOARDS

At the present time, nearly all electronic units made by soldering in mass production consist of a combination of separate components mutually connected with the help of a support plate. Each separate component may in itself be a single part, a combination of parts, a highly integrated unit or a subassembly mounted together to perform an electronic function.

The support plates have a threefold function:

(i) to support the components; in many cases, the support plates are part of the mechanical construction of the equipment;
(ii) to provide a base for the conductors which connect the separate components;
(iii) to assist in the heat dissipation of the components mounted on the plates.

The support plates may or may not be provided with holes. The conductor pattern may be on one face, or on both faces, and in multilayer boards conductive patterns are also present in the interior of the plates.

Table 8.1 shows 5 configurations for support plates and mounted components.

Table 8.1

Configurations

CONFIGURATION	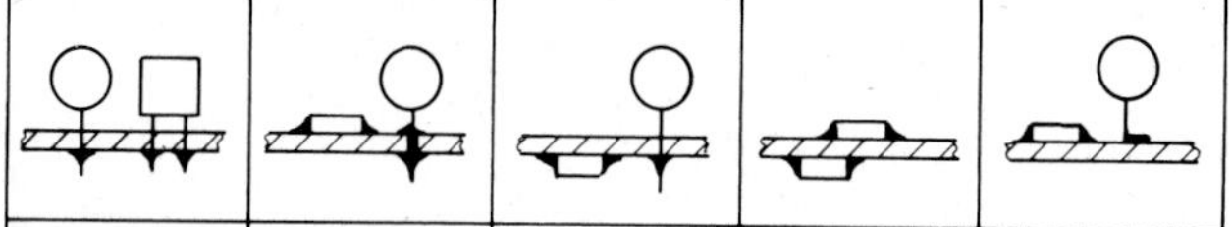				
	I	II	III	IV	V
COMPONENT	ABOVE	ABOVE	BOTH SIDES	BOTH SIDES	ABOVE
JOINT	BELOW	BOTH SIDES	BELOW	BOTH SIDES	ABOVE
EXAMPLES	SINGLE SIDED BOARD	DOUBLE SIDED BOARD	SINGLE SIDED BOARD	DOUBLE SIDED BOARD	THICK FILM CIRCUIT

he different positions of the components on the support plates determine what ossibilities exist for applying a specific soldering process.

The mounting and soldering of components on printed (circuit) boards rovided with holes is the main technique in the production of electronic ssemblies for a whole range of equipment, from cheap entertainment sets to ighly professional systems. Three Chapters in this book pay explicit attention to is subject, namely Chapter 8 on design of the printed pattern, Chapter 9 on the oldering techniques and Chapter 12 on inspection of soldered joints. These hapters concern mainly the configurations I, II and III of Table 8.1.

Components can be mounted by hand or with automatic machines, not iscussed in detail in this book [see for instance Leonida, Erickson, Anon. ef.26], the latter method particularly on single-sided boards, giving more eproducible soldering results than hand mountings. Moreover, in hand mount-ıg trivial mistakes are made that are absent in automatic mounting.

In thick film technology, conductors are formed by a process of screening a uitable paste onto the support plate followed by firing in air. The metallic onductors obtained in this way are solderable, though the level of solderability is uch lower than that of copper conductors on a printed board. The separate omponents are connected to the solder lands on top of the substrate in a reflow oldering operation, which follows the thick film process steps [Holmes *et al*]. fter soldering, configuration V (see Table 8.1) has been realised.

Thick film circuits are generally made on ceramic substrates of alumina, a ommon size being $0,7 \times 50 \times 50$ mm^3. The alumina combines strength, stiffness nd high heat conductivity (see Table 8.2). The faces of the substrates are mooth, but the slightest curvature or camber of the substrates affects their uitability for specific soldering processes.

Metallic support plates combine certain useful characteristics such as strength, rigidity, dimensional ability, precisely known and relatively low thermal expansion, high resistance to heat, good thermal onductivity (during soldering and use). Owing to their strength and rigidity the plates can very well ovide other supporting functions as well as bearing components, whereas electrical and magnetical ielding are possible.

One type comprises porcelain-coated steel substrates, having a conductive pattern made by an Iditive process, and plated holes if necessary. These plates can be wave soldered in the same way as ommon printed boards or can be used as substrates for thick-film technologies [Spector, nyshkevych].

Another type comprises copper-clad aluminium plates without holes, to be used for the surface ounting of components, for instance of audio power modules and voltage regulators. The copper il of 35 μm thickness is adhered to the heavily anodised aluminium plate of 1 to 2 mm thickness ing an epoxy, and can be etched to produce the conductor pattern. Various techniques can then be ied to make the electronic circuit (IMST = insulated metal substrate technology) [Miura *et al*].

Despite the attractive combination of properties and the low cost potential in certain applications, ie metallic substrates are not widely used (at present), mainly because of the total cost of this icommon technology, including the many implications for the product design. Some technical awbacks associated with these substrates are their relatively high weight, their maximum operating equencies (a few hundred MHz for porcelainised steel and a few MHz for insulated aluminium), fficult repair if necessary, and for the porcelainised steel plates also the lack of flatness of coat pecially at the edges of the plates and holes (if present).

.1 PRINTED BOARDS

A printed board, often referred to as a printed circuit board (PCB) or printed iring board (PWB), is an insulating plate carrying a desired conductive circuit attern on its surface (*i.e.*, printed wiring). The (printed) conductors, also called

tracks, consist of copper strips adhering to the insulating substrate and may b
plated with a tin-lead alloy.

A distinction is made between:

(i) single-sided boards: The printed wiring is applied to one side of the boar
only. The boards are usually provided with holes;

(ii) double-sided boards: The printed wiring is applied to both sides of th
boards, whilst in most cases the wiring on both sides is connected by
metallisation of the walls of the holes, thus producing so-called plated hole
or plated-through holes (PTH);

(iii) multilayer boards: These are double-sided boards provided with addition:
conductor layers inside the board. The conductor layers are mutuall
connected as required by plated holes. A common construction consists c
four or five layers: on the faces the pattern for carrying the electron
signals and inside the board two or three layers for the power connectio
(ground and voltage levels);

(iv) flexible boards: Boards of either of the three preceding types, but using
flexible base material, such as polyester or polyimide.
(Pieces of rigid and flexible boards may be connected to give so called "flex-rigid").

The two sides of the board are known as component side and solder side. Wel
established standards [Spec. Ref.7] define the component side as the side c
which most of the components are placed, and the solder side as the opposi
side. These definitions apply in most cases and create no uncertainty, but they a
no longer correct for single-sided printed boards with leadless componen
soldered to the 'copper' side.

The number of joints on the boards varies from below 1 per cm^2 for simp
single-sided boards to 5 per cm^2 for common double-sided boards. Special boar
may have over 10 joints per cm^2. Board sizes range from very large ones having :
many as 10000 joints to small ones with fewer than 100. Assembled boards with
high mounting density often contain a mixture of different components, part
mounted in the holes of the boards and partly mounted on the surfaces (on one c
both sides).

The opposite page shows such a soldered double-sided board for a profession.
portable TV camera, containing a large variety of components, *e.g.*, capacitor
resistors, adjustable resistors, coils, transistors and integrated circuits.

More than 80 leadless components and components with short leads may b
seen (see Chapter 8.2). These have been reflow-soldered to the component side c
the board before the wave soldering of the other components with leads. Th
board illustrated has 1950 soldered joints (1350 in plated holes and 600 on top c
the board), which is 11 joints per cm^2. The board dimensions are 100×175 mm

The printed conductor pattern on one or both faces can be produced in
'subtractive' process by selective chemical removal (etching) of unwanted copp
from a copper clad substrate, or in an 'additive' process by plating copper o
previously sensitised areas [Mansveld *et al*, Beckenbaugh *et al*, Egerer].

The copper thickness is usually 35 μm (305 g/m^2) though in rare cases 70 or 17
μm is applied. The use of thin foils is forecast to increase considerably.

Processes for making printed patterns on boards are not discussed in this boo
[see Coombs, Leonida, Herrmann], nor is the identification of the various typ
of defects that occur in printed boards [see Jawitz].

Depending on the specific application of the board, the printed conductors can range in width from 0,1 to 3 mm. At a conductor width above 3 mm the risk exists of solder spikes, because the flux is pushed aside too much by the solder, whilst a width of less than 0,3 mm favours the formation of solder balls.

The space between adjacent printed conductors, between printed conductors and regions where joints must be formed (solder lands), and between adjacent solder lands is called conductor spacing (or creepage distance). The magnitude of this conductor spacing is often more important from the soldering engineering viewpoint than the width of the printed conductors.

A number of base materials are commonly used including:

(i)   phenolic paper laminate;
(ii) epoxy glassfibre reinforced laminate;
(iii) polyester glassfibre reinforced laminate.

The choice of material for a certain application depends on its electrical and mechanical properties and on the price.

Preferably, board material is used having a thickness of 1,6 mm. If the boards are so small that deformation is negligible, a thinner laminate may be used. On the other hand, flexible boards are sometimes required. Printed boards always have a relatively low stiffness because the Young's moduli of the materials used are low (Table 8.2). Consequently, the boards are bent by their weight and by the weight of the components mounted on them. Moreover, these types of materials are very weak at the soldering temperature, and large deformations are observed when printed boards travel across a hot solder bath at about 250°C.

Table 8.2

Properties of Some Substrate Materials

	Polyester Glass-fibre Laminate	Phenol Formaldehyde Paper Laminate	Epoxy Glass-fibre Laminate	96% Al_2O_3	Copper	Tin60–Lead40 Solder	Units
Heat conductivity, λ	0,1	0,2	0,3	35	370	50	W/mK
Thermal diffusivity, a	0,05	0,1	0,1	8	103	33	$10^{-6}m^2/s$
Density, ϱ	2000	1350	1850	3700	8900	8500	kg/m³
Specific heat, c	1000	1600	1600	1180	380	176	J/(kg. K)
Heat required to raise 1 mm³ from 20°C to 200°C	0,36	0,38	0,86	0,78	0,61	0,69	J
Modulus of elasticity, E	7–15	8–16	14–25	500	130	32	$10^9 N/m^2$
Expansion coefficient (in plane of board)	20–30*	15–30*	10–12*	6	17	25	$10^{-6}/K$

Data are only approximate, as they depend on the actual type of material [see also Harper].
*These figures are influenced by internal stresses built into the laminate during its fabrication.

8.1.1 Flatness of Printed Boards

The immersion depth of a printed board in a solder bath during soldering is generally chosen as half the board thickness ($= 0{,}8$ mm). The permissible tolerance in the vertical position of the lower face of the boards with respect to the solder surface is 0,5 mm. This tolerance is for the sum of variations of the printed boards, the printed board holders, the conveyance mechanism and the solder surface. Without special precautions, such as clamping of printed boards in carriers, it will in general be impossible to satisfy this 0,5 mm tolerance requirement.

Possible effects of excessive warp of printed boards are:

(i) Sagging near the board edges incurring the risk of solder flooding the component side of the boards;
(ii) Sagging in the centre of the printed boards, allowing solder to flow through any apertures in boards and so to flood the component side, and causing component terminations to project sufficiently to interfere mechanically with parts of the soldering machine;
(iii) Component terminations projecting from the conductor side may be cut to different lengths;
(iv) Distortion of the form of the solder wave, thereby reducing the quality of the soldered joints.

A judicious design of a printed board will assist in limiting warp. Greater bending occurs, and hence more effective clamping measures are necessary, in the case of:

(i) greater width of the printed boards;
(ii) thinner printed boards;
(iii) printed boards with one-sided copper coating;
(iv) printed boards of laminated paper in comparison with glass-fibre reinforced epoxy material and (to a lesser extent) with glass-fibre reinforced polyester material;
(v) printed boards with heavy components.

8.1.1.1 WARP OF BOARD LAMINATE

The permissible warp of the printed board bulk laminate stated in the material specification is nearly always too large for acceptable machine soldering results. Moreover, before the printed board is cut from the bulk sheet, it is not known whether the conductor side of the printed board will have a convex or concave warp. These considerations render it imperative for the printed board assembly department to take precautions to counteract the effects of printed board warp.

A few parameters that determine printed board warp (Table 8.3) are:

(i) Thickness of bulk printed board laminate: for thinner printed board laminate a larger warp is permitted than for thicker material;
(ii) Single-sided or double-sided copper clad: single-sided copper-clad laminate is allowed to have larger warp than double-sided copper clad laminate;
(iii) Nature of bulk laminate: for paper-base laminate the as-received condition will as a rule exhibit about twice as much warp as for epoxy glass-fibre laminate:

(iv) Size of printed boards: when the size of printed boards increases, the absolute value of the warp increases; this imposes a definite upper limit on printed board dimensions.

Table 8.3

Maximum Permissible Warp

Base Material	Type	Thickness 0,8 mm	1,6 mm
epoxy-glass	double-sided	2%	1%
	single-sided	10%	5%
phenolic paper	double-sided	5%	2,5%
	single-sided	10%	5%

Printed boards of which the dimension expected to be at right angles to the direction of travel across the solder bath is more than 250 mm, as well as printed boards carrying relatively heavy components, such as transformers or choke coils, need to be supported in the centre during soldering. This must be taken into account at the design stage, by locating the heavy components as often as possible near the edges of the printed boards.

There is also the possibility of providing the printed boards with one or more stiffening ribs. The latter provision is recommended when the boards must exhibit minimal warp in service. If metal ribs cause problems with respect to electrical insulation, RF phenomena, *etc.*, non-metallic ribs can be employed. Especially in the case of large boards, care must be taken that sufficient free space is left along the edges for support by the soldering jig.

8.1.1.2 BENDING OF PRINTED BOARD UNDER LOAD OF COMPONENTS

A printed board having a thickness of 1,6 mm, mounted with components such as resistors, ceramic capacitors, transistors, ICs, small switches and small coils, has a weight of approximately 0,1 kg/dm². If the component mixture comprises a definite percentage of heavier components, for instance potcore transformers, the weight of the assembled printed board may increase to approximately 0,2 kg/dm².

Deflection of printed boards is determined by the following equation:

$$y = f.\frac{Q.l^4}{E.d^3}$$

in which: y = deflection of board, l = length of board, Q = mass per unit surface area, E = modulus of elasticity and d = thickness of the board (in m, kg/m² and N/m²). The factor f depends on the situation (f is expressed in N/kg):

f = 1,53 if the printed board is supported at 2 opposite sides, a distance l apart;

f = 0,43 if a square board is supported at 4 sides in such a way that a movement of the printed board edges in the vertical direction is not possible (the corners then showing a tendency to rise);

f = 0,17 if a rectangular board having a length/width ratio of 1,5 is supported at 4 sides as stated;

f = 0,07 if the board having a length/width ratio of 2 is supported at 4 sides as stated.

From this the values given in Table 8.4 can be calculated. The Table shows the importance of an appropriate support of the boards in the carriers. Corners must be held down if small deflections are desired, and also if *l* is relatively large, because of the fourth power of *l* in the formula.

Table 8.4

Deflection of Board Under Load

Support	Length 300 Width 300	Length 200 Width 200	Length 200 Width 133	Length 200 Width 100	mm
2 sides	1,5	0,3	0,3 or 0,06*	0,3 or 0,019*	mm
4 sides, corners down	0,42	0,08	0,032	0,013	

Deflection for $Q = 10$ kg/m^2; $E = 2 \times 10^{10}$ N/m^2 and $d = 1,6$ mm
* Depending on which sides are supported.

8.1.2   Distortion Caused by Temperature Differentials

When in the machine soldering process the conductor side of a printed board contacts the molten solder, the conductor side of the board rapidly assumes the temperature of the solder, whereas the component side of the board continues to be at the temperature imparted to it by the preheater station. Consequently, for a definite period of time, there is a temperature gradient of more than 100°C across the printed board, producing substantial deflections of the board, proportional to the square of the support span.

Large deflections are actually encountered as the experimental results (plotted in Figure 8.1) demonstrate. In these experiments, paper-base and plastic-base printed board laminate materials, with and without copper plating or cladding, were passed through a wave soldering machine while deflection (rise of arc) of laminates was recorded.

In general, there is a deflection of 0 to 1 mm during preheating of the printed boards. This deflection recovers as soon as the printed boards have warmed up uniformly. On contacting the solder wave, the printed boards are subject to a second deflection, now of 0 to 4 mm.

The preheat serves the very useful function of reducing the temperature gradient from bottom to top of the board. Some heat passes to the top of the board during the relatively long preheating time, which would not be possible during the short exposure to the solder wave. Thus the preheating reduces the tendency of the board to bend in the wave. In extreme cases, on large boards, bow in the board could lift part of the underside right out of the wave, preventing soldering.

The permanent deformation of the soldered printed boards bears some relation to the fact that certain types of printed boards become 'as soft as a dish-cloth' at elevated temperature, particularly epoxy-glass laminate that already begins to soften at about 100°C, which is accompanied by considerable changes in the coefficients of thermal expansion [Franz *et al*].

Forced air cooling immediately after soldering reduces the final war
[Waltner]. The metallisation inside the holes increases the rate of achievin
thermal equilibrium between solder side and component side of the printe
boards, thereby reducing their deflection.

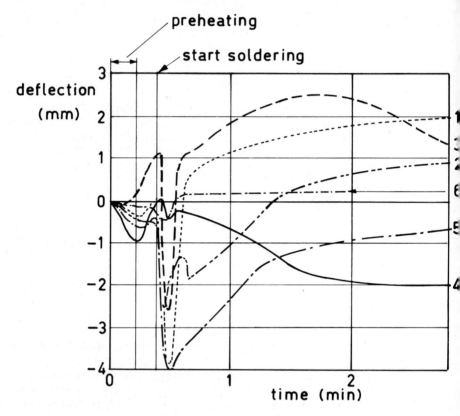

Fig. 8.1 Deflection of copper clad laminates during wave soldering. The boards of 150 × 150 m
were supported at the two sides parallel to transport direction, while the deflection was measured i
the middle of the boards. Curve 1: phenolic paper, 1,6 mm with copper clad; 2: epoxy-glass, 1 m
with copper clad; 3: polyester glass, 1,2 mm with copper clad; 4: polyester glass, 1,2 mm; 5: epox
glass, 1 mm; 6: phenolic paper, 1,6 mm.

The printed boards to be soldered are at room temperature when they ar
placed in the board carriers. In the course of the actual soldering operation the
will assume an average temperature of approximately 200°C, so that their lengt
will increase by about 0,5%. If a printed board at room temperature is alread
such a tight fit in the board carrier that either expansion of the printed board o
difference in expansion between printed board and board carrier cannot b
accommodated, then the printed board will deflect upwards or downwards. It ca
be calculated [Southwell] that if this expansion of 0,5% has to be compensate
for by deflection alone the deflection will be 4% of the board length. This caus
of deflection of printed boards can be entirely eliminated by appropriate desig
of the board carriers.

The permanent bending of the soldered board, as shown in Figure 8.1, may sti e followed by additional bending as a result of temperature variations of the oard during service.

The curves shown in Figure 8.1 do not result solely from the soldering heat, but are also influenced y the internal stresses from the production process of the laminate, which are still present in the aterial before soldering. As such, these curves should not be considered typical for the given aterials.

A temperature treatment of phenol-paper laminate will always produce a shrinkage of the material. or instance, a 1 hour treatment at 100°C, as applied for the curing of solder resist and the drying of rinted ink, gives a shrinkage of about 0,02% parallel to the fibre direction and twice this value at ght angles to the fibre direction. The internal stresses have not yet completely vanished after oldering. A subsequent thermal cycling (*e.g.*, between 25°C and 100°C) will distort single-sided oards so that their solder side becomes convex. The degree of curvature increases with the percentage f the surface area which is covered with copper conductors.

.1.3 Drying of Boards with Plated Holes

The boards emit gases during the soldering operation, which derive from arious sources, such as absorbed or trapped water, organic inclusions in the lectroplated coatings and volatile compounds of the laminate material. The ases evolving from free board surfaces will not harm the joint formation and are imply added to the flux fumes.

In the case of plated holes, gases from the board material will also evacuate via he hole walls whose metal coat can have various degrees of porosity, and the gas ill then penetrate into the molten solder in the hole, thus generating gas nclusions (gas pockets) and blowholes in the soldered joints [Bulwith].

The main source of gas is water, originating in the board manufacturing rocesses. The amount of water to become free during soldering depends on the ype of board material chosen and on the quality of the drilling operation of the oles. In drilling with dull drills the board material is not cut away properly but is meared out while fibres will be torn loose, thus giving many capillary spaces in vhich salt residues and water may accumulate. These capillary spaces are later vergrown by the hole plating, whose porosity will affect the rate at which the vater can escape during the short soldering time.

If too many blowholes are found after soldering the immediate action should •e to try to eliminate the water by heating (predrying) the boards before placing •f the components and soldering.

Predrying of boards can or may be carried out in a ventilated oven. Drying emperature and time are dependent on the substrate material, the type of netallic coating employed, and the prime requirement of maintaining wettability. n practice, these requirements are met by a drying time of 16 hours at a drying emperature of approximately 105°C for boards with a tin or a tin-lead coating. 'or boards that are only copper-clad, the drying temperature is either 80°C or 05°C (maximum), depending on the flux used in the soldering process. Drying or 40 hours at 80°C is equivalent to 16 hours at 105°C.

After the predrying of boards, the subsequent process steps up to and including oldering should be executed within as short a time as possible to prevent the ubstrate material reabsorbing moisture from the atmosphere (Figure 8.2). Thus, or instance, boards predried during the night should preferably continue their rocessing during the immediately following daytime shift.

Predried boards can be stored in a ventilated oven at a temperature from 45°C o 70°C or in a drying cupboard.

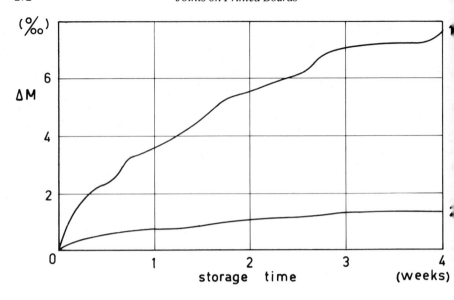

Fig. 8.2 Increase of board weight in a common factory atmosphere of 20-25°C and 50-70% relative humidity, after drying for 16 hours at 105°C. Two curves are shown: for phenolic paper (1) and epoxy glass-fibre laminate (2). Note the irregularities in curve 1 due to the effect of weekends with lower temperature and higher relative humidity.

8.2 COMPONENTS

Printed boards were developed for the mounting of electronic components provided with leads, *i.e.*, with wire-shaped terminations. The use of these printed boards influenced the introduction of new shapes of components particularly suited to mounting on them, *i.e.*, components with radial leads instead of axial leads. The most recent development is the application of leadless components on printed boards, mounted on either side of the board without utilising component holes. Approximately 10^{11} passive components are being produced annually, roughly a half of which are resistors, a quarter capacitors, one eighth electrolytic capacitors and another eighth remaining components.

The active components (transistors and integrated circuits) were developed after the introduction of the printed boards, and as such are nearly all designed for use on these boards, having radial leads or terminations in line.

Table 8.5 presents a survey of types of components with typical examples based on their lead lengths and number of lead-outs. The various components are briefly discussed in the following paragraphs; more comprehensive reviews can be found elsewhere [see Leonida, Anon. Ref. 26].

Table 8.5

Types of Components

Type	2 Lead-outs	3 or 4 Lead-outs	Many Lead-Outs
ong leads (ound or ctangular)	Radial components, axial components	Transistors, rectifier bridges	DIL, SIL
MD with ort leads	Electrolytic capacitors	SOT-23, SOT-89	SO, LDCC
adless MD	MCC, MELF	Adjustable resistors	LLCC

e acronyms are defined in the text.

2.1 Passive Components with Leads

Regarding design, components fall into two groups:

(i) those with axial leads;
ii) those with radial leads (Figure 8.3).

These components differ considerably in shape and dimensions, but one thing ey have in common is that their leads are inserted through holes in the printed oard before the components are finally attached to the solder lands.

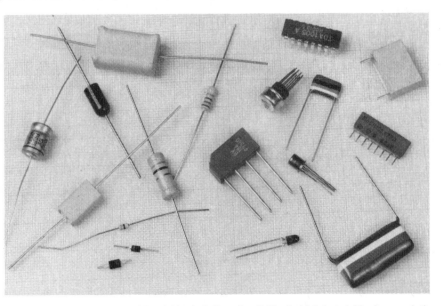

g. 8.3 Various components with axial leads (left) and radial leads (right). Axial leads are pointing the opposite direction, radial leads in the same direction. The word 'radial', though commonly used, is not particularly apt. Note the mm grid.

For the most part, the leads are made of copper with a solder coating, which applied by electroplating or hot dipping during the final stages of wire productic (see Chapter 6), before the wires are connected to the component bodies. For number of components other materials are used, such as manganese-nickel a nickel-iron (mostly coated with solder), for reasons of stiffness or he conductivity. Common diameters of the (copper) leads are 0,6; 0,8 and 1,0 mi

8.2.2 Passive Components Without Leads

Passive components of very simple form without wire terminations but wi metallised bonding pads, such as multilayer chip capacitors (MCC), have bee known for many years, especially for mounting on alumina substrates. Th components may be connected by soldering or by bonding with conductiv adhesives [Dreyer *et al*, Kinser *et al*]. A substantial increase is expected in the u of these components with soldering pads, as both capacitors and resistors as we as active components, because their application on common printed boai laminates for professional and consumer products is being practised more an more widely.

Leadless components are mainly available in two shapes:

(i) With a more or less rectangular shape, having metallised soldering pads, fc instance of fired palladium-silver paste. There is a large variety of thes components (often called chips), common dimensions for multilayer chi capacitors and chip resistors being 1,25 mm × 2 mm and 1,6 mm × 3,2 mn both with a height of about 1 mm (masses respectively 6,5 and 10 mg);

(ii) With a cylindrical shape, having pretinned metallic caps. These componen are called MELF (Metal Electrode Face bonding) components [Honda] an have sizes of for instance 2,2 mm diameter and 6 mm length, or 1,4 mi diameter and 3,5 mm length (masses respectively 68 and 22 mg). Besid MELFs, tubular 'chips' are also being used.

The leadless components of both shapes are available as ceramic capacitors, T and Al capacitors, resistors [Ijiri *et al*], fuses, diodes and bridge conducto (Figure 8.4). Recently, other shapes of leadless components have been intrc duced, *e.g.*, for wire-wound-type 'chip' coils [Takeno, see also Anon. Ref. 28

Some of the advantages of leadless components can be summed up as follow

(i) The small dimensions are useful for high frequency electronics;

(ii) The small dimensions make it possible to mount with a high componer packing density, combined with a small mounting height. Smaller boarc lead to smaller and thinner products [Denda *et al*], to smaller cabinets an to smaller floor spaces for large systems;

(iii) The shape is simple and identical for different components, enabling a easy and cheap mechanisation of the placing;

(iv) The simple shape of the components offers a certain freedom of patter design, especially if 'jumpers' are also to be applied.

(v) The components are highly reliable and have good humidity characteristic

g. 8.4 Examples of leadless components and components with small leads. Note block-shaped chip pacitors and chip resistors, MELF components, transistors in SOT-23 package (bottom, see Fig. 5) and in SOT-89 package, and ICs in SO packages (examples with 8, 14 and 28 terminations). Note the mm grid.

Some disadvantages of leadless components are:

(i) as yet a higher price and an incomplete product range;
(ii) their placing by hand, if necessary, is difficult;
(iii) the technology for mounting in mass production awaits further developments, especially for their application on printed boards (see Chapter 9.5.3).

2.3   Active Components

The encapsulation commonly used for integrated circuits (ICs) is the DIL, with ual in-Line terminations, also called DIP (P for package), or the SIL, with one ries of Single in-Line terminations. These components are intended to be ounted in holes in the board. The terminations of SILs or DILs have a ctangular cross-section of about 0,3 mm × 0,5 mm, a length of 3 to 4 mm, and e placed 2,54 mm apart (Figure 8.5). Various numbers of terminations are und: 8, 14, 16, *etc*. Large models of the DIL may even have more than 50 ·minations.

Transistors are usually available with radial leads and a large number of ckages can be used.

However, packages for ICs and transistors with small or very small soldering ·minations are rapidly becoming more important [Rydwansky]. SO-packages mall Outline) as shown in Figure 8.4 have been developed at Philips in the early venties. They have terminations with sizes of about $0{,}25 \times 0{,}4 \times 1{,}5$ mm^3 at a tch of 1,27 mm, and offer a substantial reduction of the mounting area over the

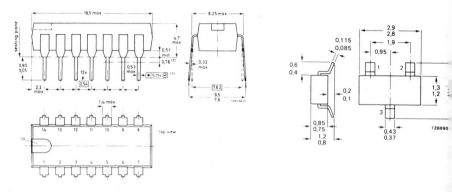

Fig. 8.5   Example of DIL encapsulation (left) and transistor with small terminations (SOT-23, right)
The distance of 0,1-0,2 mm between the support plate and the body of the SOT-23 is now being
changed to a smaller value regarding the mounting process described in Chapter 9.5.3.

conventional packages, as is demonstrated in Table 8.6 [Resendes]. A recent
extension of the SO-family is the VSO-40 (very small outline) having two rows of
20 terminations at a pitch of 0,762 mm (30 mils), a plan area of body of 110 mm
and a component mass of 560 mg, see also Figure 10.15. The SOT-23 package for
transistors, with a mass of 7 mg; has even smaller terminations (Figure 8.5). SO
and SOT-23 packages have been developed for the mounting on the surface of
thick and thin film circuits, but these components are now also being mounted on
printed boards by reflow soldering and by wave soldering (see Chapter 9.5.3).

   Any device in a common DIL-package can, in principle, be made available in
an SO-package with the same number of terminations. It is expected that in the
future many ICs will become available only for surface mounting. The
terminations of the DIL, SO and SOT-23 packages may be of the same material
viz. solder plated nickel iron. Their solderability, however, may differ
considerably, because of injury to the plating of the small leads of SO and
SOT-23 caused by the bending tool.

   One of the smallest encapsulations is the flat package (flatpack multiple-lead
component). The body of such a component can be as small as $6 \times 3 \times 0,8$ mm;
larger flatpacks may have up to 100 lead-outs. The component leads are normally
relatively long flat ribbons lying in one plane and protruding from two or from all
four sides of the component.

   To obtain a high packing density of ICs on support plates, chip carriers can be
used [Pinner, Bauer *et al*, Erickson, Stafford, Fennimore, Val *et al*]. These are
small rectangular or square boxes with soldering pads on their periphery (Figure
8.6). Carriers are made of ceramic or plastic and the IC-chips are mounted in
these and bonded to the inside pads which are interconnected with the soldering
pads. The carriers can then be closed with a cover and the ICs can be measured.

   A critical feature of chip carriers is the thermal expansion mismatch between
the chip carriers and the support plates [Engelmaier, Rossi *et al*], resulting from
different coefficients of thermal expansion of the materials involved, and from
different temperatures associated with non-homogeneous heat dissipation. The
different thermal expansions may easily cause relatively large deformations in the
small soldered joints, so that cracks are readily formed. The stresses in the joints
are directly related to the rigidity of the construction, which can be reduced in

Table 8.6

Comparison between the Size and Space Required by SO and Standard DIL Packages

Number of Pins	8		16		28		
Package Type	SO	DIL	SO	DIL	SO	DIL	
Plan area of body	20	70	40	140	140	500	(mm²)
ratio		3,5		3,5		3,5	
Board area	31	80	62	175	192	590	(mm²)
ratio		2,6		2,8		3,1	
Body thickness	1,45	3,1	1,45	3,6	2,55	3,9	(mm)
Height above printed board	1,75	4,2	1,75	5,1	2,65	5,1	(mm)
Mass	60	600	130	1200	700	4300	(mg)
ratio		10		9		6	

Fig. 8.6   SEM picture of an empty chip carrier soldered on a printed board. The joints were made by condensation reflow soldering. Dimensions of the carrier are $9 \times 7 \times 1$ mm³. The mass of the part shown is 180 mg.

carriers with flexible leads are used instead of rigid soldering pads (Figure 8.7) [see also Brodsky *et al*, St. Louis *et al*, Schoenthaler], or if the substrate is provided with a special layer of a compliant material beneath the copper surface layer [Rafaie, Fishman *et al*].

The differences between the coefficients of thermal expansion of the suppor plates and the chip carriers can be minimised by adapting the plate materia Examples are laminates based on a special fabric and a resin (*e.g.*, Kevlar* fabri and polyimide resin), in which the negative or low expansion of the fabric and the positive expansion of the resin are balanced to yield an overall expansion matched to that of the carriers and clad metal substrates (*e.g.*, copper clad invar) with the wanted thermal expansion, having extra advantages such as high heat conduction and shielding capabilities [Dance, Dance *et al*].

In 1982 chip carriers represented far less than 1% of all types of hermeti packages, but it is expected that over the next decade they will predominate fo various high reliability applications, particularly in the leaded version.

Fig. 8.7 Underside of a ceramic chip carrier with flexible terminations and dimensions of about 12 mm × 12 mm × 3 mm. Similar carriers have also been designed with 20, 28, 44, 68, and 84 leads in ceramic as well as in plastic versions.

The progressive integration of the components demands an increasing number of component lead-outs. Very large-scale integration (VLSI), especially of memories, necessitates the use of more than 200 connections. A component having 100 leads on its periphery in 1 mm pitch (lead width 0,5 mm) occupies an area of more than 25 mm × 25 mm. The outer dimensions of the package can be limited by using a finer pitch or staggered rows of leads, but pin-grid arrays or pad-grid arrays are more effective over 100 lead-outs [Lyman, Hargis *et al*, Amey, Messner].

The choice of the package determines the mounting technology, *e.g.*, surface mounting for chip carriers or plated-hole mounting for the pin-grid arrays. A visual inspection of all soldered joints is not always possible. The hidden joints can only be assessed electrically, and the confidence in reliability of these joints can only be justified by the applied soldering process.

---

*An aramid polymer produced by Du Pont.

The components without leads or with very short leads, intended for surface mounting, both passive components and active components, are sometimes called SMD (Surface Mounted Devices) [Anon. Ref. 24]. Some other acronyms are LCC (Leadless Chip Carrier) and LDCC (Leaded Chip Carrier).

It is noted that a truly high packing density cannot be obtained merely by choosing small component packages, such as SOs, but that a well adapted conductor pattern, having small solder lands and small connections between both sides of the board, is also needed (see also Figure 10.22).

2.4 Electrostatic-Sensitive Devices

This group of devices comprises many kinds of MOS-ICs, FETs, *etc.*, of which the thin insulating glass layers inside the devices may easily be destroyed by an electric force. This damage may be due to many causes, not only soldering. The most sensitive devices will even be destroyed by voltages below 50 V. In reality the devices are destroyed by an electrostatic discharge, but a description of the exact mechanism of the effect is beyond the scope of this work.

Electrostatic potentials have various sources. Many materials common in industrial environments generate high voltages when subjected to friction. These material combinations and the relative movements are unavoidable. Human static potentials are known to reach voltages far over 5 kV.

Another source of high voltages can be traced to transient voltage spikes, originating from switching of electrical equipment. These pulses, occurring for only a short period of time on the supply lines, are transported by one path or another to the sensitive components.

Many devices have built-in protection networks to reduce the chance of damage. However, the added networks may have an adverse effect on the operating characteristics of the device, so that a compromise must always be effected.

The measures to be taken against damage of the components are extensive but straightforward [Berbeco, Lunt]. It goes without saying that the devices should be delivered packed in adequate antistatic or conductive boxes, provided with a warning label of which an example is shown. All handling of unpacked devices

Warning label in accordance with IEC Publication 417, symbol number 5134. (Caution, Observe precautions for handling.)

must take place in a working area with a special floor and on a table provide
with a conductive sheet. Floors and tables can also be sprayed with an 'antista
fluid, but this affords only temporary protection. The personnel involved, th
conductive sheet and all equipment used should be continuously connected t
earth potential. Nylon clothing should not be worn. Handling tools should b
made entirely of conductive materials.

The components to be mounted can be temporarily inserted in antistatic mats
These can be safely transported in the factory, because no special measures ar
required provided the components are in the mats. However, storage of ICs wit
their leads in conductive foam plastic must be avoided, as the wettability of th
leads may be impaired. In the mounting sequence, the sensitive devices must b
selected last, to minimise the risk of damage. The devices to be mounted must b
taken from the protective package by special short-circuit clips which remain o
the devices until the soldered board is measured.

Because the personnel working with the devices have to be connected to eart
(mostly achieved with a wrist strap via a resistor of 0,5 to 1 MΩ), safety measure
must be taken for all equipment connected to the mains. Such equipment shoul
for instance be provided with leakage safety switches, according to local safet
requirements.

If sensitive components are handled by a machine instead of by hand damage i
less likely, as machines do not generate high static potentials.

The soldering of the boards mounted with the sensitive devices is performed i
the usual manner; the soldering equipment should be carefully grounded.

After soldering, the sensitive terminals of the device have acquired electrica
contact with the circuitry of the board and, depending on the electronic design
the risk of damage to the devices is then considerably reduced. In spite of this, i
is good practice to leave the short-circuit clips on the devices as long as possible
to touch only the edges of the boards and to package and transport the soldered
boards on a piece of antistatic mat.

8.3   DESIGN OF PRINTED PATTERN

The design of the printed pattern has a major influence on the soldering results
On the one hand, the pattern must allow for the flow of solder to the area of th
joint; on the other hand, the formation of bridges must be avoided. Too often
attention is paid mainly to machine settings and flux abilities instead o
considering the thermal situation (see Chapter 3) or the layout of the printed
pattern. However, it must be remembered that the boards are not designed
primarily to be soldered with a minimum number of soldering defects; their chie
function is to provide connection of electronic components according to a
electrical functional design, preferably on the smallest possible board are
[Dicken]. The demand for higher density boards, and hence for finer circuitry i
inconsistent with the demand for a decrease in soldering defects. Still, the change
to finer circuitry will continue. Although one conductor between two holes at a
2,54 mm distance, as shown in Figure 8.29, is common, from a purely soldering
point of view it is already a somewhat critical situation, and despite this the trend
to have two or three conductors in between is emerging. This implies th
manufacture of conductors smaller than 200 μm, and the use of conducto
spacings of the same sizes. These can in fact be made, but below 300 μm th
processes become increasingly critical, constituting an inevitable reduction in th

production yield [Bartlett *et al*, Swartzell]. The following Sections will restrict their attention to the common boards with relatively coarse pattern dimensions.

8.3.1 Fillet Sizes

The quantity of solder that is retained in the soldered joint at the moment it loses contact with the solder bath depends on the capillary spaces between the component termination and the solder land on the printed board, and the plated hole if present. Various forces play a role here: capillary, gravity, inertia and viscous forces. These are all in the order of 10^{-3}N, depending on the volumes and dimensions considered. For most shapes, however, the capillary forces are larger than the others by a factor of 5 to 10, and it is for this reason that calculated equilibrium shapes provide an acceptable description of the complicated situation (see Chapter 2.2).

The solidified solder in the joint between the solder land on the printed board and the protruding component lead is called the solder fillet. Its shape and volume are determined by an intricate interaction of surface tension and capillary space, in conjunction with gravity.

8.3.1.1 PRINTED BOARDS WITHOUT HOLE PLATING

Non-metallised holes do not constitute a true capillary space. The only adhesion-promoting area inside a hole is the cutting edge of the copper foil, which may additionally be given a certain flared shape pointing into the hole interior by means of a special tool. The soldered joint in this case will have to be established by the drop of liquid solder being formed round the portion of the component termination projecting from the printed board. Consequently, for the soldering of printed boards with non-metallised holes measures must be taken to guarantee the formation of large solder fillets.

Printed boards without hole plating can be divided into:

(i) Boards having relatively large centre distances between holes, thus allowing component terminations on the solder side to be bent towards the solder lands on the printed boards. This promotes the retention of solder between terminations and solder lands (Figure 8.8a);

(ii) Boards having relatively small centre distances between holes, thus preventing component terminations from being bent towards the solder lands (Figure 8.8b). This type of printed board permits a high packing density.

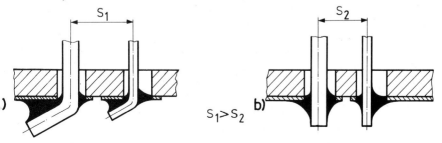

Fig. 8.8 Solder fillets on a single-sided board. The distance $s_1 > s_2$. The distance s_1 allows for the bending of the protruding leads.

In the situation in Figure 8.8b scarcely any capillary for the retention of solder is available between component termination and solder land. The soldered joint is a freehanging bridge of solder between the component termination and the solder land on the printed board. This bridge is in essence in an unstable state; it can easily collapse leaving a hole, especially if the gap between wire and hole wall is large (see Figure 8.16).

The fillet size is not only dependent on the joint design but also on the process conditions during soldering. The quantity of solder retained in the soldering area is influenced among other things by the speed at which the contact between printed board and solder bath is broken. Slow breaking allows more time for the solder to drain away from the joint, resulting in a smaller quantity of solder remaining in the soldering area (Figure 8.9). Such lean joints have an insufficient bearing capability (see Figure 8.33).

Fig. 8.9 Soldered joint on a single-sided board with too little solder in the joint. Compare this joint with that of Fig. 8.15, with the same shape of solder land and wire. Wire diameter 0,6 mm.

The quantity of solder per joint on single-sided boards is between about 1 mm^3 and about 4 mm^3, as can be derived from the weekly solder consumption and the number of joints soldered. The former figure is for small solder lands in the presence of solder resist; the latter is for large solder lands on boards without solder resist, hence including solder on the conductors.

Length of Terminations

If the length of the component terminations projecting from the solder side of a printed board is small (say, less than 0,5 mm), only a small quantity of solder can be retained in the soldering area (Figure 8.10). Moreover, the heat transfer in this case may be insufficient.

Likewise, if the length of the component terminations projecting from the solder side of a printed board is very long, again only a small quantity of solder is

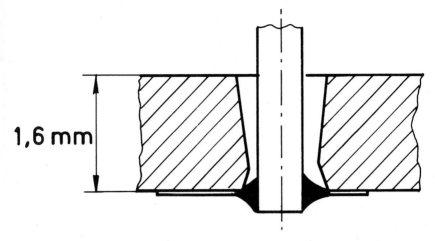

Fig. 8.10   Too small a solder fillet resulting from too small a protruding length of the lead.

retained in the soldering area because solder now flows downwards along the component terminations.

To ensure an adequate size of solder fillet the length of the component terminations projecting at the solder side of the printed boards must be between 1,0 and 2,5 mm. For printed boards with dense component packing, where the centre-to-centre distance between many terminations with their respective solder lands is only 2,54 mm (0,1 in), it is recommended, in order to prevent short-circuits, to choose a small termination length of 1,0 to 1,7 mm. If this kind of printed board is coated with solder resist, for a good inflow of solder somewhat longer terminations are desired (at least 1,5 mm). With the spacing between the solder lands exceeding 2,54 mm, to obtain optimum connections an even greater length of the terminations is to be recommended, namely 1,5 to 2,5 mm. Terminations longer than 2,5 mm are not desirable.

Size of Solder Lands and Holes

A solder land is a part of a conductor used for the connection of a component termination.

The absolute size of the solder lands on the printed boards is obviously an important consideration. A solder land having a size that is well matched to the natural drop size of the molten solder will retain a larger quantity of solder than a larger solder land, because the latter offers more surface for solder spread. A smaller solder land offers simply too little surface area.

A rule of thumb is that the diameter of the solder lands on the printed board must be three times the diameter of the hole (Figure 8.11). When holes are achieved by punching, the possibility must be taken into account of the holes having a diabolo shape. They can be thought of as consisting of two cones in line, with their apices pointing towards each other. In that case, for a printed board material thickness of approximately 1,6 mm, the smallest diameter in the printed board laminate material is approximately 0,15 mm smaller than the diameter in the copper foil. For a printed board laminate thickness of 1,0 mm, this is approximately 0,10 mm.

If insufficient space is available for the concentric arrangement of a solder land

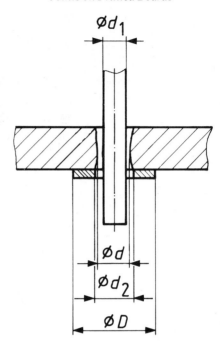

Fig. 8.11 Hole in a single-sided board. In the case of punched holes two hole diameters must be distinguished: the smallest diameter of the hole in the boards, d, and the hole in the copper foil, d_2. d_1 is the diameter of the wire. D is the diameter of the solder land: $d + 1{,}1 \leqslant D \leqslant d + 2{,}2$ mm (*cf.* Fig 8.32).

of the correct size around a hole, it is permissible to locate the hole eccentrically in the land. However, for a good soldered joint the copper land must, at its smallest width, extend for a distance of minimum 0,2 mm from the edge of the hole.

Any interruption of or damage to a solder land will result in fluid-mechanical instability of the liquid drop, *i.e.*, the solder fillet. In fact these defects at the edges of solder lands are major sources of holes in soldered joints (Figure 8.12) Care must therefore be taken to prevent printed board assembly techniques from damaging the edges of the holes. Ends of component terminations, *etc.* are for instance not allowed to exhibit burr, and must be inserted at a right angle to the board face, which is difficult in hand mounting. Automatic mounting results therefore in a substantial decrease of the soldering defects, compared with hand mounting. Damage to edges of solder lands often occurs when the holes in the board have been drilled instead of punched, *e.g.*, in small scale production or for the fabrication of a small number of test boards (!).

The quality of solder land edges after punching is influenced by the suitability of the laminate material for punching and by the ductility of the copper cladding (Figure 8.13). A substantial improvement in the quality of the edges is obtained by applying pressed-in (flared) copper [Anon. Ref. 23, see also pictures of Bud].

In this way a larger surface area is available for the capillary space, implying a better resistance to damage by component terminations being inserted obliquely (Figure 8.14).

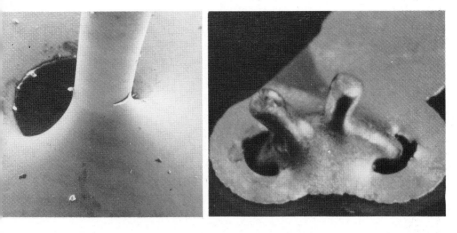

Fig. 8.12 Holes in the solder as a result of defects on the edges of the solder lands (on single-sided board). (left) This situation is aggravated by a non-ideal gap between wire and hole; (right) damage to the edges due to the insertion of kinked leads into the holes in the board.

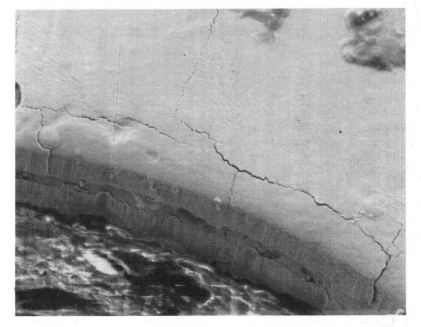

Fig. 8.13 SEM-picture of edge of solder land on a single-sided printed board of phenolic paper laminate, exhibiting cracks resulting from deficient ductility of the copper. With slightly inferior punching conditions, badly injured solder lands may be obtained, Magnification 160×.

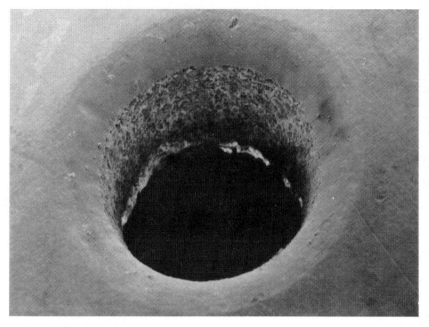

Fig. 8.14   SEM picture of a flanged hole in a single-sided board of phenolic paper laminate Diameter of the hole is 0,8 mm.

Hole punching operations, as well as post-processings on the printed boards intended to press the copper foil against the hole walls, must not violate the requirement for minimum solder land width.

Diameter of Wires (Component Leads)

The diameter of the component terminations is also a significant factor. A thick termination will retain a large amount of solder. Figure 8.15 shows an example of a correct joint on a single-sided board, having an adequate amount of solder.

If the termination of a component to be soldered to a solder land of a printed board has a diameter that is small with respect to the diameter of the hole, there is a considerable risk of the soldering area containing only a small quantity of solder. The bridging between component termination and solder land is then only a thin film and is consequently very unstable. This situation is illustrated schematically in Figure 8.16, which has been derived from a photograph of a section of an actual soldered joint. Such a thin bridge will readily break before the solder has solidified. The surface tension causes the liquid solder film to withdraw to that region of the soldering area where the termination is closest to the edge of the hole of the printed board (Figure 8.17).

A partially open joint of this nature may still perform reliably, if the component termination has such a ductility and the component body such a weight that the loads encountered by the component termination in normal practice can be adequately accommodated. At any rate such a joint with a hole is no weaker than if the original very thin solder film had not been disrupted.

The narrower the gap between termination and hole-wall, the easier it is to bridge this gap with solder. The bridge produced has a larger cross-sectional area

Fig. 8.15 Soldered joint on a single-sided board with a correct amount of solder. Compare this joint with that of Fig. 8.9, with the same shape of solder land and wire. Note in both Figures the delamination caused by the punching operation. Wire diameter 0,6 mm.

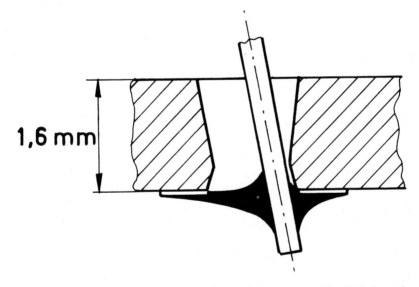

Fig. 8.16 Soldered joint with too thin a wire, producing a strong risk of hole formation.

and is thus stronger. Moreover, with increasing termination thickness, the cross-section of the solder fillet at the point of bridging is larger, thereby reducing the risk of the solder film being disrupted. The difference between the diameter of a hole in a solder land and the diameter of a component termination should preferably not exceed 0,3 mm. In that case, if the eccentricity of the termination

Fig. 8.17 Holes in soldered joints on a single-sided board, caused by an unsuitable ratio of wire diameter to hole diameter. The effect is aggravated by slight dewetting of the conductors.

in the hole is maximal, *i.e.*, if the termination touches the edge of the hole, the maximum bridging distance for the solder will be 0,3 mm. As it is very difficult to punch holes with a smaller diameter than 0,8 mm in printed board laminates of approximately 1,5 mm thickness, the diameter of terminations to be placed in such holes must not be less than 0,6 mm. Conversely, the clearance between termination and hole should not be so small that there is insufficient possibility of escape for flux fumes.

Soldered Leadless Components
    Leadless components (chip components or components for surface mounting)

Fig. 8.18 Combination of chip component and component with wire termination soldered to the solder side of a single-sided printed board. The chip has been cross-sectioned through its centre, where the adhesive is present. Thickness of the board is 1,6 mm.

re soldered using either reflow processes (mostly with solder cream) or wave soldering after the components have been attached by an adhesive (Figure 8.18). The solder gap is determined by the space between the solder land and the metallisation of the component termination, inclusive of that of the side faces of the component (Figure 8.19).

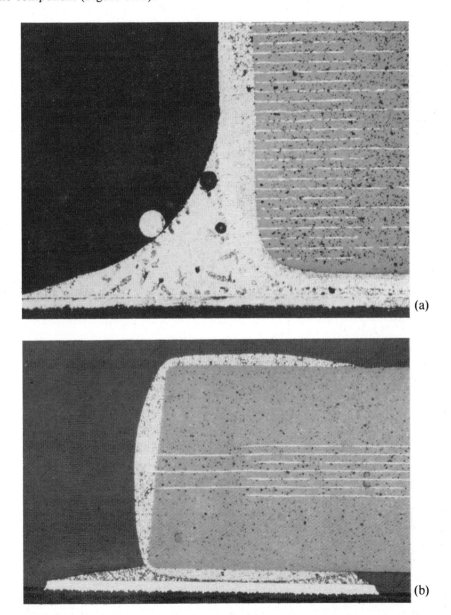

(a)

(b)

Fig. 8.19 Multilayer chip capacitors reflow-soldered to a printed board using two different amounts of solder cream. The solder in the joint (a) reaches to about half the height of the component metallisation, which is sufficient. The joint (b) contains about the minimum amount of solder to give a strong joint, but such a joint cannot be inspected. The height of the components is about 1 mm.

The amount of solder in the joint has virtually no effect on the strength of th
joint, as measured by shear or pull tests. Between 20 and 50 N are required t
break a soldered chip component from the circuit. Fracture always takes place i
the component or in the bond between solder land and laminate, unless a
extremely small amount of solder has been applied. However, in most cases on
requires wetting of the side faces and extension of the solder joint up to a certai
height on the side faces in order to be able to inspect the joints.

The dimensions of the solder lands of leadless components depend on th
tolerances of the components, the printed board and the placing machine. I
most cases suitable dimensions of the solder lands of leadless components c
metric type 3216 (= 1206 in.) are 1,3 mm length and 1,8 mm wide, 2,2 mm apar
although smaller lands are often used.

For wave soldering the minimum side-to-side distance to be realised betwee
the components is 0,8 mm for component height of less than 1,0 mm, and th
minimum head-to-head distance between the solder lands of adjacen
components is 1,0 mm. If a conductor is present between these solder lands, i
should either be small or covered with a solder resist (see Figure 12.29).

For reflow soldering it is permissible to select smaller distances between th
components than those given (Figure 10.22).

8.3.1.2 PRINTED BOARDS WITH PLATED HOLES

Soldering of components to printed boards with plated holes is simpler than t
printed boards without them, because for plated holes the shape of the solde

Fig. 8.20 SEM photograph of the topside of a perfectly soldered joint in a plated hole. The joint ha
been obtained from the same board as that of Fig. 8.21. Diameter of the wire is 0,6 mm.

llet is much less critical. In plated holes, the capillary rise between component rminations and walls of holes substantially promotes the formation of soldered ints. Once the molten solder has been brought into contact with the solid etals, the process sustains itself, provided that the thermal conditions are orrect (Figure 8.20). Owing to the fact that in a completely wetted plated hole ower fillet + plated hole + upper fillet) mechanical strength and heat transfer arcely rely on fillet size, solder land diameters can be considerably reduced. The ace thus made available contributes to the possibility of increased packing ensity. The gap in the holes required (diameter difference) for sufficient enetration of the solder to the upper edge of the printed board must never be less an 0,2 mm, the optimum gap size being 0,4 mm. Terminations with rectangular ctions may be placed in the holes with a tight fit. The remaining space suffices r the solder rise. If the terminations are of a square cross-section, all sides must ermit good soldering, for otherwise there is a chance that the small capillaries ay not be filled. Because of the fairly general occurrence of undercutting of bout 0,05 mm, it is always necessary, in order to prevent etching in the holes, to ave a minimum width at the edges of 0,05 mm around the holes if the thickness f the foil is 35 μm. Undercutting also takes place at the edges of solder lands and onductors (Figure 6.3). If the copper foil has a thickness of 70 μm instead of 35 m, then on account of the increased undercutting the minimum pattern gauge

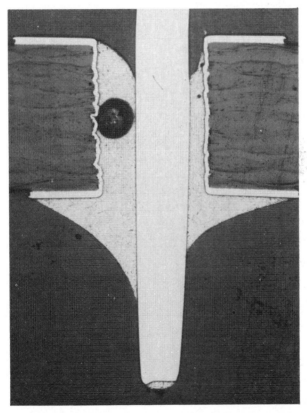

g. 8.21   Incompletely soldered plated hole, resulting from too small a soldering distance. The joint shown originates from the board in Fig. 7.33. Diameter of the wire is 0,6 mm.

must be chosen a little wider. Larger holes, *e.g.*, with a diameter of 1,3 mm, may in certain conditions 'run empty'. If component leads or wires are present in the holes the likelihood of this occurring is practically nil; it is safe to limit the difference in diameter between terminations and holes to 0,6 mm.

The solder lands on boards with plated holes are smaller than on single-sided boards, the diameter of the solder lands usually being hole diameter + 0,7 mm for coarse patterns, hole diameter + 0,5 mm for normal and fine patterns and hole diameter + 0,4 mm for very fine patterns (copper thickness 35 μm).

Upper fillet (that at component side of printed board) and lower fillet (that at solder side of printed board) communicate with each other via the capillary canal. Thus, liquid pressure in the fillets as well as curvatures of surfaces of fillets are interdependent, this being the reason for the upper fillets usually assuming a rather shallow ('flat') shape (Chapter 2.2.4 and Table 2.1). The height of upper fillets in nearly all circumstances is smaller than 0,5 mm, so that solder fillets at the component side of printed boards can be disregarded with respect to the height of mounting of components on printed boards.

Note: An incompletely soldered plated hole is still preferable to an optimally soldered joint in a non-plated hole. Compare Figure 8.21 (incompletely soldered plated hole) with Figure 8.15 (properly-filled joint in non-plated hole).

8.3.2 Printed Conductors on the Board

The conductor pattern exerts a major influence upon bridging, provided no solder resist is applied. Problems with bridging increase with finer pattern dimensions. Bridges are unintended solder connections between metallic parts such as printed conductors or protruding leads. During the soldering operation on a drag or wave soldering machine the entire board surface is in fact bridged by solder. At the end of the dwell time, the contact between the board and the solder bath must be broken, which means that the amount of solder present at the joints must decrease enough to induce spontaneous breaking of the bridges. The design of the board pattern with the capillaries at the protruding leads, together with the process conditions, determines this subtle phenomenon.

The final state of a soldering area is rarely attained via a smooth rate of reduction of the quantity of molten solder but rather via a multitude of metastable transitional states which pass stepwise from one to another. A bridge is usually a metastable transitional state. For the quantity of solder present in a definite area at a definite point in time, it exhibits the minimum surface area of liquid; but relatively small alterations in the shape of the liquid quantity are capable of disrupting the bridge, thereby forming two separate liquid quantities. Together these have the same total volume as the original single liquid quantity, but a smaller total liquid surface area.

8.3.2.1 PARALLEL CONDUCTORS

After breaking the contact between the board and the solder bath, a certain amount of solder will remain on the conductors. This amount may display a significant variation between different places on the board, depending on the precise way in which the transition states are passed through. With a large volume of solder on the conductors, bridging is more likely than with a small volume. Consider two parallel conductors covered with solder, partly bridged as shown in

Figure 8.22. The situation resembles a zip-fastener, and whether it will open or close depends on the shape and on the amount of solder present on the conductors. The stable situation in which no opening or closing occurs is present if the total surface area per unit length of the liquid solder on the two conductors to the left of point P in Figure 8.22 is equal to the area per unit length to the right of point P. At the same time, of course, the requirements of a constant volume of solder must be satisfied. On the basis of these starting points, Figure 8.22 has been calculated. The relative conductor spacing is plotted versus the relative height of the solder on the separate conductors, thus defining the neutral situations. It can be seen that the bridging becomes likely if the conductor spacing decreases, or if the amount of solder increases. However, with the common widths of conductors and conductor spacings, this kind of bridging will not occur provided a large volume of solder is not retained on the conductors during soldering.

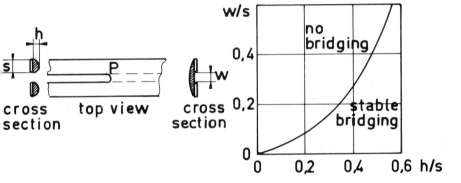

Fig. 8.22 Bridging between two parallel conductors depending on the amount of solder retained after soldering.

The solder must be able to drain as uniformly as possible over the entire width of the printed board in a coherent flow. Conductors lying transverse to the direction of transport, especially if there are several in succession, are particularly unfavourable. The solder withdraws in 'jumps' from one conductor to the other, and each time it must release the printed board correctly. At these transition states a situation exists similar to that shown in Figure 2.8. If a jump is taken badly, too much solder remains on the conductors, resulting in bridging. If the conductors lie in the direction of transport, jumping does not occur and the solder can drain along them. At an angle to the direction of transport the situation rapidly becomes less favourable. The implications for design of boards with a normal or fine pattern are shown in Figure 8.23. Values of conductor widths and spacings for very fine patterns (double-sided boards, plated holes) may be $w = 0,20$ mm and $s = 0,15$ mm.

Finer conductors and finer spacings make it possible to use smaller boards, though at the expense of an increased risk of broken conductors on the board and of solder bridges after soldering, unless a solder resist is applied [Bartlett *et al*].

A conductor spacing of 0,3 mm generally allows for the safe operation of a peak voltage between the conductors of 50 V (0,5 mm – 115 V; 1 mm – 260 V), though the breakdown voltages are considerably higher [Spec. Ref.6, Lehner *et al*]. The conductor width, w, is only in rare cases determined by the current

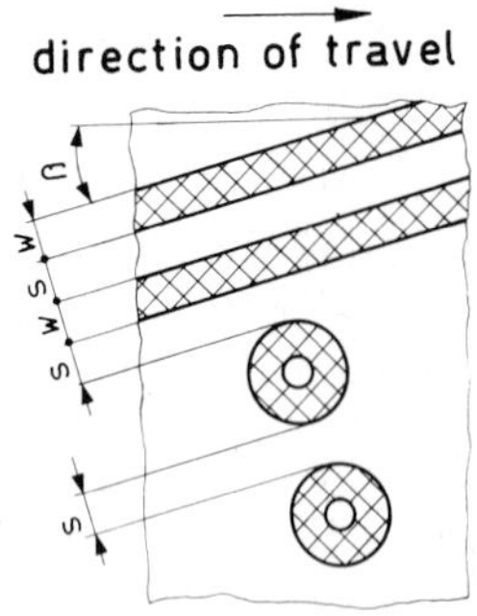

direction of travel

	fine pattern $0,3 \leqslant w \leqslant 0,5$	normal pattern $0,5 \leqslant w \leqslant 3,0$
$0° \leqslant \beta \leqslant 15°$	$s \geqslant 0,3$ preference $s > 0,5$	$s \geqslant 0,5$ preference $s > 1$
$\beta > 15°$	$s \geqslant 0,6$ preference $s > 1$	$s \geqslant 0,6$ preference $s > 1,5$

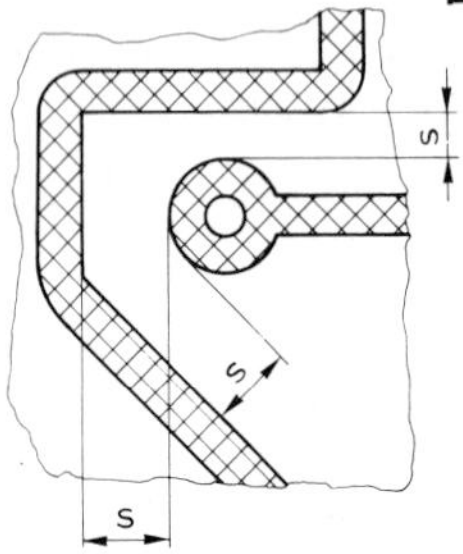

Fig. 8.23 Spacing between two parallel conductors or between conductors and soldering lands. The necessary spacing depends on the angle between the conductors and the direction of travel.

density. A conductor having a width of 0,3 mm and a thickness of 35 μm, carrying a current of 1 A, rises in temperature by only about 10; with 2 A, about 50 K [Spec. Ref.3, see also Scarlett].

The pattern of the conductors must not impede the draining and special consideration should be given to corners in which the solder may become trapped (Figure 8.24). In many cases it will be necessary, in accordance with the dimensions of the printed board, to determine the soldering direction as early as at the design stage and, in accordance with this direction of soldering, to ensure a 'flowing' arrangement of the conductor pattern.

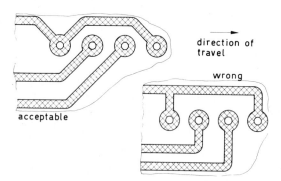

direction of travel

wrong

acceptable

Fig. 8.24 Conductors to solder lands. Draining of solder is helped by avoiding right angled corners and tracks transverse to direction of travel.

.3.2.2 SPONTANEOUS OPENING OF SHORT CIRCUITS

The pattern of conductors should be designed so that undesirable bridges are ot maintained, and attention should be paid to cases involving several closely paced conductors, above all if the ratio of width of conductor to conductor pacing is unfavourable, and if isolated parts of the pattern are enclosed by other arts. End points lying 'downstream', to which solder tends to flow and thus crease the layer thickness, are specially critical. This is also the case for the railing end of the boards, on which too much solder may be retained on exit om the solder bath. Therefore it is preferable to solder the boards with the long ide in the transport direction, thus minimising the width of the end edge. The onductors on the solder side of the boards must be designed to lie parallel to the onger edge of the boards as much as possible. If for production reasons more oards are to be soldered simultaneously, the correct direction must of course be aintained. The conductor pattern should be separated from the end edge for at ast 3 mm, and certainly at this position no transverse conductors may be resent.

Areas on the laminate material surrounded by conductors and areas between losely spaced conductors will lead to temporary trapping of flux during oldering. Flux droplets will occasionally be trapped between unplated areas of he laminate material and skins of solder which cover these areas and connect the djacent pattern parts just after the contact with the solder bath (wave) has been roken. Under the influence of the developing vapours from the flux and the aminate material, these solder skins will burst and the solder will withdraw to arying extents onto the adjacent conductors (Figure 8.25). This bursting of the kins will often be accompanied by solder spatters on the unplated laminate urface near the areas where the flux has been trapped (see also Figure 12.19). he nature and amount of flux, together with the degree of predrying, largely etermine whether this phenomenon will occur.

ig. 8.25 Burst solder skins on a printed grid pattern, associated with trapped flux droplets. Magnification about 2×. (by courtesy of G. Schouten, Hilversum).

The 'apparent bridge' is a special type of bridge (see Figure 8.26). This is a soldered connection for which it is not clear whether it was intended in the design or not. The conductor pattern should allow intentional connections to be recognised as such, by giving the conductors between the solder lands, *etc.*, a proper shape, for instance a bend.

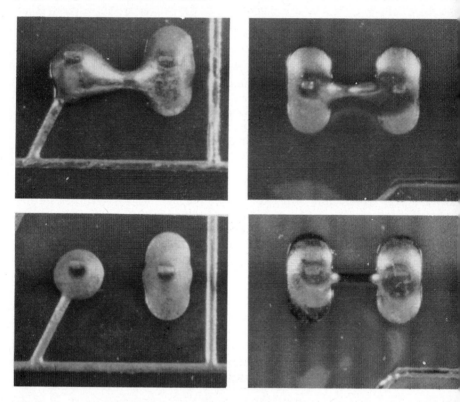

Fig. 8.26   Apparent bridges. The top-left case is a bridge and the top-right case is in fact a solder-covered conductor, as is shown by the two lower pictures. The location or the shape of the conductor between the solder lands is wrong (by courtesy of P. Langeveld, Eindhoven).

8.3.2.3   INTERRUPTED SOLDER LANDS ON SINGLE-SIDED BOARDS

A particular situation which is prone to (unwanted) solder bridging is constituted by a solder land surrounding a hole in the printed board, where it is intended to be kept free of solder in machine soldering. At a later stage in assembly a component termination must be inserted in this hole by hand and soldered with a soldering iron. Keeping this type of hole free of solder is achieved by interrupting the solder land surrounding the hole, making it fork-shaped (Figure 8.27).

Fig. 8.27   Fork-shaped solder lands on single-sided board are not closed during machine soldering. They allow for easy addition of components by hand soldering at a later stage.

8.3.3   Terminations in Close Proximity

The space between parallel component leads, positioned close together and perpendicular to the board surface, constitutes a point where a bridge could form (Figure 8.28). Not only can such a 'capillary' be easily bridged, but under certain

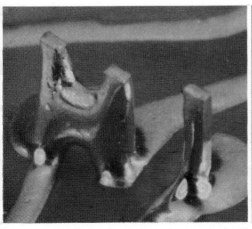

Fig. 8.28   Solder bridges between two parallel leads. The left bridge is caused by wrong joint design: leads too close relative to their length. The smooth surface of the solder indicates that the process conditions were presumbaly correct during soldering. The bridge to the right with its rough surface is the result of wrong process conditions. Compare also Fig. 12.9.

conditions such a bridge is even relatively stable. The occurrence of this type of bridge is difficult to prevent even by the application of solder resist.

The appearance of the solder surface is important; it should be uniform and smooth, showing that the solder has not been oxidised prior to solidification. If the solder surface is rough and striated, the conditions during soldering were presumably the cause of bridging (Figure 8.28).

With components having several terminations in a row at a spacing of 2,54 mm (0,1 in), for example, with print plugs or DILs, the situation is rather critical for obtaining good soldered connections that are free from short circuits. The most suitable shape for the solder lands is a circle (Figure 8.29). The terminations can be round or rectangular in two arrangements. With conductors between the

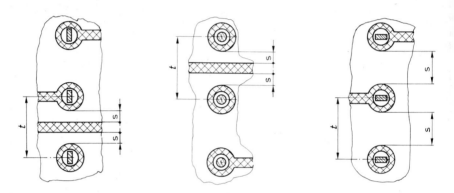

Fig. 8.29 Solder lands for terminations in-line. Conductors between the solder lands are only permitted for round terminations and rectangular terminations arranged parallel to the in-line direction. For a creepage distance $s \geqslant 0,3$ mm and $t = 2,54$ mm, the conductor width is $\leqslant 0,3$ mm and the outer diameter of the solder land $\leqslant 1,6$ mm (inner diameter of solder land $\leqslant 1$ mm).

solder lands, not all the requirements for conductor spacings of Figure 8.23 can be fulfilled, but from the layout point of view it is often mandatory to have conductors between the solder lands and to arrange the components in both directions with respect to the solder direction. From the soldering point of view the conductor spacings will then be small, with the result that this layout creates an increased risk of bridging. Conductors between the solder lands are only permissible for components with round wires or rectangular terminations with their lengths in the in-line direction. If the rectangular terminations are orientated transversely, and if conductors are also present between the solder lands, the number of short circuits is extremely large.

Experiments reported in the literature show low bridging frequencies when using elliptical or rounded-off shapes for the solder lands; however, these tests were carried out without conductors between the lands and without protruding terminations [Comerford, Ruhl *et al*]. These conditions are essentially different from production conditions. The Author's experiments reveal that, depending on the situation, ellipses are either worse than or, at best, as good as circles, but certainly not better than them.

SO-Packages

SO-packages form a separate group of components, which can be either wave soldered (after being adhered to the solder side of the board) or reflow soldered.

The wave soldering of SOs, simultaneously with various other types of components, has not yet been generally accepted, because it is difficult. The closely spaced terminations readily obtain unwanted bridges, especially those of the trailing row, if the component is conveyed transversely. It is preferable to solder the SOs lengthwise, but special measures in the conductor pattern may still be necessary to ensure a sufficient drainage of the solder from the trailing terminations.

The risk of bridging is reduced if smaller solder lands are selected. However, if the width of the lands is smaller than the width of the terminations, there will be no meniscus at the sides of the terminations when the component is placed in true position, thus making the assessment of the joints extremely difficult. Having a nominal width of the component leads of 0,40 mm (max. 0,45 mm), a land width of 0,50 mm is suitable, whereas the length of the land, for instance 2,5 mm, is not critical. These dimensions easily allow for the designing of a separate conductor between the lands, of course to be coated with a solder resist.

For reflow soldering there is more freedom to select a smaller land to land insulation distance, because the risk of bridging is smaller than with wave soldering.

Matters of placing accuracy, in relation to tolerances of the board, of the printed pattern and of the solder resist pattern, however important, are not dealt with in the present text.

8.3.4   Avoidance of Obstructions to Solder Flow

The measures to be taken may be in terms of the design of the printed board, or of additional provisions in respect of clamping of the printed board during soldering.

8.3.4.1   SHAPE OF THE PRINTED BOARD

The printed boards must have a rectangular perimeter. Any departure from this shape leads to difficulties, such as complicated construction of the soldering jig and scooping of molten solder.

In the designing of boards, it is essential to take into account the need to use board holders during soldering, so that bending of the printed boards can be kept within the specified limits.

Rectangular apertures whose dimensions exceed 30 mm in the transport direction or 10 mm in the transverse direction, and all circular apertures whose diameters exceed 20 mm, must be covered during soldering. For this purpose, blocks are loosely placed on top of the board (Figure 8.30). These are made of paper-base laminate having a thickness of 8-10 mm (not less, to avoid their being

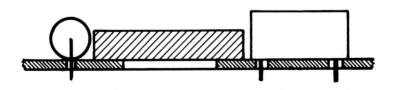

Fig. 8.30   Block of synthetic material to close a large aperture in a printed board during the soldering operation.

lifted by the solder), whereas their other dimensions must be such that the blocks completely close the apertures, and are held in position by adjacent components

8.3.4.2   ESCAPE OF GASES

The design of the printed board must provide escape ways (in the form of holes in the board) for flux vapours and other fumes or gases. Moreover, care must be taken that these holes are not obstructed or even closed by, for instance components mounted on the printed board. Especially in the drag-soldering process, flux gas can be entrapped under the board, and can impede contact between solder bath and printed board. The escape holes, if present in a sufficient number, will solve this problem. Each imaginary circular area of the printed board with a diameter of 40 mm should have at least one completely open hole with a minimum diameter of 0,6 mm, or else the same area should contain at least four holes in which terminations are mounted.

Printed boards with plated holes must, for the sake of penetration of solder have more than 0,2 mm space between the walls of the holes and the terminations. This space also suffices for the escape of the gases.

On the printed boards without hole plating, where in respect of solder penetration closing of the holes would not matter, there must be sufficient space for the escape of the gases between the walls of the holes and the terminations

Escape holes can, however, be closed inadvertently by various means such as

(i)   Incorrect wire-to-hole ratio, resulting for instance from application of a different component from that envisaged in the design. With round terminations in non-plated holes, the difference in diameter between hole and termination must be at least 0,1 mm. For rectangular (not square) terminations in round holes there is always adequate space, even if these terminations have a tight fit;

(ii) Tolerance violations such as excess encapsulant material on component terminations;

(iii) Incorrect methods of mounting of components or other hardware to the printed board.

8.3.4.3   SHADOWING EFFECT OF ONE SOLDERING POSITION ON ANOTHER

In the design of the printed board it is necessary to ensure that the solder surface is not disturbed to such an extent that it cannot reach all soldering positions. Difficulties arise especially from small soldering positions behind or between closely spaced terminations which project into the solder, in particular if no supply of solder is possible via the conductors, as when solder resist is used. To avoid the shadowing effect, the length of the terminations projecting under the printed board must be less than 2,5 mm. In addition, account must be taken of parts which are not soldered but which nevertheless project under the printed board, such as plug heads, screw heads and tags of reinforcing strips. This is also applicable to the soldering jig.

8.3.4.4   ISOLATED SOLDER LANDS

Small isolated solder lands (without holes) are in many cases screened from the older by a film of flux, the use of a solder resist further enhancing this effect. uch solder lands which have to be provided with a layer of solder must have a liameter of at least 3 mm. If this is not possible, the solder must be able to flow to he solder land via other soldering areas. The pattern of any solder resist used nust be adapted to this.

.3.5   Solder Resist (Solder Stop-off)

Solder resist is a non-wettable and heat resistant coating on a printed board aving openings at the solder lands to be soldered. The main reason for its pplication is to eliminate the influence on the soldering mechanism of printed onducting areas which do not require soldering. Preventing in this way the nderlying printed conductors in particular from exposure to liquid solder recludes solder bridging of adjacent conductors, thus removing a major cause of nalfunctioning of printed boards. It is obvious that the application of solder esist increases the freedom of design of printed conductor patterns, not only as roublesome areas are covered, but also because of a more controlled flow of the older with less spread in contact times. In the case of printed boards without hole lating, drainage from joints is restricted by the solder resist, ensuring an dequate quantity of solder in the joints.

On printed boards provided with a tin-lead plating under the solder resist, this lating will melt during the soldering operation, thereby causing permanent /rinkling of the solder resist coat (Figure 8.31). This may then even crumble off nd produce trouble in switches, *etc.* Such a problem can be remedied by eflowing the tin-lead plate prior to applying the solder resist (see Chapter 6.4.3).

ig. 8.31   Wrinkling of the solder-resist coat caused by melting of the solder plating on the conductors during the soldering operation.

8.3.5.1 PATTERN OF SOLDER RESIST

Diameter and eccentricity tolerances for openings in the solder resist patter intended to coincide with solder lands of coarse patterns are shown in Figu 8.32.

Openings in the solder resist extending to the adjacent conductors can l prevented in the printed board design by providing sufficient clearance betwee solder lands and adjacent conductor tracks [Wheeler]. Solder resist may cau small isolated solder lands without holes to be accidentally missed out i soldering. On the other hand, solder resist can isolate certain regions of th pattern, enhancing the risk of bridging within these isolated regions. In such case, it is better to leave a part of the pattern free of solder resist.

During application of the solder resist, the edges of the printed board and o the holes already present in the base material must be kept free, to prever spreading of solder resist over the edges. If in a further processing stage th printed board is divided into printed boards of smaller dimensions, this la requirement as regards edges can be ignored.

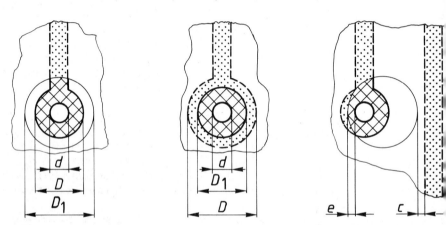

Fig. 8.32 Pattern of solder resist at solder lands. d, D and D_1 are diameters of hole in the boar diameter of solder land and diameter of opening in solder resist, respectively. For boards with plate holes: $D_1 - D \geqslant 0$ and $e \geqslant 0,05$ mm. For single-sided boards: $D \geqslant d + 1,1$; $e \geqslant 0,2$ an $d + 1,1 \leqslant D_1 \leqslant d + 2,2$ mm (*cf.* Fig. 8.11). In all cases: $c > 0$.

8.3.5.2 ADDITIONAL ADVANTAGES

Some additional advantages of solder resist are:

(i) after soldering, the solder resist coat improves the surface resistance of th printed boards and to some extent prevents it from being reduced t moisture and contaminants;

(ii) the coat promotes effective visual inspection of solder joints, in that reduces the glare-generating area and thereby operator fatigue, at the sam time directing attention to the soldered areas;

(iii) the risk of short circuits by solder slivers and similar objects is eliminate (Chapter 6.3.3);

(iv) thermal shock of the boards during soldering is slightly reduced, as is also the warp of the boards;

(v) the consumption of solder is reduced (for instance by 1 dollar cent per dm²);

(vi) the professional appearance of boards with solder resist is generally appreciated.

1e main disadvantage of solder resist is the cost of the application process.

3.5.3 COATING THICKNESS AND TYPE

Thickness of solder resist coats is approximately 10 μm. Solder resists can be of ree types (not discussed in further detail): rubber based (air drying), epoxy ised (thermosetting) and acrylate based (UV curing) [Elsberg].

The main method of application of solder resist is screen printing, especially on)ards with relatively coarse patterns. It is a matter of tolerances to have the reened pattern coincide sufficiently with the printed pattern. Deviations arise om various sources, such as the shrinkage of the boards during etching process eps, the inaccuracy of the screen manufacture, the method of reference of reen to boards, the deformation of the screen during printing and the bleeding ˙ the screened resist. Some of the sources mentioned can be eliminated by using iotographic methods, which thus are more suitable for fine patterns, though ey are much more expensive.

ite: The limits of practical technology for producing boards with very fine patterns are more often ind in the application of solder resist than in the etching of the fine lines.

ite: The slightest contamination by solder resist of areas to be soldered, either by misregistration of der resist pattern or by solder resist bleeding (unintentional flow-out of solder resist), renders these eas irreversibly unsolderable and necessitates scrapping of the printed board. The contamination is ten hardly visible or even invisible so that it is difficult to trace this source of defects.

4 MECHANICAL PROPERTIES OF SOLDERED JOINTS

Data on tensile strength and shear strength of soldering alloys afford sufficient insight into the performance of soldered joints under actual loads, in hich almost invariably creep and fatigue are the determining factors. A solder llet in a plated hole is capable of withstanding short-term forces of a few indred N [Anon. Ref.12] and solder fillets on printed boards without hole ating will support similar loads, provided that the component is loaded in nsion [Le Penven *et al*]. If, in the case of printed boards without hole plating, e components are loaded in compression or subjected to bending, tearing or eeling forces, then the adhesive bond between the solder land and the printed)ard laminate will yield sooner than the soldered joint.

If a soldered joint has an insufficient quantity of solder, there is a risk of ˙eaking of the joint by forces arising later on during assembly, transport or use f the equipment. Figure 8.33 shows an example of such a broken soldered joint 1 a single-sided board. These weak, but not yet broken, soldered joints can only : detected with difficulty by visual inspection, especially if the situation is not so :treme. Forces on the joints, particularly on single-sided boards, must be /oided. Mechanical aligning of components as well as cutting off excess length ˙ component terminations after soldering is not recommended, both processes

being likely to induce inadmissibly high stresses in soldered joints. If certa
precautions are taken, component terminations may be bent to a limited exte
for instance for electrical aligning purposes. The rupture of the soldered joint
Figure 8.33 may be considered a trivial event, but even originally perfect joi
may fail eventually. In the case of long-term loading, the life of the solder
joints is not only dependent on their shape but also on the type and magnitude
the load and on temperature [Kobayashi].

Fig. 8.33   Broken joint on a single-sided board. This soldered joint was too lean, having a fillet w
only a very thin connection with the solder land (*cf.* Fig. 8.9).

In Chapter 4.7 the strength properties of solder alloys have been discusse
From the data provided, it is known that a normal soldered connection on
printed board is not well suited to withstanding a permanent mechanical loa
Given the low creep strength of the solder and the small area of attachment, t
loading of a connection will have to be lower than 0,1 N if the desired service li
is to be achieved. If heavier loads occur, such as those due to the mass of bigg
components, stress relief measures will need to be adopted. In very special case
the soldered joints can be strengthened using crimped top hats, pierced sprir
discs and washers, or by pinching the wire [Frankland *et al*]. So-called gripl
connectors are applied for the same purpose, both on single-sided and doubl
sided boards [Olsson].

8.4.1   Expected Mean Life

The life of electronic products is determined only partly by the quality of tl
soldered joints; the influence of the components is of greater importance. T
quality of a soldered product can never be better than that of its component
because the relatively heavy thermal load during soldering may damage tl
components to some degree. Properly designed joints which have been we
soldered are highly reliable. However, in reality many joints are potential failu
sources as a result of insufficient design or doubtful processing.

The reliability of separate components is expressed as the mean time between failures and its inverse is called the failure rate λ_n.

The reliability of a complex system of n components is:

$R_s = \exp - (\overset{n}{\underset{1}{\Sigma}}\lambda_n).t$. This R_s gives the chance that the system will perform satisfactorily during the time t.

The failure rate of components depends on their nature and on the way they are applied. For example, the failure rate of a common carbon resistor under standard conditions is in the order of 10^{-9} per hour, but under more severe conditions this figure must be multiplied by a factor given in Table 8.7.

Table 8.7

Multiplication Factors for Various Conditions of Carbon Resistors

	Ambient Temperature				Power Rating				
	45°C	*70°C*	*100°C*	*150°C*	*0,2*	*0,4*	*0,6*	*0,8*	*1*
Multiplication factor	1	5	10	25	1	1	1,5	4	10

Reliability data have been published for many components [Mattera, Masberg]. For soldered joints, properly designed and made, the failure rate is about 10^{-10} per hour [Duhm]. However, multiplication factors such as given in the Table for resistors are not known for soldered joints. The low value for the failure rate of soldered joints means that the failure of equipments is more likely to be attributable to component failure than to the failure of soldered joints. This confirmed by a series of results obtained from radio sets in a half-year simulation test. About 5% of the failures were due to soldering defects of the machine-soldered and reworked joints, and 5% were caused by a relatively small number of hand-soldered connections. The other failures (90%) had causes not related to soldering but to board defects (20%), mounting defects (20%), and component defects (50%). However, with improper joint design or bad soldering processing, the percentage of faults caused by soldered joints will be much higher.

8.4.2   Cracking of Joints

The majority of defects in initially good soldered joints are caused by cyclical loading which is omnipresent. This loading arises from the variations in the temperature of the equipment associated with switching on and switching off. Some connections, such as the soldered joints of the terminations of power resistors and power transistors, may experience large temperature variations. The heat dissipation of the latter components is to a considerable degree co-determined by the component terminations and by the printed conductors to which they are connected. When the temperature in a soldered joint changes, the joint is subjected to mechanical stress due to temperature gradients and to differences in the thermal expansion coefficients of the printed board material, metallic content of the plated hole and of the component. The mechanical stress in the solder can be quite considerable. Whereas, admittedly, it gradually decreases under the influence of solder creep, it is generated anew (but in the

opposite direction) by the next temperature change. The result may be that **t**
joint starts cracking [Bangs *et al*, Dunn] and the surface of the crack **th**
oxidises, causing the electrical contact resistance to increase. The soldered **jo**
may eventually degrade to the extent where the electrical connection is **eitl**
completely lost or is so reduced as to cause various degrees of annoyance, such
crackle.

Boards with a thickness of 1,6 mm exhibit more cracks than boards **with**
thickness of 1 mm, the diameter of the plated holes having no significant **eff**
[Gonzales].

Consider a joint as shown in Figure 8.34, where the middle of the **board**

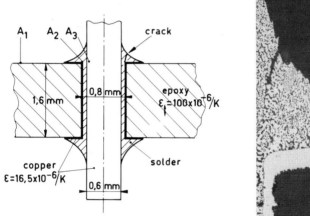

Fig. 8.34 Soldered plated hole subjected to thermal fatigue due to differences in thermal **expansi**
of the board material and the component leads; (left) shape of a hole with wire/hole **ratio** of 0,6/**C**
(right) micrograph of part of a joint showing cracks in the solder, developed during 500 thermal **cyc**
between −55°C and +100°C. The example shows two major cracks (running more or less **vertic**
and horizontally) and a clear deformation of the outer fillet surface, partly resulting from the **bend**
of the solder land. Magnification 125×.

taken as the neutral plane. The expansion coefficient of the board normal to **t**
board surface is 100×10^{-6}/K, and of the copper $16,5 \times 10^{-6}$/K. If the **board**
heated from 25°C to 100°C ($\Delta T = 75$K), the board surface remote from the **plat**
hole (for instance at point A_1) will displace $\frac{1,6}{2} \times 100 \times 10^{-6} \times 75$ mm = 6μm, **wi**
respect to the neutral plane. If the copper plating of the hole could expand **free**
the point A_2 would displace $\frac{1,6}{2} \times 16,5 \times 10^{-6} \times 75$ mm≅1 μm. However, the **h**
plating with the solder lands is firmly connected to the laminate material so **th**
the vertical displacement of point A_2 will be between 1 and 6 μm. To estimate **t**
displacement one could consider only the cylindrical part of the board **mater**
between the solder lands (width 300 μm). If the thickness of the copper **plating**
the hole is 30 μm, and if the ratio of the Young's moduli of laminate and **copper**
1:10, the displacement of the point A_2 will be about $\frac{6+1}{2} = 3,5$ μm (with respect
the neutral plane), if the solder in the joint yields. The vertical displacement
point A_2 with respect to point A_3 is thus $3,5 - 1$ μm = 2,5 μm, implying that **t**

ιear strain in the solder layer of 0,1 mm is 2,5%. This means that the solder at ιe position A_2 exceeds the yield strain every time the temperature is changed, ith the result that near point A_2 a crack will develop. The equation $^{0,4} \times \delta = 0,56$ has been given (see Chapter 4.7.3) for isothermal shear strain with cycle per minute at 25°C. For 2,5% strain the number of cycles to fracture is ɔout 2400. At higher temperatures, somewhat smaller values of N are found, so ιat for cycling between 25°C and 100°C N will be smaller than 2400. This ‐timate only intends to clarify the origin of the solder cracking and does not aim to give a correct prediction of the life of the given joint, because the ιlculation is based on too many assumptions and simplifications. For instance, ιe stress-strain situation in soldered joints is much more complicated than just a ιmple shear [Anon. Ref.12]. The plastic deformations of a specific joint depend ɔ much on its dimensions, materials, *etc.*, and on the actual temperature history, ιat its fatigue behaviour cannot be predicted precisely from the bulk solder ‐operties [Kobayashi, Munford].

On the other hand, the susceptibility to the formation of fatigue cracks is ‐esumably related to the ductility of the solder alloy used, which does not only ‐pend on composition and grain size, but also on the stability of the grain ιructure. The ternary alloy tin62-lead36-silver2 thus shows an improved fatigue ‐sistance compared with that of the eutectic tin-lead alloy [Waine *et al*].

Associated with the large cracks induced by the macroscopic expansion ‐ismatch of the constituting parts of the joint and external forces on the leads, ιere are often many smaller cracks present in the deformation zone beside the ‐rge cracks. Moreover, the surface may show distortions, such as shown in ‐gure 8.35, caused by expansion mismatch on a microscale (Chapter 4.7.3).

The cracking susceptibility of joints can be investigated with thermal cycling or

ς. 8.35 SEM photograph of part of the surface of a solder fillet on a double-sided board as in ‐gure 8.34, after 500 thermal cycles (− 55°C to + 100°C). The surface shows features such as small ιcks and 'extruded' portions of solder, which give the surface a rough appearance. Magnification
640 × .

thermal shock tests. As these tests are time consuming the thermal amplitude
increased in order to accelerate the tests, as was also carried out in the tests o
Figures 8.34 and 8.35. However, cycling with an amplitude >150K is rathe
remote from reality and may introduce uncommon effects. The results of suc
tests should therefore be assessed with great care [see Baker].

The material of the component body can have an adverse effect in that it ma
promote crack formation in the soldered joints due to different therma
expansions. This is also the case with encapsulating conformal coatings, whic
are sometimes necessary for the survival of the electronic components in high
vibration-level environments. If conformal coating is mandatory, it should be a
thin as possible and should certainly not bridge the gap between component an
board [Frankland *et al*, Gonzales]. A stress relief in component leads and th
application of expansion-absorbing spacers are useful.

The adverse effect of encapsulating material on the temperature cyclin
performance is also clear for SOT-23 packages soldered to thick-film on alumin
substrates. If fatigue cracking of one of the joints occurs, it is always the singl
lead of the SOT-23 package [Panousis *et al*].

All measures that tend to reduce mechanical loading and temperature swing ar
equally effective in diminishing crack formation. The design of mounting o
components to printed boards must inherently preclude mechanical stresses. Ver
detrimental effects can be expected from fastening the components with screw
together with using short stiff soldered connections (Figure 8.36).

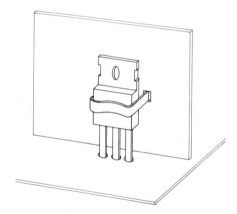

Fig. 8.36   The mounting of a power transistor. It can be achieved in two ways: if the terminations ar
soldered, the transistor must be loosely clamped (shown); if the transistor is firmly attached with
screw, the leads must be soldered with flexible wires.

With some poor designs the development of cracks proceeds extremely rapidly
The construction of Figure 8.37 is such an example, showing solder tags in
single-sided board. On the left the tag is attached only by the fillet and hence th
force allowed in the eyelet is limited, because otherwise the solder land will brea
away from the board. If there is no play at point A, this does not matter; it wi
develop in the first temperature cycle in which the different elongations are take
up by deformation of the fillet. To increase the force allowed in the eyelet the ta
can be 'shot' into the board, as shown on the right, so that it is fixed at point E
After soldering, this tag can bear a much greater force at the eyelet, but a crack i

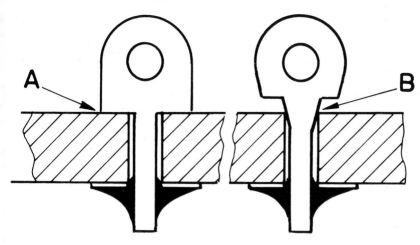

ig. 8.37 Tags soldered in single-sided board. The construction on the right in which the tag is mechanically fixed at B is prone to cracking of the joint as a result of thermally-induced stresses.

he solder fillet will soon appear, because every temperature cycle is accompanied y forward and backward deformation of the fillet until the joint is cracked Figure 8.38). A similarly unfavourable situation arises in constructions like ouble-sided boards, without hole plating, that are soldered on both sides.

If relatively rigid components, for instance screening plates, are fastened by neans of soldering, even moderate heating will exert a large force on the soldered oints causing them to crack. The electrical connection should then be reinforced y a separate flexible connection. A similar cause of solder cracking, both on ngle-sided and double-sided boards, may be encountered with soldered omponents having a relatively large number of terminations arranged in-line ich as integrated circuits in DIL and SIL version, slide-switches, long

ig. 8.38 SEM photograph of soldered joints on a single-sided board, which have cracked (as the sult of faulty construction) within a few months of normal use. The soldered pins shown are parate connectors for IC leads which have been mounted in the board in the same way as the tag shown in Fig. 8.37 (right). Spacing of soldered pins 2,54 mm.

connectors, *etc*. Stresses in their joints do not only originate from the expansion mismatch in the plane of the board, but also from the cyclic bending of the board during thermal cycling (see Chapter 8.1.2). As the end joints of the long rows of terminations then are subjected to the largest deformations, these are likely to exhibit the first cracks, having the same appearance as those shown in Figure 8.38. For the mentioned components, elevated (off-board) mounting is recommended. Moreover, it is good practice with this type of component to solder even the electrically-unused terminations to the printed board, for the purpose of distributing the forces over as large a number of terminations as possible.

Clinching of the component leads at the solder side of the board is good practice. If this is performed on boards with plated holes, no solder cracking is observed along the portion of the leads lying parallel to the conductors [Dunn] See also Chapter 12.4.1.

8.4.3 Plated Holes versus Plain Holes

Soldered joints in holes without a plating derive their mechanical strength exclusively from the size of the solder fillets and from the adhesive force between solder lands and printed board laminate. Solder lands must therefore have a surface area that is sufficiently large to handle the mechanical forces exerted directly or indirectly by the components on the soldered joints. In the process of making soldered joints on single-sided boards, the conditions should be selected such that fillets of adequate size can be obtained.

For joints in plated holes the matter of strength may seem to be much simpler, but this is appearance only. A plated hole constitutes, together with the component termination, a good capillary for retention of the liquid solder. While it is true that under short-term loads and vibrations the strength of soldered joints in plated holes is much greater, strength under cyclical loading is, however, not significantly greater than that of joints on single-sided boards without a hole plating. The latter is understandable if it is borne in mind that the soldered joint in a plated hole is composed of materials having considerably different coefficients of thermal expansion. The elongations due to temperature variation cannot be taken up elastically in the solder, so that a fatiguing plastic deformation will be present, leading ultimately to cracks. In this respect, fillets on single-sided boards are superior. Reinforcing the joints on double-sided boards by applying an extra heavy fillet at the solder side of the board is ineffective; furthermore, heavy fillets impede inspection of the soldered joints because they conceal the contour of the component termination in the solder fillet. Thus, with plated holes lean (light) fillets are preferred. In conclusion, the overall quality of simple single-sided board is not vastly inferior to that of double-sided boards for so-called high-quality work. The extra reliability of professional boards is obtained at relatively high expense.

8.4.4 Voids in Soldered Joints

The mechanical properties of joints are related to voids in the solder [Novick]. Voids are present in all soldered joints, not only in plated holes [Bulwith] but also in joints on single-sided boards. These may contain tens of voids, ranging in diameter from below 10 μm up to 1 mm (Figure 8.39). In general, porosity does not affect the reliability of the soldered joints [Keller *et al*]. Large voids, however

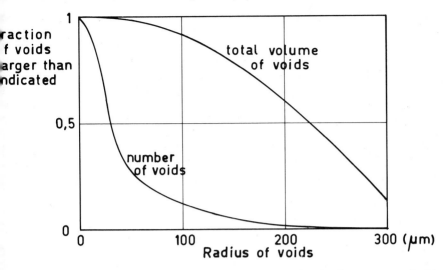

ig. 8.39   Distribution of voids in a joint on a single-sided board, showing the percentage of voids
ith a diameter larger than a given diameter. The distribution implies that in this case 50% of the total
void volume is present in one or two voids greater than 400 μm diameter.

nay inadmissibly reduce the fracture strength. Voids are the result of solder
hrinkage during solidification (about 4%). The direction of solidification will
letermine whether the shrinkage has to be accommodated in the joint or not. If,
or instance, solidification of the solder in a plated hole starts from both faces of
he board, the central part of the joint will contain one or more voids (Figures
.21 and 3.19). Outgassing in the plated holes during soldering may produce holes
n the solder. Sources of gas are moisture in the laminate (Chapter 8.1.3), and
ncomplete curing of the laminate. Another cause of voids can be entrapped flux.
This is particularly the case in reflow soldering with solder cream, which has to
ave a high flux content to obtain the desired properties (Figure 8.19 and 10.3).
/oids can hardly be prevented if flat surfaces with a relatively large area are to be
oldered against each other. It is not known to what extent entrapped gas plays a
ole here, but it is demonstrated that applying a vacuum prior to solidification,
ollowed by returning to atmospheric pressure while the solder is still molten,
roduces almost void-free solder bonds [Bascom *et al*].

.4.5   Thermal Aspects of Joint Design

The heat dissipation of the electronic components produces an ambient
emperature in the equipment that may be considerably higher than room
emperature. This temperature exerts its influence on the solder joints by thermal
tresses. Dissipation of the components is to a considerable degree co-determined
y their terminations and by the printed conductors to which they are connected.
or resistors having a few watts dissipation, their body temperature may attain a
alue of over 250°C. At an ambient temperature of 70°C, which is quite common,
he soldered joints connecting the terminations to the printed board can then,
ven with elevated (off-board) mounting of the resistors, easily exceed 100°C. If
everal resistors of this rating are situated close to each other, matters are even

worse. The net effect of all these influences depends on the design of the printed board as well as on its environment. The heat of the resistors is dissipated by radiation, convection of air, and conduction (through the leads to the conductor on the board), an approximate ratio for these three being 1:1:2 (1 for each lead). As a result, the joint temperature is distinctly above the ambient temperature, as is shown in Figure 8.40 for three ways of mounting horizontal resistors on a vertical board. The effect of the conductors on the board and the length of the leads between body and board can be seen. The kinks applied in the leads, and consequently the longer length of the leads, not only produce a lower joint temperature at the same dissipation but also result in lower forces in the joints. At the same relative displacement of the component body with respect to the joints, the force with the longer leads is $(\frac{10}{16})^3 = \frac{1}{4}$ times, because the bending force decreases with the third power of the length.

Components that generate a lot of heat must be fastened using long terminations, or else mounted on special racks, strips, *etc*. Moreover, with these components mechanical loading must be minimised by means of a suitable termination design that incorporates stress relief.

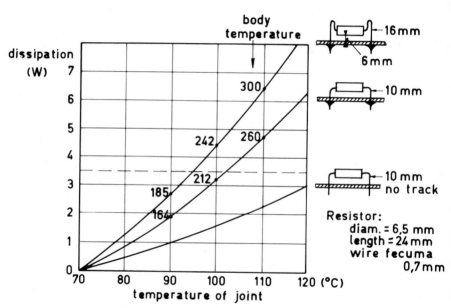

Fig. 8.40 Temperature of joints of power resistors at an ambient temperature of 70°C, with the resistors mounted horizontally on a vertical board. In the situation without tracks on the board the resistors were powered using thin separate wires. Note the marked effect of the mounting methods and the presence of conductors on the board.

Chapter 9

MACHINE SOLDERING OF PRINTED BOARDS

For mass production purposes machine soldering methods are used and two groups of methods can be distinguished. The methods of the first group are for assembled printed boards and involve application of solder and heat simultaneously to the parts to be soldered. The methods of the second group, discussed in Chapter 10, are the so-called reflow soldering methods, in which the solder and the heat are applied separately.

9.1 MACHINE SOLDERING

A soldering machine for the soldering of assembled printed boards consists of a number of separate units (Figure 9.1):

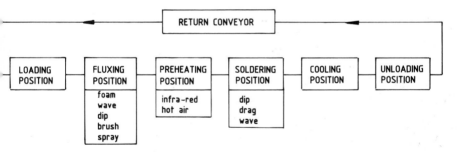

Fig. 9.1 General cycle of a soldering machine. The various units are discussed in this Chapter.

(i) Loading position, to place the boards to be soldered in the machine;
(ii) Fluxing position, to apply a uniform layer of flux to the boards;
(iii) Preheating position, to bring the flux to the desired condition and to preheat the boards;
(iv) Soldering position, to perform the actual soldering operation;
(v) Cooling position, to cool the products, thus reducing the risk of damage by the soldering heat remaining after the formation of the joints;
(vi) Unloading position, to remove the soldered boards from the machine.

In order to guide the boards to be soldered along the machine, a transport system is employed, which makes use of jigs (carriers) or so-called fingers, in which the boards are placed. With an adequate return transport system the

313

loading and unloading positions can be located at the same place or in close proximity to each other. The six positions in the soldering machine are also called 'stations'.

The methods for machine soldering of printed boards are:

(i)   Dip soldering, in which the assembled boards are soldered by lowering them in a vertical direction onto a static solder surface;

(ii) Drag soldering, in which the assembled boards are soldered by dragging them in a horizontal direction across a static solder surface;

(iii) Wave soldering, in which the assembled boards are soldered by dragging them in a (nearly) horizontal direction across the crest of a wave of flowing solder which is generated by forcing the solder from a sump upward through a nozzle.

For the majority of applications dip soldering has been replaced by drag soldering or wave soldering [Bud].

Besides the aforementioned soldering methods the literature persistently includes drawings of the cascade soldering method. The Author has, however, never seen such a cascade in reality.

9.1.1   Process Parameters

In most machine soldering techniques the process parameters are insufficiently defined, and therefore machine settings are often obtained in test runs. However, process parameters are subject to a complex interaction of many factors, not only determined by the particular type of machine but also by the design of the products to be soldered. Trial and error setting of the machine implies that for every new product it is necessary to revise the machine setting. The actual effect of these trial and error trimmings is that, for essentially similar boards, different settings are used on similar machines, this being poor engineering practice.

The considerations regarding heat given in Chapter 3 result in temperature-time boundaries constituting an area of safe operation. These boundaries depend on the particular product, but for most machine processes the temperature of the solder bath must be chosen between 240 and 270°C and the dwell time between 2 and 4 seconds.

Times and temperatures employed in the various processing steps are the main process parameters (Figure 9.2).

The preheat temperature, which is the temperature assumed by the boards at the end of the preheating period, is used to specify the conditioning of the flux, but the preheat time is never stated explicitly, so intentionally omitting the (unknown) influence exerted by the time.

In machine processes such as wave, drag and dip soldering, the dwell time is the nominal duration of the time of contact between the molten solder in the soldering machine and the parts to be soldered. This concept does not account for the practical phenomena by which the actual contact time may, locally, deviate substantially from the dwell time. The formation of gases from solvents tends to decrease the real contact time, whilst geometric distortions of the solder surface, particularly by the wetted component leads, in many cases increase the contact time.

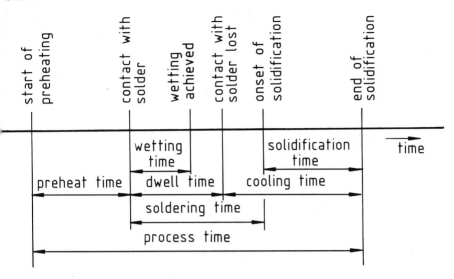

Fig. 9.2 Visualisation of the various time concepts used in machine soldering.

The dwell time and the soldering temperature determine the total heat flow to the soldering area.

The terms dwell time, contact time and soldering time are often interchangeable, but their meaning can differ according to the particular process concerned.

The term soldering time is used in several senses. In general, it signifies dwell time, sometimes it means heating time, but in other cases it may be used for the total process time, for instance in reflow soldering processes. It can also denote a definite time, measured in solderability testing, in which case its meaning is wetting time, that is the minimum time required to achieve a recognisable degree of wetting.

The soldering temperature in most cases refers to the temperature of the solder bath, though it may also represent the maximum temperature reached in the soldered joints.

The time during which the solder in the joint is in the liquid state (*i.e.*, the time between the moment of first contact between the parts to be soldered and the solder, and the moment that the solder in the joints starts solidifying) is most important for the metallurgical effects, such as dissolution of coating or growth of intermetallic compounds, and for the occurrence of thermal damage. This time is seldom mentioned explicitly. The parts losing contact with the solder bath have accumulated heat which subsequently penetrates into the component bodies. Hence, the temperature of the component bodies continues to rise for a period after the end of the dwell time, and only later starts decreasing. Forced cooling after soldering reduces the maximum temperature reached in areas on the component side of the board which are at some distance from the soldered joints, resulting in less warp [Waltner]. However, forced cooling may cause unequal contractions which will initiate cracks, particularly when the side of the joint remote from the cooling is just above or below the solidus. Forced post-soldering cooling is often unnecessary.

Figure 9.3 contains some temperature-time traces measured during a wave soldering operation, showing that areas which are only a few millimetres apart attain quite different temperatures. For trace (1) a preheat time of 100 seconds is obtained, a dwell time of 4 seconds, a solidification time of 5 seconds and a time between start of dwell time and onset of solidification time of 15 seconds.

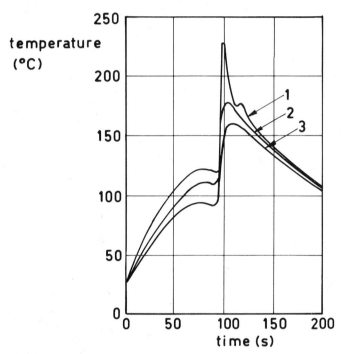

Fig. 9.3 Temperature-time traces of three locations on a double-sided printed board. (1) in the plated hole; (2) at a conductor on the component side of the board, 4 mm from the hole; (3) at the epoxy on the component side of the board, 4 mm from the hole.

9.1.2   Materials Used in Machine Soldering

Solder alloys and fluxes are discussed in Chapters 4 and 5 respectively and only a few aspects relevant to machine soldering are dealt with in the following text.

9.1.2.1   SOLDER ALLOYS

For machine soldering tin60-lead40 solder is generally used, this having a melting range between 183° and 189°C. For the soldering of boards with plated holes the eutectic solder is sometimes used, because this composition has the lowest melting point (183°C) and therefore the lowest operating temperature. The composition of the eutectic alloy can after a lapse of time become enriched with lead owing to dissolution of the non-eutectic solder coating from coated component terminations (see Chapter 6.3.4), and to preferential oxidation of tin especially if dross removal is practised (see Chapter 4.5.2). The tin-lead ratio of the bath can be checked by a density determination, and if necessary corrected.

(see Appendix to Chapter 4). In general, however, regular correction is not recommended. The correction alloy held in stock always means a risk of error. The alloy tin49-lead48-bismuth3 imparts a matt finish to the soldered joint after solidification, thus rendering visual inspection less fatiguing. The extended melting range from 178°C to 202°C of this alloy may be objectionable (see also Chapter 4.4.7).

Impurities in the Bath

Several metallic impurities in the bath can be detrimental to the soldering process. As a rule these impurities, originating from auxiliary tools, components and boards, will gradually increase in concentration (see Chapter 4.6) until a dynamic equilibrium concentration is reached. This is usually the case within a few months. It is wrong to replace solder baths indiscriminately, for instance on a regular basis. Replacement should only be considered if a change in the soldering results gives rise to suspicion that the bath is too contaminated. Only when this suspicion has been confirmed by chemical analysis should the bath be replaced. A density determination is not suitable for detecting contamination, the presence of which should be verified by optical emission spectrometry, X-ray fluorescence spectrometry or atomic absorption spectrometry.

Table 9.1 gives the maximum tolerable impurity levels for normal soldering baths [Spec. Ref. 9; *cf.* Becker]. Much lower contamination levels are sometimes specified, but it is doubtful whether this is realistic, (see also Chapter 4.4).

Table 9.1

Maximum Tolerable Concentration of Contamination in Solder Baths

Element	Percentage
antimony	0,5*
copper	0,3
bismuth	0,25*
iron	0,02
nickel	0,01
arsenic	0,03
aluminium	0,006
cadmium	0,005
zinc	0,005

*Antimony and bismuth are sometimes added intentionally to the bath to produce a content higher than that given in the Table. If there is antimony in the solder, say 0,3%, the aluminium content will be very low (<0,001%).

The maximum contamination levels in Table 9.1 by no means imply that fresh solder for replenishment of the bath is allowed to exhibit these contamination levels. The ultimate contamination of the bath is understood to be constituted by the take-up of contaminants into the solder bath in operation and by the composition of fresh solder added to the bath to compensate for solder consumption.

Oxidation of Solder

A solder bath is always covered with a natural oxide film, whilst the inevitable turbulence of the liquid solder in a wave-solder bath generates additional oxide and dross (see Chapter 4.5.2).

A layer of dross on the solder bath will not inhibit further dross formation. On the contrary, depending on the shape of the wave, the dross present may enhance turbulences and so increase the rate of dross formation. Therefore the dross should be removed regularly. Moreover, if the layer of dross on the bath becomes too thick, there is a chance that dross particles will be pulled into the solder stream where they will abrade the walls of the channels and the surface of the pump impeller. Dross particles in the solder are liable to impede the solder flow and will easily adhere to the board surface, thus contributing to various kinds of soldering defects.

A few hints for dealing with the oxide problem are given in the following text. The effectiveness of skimming the oxide film from the solder bath is, among other things, dependent on the ratio between the width of the printed board (or board plus soldering jig) and the width of the soldering wave or solder bath, while it cannot be ignored that the shape of the leading edge of the soldering jig also has a part to play.

The streaming of the solder in a wave soldering machine easily leads to undesired turbulence. The more quietly the solder flows into the solder bath the less the oxide is formed, because the quantity of oxide generated is to a high degree governed by the flow characteristics of the wave. A low height of the nozzle above the surface of the solder in the bath is of course favourable, but a really low nozzle is only possible with horizontal conveyance. In other cases, the height of the solder wave is reduced by locally raising the level of the solder bath. This can be achieved by applying a system of side plates to the nozzle with adjustable openings to the main bath. From time to time the dross must be removed from the solder bath. Containing more than 95% of solder metal, this dross should not be thrown away as it can usually be sold at about half the price of the solder.

The application of oil on the solder bath or in the wave reduces the formation of oxides (see Chapter 9.5.2); special synthetic products are available for the same purpose. Covering the solder bath with a layer of glass marbles with a diameter of about 2 cm may also be effective in reducing the dross formation, for instance to one-third.

A new wave-soldering technique has been reported [Getten *et al*] in which the formation of dross is eliminated by applying such a thick layer of protecting liquid that the bath and the wave remain continuously covered. The assembled boards are immersed in the liquid, which acts at the same time as a fluxing and preheating fluid, and are brought into contact with the solder while still immersed. The temperature limitations of the liquid (activated glycerine) unfortunately, preclude the use of common tin-lead solders, restricting the process to low-melting alloys.

9.1.2.2   FLUXES IN SOLDERING PROCESSES FOR PRINTED BOARDS

The choice of the appropriate flux is of prime importance to the soldering system [Schneider]. Many major issues depend on the type of flux chosen. A factor governing the choice is the solderability of components and boards. When solderability is good, a mildly active flux will be suitable, but when solderability is poorer, an effective flux is required (see also Chapter 7.1).

Flux choice moreover has its implications as regards the need for washing of boards after soldering. For water soluble fluxes, washing is always necessary. If washing is not performed thoroughly, severe problems may arise in service due to corrosion or short-circuiting caused by conductive flux residues.

For the rosin-based fluxes, the need for washing depends on the activity of the flux. There is no objection to low-activated rosin flux residues in many cases being left on the board, where they will undoubtedly provide some protection (though the protection decreases with time). The decision as to whether the flux residues may stay or must be removed can be based on the results of climatic tests on soldered comb patterns. In practice, a choice is made between an RMA and an RA type flux, depending on climatic demands and solderability. For detailed information on flux compositions and corrosion by flux residues reference should be made to Chapter 5.

9.1.2.3 OILS

In the wave soldering process, oil can be used on the bath and on the wave (compare Chapter 9.5.2).

Tinning Oil

Tinning oils usually consist of a mixture of mineral oils and fatty acids. They have a high flashpoint and a long service life at a solder temperature of 250°C, which means that the oil suffers little decomposition and has a low evaporation rate. The oil should be thoroughly mixed prior to use.

A tinning oil shows a mild fluxing action, to a greater extent than a normal mineral oil [ten Duis]. The viscosity of the oil will increase in time, because the base oils, being unsaturated hydrocarbons, can conceivably polymerise.

Moreover, the formation of tin and lead oxides in the bath cannot be entirely avoided; the oil will then form soaps with these oxides which are dispersed in the oil [Stayner], for instance by the reaction:

$$SnO_2 + 4\,RCOOH \rightarrow [RCOO]_4Sn + 2\,H_2O$$

During its lifetime at high temperature the oil will oxidise, causing its acid level to increase. Replenishment is therefore necessary once a week (40 hours' use). A thickness of oil of 10 to 20 mm on the solder bath is recommended.

Injection Oil

Widely used as injection oils are the purely vegetable peanut oil or the tinning oil previously mentioned. The service life of injection oil is of less importance, because this oil is in contact with the solder wave for a short time only. It is, however, important to ensure that the oils are virtually chemically inert, because the part of the oil that remains on the boards would otherwise deteriorate the board, soldered joints and electrical properties. Furthermore, the oil residues remaining on the bath must not react with the tinning oil.

9.1.3 Ecological Aspects of Machine Soldering

Fluxes consisting of a solution of colophony in ethanol or isopropanol liberate fumes which in general are not offensive. Yet, preventive measures will be necessary when working with these materials if:

 (i) Work is carried out in small, poorly ventilated rooms;
 (ii) Processed boards have a large surface area and solder baths have a large evaporating surface area;
(iii) Environmental temperature in work area attains unacceptably high values
(iv) Large amounts of vapour emanate from tinning oil on the solder bath;

Some fluxes are subject to decomposition in the course of the soldering operation, thereby giving off substances that irritate human mucous membrane or produce an unpleasant odour. In addition, in some cases chemical compound are liberated to which some people are allergic. Consequently, in many instance an exhaust system must be provided [Anon. Ref.15].

Certain soldering fluxes, particularly those used for the less readily-wettable metals, contain highly aggressive substances (although as a rule these fluxes are not used for machine soldering of printed boards). If such fluxes come into contact with the skin, the flux should be removed immediately by washing with large quantities of water. If flux spatters go into the eye, these must also be removed immediately by washing with plenty of clean water, and a qualified medical practitioner must be summoned. Cleanliness of the eyewash water is most important, to avoid the risk of conjunctivitis if the flux has already damaged the eye. Freshly prepared deionised drinking water is probably safest for this purpose.

The gaseous waste of fumes and vapours originating from the soldering process will not as a rule adversely affect the environment to any appreciable extent because the quantities involved are of negligible magnitude. Neither will the liquid and solid waste originating from fluxes and solder cause difficulties provided that they are discharged in an appropriate way [Langan], *i.e.*, in accordance with local public regulations (see also Chapter 4.1.4 and 5.8).

Various materials used in machine soldering present a fire hazard, especially at high temperatures, but in practice fire accidents are rare.

Vent System

The vent system (fume extraction system) must fulfil a number of requirements:

 (i) It must conform to local safety regulations;
 (ii) It must remain operative for 1 hour after shutdown of the machine preferably by means of a separate timer;
(iii) It must cover at least the fluxing station, the preheating station and the soldering station.

Across the full length of the vent system, boards on the conveyor must be visible and accessible, for instance by means of sliding, removable or folding glass windows. Vent hoods need not be completely closed but should be fairly spacious to prevent strong local turbulences. If the machine vent system contains filters, there must be a maintenance schedule for their cleaning and replacement.

9.2 APPLICATION OF FLUXES IN SOLDERING MACHINES

For mass soldering, the flux is applied in liquid form, because in this way the flux can be easily applied to large surface areas and to a large number of soldering points simultaneously. The flux is generally supplied from a large container of 30-50 litres to the fluxing unit from which it must be applied to the boards in a homogeneous layer with a certain thickness. The retention of the correct amount of flux on the boards immediately before soldering depends on two factors:

(i) The layer thickness of the flux, which is the result of the flux application method;
(ii) The fraction of solvent in the flux, which has to be evaporated after flux application.

Depending on the type of flux used, an amount of solid flux agent between 0,7 and 3 g/m² is required for soldering. This corresponds to a wet flux layer thickness of 3 to 20 μm. During soldering, the amount of flux is decreased owing to the washing action of the solder. An important point is that there must be sufficient flux on the boards to ensure a bridge-free exit of the boards from the solder bath or solder wave.

An excessive amount of flux on the boards is not only a waste of material, but also adversely affects the soldering process. Part of the flux will drip onto the hot preheater, thus polluting the elements and increasing the risk of fire, and the rest cannot be dried adequately in the available time so that it will produce the unwanted effects described in Chapter 9.2.7.

The commonest fluxing methods in current use are: Foam, Wave, Dip, Spray, and Brush fluxing.

The foam, wave and dip fluxing systems are best suited to boards with plated holes, since these provide a continuous layer of flux on the solder side of the board, promoting capillary penetration of flux into the holes. As the brush and spray fluxing systems give only droplets on the surface, there is risk of insufficient penetration of flux into the plated holes. Therefore these systems can cause poor soldering quality that is due to defective filling of plated holes with solder.

9.2.1   Foam Fluxing

Foam flux is generated from a liquid flux by means of an aerator, *e.g.*, a tubular porous stone. Low-pressure air, forced through the pores of the stone immersed in the flux, generates fine bubbles which are guided to the surface of the boards by a chimney nozzle. The boards to be fluxed are passed across this nozzle so that their solder sides contact the foam, while the bubbles burst thereby applying an even coating of flux to the boards. The bursting of the bubbles also causes the flux to penetrate into the plated holes. Excess flux flows back into the flux sump along the outside of the funnel and meanwhile the remaining foam bubbles must collapse (Figures 9.4 and 9.5). The conveyor speed and the dwell time of the board in the foam have almost no effect on the amount of flux deposited on the board.

To obtain an optional dosage the flux must have a specific concentration (solvent to flux ratio), which may usually be controlled by observing the density. The density of the flux must be kept within close limits. If the flux viscosity is too high, the foam bubbles will not collapse correctly and may even overflow. A correct foam consists of homogeneous bubbles with a diameter of between 1 and 2 mm. In this respect, the porous stone is important, as its pore structure determines the bubble homogeneity and hence the foam quality. Diffusion stones, having much greater air resistance, are better than porous plastic tubes. The stone must be exchangeable, to facilitate cleaning with solvent after use. The

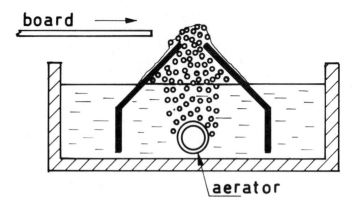

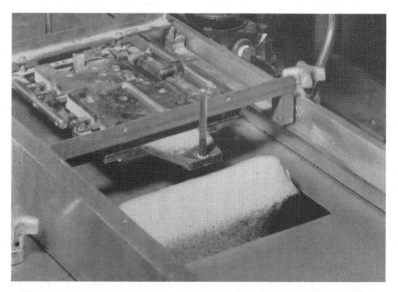

Fig. 9.4 Principle of foam fluxing. A mixture of flux and air is propelled upwards through a inverted nozzle which functions as a guide. The boards to be fluxed are moved across the foam crest

flux level must be 10-25 mm above the top of the stone, and the air pressure must be kept as low as possible, below 0,3 atmosphere, depending on the stone. A fin adjustment valve is indispensable. The applied air must be freed from water (se Chapter 9.2.6) by drying at the compressor intake from the atmosphere and th air line from the compressor must incorporate an oil filter to remove compresso lubricant, which may not necessarily be compatible with the flux.

Fig. 9.5 A foam fluxer. (The board is moving from top-left to bottom-right.)

The foam height above the nozzle should be adjustable between 0 and 15 mm (normally 6 mm). For boards with long protruding leads this system canno therefore be used, unless the foam blanket is enlarged by the use of a bristle brush nozzle. This addition, however, has the disadvantage of interfering with component leads, thus dislocating components.

Advantages

   (i) It can be incorporated in a continuous process;
  (ii) The height setting of the foam crest is not critical;
 (iii) Overdosage is easy to avoid;
 (iv) Plated holes are reliably moistened without excessive deposit of flux on the component side of the board.

Disadvantages

   (i) Not all fluxes exhibit the correct foaming action;
  (ii) Regular compensation for evaporation losses of the solvent is necessary;
 (iii) It is unsuitable for use on warm boards (even warm board fixtures should be avoided);
 (iv) Silicone compounds, present as silicone oil from switches or as heat transfer paste, destroy the foam, so that fluxing may become insufficient in contaminated areas.
  (v) Because the solvents mostly used for foam fluxing have a high boiling point, a long preheat station is necessary, preferably with hot air circulation.

9.2.2   Wave Fluxing

Flux can be applied using the liquid-wave principle to form a double-sided wave (Figure 9.6), the washing action of the flux wave promoting flux coverage. The fluxing unit should be equipped with an adjustable wave height control and an adjustable delivery pump to maintain the liquid level in the flux unit. A soft exit wipe-off brush is also needed, to remove excess flux deposit from the board.

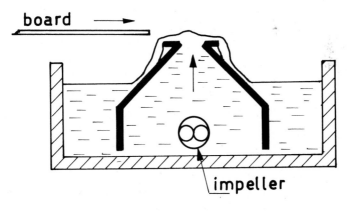

Fig. 9.6   Principle of wave fluxing. The boards to be fluxed are passed across a wave of flux (*cf.* Fig. 9.14).

Wave fluxing is generally preferred for dense circuitry with plated holes. When the length of leads to be soldered exceeds 15 mm, wave fluxing becomes preferable and is almost essential if plated holes are also present.

The solids content of a rosin flux for a wave fluxer is limited to 60 mass per cent whereas for foam fluxing it is usually limited to 35 per cent.

Advantages

   (i) It can be incorporated in a continuous process;
  (ii) Any liquid flux can be applied in this way;
 (iii) It is suitable for boards with plated holes;
 (iv) It is suitable for warm boards and warm board jigs.

Disadvantages

   (i) The height setting of the crest is rather critical, on the one hand involvin
the risk of failing to contact the boards and on the other hand of moistenin
the boards excessively so that the flux penetrates to the component side c
the boards (especially objectionable with boards that are not cleaned afte
soldering);
  (ii) The relatively high loss of solvent necessitates regular compensation fc
solvent evaporation losses;
 (iii) There exists a risk of flux penetration into the interior of certai
components.

9.2.3 Dip Fluxing

The flux is applied by dipping the solder side of the boards into the liquid flu:
surface. The flux is stored in a container with an open top and while not in us
this container must be covered, to avoid excessive evaporation of the flux solvent
This system can not really be used in automatic soldering processes, but if ;
separate fluxing station is included, it may be acceptable.

9.2.4 Brush Fluxing

A cylindrical brush is rotated with its lower side dipping into the flux while th
boards to be soldered pass across its upper side. A variant of this system is a fas
rotating brush from which flux spatters onto the boards. Brush fluxing is no
suitable for the fluxing of plated holes. The rotating action must be commandec
by the carrier on the soldering machine.

9.2.5 Spray Fluxing

Several methods of spray fluxing exist. The most common spray fluxer involve;
a drum consisting of a fine stainless steel screen, rotating in liquid flux, while ai
is blown into the drum (Figure 9.7). The air stream which passes the steel screer
generates a spray of flux in the direction of the boards that are passed across th
fluxing unit.

The amount of flux deposited on the boards, at a certain conveyance speed, i;
controlled by the speed of rotation, by the air pressure and by the density of th
flux. The flux layer thickness ranges from about 5 to 30 μm, but below 6 anc
above 20 μm it tends to be inhomogeneously distributed. To obtain ;
reproducible amount of flux on the boards, the pressure nozzles need carefu
adjustment. The speed of the rotation of the drum must be adjustable from 3 tc
20 rpm, and the air pressure from 0,5 to 1 atmosphere. During operation th

motor is activated by the approaching carrier on the soldering machine. The motor must have ample power to enable it to set the drum in motion even after a long period of rest.

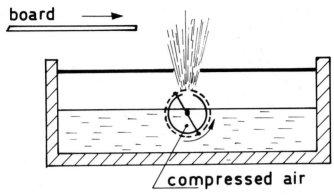

Fig. 9.7   Principle of spray fluxing. The boards to be fluxed are passed through the spray of flux droplets.

Advantages

(i) It is suitable for nearly all liquid fluxes and with a proper alcoholic solvent a short preheat will suffice;
(ii) It gives reproducible results and adjustable dry flux layer thickness, including very thin layers;
(iii) Flux does not penetrate into small holes on the component side of the boards and consequently no risk exists of reducing the component quality by contact with flux;
(iv) Long protruding leads are allowed.

Disadvantages

(i) It is unsuitable for boards with plated holes because the flux penetrates insufficiently into the holes;
(ii) There is a substantial loss of flux because any excess flux issuing from the spray chamber is not recovered; the system needs frequent cleaning;
(iii) Large holes in the boards must be closed to prevent excessive fluxing of the component side of the board.

9.2.6   Controlling the Correct Flux Density

One of the main control factors for fluxes used in machine soldering is the flux density which gives information about the solids content of the flux.

The flux density depends on the nature of the solvents used, and these may have different densities and different rates of evaporation. Moreover, the flux density may depend on the water content, resulting from condensation. Figure 9.8 shows the density of a rosin flux (with isopropanol as the solvent) as a function of concentration, for various water contents.

In a large container the consistency of the flux will be more constant than in a

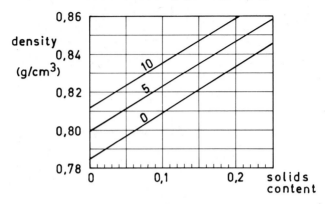

Fig. 9.8 Density of fluxes of rosin in isopropanol at 20°C, and containing 0, 5 and 10% of water. (Solids content and water percentage are expressed with respect to the total mass of rosin, isopropanol and water.)

small one. Slow density variations can be corrected from time to time, remembering to allow for the water content. An automatic density control requires special equipment, but this can be easily combined with the fluxing system. (Figure 9.9 shows an example.) Such density controllers are commercially

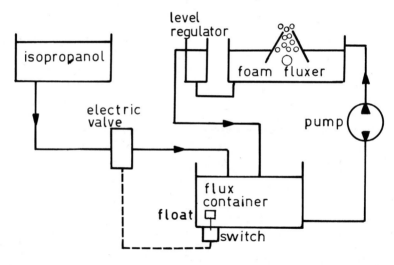

Fig. 9.9 Flux density and level controller. The density of the flux is monitored, and when necessary isopropanol is injected to bring the flux to the desired density.

available. However, it should be noted from Figure 9.8 that if the system only controls the density of the flux, the solids content of the flux may still change owing to a changed water content.

The water content of isopropanol-containing rosin fluxes may be determined as follows. A sample of the flux of 10 ml is mixed with 10 ml of heptane. Next, deionised water is added stepwise to this mixture, during which time it is thoroughly stirred, until it becomes turbid and shows separation. If this takes place with a water addition of 1,0 ml or less, the flux is no longer suitable for use and requires to be renewed. The amount of water in the flux can be calculated, considering that about 1,5 ml of water can be added to a water-free flux before separation occurs.

9.2.7   Drying of Applied Flux (Preheating)

To achieve optimal quality with machine soldering methods it is necessary to dry the flux immediately before soldering. Predrying of the flux and simultaneous preheating of the printed boards serve several purposes. The drying results in the evaporation of the greater part of the solvent from the flux. If the solvent evaporation function is assigned to the solder bath, the bath cools down owing to withdrawal of the heat required for evaporation. The vapour originating from the solvent precludes good contact between board and solder, so producing inadequate and irregular heat transfer, and possibly generating pores in the soldered joints. The boiling of the solvents causes the solder to spatter resulting in solder particles being deposited in unwanted areas.

Drying brings the flux to the correct viscosity. If the viscosity of the flux is too low, the flux is prematurely expelled from the boards by the solder. This may cause poor wetting and also increase the risk of bridging and webbing. The drying accelerates the chemical reaction of the flux with the surfaces to be soldered and it advances the moment of onset of activity of the flux.

Preheating the boards to a temperature of 80°C to 90°C lowers the thermal shock during soldering and reduces bending of the boards during soldering (see Chapter 8.1.2). An added advantage is that in this way less heat is withdrawn from the solder bath. The preheating is always expressed in terms of the maximum temperature reached on the component side of the board. This can be easily measured with temperature-sensitive paint or tape [Anon. Ref.25]. The optimum preheat temperature will depend on the design of the product to be soldered, on specific heat, vaporising temperature of the flux solvent, latent heat of evaporation, production speed, and other factors. For example, thick multilayer boards require higher preheating to dry and activate the flux in plated holes in order to assure penetration by the solder.

The effect of the predrying treatment, however, depends not only on the maximum temperature reached, but also on the duration of the preheat period. Moreover, streaming hot air is much more effective in removing evaporated solvent than infra-red heating. These aspects have never been fully worked out, and thus the purpose mentioned of 'bringing the flux to the correct viscosity' can not in fact be accompanied by a statement concerning what is to be understood by 'correct'.

If a rosin flux is preheated for too long, the colophony will oxidise and polymerise. The subsequent soldering process will then proceed slowly, because the colophony melts insufficiently and thus is not easily replaced by the solder. Fluxing a second time will eliminate the effects of unsuitable pretreatment.

For acid fluxes the preheating is not so critical, because their chemical action is more rapid than that of rosin fluxes.

The predrying can be carried out in three ways:

(i) Convection heating with forced hot air;
(ii) Radiation heating with heating coils, infra-red tubular quartz lamps, or hotplate panels;
(iii) Combination of hot air and radiation.

The preheater is sometimes lined with an aluminium foil which can be changed regularly in order to remove the flux drippings. Otherwise the dripped flux should be removed frequently to maintain the efficiency of the heat transfer.

The preheater must be capable of heating the board to such an extent that the component side assumes a temperature of 80°C ± 5°C. Heating must be uniform. The solder side of the board should not be allowed to reach a temperature higher than 130°C, a requirement which limits the rate of heating.

Suppose boards of a width of 300 mm and a thickness of 1,6 mm are heated to an average temperature of 100°C ($\Delta T = 80$), at a conveyor speed of 2 m/min ($v = 0,033$ m/s), then a power of 2560 W is needed. ($Q = \varrho c V \Delta T = 2 \times 10^6 \times 0,3 \times 0,033 \times 1,6 \times 10^{-3} \times 80 = 2560$ W (see Chapter 3.1)). In this case, depending on the efficiency of the heater system, a total power capability of about 10 kW must be installed.

The preheat temperature depends only slightly on the amount of flux present on the board. However, in the case of IR-heating, the area of copper on the board has a distinct effect on the final temperature because of the heat reflection by the copper. With an unchanged power setting and conveyor speed the following preheat temperatures were obtained on epoxy glass boards, either completely covered with copper or with the copper fully removed. In the former case, with 2,5 g/m^2 of flux (solids) and without any flux, 60°C and 50°C were obtained respectively (the heat necessary to evaporate the flux solvent being more than compensated by the larger heat absorption of the flux). In the latter case a temperature of 85°C was obtained, irrespective of the flux amount.

The preheater is a significant energy waster, which could for instance be improved by powering the elements only when boards are conveyed in the machine. However, common heater systems have too large a thermal mass and hence are too slow for this purpose. Fast-response quartz preheaters would be suitable, but these are more expensive.

The capacity of the preheater must be such that the specified board temperature can be realised at the highest speed of travel, whereas controls must be provided to prevent this temperature from being exceeded at a lower speed of board travel.

Some machines, especially the 'mini soldering machines' with a narrow solder wave at right angles to the direction of travel, are too short to achieve the specified preheating temperature if the conveyor movement is not interrupted.

9.3 DIP SOLDERING

In dip soldering, the assembled board, in an almost horizontal position, is lowered vertically until the solder side of the board contacts the molten solder in the bath (Figure 9.10). After maintaining contact for the required dwell time, the board is lifted clear of the bath. The sequence of operations in dip soldering, like fluxing, flux drying, soldering and board transfer is usually not mechanised.

The following operations are generally performed automatically:

(i) Skimming any surface contaminations from the solder;
(ii) Lowering the board and bringing its solder side into contact with the surface of the solder;
(iii) At the end of the dwell time, lifting the board vertically from the solder bath.

The production capacity attainable with this method is approximately 120 boards per hour. Gas bubbles can escape better when the board is lowered at an angle of about 30° to the horizontal into the solder bath, this angle then being lecreased to zero. Risk of bridge formation is reduced by again performing a ilting motion when withdrawing the board from the bath, but this time in reverse order (Figure 9.10 right).

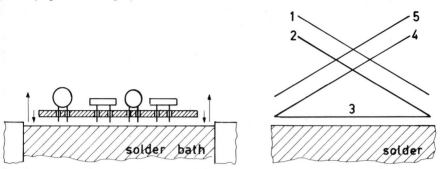

Fig. 9.10 Principle of dip soldering. 1 to 5 are successive positions of the board. Compare the movement of the board with drag soldering (Fig. 9.12).

Some machines have been modified so that within one cycle the board is dipped twice in succession, the interval between the two dippings creating an added opportunity for gas bubbles to escape. Another feature introduced into this type of machine is the so-called solder dripping grid, intended to decrease the risk of bridging on the soldered board. The dripping grid consists of a series of parallel plates, preferably made of solder coated alloy of iron-nickel-cobalt, 1 mm thick and 15 mm high, 2 mm apart. The grid is located in the solder bath and can make a limited reciprocal vertical movement, but is never out of contact with the solder bath. At the moment the board is lowered onto the bath, the grid is in its lowest position. After the dwell time the grid ascends, contacts the board and lifts the board free from the bath. Excess solder adhering to the board is caused to flow back into the bath via the grid.

Advantages and disadvantages of dip soldering are:

(i) The cost of investment is relatively low;
(ii) The operation and maintenance of the machine are simple;
(iii) Dip soldering is capable of producing well-filled soldered joints on single-sided boards; it is less suitable for boards with plated holes because of insufficient heat transfer to the component side of the boards;
(iv) If not automated, the overall process is strongly susceptible to any inconsistencies in the performance of the human operator;
(v) Gas bubbles evolving from the flux impede intimate contact between the surfaces to be soldered and the solder, thus retarding or even preventing the establishment of the soldered joints;
(vi) If the conductor spacings on the boards are small, dip soldering involves considerable risk of bridging between the conductors;
(vii) The level of the solder bath is critical if the dipping is carried out automatically.

9.4 DRAG SOLDERING

This method essentially involves the assembled board being lowered into the solder bath until it makes contact with the solder. Subsequently the board is dragged a predetermined distance along the surface of the bath, after which it is lifted from the bath (Figure 9.11).

The board is lowered into the solder bath at an angle of about 15° to the horizontal; from the moment the board contacts the bath, this angle is gradually reduced to zero. The purpose of this slope is to provide an opportunity for gas bubbles to escape. Board transport may be interrupted while the board is in contact with the solder bath for a predetermined time. The raising of the board from the solder bath, while at the same time tilting the board gradually to a small angle to the horizontal and moving the board at a suitable speed, allows excess solder to flow back from the board into the solder bath. The speed of withdrawal of the board from the solder bath determines the quantity of solder remaining in the soldered joints on the board. A high speed of withdrawal leaves a lot of solder on the board; a low speed leaves less solder on the board.

Optional possibilities are a variable drag distance of the board, and a special device for lowering and raising the board while holding it in a truly horizontal position (no tilt).

The flux is usually applied by foam-fluxing in-line and the surface of the solder bath is skimmed each time just before a board passes, for instance with a suitable device attached to the board carrier. The production capacity attainable with this method is approximately 125 boards per hour.

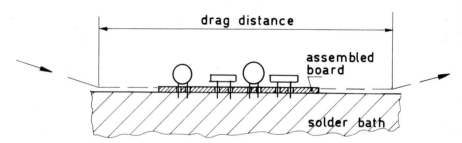

Fig. 9.11 Principle of drag soldering. The assembled board is brought into contact with the solder in a long solder bath and is then dragged along the length of the bath.

Advantages and disadvantages of drag soldering are:

(i) It is a continuous process and the soldering is virtually independent of human attendance;

(ii) It needs little maintenance, moreover requiring no special skill;

(iii) The level of the solder bath is critical (this can be overcome by utilising an 'overflow solder bath' [Nakajima]);

(iv) The heat transfer is better than with dip soldering owing to the motion of the board relative to the bath, but the heat transferred to the component side of double-sided boards is still insufficient or only just sufficient;

(v) Gas bubbles evolving from the flux may impede wetting of the board by solder, although to a lesser degree than is found with dip soldering;

(vi) Short dwell times are not possible.

Rate of Drainage

The escape of gas bubbles and the drainage of solder are difficult to achieve if the board is lowered and lifted while it is held in a horizontal position. Tilting the board while it is lowered or lifted has the effect that the conditions along the length of the board are not constant. The angle at which a certain portion of the board leaves the horizontal plane through the ideal solder surface depends on the location on the board considered. Suppose that a board is lifted from the bath by moving the edges of the board along a horizontal and inclined path (Figure 9.12a). The leading edge leaves the horizontal plane under an angle α, while the region near this edge is in a horizontal position. The trailing edge also leaves the horizontal plane at an angle α, but the whole board has by now been rotated through that angle α. Intermediate regions leave the horizontal plane at an angle between 0 and α depending on their location on the board. This angle is found by considering the vectors of the (constant) horizontal conveyor velocity and the vertical velocity, which increases from the trailing to the leading edge. The vertical velocities of three locations on the board during rotation are shown in Figure 9.12b. From the distribution of vertical velocities along the length of the board it is easy to obtain the vertical displacement of points along the length of the board.

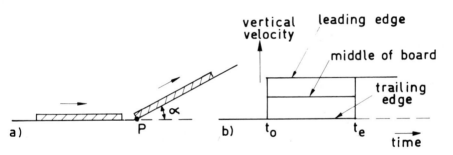

Fig. 9.12   (a) movement of board in drag soldering; (b) vertical velocity of the board. t_o = time at which the leading edge reaches point P; t_e = time at which the trailing edge reaches point P.

The contact between board and solder is broken when the board has been lifted a certain distance above the nominal plane of the solder surface, depending on the amount of copper on the printed board. In the case of full copper the shape of the elastica (discussed in Chapter 2.2.1) indicates that the height of the lifted solder will be about 4,4 mm. For boards with a conductive pattern, and perhaps a solder resist, the average height of the lifted solder is smaller, possibly about 2 mm. The path of the point of drainage for this condition has been calculated, assuming an angle of inclination of 12° and a board length of 300 mm. Figure 9.13 shows this path versus the horizontal displacement of the board. This figure indicates that the velocity of the point of drainage varies strongly along the length of the board, signifying that the circumstances under which the joints must be formed are not constant over the board. The same is valid for dip soldering with tilting of the board.

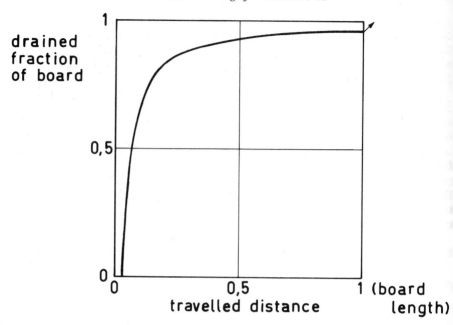

Fig. 9.13 Drained distance on a board versus the horizontal displacement of the board under conditions discussed in the text. The position 0 on the axes corresponds to the moment when the leading edge reaches the point P in Fig. 9.12a, the position 1 when the trailing edge reaches this point.

9.5 WAVE SOLDERING

In wave soldering, a stationary, continuously replenished wave of molten solder is generated, while the boards to be soldered are moved in one direction across the crest of the wave (Figure 9.14) [Pat. Spec. 798, 701 (1955)].

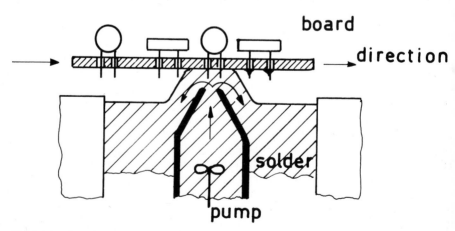

Fig. 9.14 The principle of wave soldering. The board to be soldered is moved across the wave of solder which is pumped up through a rectangular orifice and which then falls back into the solder bath.

Wave soldering is the major machine method for the soldering of printed boards [Keller], but it is also used for other purposes such as the tinning of coils [Bud]. It is expected that the wave soldering technique will remain the dominant method of fabricating printed board assemblies for many years. No significant change is anticipated in the near future [Anon. Ref.4].

In wave soldering, the dwell time is determined by the width of the area of contact between the solder wave and the solder side of the board as well as by the speed at which the board is transported. The board is transported in a truly horizontal direction or at a small angle, for instance 7° upwards. The solder wave is generated either with the aid of a mechanical pump, or by applying Lorentz forces, generated by electric currents and magnetic fields. Molten solder is pumped upwards from a sump into an ejection chamber equipped with baffles for flow diversion, and out through an ejection nozzle. After reaching its summit, the molten solder falls down along one or two of the outer sides of the ejection chamber and back into the solder sump.

The production capacity, expressed in linear throughput of workpiece, varies from 60 to 300 cm/minute.

9.5.1 Shape of the Wave

A closer look will now be taken at a quiet wave without oil application. While the solder is pumped out of the nozzle, apparently new free solder surface is being generated continuously at the crest of the wave, although on close examination this is not true. The surface of the wave is covered with an oxide skin which along almost the entire length of the wave remains static, except at the extreme ends. This is difficult to see at the surface, on which small movements give a deceptive impression, but the reality immediately becomes clear if small pieces of paper are put on top of the wave (Figure 9.15).

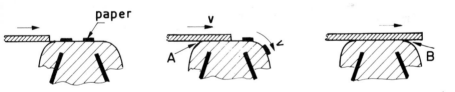

Fig. 9.15 Three positions of a board on a quiet wave without oil application. In the ideal case, the oxide skin is at rest, till it is pushed away by the advancing board.

When an approaching board contacts the surface of the wave, the oxide skin is broken and the part in front of the board is pushed forward without being crumpled. This means that the whole oxide skin moves at the same speed as the board and in this way the machine works with minimum dross formation.

Without a board on the wave the solder streams through a channel between the nozzle edge and the oxide skin on the solder. Just at the edge and at the surface skin the flow velocity of the solder is zero, while at intermediate positions there is a velocity distribution.

With a board on the wave the situation is only slightly different. The solder just below the board moves along at the same speed as the board, irrespective of the nominal direction and speed of the wave. Component leads protruding into the

flowing solder may disturb the velocity distribution at those places. The velocit\
distribution in the solder wave and its implications on solder wave behaviour hav\
not yet been worked out. It is obvious that a thorough investigation into the flui\
mechanics of the solder wave is not only of theoretical interest, but could also k\
of great practical importance.

The wave has three regions to be distinguished, these being where the boar\
enters the wave (near point A in Figure 9.15), where the board leaves the wav\
(near point B), and the part of the wave between the two points A and B, calle\
the heat transfer zone [Manko].

Near point A the surfaces to be soldered must be cleaned by the action of th\
flux so that between point A and point B wetting can be achieved. The area nea\
point B is called the peel-back area or the back-wash region.

During passage across the wave crest the boards and the components heat u\
meaning that somewhere between the points A and B wetting is achieved an\
holes, if any exist, are filled with solder. In the region between the points A an\
B, the board is totally bridged by the solder and the solder has displaced the flu\
from the conductors, but between the conductors flux is still present and is take\
with the boards from A to B. The situation at point B is more complicated an\
needs further consideration. The extreme cases that can occur are boards withou\
copper and boards completely covered with copper which is readily wetted. In th\
former case the solder will lose contact with the board at point B_1 in Figure 9.1\
and in the latter case the solder is carried along with the moving board as far a\
point B_2. The distance between the points B_1 and B_2 may easily exceed 25 mm.

Because the fraction of copper on the boards and the configuration of th\
conductors vary, the actual position of the point of separation (B) varies betwee\
the points B_1 and B_2 in a highly irregular manner. Thus the actual position c\
point B is unpredictable. If for a given period the position of B remains the sam\
with respect to the nozzle edge, the relative movement of the solder is mainl\
vertical, as indicated in Figure 9.16, for instance over a distance of 10 mm.

A critical peel-back situation occurs when the solder meniscus has to retrac\
abruptly in the direction of point B_1. The amount of solder in the back-was\

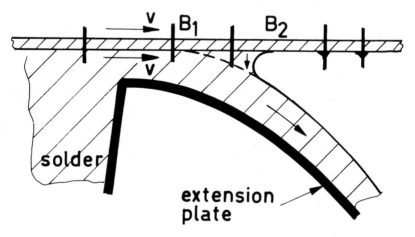

Fig. 9.16 Situation at the point where the soldered board leaves the solder wave. Depending on th\
quantity of copper and the configuration of the copper conductors on the board, the point c
separation lies somewhere between the points B_1 and B_2.

·egion must then decrease suddenly, involving the possibility of bridge formation.

The vertical velocity (or distance) of the solder near the point B_2 is important. Too abrupt a change implies that there is not enough time for bridges to open, because the contact with the solder wave is lost before sufficient solder has flowed off. This is moreover influenced by the oxide skin on the surface of the solder, and hence by the flux that is still present at this point [Zado]. Oil applied on the wave will also play a role (see Chapter 9.5.2).

An improved version of the wave soldering process has been introduced recently by Hollis Engineering Inc. In this case, a hot-air stream is directed at the peel-back area of the wave with the purpose of breaking bridges and removing icicles, while preserving good joints. This is possible in principle, because the stability of the unwanted bridges and icicles is low and can easily be disturbed without affecting the intended joints, especially those in plated holes which are considerably more stable if properly designed. The application of the extra air stream in wave soldering has indeed been reported to provide a substantial reduction in the number of short circuits [Comerford, Keller]. The need for application of this technique depends on the board design, especially on the density and complexity of the circuitry. If by other measures a low frequency of defects like bridges has already been obtained, any remaining defects are likely to be of a more stable type that cannot be disturbed by an air jet. To generate the hot-air stream an air knife is used, similar to those used in hot-air levelling, but with lower air velocity and higher air temperature.

Drawbacks to the addition of the hot-air facility are that the soldering equipment consumes more energy, becomes more complicated and thus more expensive, with extra machine parameters to be controlled.

As the shape of the wave near the back-wash region influences the tendency for bridge formation, the manufacturers of wave soldering machines have developed various nozzle designs, each capable of generating specific wave shapes [Bud]. On a single machine it is often possible to mount a number of exchangeable nozzles, although in practice this facility is litte used.

Four groups of wave forms are discussed as follows:

9.5.1.1 DOUBLE-SIDED WAVE

The double-sided wave is also called the standard wave or T-wave which is usually provided with extension plates (Figure 9.17 left). The molten solder flows

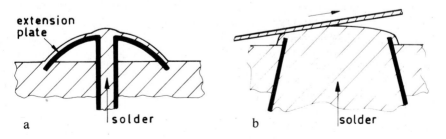

Fig. 9.17 Double-sided wave with horizontal conveyance (a) and inclined conveyance (b). Angles of inclination are usually between 5° and 9°; the nozzle is often tilted backwards over an angle equal to half the conveyor inclination.

back into the solder bath along both sides of the nozzle. If the board is conveyed horizontally across such a wave, the drainage of solder is prevented at the point where the board leaves the wave, because the separation between the falling surface of the solder wave and the board is very rapid on account of the large angle between those two. This situation involves the risk of formation of bridges and icicles. If the board is guided at an angle to the horizontal through the solder wave (inclined conveyance), this has the effect of an increased drainage of the board resulting in joints containing less solder. For joints on boards with plated holes this is of no consequence, because the strength of these joints depends little on the fillet size. In this case it is even an advantage to have lean joints, because these produce fewer bridges, better possibilities for inspection, and a reduction in solder consumption. For single-sided boards where better-filled joints are desirable horizontal conveyance may be appropriate. The angles of inclination are usually between 5° and 9°.

9.5.1.2 EXTENDED WAVE

Drainage of the solder is also assisted by positioning the point at which the board leaves the wave in the neutral zone of the wave, where the relative speed of the board with respect to the solder can be adjusted to virtually zero. This is attainable if the aperture of the nozzle is sufficiently wide (Figure 9.17 right), or if a long extension plate is used near the region where the board leaves the wave (Figure 9.18).

A wider wave permits of greater contact length and hence of higher transport velocity and higher production rate, with the same dwell time.

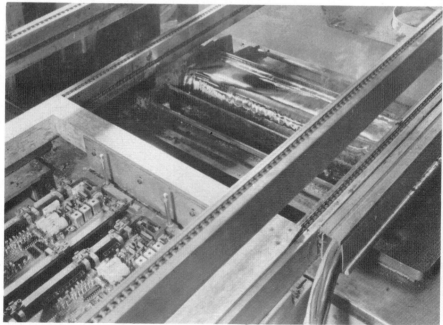

Fig. 9.18 Extended solder wave. The carrier with the boards shown is moving from bottom-left to top-right and is above the end of the preheat zone. In this machine the conveyor is inclined. Note the return conveyor.

Another example of extended waves is the 'Lambda Wave', introduced by Electrovert Inc. in the seventies [Can. Patent 974.331 (1975)] and which makes use of fairly large front and back plates as is shown in Figure 9.19. As a result of the specific shape of the wave, the solder flow accelerates in the direction opposite to the board travel, thus providing an effective washing action which promotes wetting.

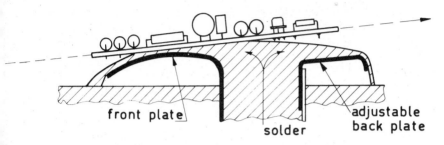

Fig. 9.19 Lambda wave. By adjusting the front and back plates, optimum entry and exit conditions can be obtained.

However, other wave designs are also referred to using the same name, such as hat shown in Figure 9.20. The back plate of this type of nozzle can be adjusted such that no solder flows across the back plate (backflow) without a board on the wave, which minimises the dross formation. When a board is on the wave, the

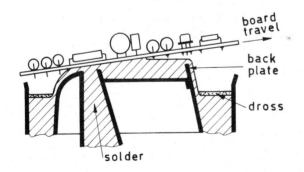

Fig. 9.20 'Lambda wave'. The adjustment of the back plate and the pumping rate influence the character of the wave (*cf.* Fig. 9.19).

older is driven up to produce a horizontal velocity of the solder to the right, qual to the board velocity. This condition changes when the trailing edge of the oard enters the wave, and the adjustment of the back plate thus also gives a means to control the peel back of the solder from the trailing part of the board.

Figure 9.21 depicts a soldering machine with the fluxing position, the reheating position and the soldering position in an almost completely closed abinet (separate parts not recognisable in the picture). The inclined conveyor xtends along the full length of the cabinet.

Fig. 9.21 Complete wave-soldering machine. The machine shown is the 'Ultrapak system' Electrovert, provided with the Lambda wave (by courtesy of Electrovert, Canada).

9.5.1.3 SINGLE-SIDED WAVE

This principle is implemented by inclining the nozzle so that a unidirection wave is generated with only one falling surface (Figure 9.25). The direction flow of the solder is opposite to the direction of travel of the printed board.

An extreme example of the single-sided wave is the 'jet-wave' in which tr solder is pumped out of the nozzle at a relatively high velocity, so that a jet solder can be directed against the board to be soldered.

9.5.1.4 DOUBLE-WAVE NOZZLE

The wave soldering of leadless components and components with very sma leads places two opposing demands on the solder wave. On the one hand tr solder in the wave must have a certain minimum thrust in order to reach a component terminations (Chapter 9.5.3.3), which implies a turbulent wave. O the other hand a quiet wave is desired to avoid bridging. Both demands can t satisfied with a standard double-sided wave, but this situation is rather critica Several manufacturers therefore offer special nozzles for chip soldering, givin two separate waves in one solder tank at a few centimetres' interval [Euro. Pa

ppl. 0 055 323 and 0 058 766 (1981)], (Figure 9.22). The two waves of the
ɔuble-wave nozzle may be generated using one pump for both, or using two
ɹmps. In the latter case control is easier, but this solution is more expensive. The
fect of the double wave can also be produced by placing two separate solder
ɩnks (each with a nozzle and a pump) close together in a machine of sufficient
ɩgth.

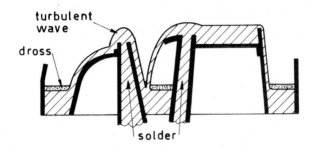

ig. 9.22   Double-wave system for the soldering of leadless components to the solder side of printed
ɔards. The solder streams discharged through the two nozzle orifices shown are generated by two
   separately adjustable pumps or by one pump with the use of suitable gates in the channels.

5.2   The Use of Oil in Wave Soldering

In many cases oil is used as an additive in wave soldering with the following
ɩtentions:

(i)   To provide a barrier against oxidation of the molten solder in the bath
      (tinning oil);
(ii) To provide an oxide barrier in the form of an oil film on the solder wave
      surface (injection oil);
iii) To adsorb and carry away any oxides formed.

Oil, injected into the wave, has a much lower density than the molten solder
ɩnd will rapidly move to the surface, thus apparently reducing the surface tension
f the solder. The result is that excess solder is more easily pulled back from the
ɔoards by the solder wave in the back-wash region, where the board loses contact
·ith the wave [Stayner, Manko, Boynton]. This implies a substantial decrease in
ɩe chance of short circuits. In addition, the establishment of light (lean) solder
llets is promoted, which is an advantage in the case of plated holes. The size of
ɩe fillets and the number of solder bridges decrease in the order: horizontal
ɔnveyance without oil, inclined without oil, inclined with oil [Bernard].

The disadvantages of the application of oil are:

(i)   Contamination of the machine with decomposed and thickened oil, which is
      difficult and dangerous to remove;
(ii) Consumption of oil;
iii) More complicated operation of the machine;

(iv) Excessive oil residues on the soldered products will necessitate extra pos'
treatments, such as washing with organic solvents.

The first drawback mentioned is the major one experienced. The variou
methods of oil dispensing and metering to the solder wave continue to be a matte
of controversy and a compromise will always have to be established betwee
conflicting factors. It is noted that the application of oil onto or into the solde
wave seems to be declining [Strauss]. With boards having relatively larg
conductor spacings and with a quiet wave, it is certainly possible to solde
without oil on the wave.

The injection oil can be supplied to the solder wave in various ways: by o:
intermix, by oil injection or by application of the oil directly onto the wav
surface.

9.5.2.1   OIL INTERMIX

The oil is sucked into and dispersed in the solder by the pump through a ventu
system (oil intermix principle), resulting in an oil film being generated at th
surface of the wave (Figure 9.23). This method has the disadvantage that the o'
metering cannot be closely controlled, whereas the quantity of oil added to th
solder is, among other things, dependent on the pump discharge rate. At a lo'
discharge rate it is impossible to obtain a good intermix.

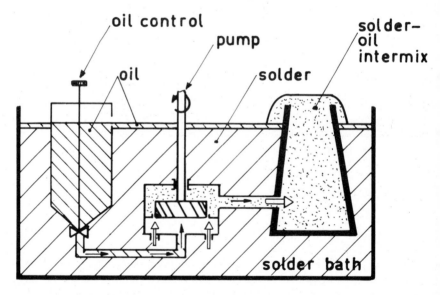

Fig. 9.23   Intermix of oil in the solder wave using the solder pump to suck the oil into the solder. → oil, ⇒ sold

The oil can be supplied in two ways. The first is by sucking it off the surface o
the static solder in the bath. However, this is tinning oil which is continuousl:
subject to contamination and therefore will be liable to cause clogging of th

ransport channels. In the second method the oil is sucked from an external oil essel containing peanut oil or fresh tinning oil, preferably preheated.

.5.2.2   OIL INJECTION

The oil is injected from an external oil vessel at a small, controllable verpressure (approximately 0,5 atm) into the solder channel at a point situated a ew centimetres below the surface of the wave (Figure 9.24). Dependent on the rocess conditions, the oil consumption may vary from 0,5 litre per week to everal litres per day.

The advantages of oil injection over oil intermix are that the oil supply is ndependent of the pump rate and is easily controllable. Moreover, the injection il can simultaneously serve the purpose of tinning oil for the static solder bath, vith the benefit that the oil on the solder bath is continuously being replenished.

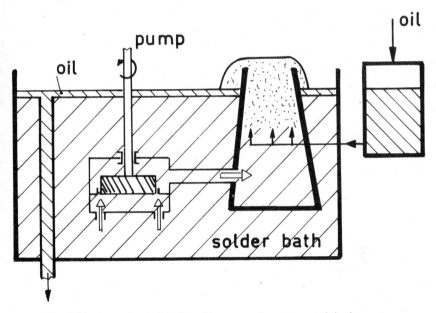

Fig. 9.24   Intermix of oil in the solder wave using a separate injection system.

.5.2.3   OIL DIRECTLY TO THE WAVE SURFACE

The simplest way to supply oil to the solder wave is to drip it on top of the wave rom a separate oil reservoir. An air pressure (0,5 atm) above the oil in the eservoir and an adjustment valve in the oil tube facilitate a precise control of the il supply.

A method only feasible when the solder wave is of the single-sided nidirectional type has been sketched in Figure 9.25, where the oil is supplied lirectly to the surface of the solder wave via a controllable narrow gap. The [uantity of oil sucked by the wave is determined by the shape of the gap and the older flow in the wave.

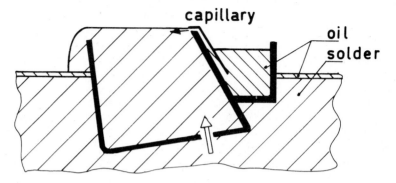

Fig. 9.25 Application of oil directly to the solder wave.

9.5.3 Soldering of a Mixture of Components to Both Sides of a Printed Board

The common wave soldering process is also used for the soldering of multilayer chip capacitors, chip resistors, MELF components, SO and SOT-23 components, *etc.* (see Chapter 8.2), to the solder side of printed boards, simultaneously with other components placed on the 'component' side with their leads protruding through holes in the board. By this means, configuration III of Table 8.1 is obtained. This configuration makes it possible to mount discrete components on single-sided boards to a very high density [Fletemeyer] and is suited to the production of the densely-packed circuits used in portable TV-cameras, car radios, *etc.* The components on the solder side of the board are fully immersed in the molten solder during the soldering operation, leading to the reference to soldering of components 'through the wave' or immersion wave soldering (Figure 9.26).

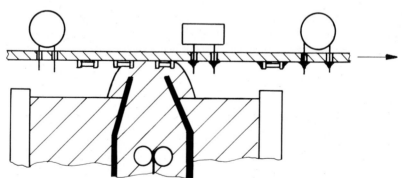

Fig. 9.26 Soldering method for a combination of leadless components and components with leads on both sides of single-sided printed boards (*cf.* Fig. 9.14).

To be able to use this soldering method, the components on the solder side of the boards must have been previously attached in their correct positions. This is achieved using an adhesive, a common procedure consisting in small droplets of dhesive being applied to the boards (between the solder lands), after which the adless components are placed in position, for instance using vacuum pipettes, hich can pick up the components and can be rotated and moved in horizontal nd vertical directions [Klein Wassink *et al*]. The devices for surface mounting an be placed sequentially by a computer controlled 'pick and place' machine, ke that used for thick film hybrid circuits. In mass production many mponents, *e.g.*, fifty, may be placed simultaneously in one movement of the acing machine. The actual construction of the placing machine, which is not scussed here in further detail, is influenced by the particular way in which the mponents are supplied (bulk, tapes, reels, cartridges), the number of mponents on the board, the packing density and the number of boards to be ounted.

5.3.1 APPLICATION OF ADHESIVE

The possibilities of applying the adhesive depend strongly on the types of mponents that are to be connected simultaneously, and on the fraction of adless components. In cases where only chips or chip-like components are to be ounted, screen printing can be used [Denda *et al*]. If a combination of mponents with wire terminations and leadless components is to be soldered, it ust be decided which components are to be placed first. Starting with the wire mponents gives no problems with automatic insertion. The components for rface mounting can be placed at a later stage on the solder side of the board in e areas which have been left free between the leads of the inserted components. this case the adhesive cannot be screen printed but should be discretely applied y dispensing or by pin-transfer (stamping), or it should be applied to the eparate components. Starting with the leadless components permits an easy pplication of the adhesive by screen printing, but makes the mechanical sertion of the other components much more difficult. Moreover, this requires a rger area on the solder side of the board, because the clinching or bending evice of the insertion machine needs a certain amount of free space around the rotruding leads.

Any contamination by adhesive on the metallisation of the components and on e copper of the solder lands impairs the wetting with solder, restoration of ettability being impossible.

Various adhesives can be used, to be polymerised by ultraviolet rays, by heat or y both. The adhesive should be applied in droplets thick enough to bridge the istance between the board and the bottom of the components and it should be fficiently tacky to withstand the forces during handling of assembled boards in e non-cured condition. After curing the bonds should be sufficiently strong (at)°C) to withstand any forces occurring during mounting of other components, nd to withstand the forces, mainly due to differential thermal expansions, ccurring during the soldering operation (at 250°C).

The combination of several techniques of a different nature in one mounting chnology represents a disadvantage. The application of small droplets of dhesive, the problems of adhesive potlife and cleaning of equipment (and the andling of adhesive in general) are not particularly appreciated by the personnel sually involved in the manufacture of soldered printed boards.

9.5.3.2 PROCESS

A complete process may consist of the following steps:

(i) Automatic insertion of components with leads in the holes of the board, clinching the leads;
(ii) Application of adhesive to appropriate places on the board;
(iii) Placing of components for surface mounting on the places provided with adhesive (Figure 9.27);
(iv) Curing of the adhesive;
(v) Addition of components by hand mounting, if any;
(vi) Application of flux and preheating of flux;
(vii) Soldering as usual (or if desired, soldering–lead cutting–soldering, see Chapter 9.5.4);
(viii) Inspection.

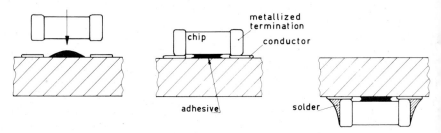

Fig. 9.27 Three stages in the mounting of leadless components on a printed board. Left: the component is placed on a previously applied droplet of adhesive; Centre: the component has been placed on the droplet of adhesive, which then must be cured; Right: the component has been soldered to the solder side of the printed board, while the adhesive remains between component and board.

The aforementioned process involves a mixture of components in a combination of connecting techniques. The leadless components should be suited to the immersion treatment during the soldering operation, in which the temperature ranges from 240 to 270°C and the contact time from 2 to 4 seconds (see Chapter 9.1.1). This implies adequate resistance to soldering heat and resistance to solder leaching. Many components do in fact satisfy these requirements.

When the board bearing the adhered components encounters the molten solder, every component termination and solder land should be contacted by solder. This does not happen automatically at the minute soldering terminations, which are in fact 'hidden' behind the component body, of for instance the SOT-23 package. The molten solder can only reach these terminations if it is curved inwards at the corners between the board and the component bodies. Drag soldering generally fails in this respect, because the pressure in the solder is insufficient to realise the necessary curvature.

9.5.3.3 SOLDERING DEFECTS

After soldering, a number of soldering defects may be observed:

(i) *Surface mounted components moved out of correct position or completely gone*: These defects are not usually soldering defects, but are linked with the properties of the used coatings, the adhesive or the curing treatment. The detachment of a component is not a direct result of the force exerted upon it by the flowing solder, because this force is much too small, but is owing to thermal stresses caused by the sudden contact with the hot solder, which the bond is apparently unable to withstand;

(ii) *No solder present between component and solder land*: The absence of solder can be the result of contamination by adhesive of the metal parts to be joined, or can be caused by any other obstruction to solder flow, which means that the solder does not come into contact with the surfaces to be wetted. Trapped flux or flux fumes can be the cause of such obstructions, as can also the unfavourable shape of components with minute soldering terminations in the 'shadow' of the body. Various remedies exist, *e.g.*, the application of holes in the board to relieve the gas pressure [US Patent 4,139,881 (1979), Down] (see Figure 12.33), adaptation of conductor shape so that the solder flow is guided to the solder lands, and the use of special wave nozzles, including double-wave systems;

(iii) *Bridges (shorts) between components in close proximity*: Bridges are the result of wrong process conditions or, more commonly, too small a spacing between the components relative to their height;

(iv) *Insufficient solder in the joint*: Insufficient volume of the soldered joints has various sources, among which are inadequate design of board configuration, poor wettability of component metallisation and incorrect process conditions.

Mechanical tests on soldered boards (Figure 9.28) have shown that the combination of leadless components with ceramic bodies and boards of cheap laminate material gives reliable joints, capable of withstanding all kinds of

Fig. 9.28 Part of an experimental board of phenolic paper laminate with a thickness of 1,6 mm. The board is used for investigating various printed pattern configurations, and the influence of the conditions in the adhesive bonding and the soldering stages of the process. The board is also used for mechanical tests of the soldered joints (bending tests, cycling tests, *etc.*). The board is shown at about twice the actual size.

thermal and mechanical tests. The most severe strength test is the bending test, in which the soldered board is forced against a cylindrical surface. Intuitive objections to the fixing of rigid components to a relatively flexible material have thus proven to be unfounded, provided the components are small. Perhaps it is precisely the difference in stiffness that forms the basis of the mechanical reliability of the soldered joints. For large components flexible terminations are necessary.

9.5.4 Soldering–Cutting–Soldering

With the soldering–cutting–soldering method, components with long leads protruding through the board are temporarily attached by a first soldering operation, after which the protruding leads are cut to the desired length, followed by a second soldering operation to form the final joints (Figure 9.29) [Bud]. The second soldering operation is employed because the joints may be degraded by the mechanical load associated with the cutting operation. This method permits assembly of printed boards using components of which the leads have not been cut or otherwise processed previously. Especially when components have to be placed by hand, vertically and close to one another, long component leads are essential. This soldering method is also applied if small protruding lengths are desired.

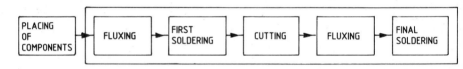

Fig. 9.29 The various steps in soldering–cutting–soldering. In the first solder step the components are fixed to make the lead cutting possible. The soldering–cutting–soldering is mostly carried out 'in line', that is using two solder baths.

The first soldering can be performed with a high solder wave, but this will cause relatively heavy oxidation, besides which such a wave is difficult to control. A static bath such as a drag soldering bath or an overflow solder bath is a more convenient alternative. The long leads, with a considerable amount of solder adhering to them, are cut to a length of between 0,5 and 2,5 mm (usually about 1,5 mm) from the board surface. This is achieved by transporting the printed boards horizontally across one or more circular cutters with vertical axes. The cutting blades are made of tungsten carbide and have a rotary speed of about 50 m/s [Woodgate]. Normally the cutting machine has a set of two or three cutters, but sometimes there is only one cutter that can oscillate perpendicularly to the board travel in order to span the width of the boards. Provisions are necessary, particularly for large boards, to prevent the boards from sagging too much. One method is to support them by rotating brushes. The board carriers are of equally great importance. A cutting disc must be ground after about 400 000 leads, and a built-in grinding facility is often provided. Dull cutting edges cause the leads to bend without being cut, which will cause short-circuits immediately, or after the final soldering (Figure 9.30). The best results, without bending of the leads, are obtained with short cutting lengths, but a cut very close to the board also has the risk of cutting in the conductors.

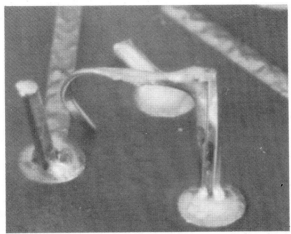

Fig. 9.30 Soldering defect resulting from a poor cutting operation. Two strands of the twisted wire have not been cut and are still present as a so-called flag. Moreover, the cutting length is excessive (by courtesy of P. Langeveld, Eindhoven).

The final soldering operation can be performed using a standard wave soldering machine. The small length of protruding leads from the boards permits a small wave height and thus a quiet wave.

Although the final joints are formed in the second soldering operation, this does not imply that the first soldering step is irrelevant to the final joint quality. If the first soldering is poor, for instance as a result of insufficient fluxing, it is not certain that the second soldering will correct this. The second fluxing is effected on the outside surface of the temporary joints but generally will not reach all places which are not yet wetted, such as the inside surface of plated

Fig. 9.31 A soldering–cutting–soldering system. A production sequence, combining component lead-locking, component lead-cutting and wave soldering operation in one in-line system (by courtesy of Electrovert, Canada).

holes. Consequently these places may be missed again in the second soldering operation.

The cut end faces of the leads in some cases oxidise to such an extent during the cutting action that they are not soldered during the final soldering operation.

The volume of the solder in the second solder bath may increase by drag-in from the first bath, in which case adequate corrective measures are needed.

The repeated soldering and the well-defined form of the protruding leads during the second soldering operation may produce a final soldering result with fewer defects compared with a single soldering operation. However, since the components are thermally loaded twice, an increased risk of thermal damage has to be envisaged. Equipment for soldering–cutting–soldering has high space requirements and demands extensive care. A complete system for the method is shown in Figure 9.31.

Instead of the first soldering operation, a similar operation is sometimes performed applying wax to fix the components before cutting. This has the advantage of a lower temperature, but the subsequent replacement of the wax by solder is difficult (especially in the holes) for thermal reasons. Moreover, the action of the flux in the final soldering operation is strongly impeded by the wax.

9.5.5   Advantages and Disadvantages of Wave Soldering

(i) It is a continuous process, affording relatively high production rates;

(ii) It is less prone to generation of gas bubbles under the boards, which can impede solder flow, than drag soldering and dip soldering;

(iii) The rapid transfer makes the process well suited to the soldering of boards with plated holes;

(iv) In the majority of applications it is capable of generating lean solder fillets, thereby facilitating the soldering of boards with high resolution patterns;

(v) The level of the solder bath is less critical than with soldering machines employing a static solder bath;

(vi) There is little limitation imposed on the dimension of the boards in the direction of travel;

(vii) Maintenance costs are high because of the necessary regular cleaning of the machine and the regular replenishing of tinning oil, if used;

(viii) The set-up of a machine requires skilled and experienced personnel;

(ix) The lay-out of the printed wiring must (preferably) be adapted to the direction of travel of the boards through the wave. The travel direction should therefore be indicated on the boards, although unfortunately this is seldom observed;

(x) If component leads project more than 2 mm from the solder side of the board, other soldering methods should also be considered.

9.6   THE SOLDERING MACHINE

The comprehensive evaluation of a soldering machine should distinguish between machine adjustments, machine parameters and process parameters. The latter parameters, as well as board design and components, determine the soldering result, whereas often only the adjustments of the machine are known precisely.

An arrangement of parameters of wave soldering is shown in Table 9.2, where

Table 9.2

Parameters of Wave Soldering Machine

Machine Adjustments (Settings of Controls)	Machine Parameters	Process Parameters (see Chapter 9.1.1)
adjustment of fluxer:	foam height: mm	
— air pressure: N/cm²	bubble size: mm	
— flux level: mm		
— baffles:		
		amount of flux on board and in holes:
adjustment of flux density controller:	density of flux: g/cm³	— before preheating: μm — after preheating: μm — after soldering: μm
adjustment of preheater(s):	power of preheater(s): kW	preheat temperature: °C
adjustment of conveyor:	transport speed: m/min.	dwell time: s
type of nozzle:	contact length: mm	
— position of front and backplates:	shape of wave:	
— solder level in tank: mm	height of wave: mm	flowing velocities of solder in both directions: turbulences:
— adjustment of pump:		
inclination of conveyor: °	falling height of solder: mm	peel-back velocity:
adjustment of bath-thermostat:	temperature of solder and its variation: T: °C ΔT: K	temperature reached: — on board: °C — on terminations: °C
type of carriers:	clearances: mm	immersion depth: mm soldering direction: warp: mm
adjustment of cooling facility:	air velocity: m/s air direction:	cooling time: s maximum temperature in the component bodies: °C

every item in the Table needs to be quantified if a particular machine is considered. Complete and satisfying evaluation of machines, however, is achieved with difficulty owing to lack of real insight to express the requirements in terms of intrinsic physical parameters. The evaluation therefore is usually done partly (at the most) and the difficulties are circumvented by establishing those machine adjustments that give useful or acceptable results in practice [Anon. Ref.18, Bester].

An ideal soldering machine does not exist. It is a well-known fact that everyone who has procured a soldering machine has had to expend a considerable and sometimes a prolonged period of time to make it function satisfactorily. Could this mean that the manufacturers of these machines do not know exactly what to look for?

Reviews of commercial equipments for wave soldering, drag soldering and dip soldering have been published recently [Karpel, Strauss, Billing]. The difficulty in comparing the various makes and types of machines is aggravated by th‹ interrelationship between the products to be soldered and the soldering machin‹ itself.

The investment costs of various types of machines differ considerably, but it i‹ beyond the scope of this book to make comparisons between the cost of th‹ various machines and methods. Per type of soldering machine as well as pe‹ manufacturer, prices exhibit substantial variations. In addition to the cos‹ criteria, the selection of the soldering method is also governed by the capacity c‹ the soldering machine. As a rule, at optimal machine setting the capacity is nc‹ fully exploited. The typical situation is that the machine is shut down for lon‹ periods interrupted by a sporadic hour of soldering, or else the machine is almos‹ 100% standby and only now and then is a board passed over it. The guidin‹ criterion must be the influence exerted by the cost of the soldering process o‹ product cost. The major components of the cost of the soldering process are th‹ price and operating costs of the machine, and the speed and degree of servic‹ offered by the vendor.

In this connection it is worth noticing that the total cost of the soldering machine and solderin‹ materials is only a small fraction of the total production cost of an assembled printed board. Some in‹ dication of the various components of this cost for two common types of board is given in Table 9.3‹

The example given of the single-sided board is representative of boards used in consumer produc‹ (television). It has 160 joints per dm^2 and a lot size of 30 000 boards. The double-sided board ‹ representative of boards in professional products (measuring equipment). It has 360 joints per dm‹ and a lot size of 2 000 boards. However, in both categories large variations in complexity are found a‹ regards number and distribution of components, pattern layout, *etc.* While comparing the boards i‹ Table 9.3 it must be realised that their electronic functions are totally incomparable. Comparin‹ boards with the same function, in single-sided and double-sided designs, is another matter.

Table 9.3

Cost of Various Production Steps (Prices are Only Indicative)

Type of Board	Prices in Dutch Florins per dm² (1982)	
	Single-Sided Phenolic Paper with Punched Holes	Double-Sided Glass Epoxy with Drilled and Plated Holes
Printed board with solder resist	1	12
Components: ICs, etc.	10	50
resistors, capacitors	15	15
Mounting (including transport)	2	9
Soldering (including transport)	0,25	0,75
Solder + flux	0,15	0,25
Touch-up (including transport)	0,5	1,5
Measuring (including transport)	0,6	12
Total factory price per dm²	29,5	100,5

Computer-Controlled Soldering

The introduction of computer aided wave-soldering machines (CAW), in whic‹ the soldering parameters are controlled with a microprocessor, suggests that i‹ might give an answer to existing soldering problems. This suggestion is no‹

verified and in fact is an overestimation of the importance of the soldering machine in the whole soldering system, as was discussed in Chapter 1.1.1.

A microprocessor can, of course, supervise very efficiently many parameters, such as flux density, flux foam height, conveyor speed, preheat temperature, solder height, solder temperature and wave height, but good control of these is often possible without a 'computer' and at lower cost [Woodgate]. The microprocessor is also said to permit of changing several (though not all!) of the aforementioned parameters almost instantaneously for individual board types, at the command of a code on the boards or on the carriers. This idea, however, is based on the opinion and illusion that it is possible to know for each type of board the set of soldering conditions that would give the best results (Chapter 12.6.3).

A machine which is fully computer controlled can only maintain the machine parameters at the required value, thus preventing maladjustments which would cause soldering defects, but this is limited in its scope and does not guarantee defect-free soldering, as the computer cannot cope with bad board design, improper selection of materials, and many other aspects that feature in Figure 1.1.

9.6.1   The Soldering Position

The important parts of the soldering position are the solder tank and the temperature control unit.

9.6.1.1   SOLDER TANK

The solder tank must have a shape that permits easy cleaning, *i.e.*, devoid of inaccessible corners, ridges, crevices, *etc.*, and it must be provided with a drain plug. (Moulds for casting drained solder must have outward-sloping walls to allow the ingot to be easily turned out.) The volume of the solder tank of a wave soldering machine depends on the width of the nozzle (measured at right angles to the direction of transport). For a nozzle with a width between 100 and 200 mm the minimum required volume of the solder tank is 20 litres. For a nozzle width up to 400 mm a tank volume of 40 litres is adequate. 40 litres of solder weigh 320 kg; added to the weight of the machine, it may be necessary to consider the maximum weight loading of the floor where the machine is located. The solder tank must have a length of minimum 300 mm in the direction of board travel in order to accommodate the widest nozzles and wave adapter assemblies.

A replenishment system should maintain the level of the molten solder in the operating condition and for this an automatic level control is recommended.

Sometimes the level in the operating tank may exceed the normal height, for instance by drag-in from one machine to the other if two machines are connected in series. In the event of this there must be provision for monitoring the level as well as a suitable overflow through which the solder and the oil can flow away when the solder pump is stopped.

The solder level and the oil level can be measured by means of a bar of solder bent at right angles (Figure 9.32). The oil on the bar of solder indicates the oil level, whilst the length of the bent part of the solder bar after melting off (10-15 seconds) indicates the solder level with respect to the upper edge of the tank. In the oil the heat transfer is insufficient to melt the bar of solder.

The machine must be so designed that in case molten solder accidentally flows over the edge of the solder pot, no hazard is created, and no machine parts are damaged. Measures must be taken so that when solder is being melted there is no

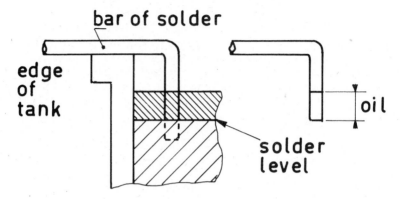

Fig. 9.32   Detail of cross-section of solder tank: method for determining the solder level and oil level.

risk of solder splashing or spitting. Hot oil may sometimes do more harm than molten solder because it penetrates the victim's clothes, whereas solder does not. Spitting of solder and oil may be rendered harmless by providing covers, but it is much better to arrange the heater elements in such a way that no high pressure is built up in the solder during melting, for instance by also heating the side walls of the solder tank.

9.6.1.2   POWER CONSUMPTION AND TEMPERATURE

A large machine must not take more than 3 hours to become operational. For bringing solder from the cold solid state to the correct operating temperature, an energy of 10^5 Joules for each kg of solder is necessary. Being equivalent to 10 Watts for a duration of 3 hours, this implies that for each kg of solder in a soldering machine at least 20 Watts of heating capacity must be installed (to heat the solder and the machine, taking into account the heat losses). The power consumption during operation is used for compensating the heat losses and for heating the boards to be soldered from the preheat temperature to the soldering temperature. The vent system should be adjusted to work just satisfactorily in order to limit the heat loss by air convection.

The thermostat must be capable of accurate adjustment, especially in the range between 240°C and 270°C. Across the full width of the solder bath contacting the printed board, with the machine fully loaded, the temperature should be maintained within ±2 K of the set value.

A safety interlock must be provided to prevent the pump motor from starting before the solder is liquid. The pump motor must also be equipped with a safety device to switch it off if the temperature of the solder accidentally rises above 300°C or drops below 200°C. It is desirable for the solder bath heater to be automatically switched off if the solder reaches an excessively high temperature in case of failure of the thermostat. All hot parts of the machine must be adequately guarded wherever possible.

9.6.2 The Conveyor

The conveyor must carry the boards to be soldered through the entire machine. For efficient operation the whole conveyor needs to be well adjusted according to the manufacturer's installation instructions. The transport mechanism must be protected against jamming by suitable means, such as breaker pins or a slip clutch. Near the charging end of the conveyor an emergency switch should be provided for stopping the transport system (and preferably also the pump, if present).

The inclination of the conveyor of a wave soldering machine, that is the angle of the conveyor with respect to the horizontal, must be adjustable. The magnitude of this angle depends on a number of factors, discussed in Chapter 9.5.1.

9.6.2.1 DIMENSIONS

The machine can of course only be integrated in an assembly line if its conveyor width conforms to the width of the assembly line. For good transport the conveyor should be supplied with chains on both sides (see Figure 9.19). The conveyor must project at least 50 cm before the fluxing station and after the soldering station, and the loading end of the conveyor must be designed so that boards are loaded in the correct position onto the conveyor. For this purpose aids like lead-in strips, *etc.* are usually required.

9.6.2.2 CAPACITY

Conveyor speed must be variable between 0,5 and 4 m/minute. The difference in speed between an empty and a full conveyor must not exceed 5% at a load difference of 25 kg. The output, expressed as the number of printed boards per hour (N), depends on the length of the boards (L), the spacing between the boards (W) and the transport velocity (v). The dwell time (t) depends on the contact length with the solder wave (l) and the transport velocity. Hence: $N = 60 \dfrac{v}{L + W}$ (boards per hour), and $t = 60 \dfrac{l}{v}$ (seconds), in which l, L and W are expressed in metres and v in metres/minute.

Example

The required dwell time is 3 seconds, the length $L = 200$ mm and the spacing between the boards $W = 200$ mm. The contact length is $L = 150$ mm. Thus the transport velocity must be $60 \dfrac{0,15}{3} = 3$ m/min, with $60 \dfrac{3}{0,6} = 300$ boards/hour being soldered.

In order to increase the output, keeping the dwell time constant, it is necessary to decrease the spacing between the boards. If there is no spacing between the boards, the output is maximal and amounts to 450 boards/hour. The output at constant dwell time can also be increased by raising the transport velocity in conjunction with a proportional increase of the contact length. However, here the conditions at the solder wave (points A and B in Figure 9.15) will be changed to such a degree that it is far from certain that the soldering results will be the same.

9.6.2.3   FINGER CONVEYOR

A special type of conveyor is the finger conveyor, in which two chains of spring strips (so called fingers) are continuously moving along the soldering machine with the desired transport velocity (Figure 9.33).

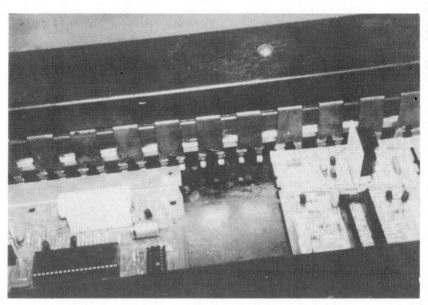

Fig. 9.33   Finger conveyance. The boards to be soldered are clamped between two chains of spring 'fingers', which move with the transport velocity.

The fingers of each chain are connected to form a continuous belt like a caterpillar track, but with vertical axis. The two chains are positioned opposite each other so that the boards to be transported can be simply clamped between the fingers; thus no carriers are required. Of course, in the absence of carriers the boards are not supported along their edges transverse to the transport direction, while at the same time the forces from the fingers act in this transverse direction. The finger conveyor is therefore unsuitable for wide boards, which will sag too much unless they are sufficiently thick to provide adequate rigidity (see Chapter 8.1.2). For a given distance between the opposite finger belts only boards of that width can be transported. For other widths the conveyor must be accommodated and means for achieving this are usually incorporated in the machine (Figure 9.34). The tips of the fingers become coated with flux when they pass the fluxing unit and they also go through the solder wave. It is necessary therefore that the fingers be made of a metal such as stainless steel which cannot be soldered using common fluxes (see Chapter 9.6.5). The fingers must be cleaned regularly to remove flux

Fig. 9.34 Complete wave soldering machine provided with finger conveyance. Note the wheel for accommodation of width of conveyor (by courtesy of Hollis Engineering, USA).

esidues and solidified solder. Many soldering machines can be delivered with either a chain conveyor or a finger conveyor.

.6.2.4 RETURN CONVEYOR

The transport and handling of the boards after soldering differs so widely from ne factory to another that no useful general advice can be given.

.6.3 The Cooling Position

If post-soldering cooling is applied, it usually involves a forced cold air stream vith a flow rate of about 1 m/s. The cooling must be uniform across the entire urface of the boards. If the cooling starts before the solder on the boards has olidified, which is sometimes necessary in view of the available length of the machine, care must be taken to prevent the air stream from moving the components on the boards. Here it is advisable to cool at the bottom side of the boards only (see also Chapter 9.1.1). The cold air stream must not flow in the direction of the solder wave, nor interfere with the operation of the vent system. These are difficult requirements because the cooling system is often located inside he vent hood for the purpose of removing flux and oil vapours generated during ooling.

Fixing of components to printed boards prior to and during soldering can be carried out in various ways:

(i) Bending (also called clinching), either partial or complete, of component terminations at the conductor side of printed boards;

(ii) Providing kinks in component terminations at the component side of printed boards.

> Kinking of component leads is not recommended for printed boards without hole plating because of risk of damaging edges of solder lands and thereby impairing soldering quality (see Figure 8.12);

(iii) Holding components down on printed boards by means of hold-down pads of a resilient material, pressed on to the component side of the printed boards.

> However, because of both the large quantity and the wide variety of components on most printed boards, this method is seldom suitable;

(iv) Transporting printed boards with components in such a way that the components are held in position by their own weight;

(v) Using adhesive or adhesive tape (see Chapter 9.5.3).

Fixing can sometimes be realised at no extra cost by means of jigs, fixtures, *etc.* used in the assembly of the printed boards.

9.6.4   Soldering Jigs

The magnitude of the warp, deflection and other geometric distortions in the printed board discussed in Chapter 8.1.1 precludes good soldering quality. It is true that part of this distortion can be eliminated by an appropriate design of printed board but to cope with residual distortion a soldering jig (carrier) is indispensable. The board carrier, having the purpose of supporting the printed board during its travel through the soldering machine, will in general have to exert a downward force on the corners of the board, to keep it flat. However, a printed board that is supported at two or four sides will still exhibit deflection in the centre. If deflection in the centre is then eliminated by an extra support, the rest of the printed board will assume a complex form which has the effect of reducing deflection to less than a quarter of the original value.

In the design of the soldering jigs, one or more of the following points must be considered:

(i) The support of the printed boards in the direction of travel;

(ii) The support of the printed boards transverse to the direction of travel;

(iii) The support of the printed boards in the centre, for instance by means of suspension strips on the component side of the printed boards;

(iv) The support of the printed boards by means of, for instance, boss-strips on the solder side of the printed boards;

(v) The clearance between the edges of the printed boards and the board carriers in transverse and lengthwise directions to allow for thermal expansion;

(vi) Protection against solder flooding of the printed boards.

A number of these points will be elaborated in the following text.

If a printed board has a width of more than 100 mm, it is advisable to provide one or more supports on the leading edge of the board carrier (Figure 9.35).

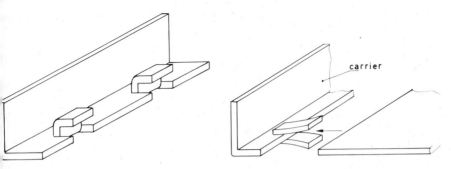

Fig. 9.35 (right) Support on the leading edge of a board carrier; (left) Reinforcement strip to be applied on the trailing edge of the board during soldering.

Because of interference with fluid flow, soldering quality in the vicinity of the supports is impaired. It is therefore recommended to use narrow supports and to limit their number to an absolute minimum.

If printed boards having a width of more than 200 mm cannot be designed with their own reinforcement strips, for soldering purposes temporary push-on reinforcement strips can be applied to the trailing edge of the printed boards (Figure 9.35 left).

Boards must always be supported in the lengthwise direction either by a device offering a continuous bearing area or local bearing areas comprising support points at intervals of 4 to 5 cm (Figure 9.36).

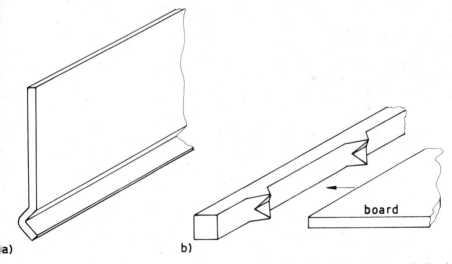

a)   b)

Fig. 9.36 Support of printed boards in lengthwise direction. (a) continuous bearing; (b) local bearing.

In general, jigs that provide continuous support of the printed board edges are, for reasons of cost, preferred to those having only intermittently placed support points. However, continuous support does have some disadvantages. The shape of the solder wave is disturbed in the vicinity of the printed board support. Consequently, in designing the printed boards the conductor pattern must be kept a sufficient distance away from the area where the printed boards will be supported. Moreover, solder bridges are likely to develop between the board carrier and the printed board conductors located close to the carrier. To cope with this problem it is recommended to provide the board carriers with a coat of PPS (polyphenylene sulphide) or PTFE (polytetrafluorethylene).

A board carrier must also be designed so that, to avoid warp of the printed boards, it has provision for accommodating the lateral expansion of a hot printed board. Where possible, a support in the centre of the boards should be provided for those having a width of more than 250 mm, as well as for boards carrying heavy components. Centre-support of a printed board is not necessary if the board is reinforced with one or more ribs. Sometimes very large boards can be supported using a carrier equipped with boss-strips on the solder side, at intervals of approximately 100 mm in both lengthwise and transverse directions (Figure 9.37).

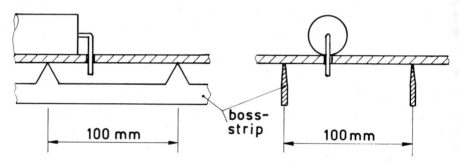

Fig. 9.37 Support of very large boards by strips at the soldering side of the board, placed vertically and in the direction of travel.

It is also possible to devise a jig supporting the whole perimeter of the printed board (a so-called passe partout jig). The soldering jig must have on its leading edge a fender device (Figure 9.38) to prevent solder from flooding the printed board. This fender has the added advantage of acting as a skimmer for removal of any oxides present on the solder wave. If the jig holds more than one printed board, the individual boards must butt closely against each other so that no opening is left through which solder may flood the printed boards.

Finally, it must be noted that a soldering jig (carrier) is a precision tool which should be treated with care and inspected regularly.

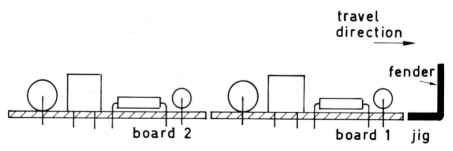

Fig. 9.38 Fender in front of the boards to be soldered. With more than one board in the carrier, the boards must be placed close to one another.

.6.5   Materials Used for the Machines

The solder tank, solder pump, *etc.* must be of such design and material that hey are resistant to the substantial mechanical forces originating from the olidification and re-melting of the solder. Machine parts that are exposed to flux s well as to solder require a long-lasting resistance to chemical attack by these ubstances. It should be borne in mind that many materials commonly considered o be non-wettable by solder may in the long term still become wetted if in requent contact with the solder, especially if these materials also come into ontact with flux.

Cast iron and ferrochromium are reasonably suitable. Stainless steel should be ;iven an oxidation or a nitriding-oxidation treatment. Titanium is the most uitable material but it is almost exclusively used for supporting points in carriers, *tc.* Aluminium is unsuitable. For those parts that are exposed exclusively to flux, tainless steel, glass or polypropylene are appropriate. Copper, brass, aluminium r iron are unsuitable for this last purpose.

.6.6   Determination of Soldering Parameters

For good soldering results the soldering parameters must be correctly adjusted nd maintained. As regards both adjustment and inspection measurement of the parameters is necessary.

.6.6.1   DETERMINATION OF THE CONTACT LENGTH IN WAVE SOLDERING

The dwell time can be measured with a test board according to Figure 9.40.)well time (*t*) depends on the contact length of the wave (*l*) in the direction of ransport, and the transport velocity (*v*) according to:

$$t = 60 \frac{l}{v},$$ in which *t* is in seconds, *l* in metres and v in m/min.

The length (*l*) depends among other things on the height of the wave. The ransport velocity can for instance be checked by determining the time which a)oint on the transport chain needs to cover a distance of 1 m.

The contact length can be adjusted using a heat-resistant glass plate in a oldering jig. In this way, the difference between the contact lengths left and right n the wave can in particular be made visible.

Note that the actual contact length between wave and metal-covered board liffers from that between wave and glass plate because of metal wetting see Chapter 7.2.3).

.6.6.2   DETERMINATION OF THE WAVE HEIGHT

The wave height can be read with a stainless steel straight edge immersed ertically into the wave until it stands on the edge of the nozzle.

9.6.6.3   DETERMINATION OF WAVE SHAPE AND ANGLE OF TILT OF THE NOZZLE

By means of a waste strip of copper-clad base material (approximately 20 cm long and 3 cm wide) a profile of the wave can be obtained (Figure 9.39). Flux is applied to the strip and allowed to dry sufficiently. The strip is held between forefinger and thumb or in tongs with the faces and short edges vertical, and lowered until one end rests on the exit edge of the nozzle. The other end is then pushed down until it rests on the entry edge of the nozzle, after which the strip is withdrawn vertically from the wave. The wave profile will now be marked with solder on the strip, and the angle of tilt of the nozzle can be measured. Because the solder readily wets the strip and climbs up, this is not a suitable means of determining the height of the wave with great accuracy, but if good wetting is shown an approximate measure can be obtained by subtracting 3 mm from the height of the wetted area.

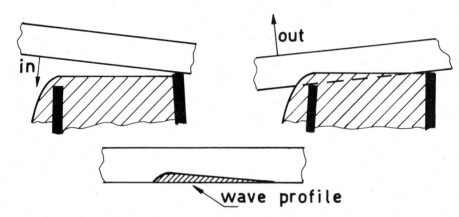

Fig. 9.39   Method for determining the shape of the wave using a piece of copper-clad material.

9.6.6.4   CHECKING THE WAVE SOLDERING AND DRAG SOLDERING MACHINE ADJUSTMENTS
BY MEANS OF A SPECIAL TEST BOARD

A special test board with accessories enables a simple check of various machine adjustments to be made (Figure 9.40). Before using the test board, flux residues from earlier tests must be removed. With the temperature gauge it is possible to determine the temperature during predrying. The clearance between the board and the nozzle edge can be measured by means of the clearance indicator. Dwell time can be measured at various points on the test board, thus making it possible to obtain ready insight into the adjustment of the conveyor, the wave and the board holders. For this time measurement, the measuring cables of the clock are connected to the solder bath and to the time test points of the test board. By placing the test board in different holders, the soldering system can be checked. Instead of a stationary time indicator it is convenient to use a battery-powered electronic clock conveyed by the test board through the soldering machine [O'Rourke].

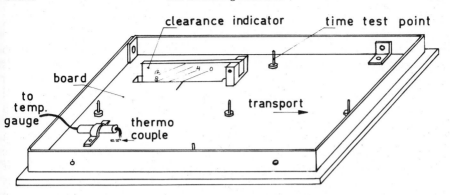

Fig. 9.40   Test board for performing measurements of dwell time, preheat temperature and clearance between board and nozzle edge. The clearance indicator is placed in its lowest position prior to the test run, and it is pushed upwards when contacting the edge of nozzle, maintaining its highest position by friction (by courtesy of G. Schouten, Hilversum).

9.6.6.5   MEASUREMENT OF THE SOLDERING TEMPERATURE

On a normally flowing wave the soldering temperature is measured with a thermometer on the exit edge of the nozzle. It is often necessary to readjust the thermostat of the bath in order to reach the desired temperature, because the adjusted temperature deviates slightly from the measured temperature. For a good machine the temperature will not vary more than ±1 K across the length of the nozzle edge.

For the correct measurement of the temperature, various thermometers can be used:

(i)   It is possible to use a mercury-in-glass thermometer, although this is not recommended because of the high risk of breakage and consequent contamination of the bath. (The temperature reading must be corrected for free length!);

(ii) A coaxial thermocouple, connected to a compensating voltmeter or a recorder, with or without cold junction compensation. This is the most accurate and reliable method of temperature measurement;

(iii) The modern electronic battery-powered temperature gauges with digital reading offer a convenient alternative. Such devices are, *e.g.*, 60 × 150 × 25 mm^3 and are provided with a 1,5 mm ϕ × 100 mm thermocouple which is immersed in the solder. The accuracy is ±1 K or ±0,5 K. Higher accuracy is not necessary, as the indication is frequently a few degrees too low in the 250°C region in any case (possibly because the curvature of the relationship between thermal voltage and temperature is not taken into account). A typical device costs approximately $250 (1982 prices).

Chapter 10

REFLOW SOLDERING

Reflow soldering is the making of joints by remelting previously applied solder, without the addition of any extra solder during the soldering operation. The word 'reflow' should not be taken too literally, as reflow soldering refers nowadays to all processes in which heat and solder are applied separately.

For the various reflow soldering methods a definite minimum quantity of solder is required, depending on the design of the joints to be formed. The field of reflow soldering encompasses mass soldering methods, as well as sequential soldering methods, both applying automatic machines as well as manual operation. Many reflow methods are available and this Chapter will discuss them in an order determined by the heating method applied (see Table 10.1). The terms 'heating from above' and 'heating from below' refer to the common configurations of the support plates, as given in Table 8.1. In most cases the components are positioned 'above' the plate.

Table 10.1

Review of Reflow Soldering Methods

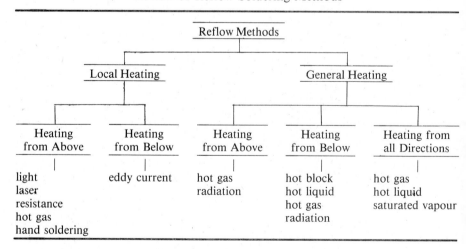

362

10.1 APPLICATION OF SOLDER AND FLUX

The solder is applied prior to the soldering operation as preforms, an electrodeposit, a layer of solder cream or a solder layer obtained by dipping. The last three methods lend themselves to mass production processes. Regarding electrodeposited solder it should be noted that the actual solder composition (and melting temperature) may differ considerably from the intended value (see Chapter 6.3.5.4), which is important if the subsequent reflow soldering is performed with a fixed maximum process temperature as in vapour phase soldering.

The flux may be contained in the solder as in the case of cream or preforms, or it may be added separately, for instance with a brush. A rosin flux can often perform two functions simultaneously, holding the components and the solder in the desired places and fluxing the surfaces to be wetted. During soldering, when the solder melts, the components generally remain in position. Once the solder has been melted the components are held in place by the equilibrium forces due to surface tensions. In the event of a small misplacing the components may even float to the correct equilibrium position. On the other hand, it is important for the solder applied at different places to melt at about the same moment. If the solder at one termination of a component melts before that at the other termination(s), which is for instance likely if the amounts of solder are not equal, the surface tension of the molten solder may turn the component upright, so that the component stands vertically on its wetted termination (Figure 10.1).

The tacky state of solder cream makes it, in principle, possible to solder light components while they are hanging. The components will not fall from the substrate or board during soldering if the ratio of suspended weight to area of contact with the solder cream is below a critical value, which depends on the state and thickness of the cream layer, and is about 100 mg/mm^2 [Takasago *et al*]. However, with hanging components inhomogeneous application of cream and unavoidable temperature gradients will in practice soon produce failures. After the component terminations have been wetted by molten solder the components will no longer fall off.

Fig. 10.1 Multilayer chip capacitor standing upright as a result of earlier melting of the solder cream on its right solder land than on its left solder land. This effect may be observed after non-uniform heating of the substrate or after unequal application of solder cream.

10.1.1 Preforms

Preforms are small objects of a given mass, made of solder, which are placed at or near the place to be soldered. Various shapes of preforms exist: discs, washers, spheres, foil, *etc.* [White, White *et al*], and the flat preforms are mostly stamped out of rolled solder strip. Preforms are available in many metal compositions and soldering flux (rosin type) may or may not be supplied as part of the preform, as either a filling or a coating [Johnson]. Figure 10.2 shows a variety of types commercially available.

Preform rings of the correct size are applied around wire terminations that require to be soldered. Flat preforms must be temporarily attached in other ways, for instance by sticking with flux.

The application of the preforms can be achieved manually using tweezers or suction tools, or by automatic techniques using vibratory feeders, vacuum transferring, multiple box jigs, *etc.* Fully automatic placing, however, occurs only in rare cases. In general, the placing is a time-consuming task and difficult to mechanise [Langan].

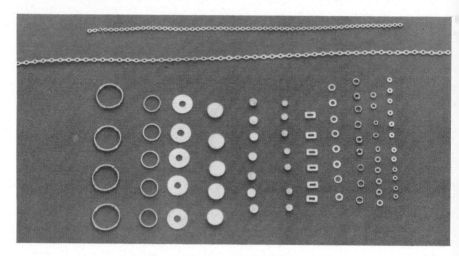

Fig. 10.2 Selection of solder preforms.

10.1.2 Solder Cream (Paste)

Solder cream is a suspension of solder powder particles in flux, to which special agents have been added [MacKay, Glaessgen, Slattery *et al*]. Its use is increasing rapidly, not only in electronics but also in many other fields of soldering.

The range of properties of currently existing solder creams is still insufficient to meet all requirements for reflow soldering. Hence, the development of new creams is desirable, for instance suitable for very rapid heating (as with a laser beam) and for very slow heating (as in an air furnace).

If the cream is heated above the melting temperature of the solder alloy contained in it, the alloy particles will coalesce to form one volume of metal. In most cases, however, this metal contains a large number of voids or flux-filled pores (Figure 10.3) [Taylor *et al*]. Most solder creams contain 75 to 85 mass per cent of solder metal, which is about 25 to 40 volume per cent. The metal particles are therefore not in mutual contact when they are homogeneously distributed. Dispensing agents are added to prevent the separation of the heavy metal from the light vehicle. However, shocks during transport may impair the stability and sometimes the cream settles, in which case uniformity of composition can be restored by stirring.

Fig. 10.3 Cross-section of a component lead which has been reflow soldered to an alumina substrate using a solder cream. The soldered joint contains a large number of holes, which is not an exception; see also Figure 8.19. Width of the lead is 400 μm.

For the application of the cream, rheological properties such as viscosity and thixotropy are important. These depend on the volume fraction, the size and size distribution of the metal particles, and the agents added.

10.1.2.1   SOLDER PARTICLES

The shape of the solder powder particles depends on the powder production process and varies from totally irregular for a powder which has been pulverised by blowing in air, to almost perfectly spherical for particles obtained from solder which has been sprayed into a liquid (Figure 10.4). By sieving the spherical powder particles, a well-defined maximum particle size is obtained. For particles with irregular shapes, the openings in the sieve only determine the smallest cross-section of the particles and consequently a large spread of the volumes of the sieved particles is observed.

The particle size is usually dictated by the 'mesh size' of the sieve through which the powder has been passed. Commonly used values of mesh sizes for

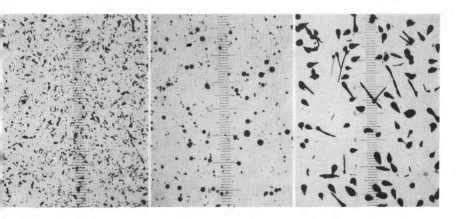

Fig. 10.4 Photographs of solder powder particles: (left) eutectic tin-lead particles with irregular shape; 300 mesh; (middle) eutectic tin-lead particles of spherical shape; 200 mesh with a wide distribution of the diameters; (right) tin62-lead36-silver2 alloy particles with an elongated shape; 200 mesh with few smaller particles (one scale division on the photographs is 27,5 μm).

solder powder are 300, 200 and 100 mesh, corresponding to openings of about 5 75 and 150 μm respectively. Coarse powders normally consist of sieve fractio and thus contain relatively few fine particles. A volume of 1 mm^3 of cream wi 80 mass per cent of metal (30 volume per cent) and spherical particles of diameter of 75 μm contains 1360 particles with a total surface area of 24 mm Before these particles can coalesce in the molten state, their surfaces must k cleaned by the fluxing action. It is therefore important that the powder particl are not oxidised beyond a certain level. High quality powder is sometimes calle 'oxide-free'.

If the cream contains spherical particles it flows easily and can be convenient applied without causing much wear to the screening equipment. To avoi excessive flow a certain proportion of the particles must be non-spherical. Th metal composition of the creams most commonly used in electronics is aroun that of the eutectic tin-lead. For soldering to thick film conductors, alloys with u to 4 per cent of silver are employed, for instance tin62-lead36-silver2, to decreas the dissolution rate of the silver from the solder lands into the molten solder allc (see Chapter 4.6.3). Apart from the alloys mentioned many other compositio are available in the form of solder cream, including many low-melting alloys.

Solder powder of polished, spherical particles with a tight particle size distribution has bee reported to present the unusual phenomenon of 'Squeaking' when it is poured from one container another or when a spoon is thrust into the powder [Anjard].

10.1.2.2 FLUX IN THE CREAM

In principle, the same fluxes are used in solder creams as for machir soldering. Owing to the relatively large surface area of solder particles, a effective fluxing is needed and a non-activated flux may be inadequate for th complete coalescence of the particles. The fluxes in the creams are characterise in the same way as the fluxes for cored solder wire and must fulfil the sam requirements of surface resistance and corrosion as apply to the correspondin types of solder wire.

Keeping small components such as chip components in position in the perio between placing of the components and soldering is assisted by the stickiness c the cream. This condition is maintained during a long period of time by selectin solvents with a sufficiently low vapour pressure, so that there is ample freedom i the interval between application of cream and placing of components (usuall within 8 hours). A waiting time of more than a month is possible if the produc are stored in a freezer at $-20°C$. If the cream becomes too dry the componen will not stick in the cream, when placed in position.

Drying of the cream, *i.e.*, evaporation of the greater part of the flux solver before soldering, but after placing of components, is very important to prevei components being blown away or moved out of true position by too rapi evaporation of solvent still present during soldering. Moreover, if the cream : heated rapidly, without predrying, it may not coalesce satisfactorily, but leav many satellites. The necessary degree of drying depends on the shape of the join and the conditions of the soldering process to follow, such as heating rate and th direction of the heat input.

Often a bake-cycle (in air) of 20 to 40 minutes at 70°C, or 5 to 20 minutes a 90°C is applied, but in other cases 10 seconds at 170°C proved effectiv Soldering may be carried out immediately after drying (preheating) or after waiting time of up to several days.

The flux residues remaining after soldering must be easily removable by luorocarbon solvents in an ultrasonic cleaning bath.

0.1.2.3 APPLICATION OF THE CREAM

Solder cream is available from the suppliers in pots of various sizes or in yringes. The pot life of the cream is an important characteristic. The cream can e applied in many ways using manual or automatic methods. It is most requently applied by screen printing, whereby the required areas (usually square) re covered with a layer of cream [Peterson, Lee]. These areas may be larger than he underlying solder lands, and during soldering the solder particles must oalesce and the solder must withdraw onto the lands. The wet layer thickness of he screened cream depends on the kind of gauze and on the pattern that is used or the screening. The layer thickness is 150±20 μm if an 80 mesh polyester or teel gauze is used with an organic lacquer mask (emulsion backed screen). It s 250±30 μm if one uses a 40 mesh steel gauze to which a metallic foil mask of 00 μm thickness has been attached (metal foil backed screen).

The difference between the thickness of the screened wet layer and the dried ayer is not large, because the solvent content of the cream is low and the powder articles soon make contact with each other while the flux retracts from between he particles.

Some examples of other methods of applying cream to the substrates are:

i)   A method similar to screen printing, but using a stencil instead of a screen [Daebler];
ii) The cream, which is available in a thin layer, is brought to the solder lands by pin-transfer;
iii) The cream is applied to the places to be soldered using a dispenser controlled by pressurised air, usually in a point to point operation. Multi point dispensing up to 68 points has been reported [Schoenthaler].

The cream can also be applied to the components to be soldered, in which case hese are dipped in a layer of cream, ensuring that the terminations are covered vith a suitable quantity.

Larger solder pads can be made on the terminations of components, such as OT-23 packages, by a transfer technique. The terminations are pressed into dots f solder cream previously applied to an unmetallised ceramic substrate. While he components remain on the substrate the cream is melted, producing solder ads around the terminations with a flat underside, thus facilitating the mounting f the components at a later stage. The components with the solder pads can be asily lifted from the substrate after removal of the residual flux [Lyman].

An amount of solder of about 1 mg per termination gives the highest pull trength of SOT-23 packages soldered on common thick films [Panousis *et al*].

Viscosity

The viscosity of the solder cream depends on the solids content of the flux, on he quantity, grain size and shape of the solder particles and on the thickener that s added to the flux to make the cream thixotropic. Viscosity must be adapted to he method of application (Table 10.2).

Table 10.2

Viscosity Ranges of Solder Creams

Application Method	Viscosity of Paste (Pa.s)	Metal Content (Mass Per Cent)
Dispenser	100–250	80
Screen	300–500	85
Stencil	400–800	85–90

As it is temperature-sensitive, at higher temperatures the viscosity will decrease markedly; it is therefore recommended to apply the cream in a temperature controlled room.

The viscosity can increase substantially during storage and use. If the flux is already found to react with the solder powder at room temperature, the flux is rendered useless. This is also the case if the surface layer of the cream hardens a a result of the reaction of flux with the powder particles in this layer (surface crusting). For this reason the cream should be stored at a lower temperature, fo instance at 5°C in a refrigerator, but should be allowed to reach room temperature in the closed pot before use, to avoid condensation of water from the air.

10.1.2.4 SOLDER BALLING TEST

The combination of metal content, flux and other constituents can be investigated by means of the solder balling test. This involves application of a do of solder cream of about 0,2 mm thickness and a diameter of 5,5 mm to a cerami or metallic substrate which is not wettable by solder. The substrate with solder cream on top is then horizontally brought into contact with molten solder c 250°±2°C for a period of 3 seconds.

During contact, all the solder powder in the cream should melt into one singl solder ball leaving no separate solder particles in the flux, with the exception c the extreme edge of the applied dot, where some small solder particles (satellites may be evident (Figure 10.5). The same requirement applies when the dot c solder cream has previously been dried in air at ambient temperature for at leas 24 hours and preferably 72 hours (a weekend).

The application of the cream involves use of a punched self-adhesive pape label and a simple metallic squeegee. The holes of 5,5 mm can be punched in th paper label with any standard paper perforator. The required thickness can b obtained by sticking two paper labels which normally have a thickness of 0,09 t 0,1 mm on top of each other, providing a total thickness without backing pape of 0,18 to 0,2 mm.

The substrate should have a thickness of 0,6 to 0,8 mm. A good therma contact between the substrate and the molten solder is realised by cleaning th surface of the bath carefully and pushing the substrate to an immersion depth c about 2 mm. Inspection of the test specimen occurs at 10 times magnificatio More than one dot of cream may be applied to the same substrate.

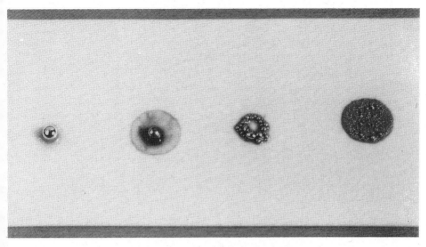

g. 10.5 Solder balling test of four solder creams on one alumina substrate, showing different grees of coalesence and satellite formation. Width of substrate 25 mm (by courtesy of J. H. J. van Dijk, Eindhoven).

).1.2.5 PRICES

Solder creams are expensive, the price to be paid for 1 kg of cream being many mes that of 1 kg of flux cored wire, reflecting the much greater amount of sting required to control the many different characteristics. The price of the eam depends on:

)   the composition and particle size distribution of the powder (standard or special);
i)   the packing (syringe or 1 kg pot);
ii) the amount of cream delivered (100 g or 50 kg);
v)   the manufacturer or the supplier of the cream.

The price of cream with a solder composition of tin60-lead40 may vary from 40 ◗ 200 US dollars per kg (1982 prices). In syringes of 100 g this increases about ireefold. For the silver-containing creams a much higher price is asked than that istified by the silver content, for instance $30 more per kg of cream for the alloy n62-lead36-silver2 in comparison with tin60-lead40.

0.1.3 Application of Solder by Dipping

The solder lands can be covered with solder by means of a dipping operation. owever, the thickness of the layer obtained by dipping varies considerably with ie rate of withdrawal [Chu], the location on the substrate and the surroundings f the solder lands. Thickness is virtually independent of the material that is ipped, provided the material is clean.

In Figure 10.6 the average layer thickness as a function of the withdrawal speed is given for copper, brass and nickel silver plates, using activated and no▮ activated fluxes (235°C).

The thickness of coating varies along the height of the specimen, the thicke▮ layer being found at the bottom. Layer thickness in areas at the bottom and at th▮ top of a dipped plate, 35 mm apart, may be respectively 6 to 12 μm and 2 to 3 μm▮ When non-wettable substrates with wettable areas are dipped, the thickness of th▮ solder coating obtained on these areas varies considerably, depending on the▮ shape and especially on the possibilities for drainage. Areas of the same size ca▮ easily display differences in solder-layer thickness of 50 μm.

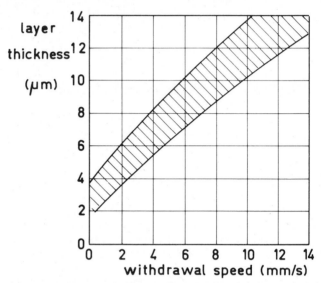

Fig. 10.6 Average layer thickness of solder coating on hot dipped plates as a function of the speed ▮ withdrawal (= dipping speed).

10.2 GENERAL HEATING FROM BELOW

The case of heating from below through the support plate has been discussed ▮ Chapter 3.2.2 in connection with the theory of heat conduction. This Chapter w▮ look at the matter from a more practical point of view. The major problem wi▮ this heating method is the variable heat transfer at the lower face of the suppo▮ plates.

10.2.1 Contact with a Hot Block

The objects to be soldered must have flat undersides to assist heat transf▮ when placed on top of a hot block. This method is normally used for th▮ soldering of alumina substrates of configuration V (Table 8.1). Numero▮ commercially available table-top machines exist for this soldering process.

The method is characterised by two problems: the magnitude of the he▮ resistance, and the lack of uniformity of the heat transfer over the substrate.

Owing to the heat resistances, the temperature of a component termination ▮ be soldered on a substrate lies considerably below that of the top face of th▮ substrate. When components with different thermal demands are soldere▮

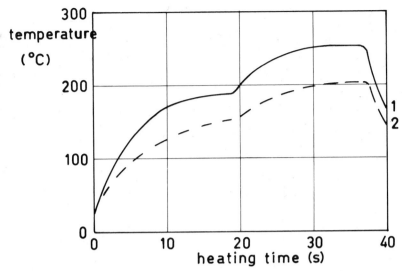

Fig. 10.7 Temperature-time traces of the top face of an alumina substrate (1) and the lead of an electrolytic capacitor (2) soldered on a belt soldering system. Conveyor speed 11 mm/s. Temperature setting of the zones 204°C and 280°C.

simultaneously, those with higher thermal demand need a longer time to reach the soldering temperature (Figure 10.7).

The non-uniformity of heat transfer results from variations in the air gap between the lower face of the substrate and the hot block of the soldering apparatus caused by curvature of the substrate surface. These variations magnify the differences in soldering conditions between components with different thermal demands, because an air gap may happen to be present just below a 'heavy' component, and a good contact below a 'light' component.

A means by which the heat transfer differences can be overcome is to convey the substrates across the heat source. In the 'belt soldering system' the substrates to be soldered are put on a PTFE belt which moves across a series of hotplates, exposing the substrates to a heating-cooling cycle [Browne]. The PTFE belt, however, creates additional heat resistances by which the heating rate is lowered and the effect of the different thermal demands is increased. The soldering conditions are substantially changed, if the substrates are held down in order to improve the contact between the lower face of the substrates and the belt, and also between the lower face of the belt and the hot plates.

The heating method applying one hot block can be extended to a system having three or four blocks at different temperatures, and in which the substrates are automatically transferred from one block to another. The idea is that in this manner a more constant heating rate is obtained. The application of additional hot blocks partly cancels the differences in air gap, but, as the final heating station is of major importance, variations of heating conditions are still encountered.

10.2.2   Heating With a Hot Liquid

An extremely uniform heat transfer is obtained when the lower faces of the support plates are brought into contact with a streaming liquid, although the heat transfer strongly depends on the liquid selected.

10.2.2.1   LIQUID METAL AS A HEAT TRANSFER MEDIUM

Very rapid heating can be achieved when liquid metal is used as a heat transfer medium. Thermal damage of sensitive components can be avoided by applying a cooling stage just after the actual soldering. Liquid metal at a lower temperature (about 100°C) can be used for this cooling.

Along these lines, processes have been investigated consisting of separate steps for the heating and cooling, realised by separate liquid-metal waves connected in series. The larger the number of steps used, the more gradual is the heating obtained (Figure 10.8).

A three-wave system consists for instance of: heating for 8 seconds at 180°C, soldering for 2 seconds at 250°C and cooling for 2 seconds at 105°C (contact times and liquid metal temperatures). Alumina substrates can withstand these thermal shocks without problems arising.

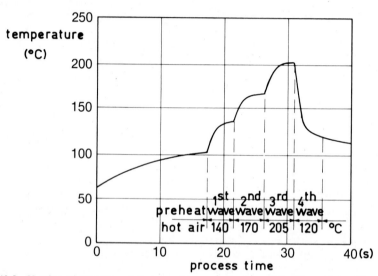

Fig. 10.8   Heating of alumina substrates making use of waves of liquid metal. In this case, three waves are used for the heating. The fourth wave is intended to cool the substrate rapidly below the temperature at which particular components are injured.

The major difficulties encountered with liquid metals as heating media are:

(i)   oxidation of the low melting liquid alloys;
(ii) spattering of the solder cream during the short heating period.

10.2.2.2   HOT OIL AS A HEAT TRANSFER MEDIUM

If very rapid heating is not desired, heating from below with a liquid can be achieved by applying a wave of hot oil in a wave soldering machine. This heating method is successfully applied for printed boards (epoxy-glass laminate), when components to be soldered are on top of the boards. The time needed to melt solder cream on the top side of the board is 24 seconds at an oil temperature of 235°C, which is in accordance with the calculations of Chapter 3.2.2. The long heating time is obtained by employing a low conveyor speed (1,5 mm/s).

Various liquids such as glycerol or silicone oil can be used (see also Chapter 10.5.2), but tinning oil is the best for thermal stability. Replenishment of this oil is necessary only once a week (5×8 hours).

The heating oils have a tendency to wet alumina substrates so that with this material the risk exists that the top faces may be partly flooded with oil. This wetting tendency can be effectively demonstrated in a wetting balance in which the bath is not filled with solder but with oil. The difference between various oils is quite pronounced. Oils with the highest heat transfer unfortunately exhibit the highest degrees of wetting. This is not surprising, since only through the close contact of molecules attained in wetting can the transfer of heat from one molecule to another readily occur.

10.2.3   Heating With Hot Air or Radiation

Infra-red heating, hot air heating or a combination of both methods is commonly used for the preheating of printed boards in wave and drag soldering machines, for which a temperature of no higher than about 80°C is desired.

Neither of the general methods with heating from below using air or infra-red is particularly suitable for reflow soldering of printed boards, because it is in general difficult to reach a sufficiently high temperature at the other side of the support plate (see Chapter 10.3). There are, however, small table-top machines provided with a heat radiator that are intended for the soldering of thick film substrates. The radiator is below the substrate (Figure 10.9) and the machine is similar to the small table-top hot block machines. The problem of variations in local heat contact found with the block method does not exist with these. However, the heating rate is strongly influenced by the absorption coefficient of the substrate surface (see Chapter 10.3.2). At a certain power setting of the machine a 'white' alumina substrate needs 45 seconds to reach a temperature of 200°C, whereas this time can be reduced to 3 seconds simply by making the surface black.

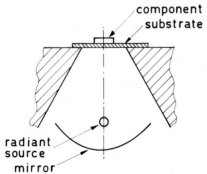

Fig. 10.9   Heating of thick film substrates with radiation from below.

10.3   GENERAL HEATING FROM ABOVE

Heating from above means that heat is directed onto the side of the substrate on which the components are located. The main methods apply radiation or hot gas, though other heating methods are conceivable. Non-selective application of heat does not imply that all places reach the same temperature, because different

positions on the substrate (board) or on the components may have different
absorption coefficients, different heat conductivities and different heat
capacities.

10.3.1 Heating with Hot Gas

The method of heating with a stream of hot gas is distinguished from that of
heating from all sides in a hot air circulation oven (see Chapter 10.5.1). As the
heat transfer between gas and the material to be heated is relatively low, the
processes using hot gas are in most cases slow. Their speed can be increased by
blowing stronger, although this inevitably has a limit. The main increase is
obtained by choosing a higher gas temperature. In doing so, the process is
typically one of the excess heating strategy, with the consequence that with
changing environmental conditions either temperature overshoot and hence
damaging of components may occur, or, if the change of conditions is in the
other direction, adequate soldering may not be obtained.

The bodies of the components positioned in the stream of gas are often heated
more rapidly than the terminations to be soldered, so that for this reason also
overheating may be encountered. Despite the objections mentioned, heating with
hot air finds use in a number of applications because it is relatively cheap.

10.3.1.1   ADVANTAGES AND DISADVANTAGES OF HOT GAS HEATING

(i)   The components cannot be mechanically damaged;
(ii)   Heat can be supplied to places which are otherwise difficult to reach. This
       allows a greater freedom of design and a greater freedom to use auxiliary
       tools such as locating jigs, provided they do not themselves have excessive
       heat capacity and thus waste the gas heat;
(iii) General as well as local heating is possible;
(iv)   The energy transfer is limited and so consequently is the speed of heating.
       The size of the objects to be heated is also limited;
(v)   There is a risk of blowing components out of position.

10.3.1.2   THE HOT GAS COMPOSITION

The gas is heated by passing it over an electrical heating element and is
subsequently blown onto the places to be heated. As air is by far the cheapest
medium, it is usually chosen. Blown over a heated product, however, it may cause
annoying oxidation. Nitrogen does not cause any oxidation, but a nitrogen
stream always takes up some air owing to turbulence.

A large volume of gas is required in order to obtain an adequate quantity of
heat. The velocity of the gas jet is limited as the products will be blown out of
position or even blown away. These objections apply to a much lesser extent in
the case of hydrogen. Hydrogen is much lighter than air but possesses the same
specific heat. This results in a lighter thrust for the same heat transfer in
proportion to the specific masses of the gases. Hydrogen also has a reducing
effect. When using hydrogen it should be taken into account that mixtures of
hydrogen and air are explosive over a wide range of concentrations, necessitating
the inclusion of a proper exhaust. A gas mixture of 75% nitrogen and 25%
hydrogen is a better choice. This mixture is still combustible on mixing with air,

ut the risk of explosion is much lower. In many cases, air is considered adequate
espite the oxidation.

).3.1.3 EXAMPLES OF HOT GAS SOLDERING

Two examples of hot gas soldering are given as follows:
Streams of hot air from blowpipes are used for the soldering of pins, for
stance wire wrap pins or connector pins, in plated holes of printed boards or
ultilayer boards. The pins are usually provided with solder preforms (rings with
ux). The blowpipes have such dimensions that, although many pins are struck
y the hot air simultaneously, only a restricted area of the board around the pins
aches the soldering temperature.

Transistors in chip encapsulation (see Figure 8.5) are soldered on top of epoxy
lass-fibre printed boards (configuration II, Table 8.1) with the aid of hot air
nives. Before the soldering operation the components are fixed to the board with
older cream. The air temperature in the nozzle exit is about 300°C (in the nozzle
ntry it is about 400°C). Conveyor speed is 100 mm/min. The temperature
ached by the transistor junction is rather close to that at which damage will
nsue and the process is critical as a result of the steep final part of the heating
urve (Figure 10.10). This heating process with hot air is not suitable for MOS
omponents, owing to the electrostatic charge generated by the air stream.

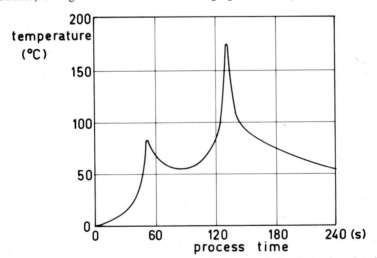

g. 10.10   Junction temperature of transistor in SOT-23 encapsulation during hot air soldering,
applying two hot air knives. Conveyor speed 100 mm/min.

After the hot air process for soldering the components on top of the board, a
ommon wave soldering process is used to solder the other components with leads
through the plated holes. In this second soldering operation the joints on
p of the board are not affected, because their temperature remains below the
elting temperature of the solder during the short time used for wave soldering.

).3.2 Radiant Heating

The infra-red (IR) heating method is an extreme example of the excess heating strategy. The ultimate temperature that the various components and the boar will reach depends on rather complex radiation conditions. Little practica information is available on the reflection properties of the materials involved an on the dependence of these properties on temperature, wavelengths, *etc.* Th absorption of a rough copper surface and of a polished copper surface are 40% and 10% respectively of that of a perfectly black surface. The absorption o solder metal also depends on wave length. Shorter wavelengths give highe absorption. At a wavelength of 1 μm the absorption is about 40%, at 0,1 μr about 80%. Solder cream has a high absorption as long as the solder particle have not melted together, and thus a 'good coupling' with the radiation i obtained. It is noteworthy that most component bodies generally become hotte than the leads to be soldered.

The advantage of radiant heating is, just as with heating by hot gas, that ther is no mechanical contact with the soldering point. Heating of the objects is eve possible through a transparent material, for instance glass, giving the possibilit of soldering in a protective atmosphere.

The adjustment of the heating equipment is simple in principle, and it i possible to vary both the energy flow and the time. Mechanisation of the proces is necessary to prevent overheating of the products. The maximum temperatur reached, however, does not depend on the machine parameters alone, but to large extent also on the conditions of the surface to be heated. With varyin conditions, varying heating results are obtained.

10.3.2.1 THE RADIANT-HEAT SOURCE

The highest radiant flux is obtained with high power incandescent filamen lamps or high pressure xenon lamps. These are 'point' sources. The filamen lamps operate with temperatures up to 3000 K. A typical life is 1200 hours at filament temperature of 2900 K.

The flux density as a function of temperature is given by the Stefan-Boltzmani law:

$\Phi = \sigma T^4$, in which:
Φ is the flux density;
σ is a constant $(5,75 \times 10^{-8}$ W/(m^2.K^4));
T is the absolute temperature.

From this formula it follows that the radiation density at 3000 K is 5 times a large as at 2000 K. The wavelength with maximum intensity at 3000 K is 0,9 μm and at 2000 K it is 1,4 μm (according to Wien's law). In the region between thes two values for the wave length, the absorption coefficient of metals changes.

The radiation from the point source is directed onto the desired area with reflector, in most cases having the shape of a half-ellipsoid. The radiation densit on a plane perpendicular to the axis of the heater has a distinct maximum at th axis. Radiation can be improved by applying condenser channel construction [Schoenthaler]. When large surface areas must be heated, use is often made o rod-shaped radiators provided with suitable reflectors, while the objects to b heated are transported across the heater by means of a conveyor.

10.3.2.2 EXAMPLES OF GENERAL RADIANT HEATING

Two examples are given.

Hybrid circuits to be soldered can be conveyed through a machine having two r more zones: one or more preheating zones and one high temperature spiking') zone. A machine with a soldering width of 100 mm and with a conveyor speed of up to 3 m/min typically consumes 10 kVA of power.

Radiant heat is also used for the fusing of solder on printed boards (see hapter 6.4.3). In this case also, use is made of a conveyor [McMillan].

0.4 LOCAL HEATING FROM ABOVE

Local heating from above means that heat is directed onto specific areas on the de of the substrate on which the components are located. The presence of the omponents puts particular limits on the possibilities for soldering, but the arious configurations will not be examined at this point.

0.4.1 Radiant Heating

White and infra-red light are good heat sources for reflow soldering. The great dvantage of radiant heating, as with heating by hot gas, is that there is no 1echanical contact with the soldering point.

0.4.1.1 FOCUSSED LIGHT BEAMS

By using reflectors, light beams can be focussed onto the workpiece. In most ases, use is made of halogen lamps or projection lamps with built-in mirrors Figure 10.11), sometimes in multiple array. The heating with light permits rotection of the parts to be soldered by an inert gas in a glass container, because he heat rays can be passed through the glass wall.

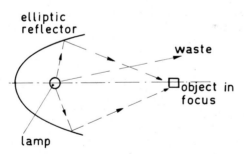

Fig. 10.11 Elliptic reflector to focus the light from the filament onto the workpiece.

1dvantages

i) Rapid and flexible adjustment is possible in experimental work;
ii) Rapid local heating is possible;
iii) Damage due to mechanical contact is avoided.

)isadvantages

i) Only local heating is possible;
ii) Precautions to prevent rapid overheating are necessary;

(iii)   In many cases white light causes an uncomfortable glare which impede
        evaluation of the adjustment or the progress of the soldering process.

This can often be avoided by use of suitable filters; arc-welding goggles are useful if the light is very
intense. 'Varilux' spectacles, which darken in proportion to the light intensity, may also be worn
Reflected glare from flat surfaces can be reduced by observing through suitably orientated 'Polaroid
sheet.

10.4.1.2   HEATING WITH A LASER BEAM

A laser can be used for microsoldering of joints. Suppose that component lead
with dimensions of $1 \times 2 \times 0,5$ mm^3 must be heated from 20°C to 220°C. Then th
energy needed is $Q = \varrho c V \Delta T = 3,5 \times 10^6 \times 0,6 \times 10^{-9} \times 200 = 0,42$ J. When th
solder land and the solder are also to be heated, the total energy is in the order o
1 Joule. Lasers can easily generate this energy.

Using a CO_2-laser (wave length 10,6 μm) and a numerically controlled beam
positioner, surface-mounted integrated circuits have been successfully soldered t
multilayer printed boards at rates exceeding 125 joints per minute, includin,
positioning time [Bohman, Loeffler]. The power setting of the CO_2 laser was 3.
W, and the heating time was 200 to 400 ms. In order to obtain a relatively larg
heating area, the beam had to be defocussed. The solder was applied as solde
cream [see also Miller].

Experiments in the Author's laboratory on similar joints with a pulse
Nd:YAG-laser (wave length 1,06 μm) have also been successful. The puls
duration, and hence the heating time per joint, was about 4 ms, with the beam
adjusted to hit the flat upper face of the leads of the component. At a highe
energy density, the joint will be damaged or destroyed by melting of th
component lead.

For a production method the positioning of the beam and the parts to b
soldered is difficult and expensive. The different places to be soldered can be h
by altering the position of the component with an X-Y positioner, or by changin,
the position of the laser beam with controllable mirrors. To reach acceptabl
production rates, automation (by microprocessor, for instance) is indispensable
Complete laser soldering systems are available (Figure 10.12). Soldering of, fo
example, flatpack ICs onto printed boards is possible at production rates te
times as high as those for hand soldering. The short heating period minimise
heat damage to the soldered components.

With heating times of about 250 ms, dispensed or screened solder cream can b
used for the soldering of flat packs, SO-packages, etc. The process parameters i
general are not critical [Burns *et al*]. With much shorter heating times, boiling o
the flux solvent in the cream may be so violent that solder or parts will be blow
away. This will not happen with reflowed solder on the solder lands, but then th
(vertical) positioning of the components will be more difficult than with cream
because the gaps between terminations and solder lands may lead to one or mor
terminations being left unsoldered.

Soldering with a multiple laser beam seems very attractive and has been announced some time ag
although no actual production is known. In this case, the laser beam is split with a hologram so tha
specific places, for instance on flat component leads, are heated simultaneously. Problems are preser
in the dissipation of the optical system, in particular in the hologram, and in the rather exot
combination of a high energy beam with one capable of producing radiation for holography.

Fig. 10.12 A complete bench-top system for laser microsoldering (Apollo LMS-1). It combines a vertically-mounted flow gas industrial 20W CO_2 laser with a numerically controlled and fully programmable X-Y table. The closed circuit television system simplifies adjustments. Connections can be soldered at the rate of four per second (by courtesy of Apollo Lasers, Inc.).

10.4.2   Resistance Heating

In resistance soldering an electric current is passed either through the parts to be soldered or through a heater element, which is gently pressed against the spots to be heated [Welch]. In the first case the heat is developed owing to the resistance of the parts themselves or to their contact resistances, whilst in the second case the heat of the element is transferred by conduction. One of the applications of resistance soldering is soldering of integrated circuits in flatpack version to printed boards [Andrade *et al*]. Although success has been achieved with solder layer thicknesses between 5 and 8 μm, at the moment a trend towards thicker layers is observed. With these thicker layers the sides of the leads also are wetted with solder, thus improving possibilities for inspection. To comply with this demand it appears that with lead dimensions of $0,40 \times 0,15$ mm^2 a layer thickness between 15 and 30 μm is required.

Electroplated solder layers which have served as etch resist on printed boards show insufficient solderability. Hot-tinned layers are preferred. Suitable layers are obtained by passing the boards across a wave soldering machine. In this way, layer thicknesses from 20 to 50 μm are possible. With layer thicknesses above about 30 μm the positioning of the leads becomes rather difficult.

Advantages:

(i)   The amount of heat can be accurately controlled;
(ii)   Heating times are short;
(iii) Heating is very local.

Disadvantages:

(i)   The heat may not reach the right spots owing to variations in contact
       resistances;
(ii)   The number of joints which can be soldered simultaneously is limited.

The most important resistance reflow soldering methods are:

(i)   parallel-gap soldering;
(ii)   single-point soldering;
(iii) multiple-lead soldering.

In these soldering methods, the electrodes (heater elements) in contact with the parts to be soldered are made of a material (*e.g.*, molybdenum, tantalum, cobalt copper, beryllium copper) that is not wetted by molten solder.

10.4.2.1 PARALLEL-GAP SOLDERING

In parallel-gap soldering use is made of two adjacent electrodes which press the leads of the component to the conductors on the substrate (Figure 10.13).

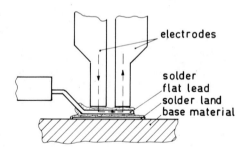

Fig. 10.13 Parallel-gap soldering. The heating current is directed through the leads and the conductors to be soldered. The pressure should be released after solidification of the solder.

Variation of the various contact resistances seriously influences the process. As the contact resistance varies with the contact pressure of the electrodes on the leads, the pressure is an important process parameter.

To obtain an electrode pressure as constant as possible, the electrodes should be spring loaded to compensate for irregularities of the component leads. The adjustment of the distance between the electrodes depends on the thickness of the component lead to be soldered. This distance should be approximately 1,5 times the thickness of the lead. It is necessary to supply a sufficiently long energy impulse, varying from 0,1 to 2 seconds, depending on the thickness of the component lead and on the dimensions of the solder lands. Generally an alternating current is used for the energy supply.

10.4.2.2   SINGLE-POINT SOLDERING

In principle, single-point soldering is the same as soldering with a soldering iron. The great advantages, however, are the dimensions, tip diameters of 0,12 to 0,5 mm being possible. Two adjacent electrodes are connected by means of a molybdenum strip or cylinder through which the electric current is passed (Figure 10.14). Some equipments have a thermocouple mounted in the molybdenum body, which measures the temperature of the tip and thus allows for controlled operation. Very short heating times are possible but this is economically less important in relation to the total soldering process time. As the heat transfer takes place by conductance the solder lands and the leads to be soldered should not have a high thermal demand, because otherwise the connection is insufficiently heated.

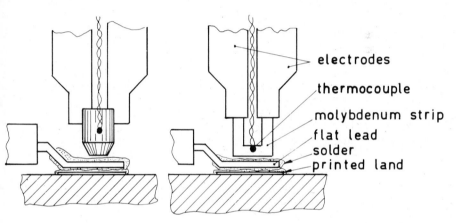

electrodes

thermocouple

molybdenum strip
flat lead
solder
printed land

Fig. 10.14   Device for single-point reflow soldering. The heat generated in the element is conducted to the component lead to be soldered.

10.4.2.3   MULTIPLE-LEAD SOLDERING

The technique of multiple-lead reflow soldering has been specially developed for the soldering of integrated circuit flatpacks to printed boards. It is an extension of the single-point soldering technique, in which the soldering tip has been built in such a way that a number of leads can be soldered simultaneously (Figure 10.15).

A strip or wire is heated either by a controlled current to maintain a constant temperature or by a brief electrical impulse each time the strip is placed in the soldering position. The latter method is sometimes called impulse-soldering (though the world 'impulse' has a more general meaning [see Lindner]). The temperature distribution along the length of the heater element, as shown in Figure 10.15, can be adjusted by making suitable saw cuts in the strip; rod or wire shaped elements can be adjusted by changing the cross-section locally.

Two or more strips can be put together, so as to form a combined element.

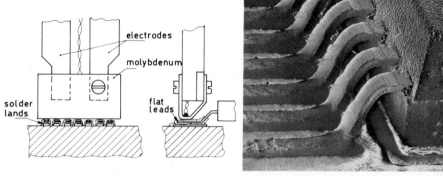

Fig. 10.15 Multiple-lead reflow soldering: (left) drawing of heating device having a molybdenum strip, heated by an electric current. The strip is pressed onto the leads to be soldered to obtain adequate heat contact. Note the thermocouple in the centre of the strip; (right) SEM photograph of some leads of a VSO-40 package, soldered to a printed board to which solder had been applied by wave soldering prior to reflow soldering. The flat parts of the leads are 1,5 mm long, with a cross section of 0,35 × 0,20 mm². The 20 leads at one side of the package (pitch 0,762 mm) were soldered using an electrical impulse of a duration of 2 s (leading to a maximum strip temperature of 400°C) and a force of 50 N (by courtesy of M. M. F. Verguld, Eindhoven).

Several manufacturers offer equipment with which it is possible to solder the four rows of leads of a quad flatpack to a printed board in one single operation. The more juxtaposed leads that are soldered simultaneously, the more critical are the requirements for the alignment of the leads and the strips. The heating time is only a small part of the total process time, which, including the placing of the components, aligning, fluxing and soldering, may be about 30 seconds.

10.4.3 Heating with Directed Streams of Hot Gas

Heating with directed streams of hot gas is similar to general heating with hot gas (Chapter 10.3.1), the only difference being that in this case the hot gas is blown through a small orifice so that a directed jet of hot gas strikes the soldering point. True local heating, however, is essentially not achievable. To attain an acceptable heating rate the gas temperature must be rather high (400°C to 700°C), with the risk of damaging components in the vicinity of the place to be soldered. If these components are not heat-resistant, they can be screened from the hot gas, but as the gas has to flow away somewhere the problem of unwanted heating of the surroundings of the soldered joints persists. Consequently, there is always a risk of components which were soldered previously being unsoldered (loosened) and moved out of true position.

In hybrid technology, hot gas is used in a variety of applications and several semi-automatic hot gas bonders exist [Phillips, Albon *et al*]. Alumina substrates are usually preheated to a temperature of 100 to 150°C before hot-gas soldering is carried out.

10.4.4 Inductive Heating

In inductive heating of the locations to be soldered, a high-frequency alternating current of some MHz is used which generates an alternating electric field in and around a coil. Metallic objects placed inside this field are heated by eddy currents. The objects are therefore not actually heated from below or from above, but from inside, irrespective of the location of the coil.

The parameters of this heating process are the shape of the coil, the frequency, the location of the object in the field and the duration of the energy pulse. The rapid transfer of great quantities of energy, resulting in quick heating even of larger objects like printed boards [Wolf], is characteristic of the method (Figure 10.16). The heating process must be automated to prevent overheating.

Fig. 10.16 SO-28 component connected on a test board by inductive heating. The coil was situated below the board. Frequency about 1,3 MHz, heating time 0,3 s.

Advantages

(i) Rapid transfer of great quantities of energy is possible;
(ii) Local heating of surface zones is possible.

Disadvantages

(i) Fixing of the object with respect to the coil is necessary;
(ii) For each specific application a different shape of coil is required;
(iii) The shape of the coils is often complicated and their fabrication requires well-trained personnel;
(iv) The parts are easily overheated;
(v) For small series the cost is high;
(vi) The components may be damaged by the HF field.

10.5 HEATING FROM ALL DIRECTIONS

In these heating methods the products to be soldered are immersed in a hot fluid (gas or liquid). In such cases the medium is at a constant temperature and the products are heated until they have almost reached the temperature of the medium. The methods thus use an asymptotic heating strategy (see Chapter 3.1.1).

10.5.1   Heating in Hot Gas

The hot gas (air) is at a constant temperature as in a hot air circulation furnace and the mounted support plates are conveyed through the furnace in a continuous flow.

The distinction between this heating method and those discussed in Chapter 10.3.1 is sometimes not easy to make, because many intermediates exist.

The method of heating in hot air has been used for many years, particularly for the soldering of pins in boards [Weltha]. In this way 7500 pins with a length of 50 mm can be soldered per minute, in a soldering zone with a width of 0,6 m. Conveyor speed is 0,4 to 0,6 m/min. The air velocity in the equipment is 500 m/min, generated with a blower, and the air temperature is about 300°C. The power consumption of such equipment is considerable, being over 10 kW.

Despite the high air velocity, the ultimate soldering temperature reached is less than the air temperature, owing to the limited heat transfer capability of the hot air.

Similar equipments to those described are employed for hot air fusing of electroplated printed boards [Scagnelli *et al*]. The apparatus is provided with a large fan to produce the air circulation, so that the maximum temperature of the boards is reached in about 2 minutes. The equipment has a conveyor with a length of 5 m, the actual hot air compartment having a length of about 2 m. The width of the conveyor is 0,9 m, and its speed is about 2 m/min.

Thick film circuits can be soldered in an air furnace, for which the process time is about 5 minutes. The prolonged heating time in such furnaces makes the method unsuitable for use with solder cream, as the flux is almost exhausted before the solder melts.

10.5.2   Heating in a Hot Liquid

In this heating method the mounted parts to be soldered are completely immersed in a hot liquid at soldering temperature [Schoenthaler]. Various liquids are used, including mineral oils, peanut oil and polyethylene glycol. There is, however, no ideal liquid because ultimately all liquids degrade at high temperature.

The equipment must be designed to handle the combustible liquid in a safe manner and provided with a means of trapping the exhaust fumes, which include the reaction products of the degraded liquid. For these reasons a liquid immersion-heating facility has fairly large proportions and occupies considerable floor space.

The thermal response time of the heating method for multilayer boards is about 30 seconds (Figure 10.17).

After the soldering treatment the products must be washed in order to remove the residues of the liquid. Polyethylene glycol is miscible with water and hence can be washed with water. The same is true for various proprietary products (*e.g.*, Lonco 240). The washing facilities, including water purifier, need a lot of space. Soldering with hot liquid as a heating medium has been used for the soldering of pins in backpanels for many years.

The method is well suited to soldering experiments in a laboratory. The glycol is put in a beaker of about 1 litre capacity and heated on a heating plate to the desired temperature, which can be simply measured with an ordinary thermometer.

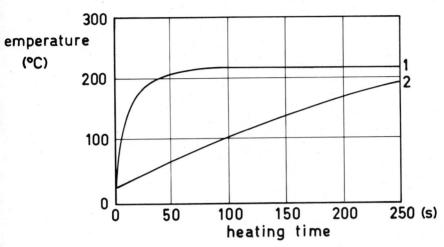

Fig. 10.17 Thermal response of multilayer boards in hot polyethylene glycol (1) at 20 m/min and in a hot air furnace (2) with air velocity 500 m/min.

10.5.3   Heating in Saturated Vapour

Soldering in a saturated vapour is also called vapour phase soldering or condensation soldering [Pfahl *et al*]. It was developed at Western Electric (Princeton) in the early 1970s. Parts to be soldered are immersed in a saturated vapour which condenses immediately on the relatively cool parts, thus releasing the latent heat of vaporisation. The temperature of the saturated vapour is the same as the boiling point of the fluid used and since heat transfer is due to the phase change from vapour to liquid it is extremely rapid, giving heat response

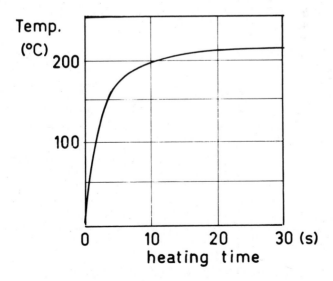

Fig. 10.18   Heating of an alumina substrate with a thickness of 0,7 mm in condensing vapour. Soldering is achieved within about 8 seconds (*cf.* Figure 10.17).

times typically below 10 seconds in the case of small parts and up to 45 second for more massive assemblies (Figure 10.18). As soon as the parts reach th temperature of the vapour, condensation stops, no more heat transfer takes plac and there is no further increase in temperature. Thus, the system does not nee temperature controllers. Any change of power input to the system results in mor or less vapour being generated but gives no change of temperature. Temperatur is strictly related to the boiling point of the fluid used. This constan temperature/variable energy concept is unique in heat transfer technology Furthermore, since the vapour entirely surrounds the part, condensation take place simultaneously on all surfaces resulting in very uniform heating.

10.5.3.1   THE EQUIPMENT

In its simplest form the soldering equipment is constructed as shown in Figur 10.19. Basically it comprises a rectangular vessel with a heater element near th bottom and a cooling coil near the wall at about two thirds of the height. Th level of the liquid is above the heater element. On switching on the heater elemen the liquid boils and the vapour rises in the vessel and condenses against th cooling coil to form droplets that fall back into the liquid. In the idling state th vapour is circulating inside the vessel, while the power is kept so low that thi situation is just maintained. As soon as a cold object is brought into the vapou zone, vapour will condense on this object also. The heating rate is determined b the rate at which vapour is generated by the heater element, so that for a rapi heating the power must be raised temporarily. The increased circulation of th vapour and the whirling caused by the downward and upward movements of th product and its support make some vapour loss inevitable.

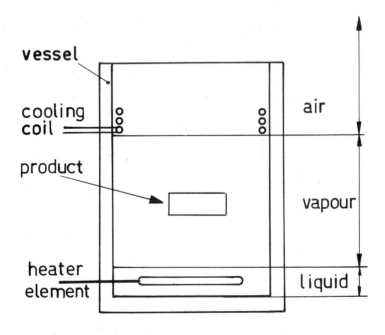

Fig. 10.19   Simplest form of a condensation soldering system, having only one cooling coil.

Production equipments in actual use, however, are much more complicated [Wenger *et al*, Karpel]. They have facilities to minimise the vapour losses by applying a secondary vapour blanket of trichlorotrifluoroethane (Freon-TF, boiling point 48°C), which floats on top of the primary vapour. This is controlled with one or more additional cooling coils and an injection system for the secondary fluid. Furthermore, systems are applied for filtering flux residues from the primary fluid, either continuously via a heat exchanger or daily after each working period, and for stripping of acid from the secondary fluid (Figure 10.20).

Fig. 10.20 Vapour phase soldering system (HTC model 1416). The system shown handles products up to 360×460 mm^2. Size of cabinet is about $1 \times 1 \times 2$ m^3. It incorporates primary fluid filtration, automatic secondary blanket control, acid and water stripping and continuously variable power control. Principal uses are the soldering of backpanels, flexible circuits, thick film hybrids, *etc*. (by courtesy of HTC, Concord, Ma. USA).

Constructions have recently been developed and patented to avoid the batchwise operation of equipment such as that in Figure 10.20. The objects to be soldered are conveyed along a more or less horizontal path through the vapour phase soldering equipment [Europat. 0 000 284, 0 023 107, US Pat. 3866307, 39004102], see Figure 10.21. The same type of equipment is used for the solder fusing of printed boards (see Chapter 6.4.3).

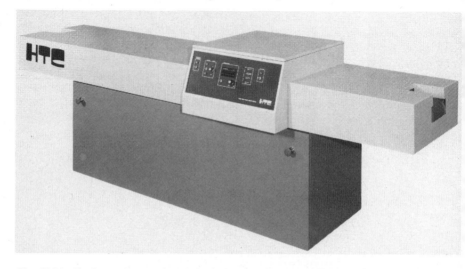

Fig. 10.21 Single vapour, continuous in-line soldering system (HTC model IL6). It incorporates primary fluid filtration, and acid stripper. The conveyor is 152 mm wide with a speed adjustable to 1,8 m/min. The system is intended for thick film hybrid circuits, surface mounting of chip carriers and other leadless components (by courtesy of HTC, Concord, Ma. USA).

10.5.3.2   THE FLUID

The boiling temperature of the fluid at atmospheric pressure should be well above the melting temperature of the solder. One particular fluid that can be used is perfluorotriamylamine, $(C_5F_{11})_3N$, which is available under the trade name 'Fluorinert' FC 70 (3M Company). This fluid has a boiling point of 215°C, a liquid density of 1940 kg/m^3 and a molecular weight of 820. At 25°C the vapour pressure is lower than 13 Pa. A similar liquid is 'Galden' LS (Montedison Company) having a boiling range of 218°C to 228°C. Another fluid is FC 71 with a boiling point of 253°C.

The fluid is very expensive (about \$150/litre), but with proper equipment and good process control the consumption, though still considerable, can be limited. Vapour losses on large production batch systems are reported at 250 g per hour per 30 cm × 30 cm of top opening [Wenger *et al*]. When a properly regulated secondary vapour blanket is employed, the primary vapour losses represent only 10% of the total loss, the balance being secondary vapour. Measurements carried out on single vapour continuous in-line systems demonstrate that, for a given product throughput, the losses are lower than those reported for dual vapour batch systems [Peck].

The heavy vapour is inert, non-flammable and non-explosive, so that during the short heating period absolutely no oxidation of the parts (and the flux) occurs. After the dwell time the soldered parts are wet with condensed liquid, but, when the parts are held in the secondary vapour region for a sufficiently long period, this liquid on the parts will evaporate so that completely dry soldered products are obtained.

10.5.3.3 VAPOUR PHASE SOLDERING

Because of the high heat-transfer rate from the condensing vapour, the relatively low soldering temperature of the vapour phase soldering method is not objectionable, providing solderable coatings of the components are adapted to it (see Chapter 7.7.1.1). The low temperature may be an advantage because the total heat input to the components is clearly limited. The heating is rapid, which will cause thermal gradients, especially in thick products, during heating but at the final temperature the temperature gradients (and therefore the stresses) vanish.

The vapour phase soldering method with its very uniform heating is particularly suitable for soldering complicated products of any shape, including all types of support plates with densely packed surface mounted devices. Examples are thick-film hybrid circuits on alumina, and printed boards with chip carriers on one or both sides (see Configurations II, IV and V of Table 8.1). Figure 10.22 shows part of a board of epoxy glassfibre reinforced laminate mounted with many components. Although, of course, other soldering methods could in principle be applied here, the vapour phase method is clearly the first choice.

Fig. 10.22 Double-sided board with surface mounted components connected by vapour phase soldering. The part of the board shown carries chip resistors, multilayer capacitors, SOT-23 transistors and SO-packages. The board has very fine conductors, including many small plated holes for the interconnection of both sides of the board (by courtesy of B. Szabo, Hilversum).

The soldering of chip carriers and other surface mounted components can readily be carried out without the use of jigs or fixtures if suitable techniques are employed. The use of rosin based solder pastes, screened onto the substrate, followed by component placement and drying results in an assembly in which the parts are temporarily 'glued' together. Precise positioning of the parts is not critical since, once the solder is molten and has wetted the metallised areas, its surface tension will automatically tend to align the parts (see, however, one component in the top right of Figure 10.22). The surface tension forces are sufficiently high to allow the soldered assemblies to be inverted and processed a second time without the components falling off. The mounting of components onto both sides of a substrate for maximum utilisation of space is therefore a very practical matter when vapour phase soldering is used [Spigarelli].

If flux residues are considered objectionable these must be washed away, which is easier than after most other soldering processes because in vapour phase soldering the fluxes are heated to a lower temperature and under exclusion of air.

10.5.3.4 HEALTH ASPECTS

The decomposition of the fluid is very limited below 250°C, but at higher temperatures, for instance at hot spots of the heater elements, a number of fluorinated decomposition products are formed, including perfluoroisobutylene, (sometimes referred to as PFIB) and carbonyl fluoride [Turbini *et al*]. The perfluoroisobutylene, $CF_2 = C(CF_3)_2$, in particular is toxic and causes high fever. The symptoms are similar to those produced by the decomposition products of polytetrafluoroethylene ('Teflon Fever'). Carbonyl fluoride, COF_2, affects the mucous membranes of the bronchi.

The precautions that should be taken are twofold:

(i)   Minimise the formation of the harmful compounds;
(ii) Avoid inhalation of the compounds.

Hot spots on the heater elements are avoided by keeping the fluid clean and free from flux residues, which can be achieved by daily or continuous filtering. Measures must be taken to ensure that the elements can never boil dry, for instance by applying a fluid-level monitor. The vapours which escape from the equipment must be effectively exhausted, without creating turbulences in the vapour phase equipment. Smoking in the working area should be strictly prohibited, as otherwise harmless vapours, if present, decompose in the burning tobacco and are fully inhaled.

General working hygiene is of utmost importance to prevent contamination of the hands and of the tools used. When installing a vapour phase equipment local health regulations should be complied with, and persons working with or near the equipment should be instructed on the correct procedure in the event of an accident. With adequate precautionary measures, as discussed in this paragraph, vapour phase soldering does not represent a health hazard.

Chapter 11

MANUAL SOLDERING

Manual soldering with a soldering iron is used for small scale production (for instance special products), for addition of extra components to a machine soldered assembly, and for all types of rework or repair soldering, including de-soldering.

In most cases the solder is applied in the form of flux-cored wire, the quantity of which is determined by the operator while he makes the joint.

11.1 FLUX-CORED SOLDER WIRE

A flux-cored solder wire is a wire of solder alloy containing some longitudinal cavities along its length which are filled with flux. The flux is solid (or pasty) at room temperature, but when a piece of solder wire is melted the flux is released in liquid form, so that it can perform its cleaning action. Later on the flux will solidify on the joint just made, and it will usually not be removed.

Solder wire is produced in many alloy compositions, with diameters ranging from 0,25 mm to 3 mm. For electronics mostly a diameter of 1,2 mm is used and the alloy composition lies at or close to the eutectic composition (see Chapter 4.1.3).

The flux in cored wire for electronic soldering has usually a proprietary composition based on a resin with several additions. The amount of flux is 1 to 4 mass per cent (3 mass % is equivalent to about 20 vol.%). Most of the required properties of fluxes in cored wire are the same as those of fluxes in machine soldering, such as sufficient efficacy and limited corrosivity (see Chapter 5), but there are also some special properties, such as the spattering behaviour (see also Chapter 5.9). The spattering of the flux could be quantified as the ratio of the mass of the spattered flux droplets to the mass of the flux in the considered piece of wire.

The homogeneity of the distribution of activator and the continuity of the flux cores depend on the processing of the wire, for which one should rely on approved suppliers.

The amount of flux in a wire can be determined by melting a known mass of wire in, for instance, glycerol or polyethylene glycol. After solidification the metal no longer contains flux and can be washed and weighed.

The continuity of the cores in a wire can be investigated by dissolving the metal from a piece of wire in mercury (amalgamation). In doing so the cores remain, which then can be inspected.

Spattering can be determined by feeding a piece of wire vertically through a hole (about 5 mm) in a metal plate (about $65 \times 65 \times 0,5$ mm^3), which is 10 mm above a bath of molten solder at 300°C. The feeding should be done stepwise, centimetre by centimetre, while after each feeding period (25 mm/s)

391

the wire is withdrawn 10 mm for a period of 4 seconds. The plate is to be weighed before and after the test and it should be noticed whether besides flux metal has also been deposited. Spattering should be less than 20% by mass of the flux in the wire.

11.2   TEMPERATURE OF THE TIP

Soldering irons are heated by an electrical element. For soldering irons used outside the field of electronics other heating methods are also used. The heat must be transported from the element to the tip with which the soldering is done.

The metallic piece with a tinned tip, acting as heat store and heat conductor, is called a soldering bit. The temperature of its tip must be considerably higher than the soldering temperature, because the heat transfer from the tip to the joints is relatively poor.

The heating is carried out by one of the following methods:

(i)   The element is connected to a fixed voltage, so that the tip reaches a certain equilibrium temperature, determined by the power input and by the heat loss as a result of convection and radiation;

(ii)   The element is connected to a power source with two voltage levels, one high when the iron is used, and one low when the iron is on stand-by.

(iii)   The temperature of the tip is controlled to a specific temperature.

11.2.1   Constant Power Source

When the element of a soldering iron is powered, the tip will gradually reach its maximum temperature. When this idling temperature has been reached, the full power is dissipated by the element body and by the shaft of the soldering tip.

Suppose that the tip temperature is 400°C and that the cylindrical shaft has a length of 35 mm, then the temperature of the shaft right beside the element will be

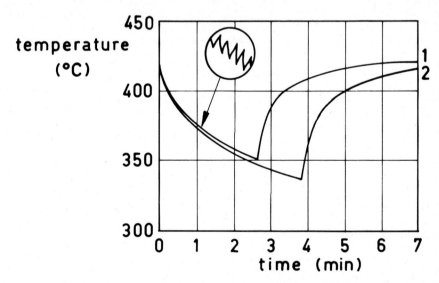

Fig. 11.1   Temperature of tip of soldering iron. Idling temperature of tip 430°C. (1) soldering of 80 joints on a printed board (wire 0,6 mm); (2) soldering of 75 joints on solder tags (wire 0,8 mm).

about 10°C higher than at the tip. The temperature of the tip will fall considerably if heat is extracted from it for the formation of soldered joints (Figure 11.1). If this extraction of heat is continued, the temperature will assume a new equilibrium value, the lowest working temperature. In normal practice, the tip temperature will vary irregularly between the two equilibrium values [Becker, Sylvester, Urban].

An improvement is obtained if the power source can be switched between two levels. The switch can be activated automatically when the soldering iron is lifted from its stand. The efficiency of the soldering iron (the ratio of useful heat output at the tip to the power input at the heater element) is zero at the maximum temperature and about 50% during soldering. Soldering irons are usually classified by their energy consumption (wattage) rather than by the temperature reached during idling or the temperature maintained at specific operational conditions. A soldering iron of 25 to 50 Watts suffices for the soldering of common electronic components. Smaller irons are seldom necessary, although they may sometimes be used for minute connections with leads of 0,3 mm diameter. Irons with wattages over 100 W find application in the soldering of thick wires (2,5 mm^2) and heavy connecting parts.

11.2.2 Controlled Tip Temperature

Soldering irons with a controlled tip temperature show much smaller temperature variations than the uncontrolled irons; for instance a variation of 25 K is common. This is achieved by arranging that the heating rate below the maximum temperature is much higher than that of the uncontrolled irons.

Various control methods include the following:

(i) Measuring the tip temperature with a thermocouple and controlling the electric power, for instance via a thyristor, with means for gradual adjustment;

(ii) Applying a magnetic switch in the soldering iron, the switching action being based on the attraction between a permanent magnet and a piece of ferromagnetic material of which the Curie point is close to the working temperature of the iron. Exchangeable switches, adjusted to different temperatures, are available;

(iii) Using a heating element of a suitable material with a positive temperature coefficient (PTC material), which exhibits a steep increase in electrical resistance at the desired temperature [Andrich].

11.2.3 Tip Design

To minimise the temperature drop along the length of the soldering shaft, the shaft material must have a high conductivity. Copper appears to be the only realistic choice. Attempts with other materials, for instance composite material of molybdenum wires with copper in the spaces between the wires, have invariably been disappointing. The problem with copper is that it dissolves in the molten solder. During the soldering operation the solder is renewed regularly, which enhances the dissolution rate. The addition of copper to the solder alloy decreases the dissolution rate of the copper of the tip [Sharples]. This rate of dissolution of the tip can be studied with a set-up as illustrated in Figure 11.2.

Fig. 11.2   Test equipment for soldering tips. The soldering iron is reciprocated against the solder wire by means of a rotating cam. Cycle time 2 s. The wire is shifted forward by about 10 mm/cycle.

Nowadays soldering bits tend to be made of plated copper, the copper being covered with a layer of iron, or iron and nickel. Despite the very low dissolution rates of these platings, the life of plated tips is limited. Once a hole has been formed in the plating the dissolution of the copper underneath proceeds relatively rapidly, as is demonstrated in Figure 11.3, which shows a tested soldering tip.

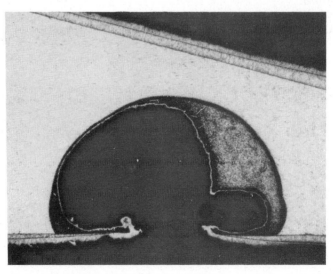

Fig. 11.3   Cavity formed in a soldering tip by the dissolution of copper into the liquid solder. Note that the protective iron plating in the top region of the cross-section is still undamaged.

Because the solder wire has always been fed to the same area of the tip, the plating has been locally damaged. After penetration of the plating the copper dissolves to leave a cavity.

Various tips from different manufacturers were tested in the set-up shown in Figure 11.2, applying repeated programmes each consisting of a heating period of 15 minutes, a soldering period of 60 minutes (soldering every 2 seconds) and a cooling period of 30 minutes. The tips tested had life spans from below 10000 to above 50000 cycles before breakdown.

An important parameter determining the life of the tip is the thickness of the plating which must be 100 to 500 μm, but the quality of the plating also plays a role.

The plating has no significant effect on the thermal resistance of the tip. It can of course easily be damaged by mechanical ill-treatment. A soldering iron should not be used as a lever. A well-tinned soldering tip is indispensable for making good joints. Cleaning should never involve a file or a steel brush, but only a cloth or a wet sponge.

Bits for soldering irons are commercially available in a variety of shapes (Figure 11.4), including special hollow bits for suction soldering irons used in desoldering and repair. Standardisation of the tips has been proposed [Becker] but has not yet been realised.

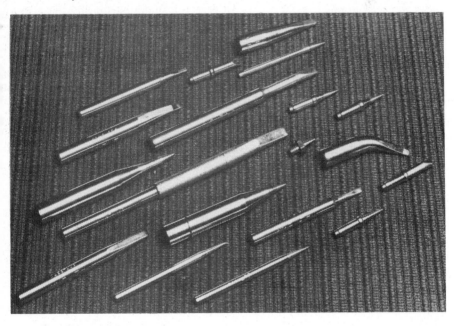

Fig. 11.4   A selection of exchangeable bits for soldering irons (by courtesy of Plato Products, Inc.).

11.3   THE USE OF THE SOLDERING IRON

This Section is not intended as an extensive guide for manual soldering. To solder correctly is a matter of skill, obtained by training and experience [Maykuth]. Many companies have instituted soldering courses for the training of their employees [*e.g.*, Anon. Ref. 10]. These courses are often supplemented by or based on a film on soldering [*e.g.*, Anon. Ref. 11], some of which are available on a loan or rental basis.

Three aspects of manual soldering are important:

(i) How to operate the soldering iron;
(ii) How to connect wires to various connecting parts, terminals, *etc.*;
(iii) How to solder various components to printed boards.

The correct choice of metal and flux composition is as important for manual soldering as for machine soldering.

11.3.1 Basic Rules for Hand Soldering

Some rules applying to use of soldering irons can be formulated along the lines of the basic aspects of soldering (see Chapter 1.2).

Rule 1 (Thermal Aspects): *Make a Good Heat Contact Between the Soldering Tip and the Parts to be Soldered.*

The soldering tip must be placed as close as possible to the part with the highest heat demand. As good contact can only be achieved via the molten solder, the solder must be applied in the space between the soldering tip and parts to be soldered.

Rule 2 (Wettable Surfaces): *Let the Flux Perform its Cleaning Function at the Correct Places.*

Cored solder must be added in such a way that the flux comes free at the surfaces to be soldered. Rules 1 and 2 have the same consequences as the flux also assists in transferring heat.

Rule 3 (Solder Flow): *Maintain the Contact Between the Soldering Iron and the Joint Until Good Spreading of the Solder has been Realised.*

Most defects in hand soldering originate from insufficient heat, often too low an iron temperature. Using a higher temperature for a shorter time will result in less damage to the component. Certainly, overheating is possible, but in practice it seldom occurs.

Rule 4 (Adequate Quantity): *Apply Such a Quantity of Solder that the Contours of the Wires Remain Visible.*

The solder fillet must be concave (hollow). The length of solder wire necessary is easily estimated by the feel while the joint is being made. Extra solder must not be added later; the joint must be formed by flow and spreading of the solder added initially.

Rule 5 (Immobility): *Do not Allow the Parts to Move During Solidification of the Solder.*

The end of the period of solidification of the solder can be observed by a sudden change in the appearance of the solder surface.

11.3.2 Soldered Connections to Terminals

Many different connecting parts and terminals are used, including cup terminals, pierced terminals, turret terminals, bifurcated terminals, hook terminals and eyelets, to which wires are soldered by hand soldering. These erminals are mainly applied in professional equipments in which high-reliability connections are required. The design of the joints on these various connecting parts is not discussed here. Details can be found, elsewhere, in the literature [Anon. Ref.9, Spec. Ref.9].

11.3.3 Manual Soldering to Printed Boards

The requirements to be met by joints hand soldered on boards are the same as those for joints formed by machine soldering. This means that the inspection criteria are also the same (see Chapter 12.5). The fillets must be bright, shiny (see Chapter 12.2.3) and concave, so that the contour of the conductor is discernible in the joint after soldering. When leads are soldered into plated holes, more heat is needed to fill the holes than is needed for joints on single-sided boards.

11.3.4 Soldering of Electrostatic-Sensitive Devices

Electrostatic-sensitive devices can easily be damaged, even during unpacking and mounting (see Chapter 8.2.4). The equipment used for soldering, especially the soldering irons, should be properly designed to prevent this. The quality of the insulating materials used in the soldering irons (*e.g.*, sintered magnesia) is decisive for the AC current leakage [Kaufman].

Soldering irons should be well grounded, via a safety resistor of minimum 100 kΩ. A clamped connection of the grounding conductor to the soldering iron may become insulated as a result of oxidation, and to prevent this it is found preferable to weld the conductor. Voltage spikes from the switching of the soldering iron can be completely avoided by using either continuously-powered irons, or irons which switch only at the zero voltage on the AC sine curve [Swanson]. The latter alternative requires the use of thyristors or controlled rectifiers as thermostat switching elements. Transformers with special shielding and application of zener diodes can reduce the peak values of voltage pulses from elsewhere.

11.4 DESOLDERING

Desoldering is an operation to remove defective or mismounted components from printed boards. It is expensive for various reasons:

(i) Attention must be paid to the fact that the correct component is removed;
(ii) Great care should be exercised so that the remaining components and the board suffer no damage, either thermally or mechanically [Scarlett];
(iii) The number of operations required to complete the removal is large, and each separate step should be performed with care.

Components with many terminations (*e.g.*, DIL-components) are especially difficult to remove. Tools for their removal include suction soldering irons, solder suckers, solder wick and other special devices or special equipment [Walgren].

A solder sucker is a kind of suction pump with a PTFE orifice, which is placed in the molten solder to be removed. The pump works with a squeeze bulb or a plunger mechanism. Those with negligible recoil effects are the most suitable.

A suction soldering iron is a soldering iron with a hollow tip to which a suction pump has been added. Exchangeable bits having different dimensions are available. An adjustable sucking capacity is preferred. Suction irons as well as solder suckers exist in many versions from various manufacturers.

Solder wick consists of woven copper wires impregnated with flux. The wick is pushed against the solder with the tip of a hot soldering iron and the molten solder is sucked up into the wick by capillary action [McBride]. Solder wick is suitable for the removal of solder from joints on single-sided boards, but is less appropriate for plated holes in double-sided or multilayer boards.

More complex equipment for desoldering exists in the form of a system with a regulated hollow soldering bit, combined with an automatic pumping unit that can produce a controllable continuous air flow with a choice of either sucking or blowing (Figure 11.5). Such a system can also be used to provide a hot air jet which offers the possibility of delicate heating.

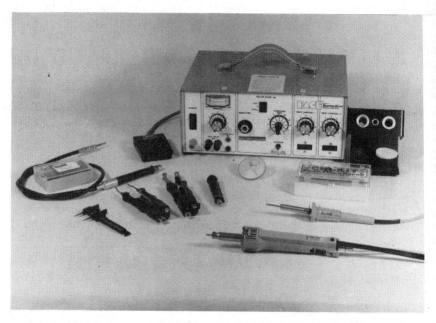

Fig. 11.5   Rework and repair system (Pace PRC-151 BE), provided with soldering iron, suction iron, heat tweezers and miniature machine unit, all to be connected to the power source unit with zero-power switching for spike-free operation (by courtesy of Pace, Inc.).

For the removal of components from a printed board it is possible to loosen the component leads one by one. The method to be used depends on the actual situation, and on whether it is hoped to save the component. Two techniques are described.

In the first method the components are destroyed. The connecting leads on the component side of the board are cut with sharp pliers; the wire is removed from the hole by means of a temperature-controlled soldering iron and tweezers; the solder is removed from the hole by one of the methods described, and the holes are checked for clearance.

In the second method the solder is removed from each of the component leads by one of the methods already mentioned, and the component is removed after checking that all leads are loose.

Multi-lead components can be removed without cutting their leads and without sucking the soldered joints out individually, by using special equipment. DIL-packages can be released by applying heat either from the component side of the printed board or from the solder side.

In the first method a pair of tongs with wide heated jaws can be used, the jaws having a width at least equal to the length of the component to be desoldered. These jaws are placed outside the DIL, close to the component terminations on both rows of solder lands on the component side of the board. After the solder has melted, the jaws are pushed against the terminations while maintaining contact with the molten solder, and the component can then be lifted out [Vandermark]. The holes must be emptied before a new component can be mounted.

The second method involves use of a small solder wave with the dimensions of a DIL and with an adjustable board holder to position the board correctly above the wave. The IC connecting pins to be desoldered are fluxed at the solder side of the board and the board is positioned in the holder. The IC is located above the nozzle at the appropriate distance. After the pump has been started for a few seconds, the wave comes into contact with the board. The solder is then allowed to flow against the board for about 3 seconds (250°C), during which time the IC is removed with tongs. Finally, the wave is lowered and the holes are blown empty.

Methods for repair or modification of conductors on printed boards are not discussed in this book. Reference is made to the literature [Anon. Ref.19, Coombs].

Chapter 12

THE QUALITY OF SOLDERED JOINTS

A soldered product will function correctly, apart from adjustments, if a number of elementary requirements are satisfied relating to:

(i) the interconnecting pattern (complete and unbroken);
(ii) the components (present and within their specification);
(iii) the soldered joints (all joints present, but no evidence of bridges or short circuits).

If the product does not function after soldering, action is needed which is generally termed as repair, rework or touch-up. The words rework and touch-up are most commonly used in respect of the soldered joints immediately after these have been formed. Reworking is carried out in order to remove short circuits, to make joints that have failed to form during the preceding machine soldering operation, and to improve those joints which do not have the desired shape.

Increasing numbers of automatic test methods are being introduced in the manufacturing process: component testing, bare-board testing, testing for missing or wrong components, connectivity and bridging testing, in-circuit testing of components, functional testing, *etc*. Depending on the situation, the kind of product and the number of products, a specific choice can be made from the available testing methods (testing mix) to yield the lowest total costs. This often turns out to be the sequence: connectivity testing→in-circuit testing→functional testing [Davis]. In many cases, 100% component testing and bare-board testing before soldering will lower the overall costs [Heller *et al*, Binnendyk].

This Chapter will concentrate on the soldered joints proper, and with bridges, icicles, *etc*. Side-effects of the soldering operation, such as discolouration of insulating material and residual flux, are not considered.

12.1 INSPECTION OF SOLDERED JOINTS

In soldering, various defects may occur. In the case of isolated defects it is often difficult to indicate a specific cause, whereas, with those which occur more or less systematically, it is usually possible to establish a relationship of cause and effect. Regular analysis of these defects provides information enabling improvement and control of product and process to be made.

When a joint produces an electrical connection between the parts to be joined, it does not necessarily mean that the joint will be reliable in the long term. This is only the case if the shape and metallurgical structure of the joint are also 'good'.

After the soldering process, inspection of the soldered joints is required. ıtomatic methods for testing the intrinsic quality of the soldered joints are so r still a matter for research. In practice, the generally accepted method for sessing joint quality, without destroying the joints, is visual inspection.

.1.1   Automatic Inspection Methods

If joints fail owing to thermal cycling, the strain amplitude will be the ɪminant cause. The deformation of the soldered joints under thermal load can measured in a non-destructive manner with an optical correlation technique ɪlography). A comparison of data from such non-destructive testing with data ɔm subsequent destructive testing indicates conclusively that the propensity of e soldered joint to fail under thermal cycling is indicated by the results of the ɪn-destructive testing of that joint [Espy]. The same technique has been used for e inspection of soldered seams of hermetic microcircuit packages [Wagner].

After cracks have developed in the soldered joints they can be detected, even if ɛy are below the surface. When heating the joints using an external radiation ɪurce, such as a laser, faulty areas and good areas will absorb the heat in fferent ways, and will also re-emit heat in different manners, thus providing a ɛrmal picture of the soldered joint that is representative of the structure below e surface [Anon. Ref. 6 and 7, Vanzetti *et al*]. This method is called ɛrmography [Henneke *et al*].

Cracks in the soldered joint interfere with acoustic transmission and in inciple permit application of acoustic microscopy. With this technique high ɛquency sound waves are transmitted through the specimen, while a focussed ɪer beam scans the surface to detect oscillations of the surface [Anon. Ref.20]. ɔmmercial equipment (Sonomicroscope) is available, but its use for soldered ints is restricted because of their complicated shape; the method only works ɛll if the surface being examined is flat.

Soldered joints with cracks have a lower fracture strength than sound joints. ɪe change of heat resistance, which is related to the presence of cracks, in theory ɛsents a non-destructive detection method. Moreover, if such cracked joints are aded, they produce acoustic signals which can be detected and analysed chmitt-Thomas *et al*, Harman].

The test methods referred to and others that are under discussion, such as diography, fluoroscopy, phosphorescence and infra-red photography, are not t sufficiently developed for use in production quality control.

Destructive inspection of soldered joints by making cross-sections is only rried out in special cases. This Chapter includes some drawings of cross-ctions, serving to clarify the text, but not serving as inspection criteria.

.1.2   Visual Inspection

The inspection of the appearance of joints after soldering does not yield full sight into joint quality. In general, the boundaries between decisions of ɪproval, rejection and rework are poorly defined. They depend on the kind of ɔduct and on the field of application, as well as on the product philosophy that locally operative.

The problem with visual quality assessment is that the aspects to look for have ɔt been fully established, and that it does not really answer the question of

whether the mechanical and electrical performance of the joints will b
satisfactory. As a consequence, visual inspection is subjective, and the ensuin
range of judgements can be wide [Anon. Ref.12]. Moreover, visual inspectic
does not offer a complete picture of the situation because not every defect
visible (hidden defects) and, indeed, even visible defects may be overlooked. It
therefore difficult to decide which criteria are required to ensure a realist
prediction of long-term joint performance. Too often a non-ideal appearance
mistakenly regarded as unacceptable [Keller]. Doubtless the starting point of th
assessment should be to check the existence of a good path for electric curren
which in fact is the main purpose of the soldered joint; yet this does not in itse
guarantee long service. Instructions for inspection and rework practice must b
unambiguous, which implies that they will in many cases be simplifications i
order to make them easy to apply.

Representative photographs showing correct and faulty configurations can b
of great assistance towards a proper understanding and several companies mak
use of such photographs [Anon. Ref.3, Duhm]. An attractive and helpful set c
twenty colour pictures is available as slides or in book form from th
International Tin Research Institute [Anon. Ref.2].

The following sections contain descriptions and photographs that will assi
visual inspection of soldered joints. Some descriptions and captions to the figure
are clearly valid, but others are currently a matter of dispute among solderin
engineers, whose views may deviate from those of the Author.

12.2   GOOD SOLDERED JOINTS

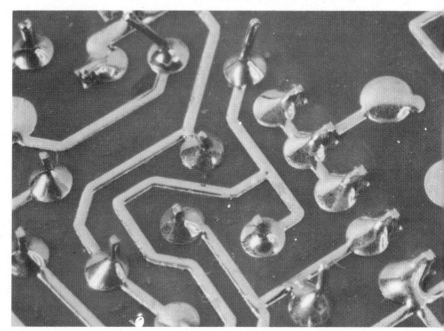

Fig. 12.1 A number of good soldered joints. The whole gives a homogeneous impression. Sold
fillets have a regular shape and a smooth surface. A few terminations protrude beyond the lim
imposed by the rules given in Chapter 8.3.1.

A good (reliable) soldered joint will, during the life of the equipment in which
ιe joint is situated, perform both its mechanical and its electrical functions
·ithout failures.

Visual aspects of good soldered joints are:

(i) good wetting;
ii) correct amount of solder;
ιii) sound and smooth surface.

In principle these aspects apply to all soldered joints, irrespective of the way in
ιhich they were made.

All soldered joints on a printed board should give a uniform impression
dependent of their location on the printed board (Figure 12.1).

2.2.1 Good Wetting

Solder should flow evenly over the surfaces to be soldered and run out thinly
ιwards the edges of the joint (Figure 12.2). The contact angle should be well

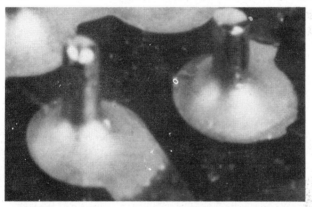

g. 12.2   Good soldered joints. Along the edges of the solder fillets flux residues are visible, which
should not be confused with dewetting.

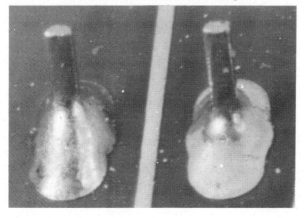

g. 12.3   Good soldered joints on oval solder lands. (Oval solder lands are in general not
recommended.)

under 30° if the surfaces are sufficiently large. If the surface to be soldered small in relation to the amount of solder, it will not always be possible to meet t requirement of a small contact angle owing to the limiting of the solder fillet the edge of the solder land (Figure 12.3).

12.2.2 Correct Amount of Solder

Sufficient solder should be present at the joint and an excess of solder shou be avoided. The solder should wet the whole periphery of the termination to soldered (Figure 12.4).

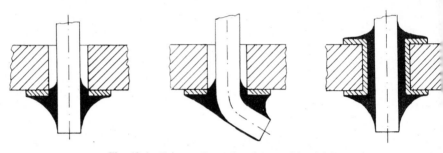

Fig. 12.4   Cross-sections of optimum soldered joints.

The shape and periphery of the parts joined should remain recognisable in t contour of the soldered joint. This applies in particular to terminations components which are bent at the solder side of printed boards without hc plating.

Solder should penetrate completely through the plated holes of double-sid printed boards. Plated holes in single-sided printed boards should be filled up the level of the plating, which should extend to at least three quarters of the boa thickness. In the case of single-sided printed boards without hole plating, t solder should as a rule have flowed over the entire solder land. From the edge the solder land the thickness of the solder coat should increase uniformly up the termination. The visible height against the termination should approximately equal to the diameter of the termination. For printed boards wi plated holes this is not a requirement, but could still be a good indication of t quality of the joint.

12.2.3 Sound and Smooth Surface

The surface of the solder should be uninterrupted and smooth, apart fro minor irregularities which should be recognised as a normal occurren [Thwaites]. Generally speaking, eutectic (or virtually eutectic) tin-lead solder uniformly shiny in appearance (except at the centre of the shrinkage dimpl However, after slow cooling the surface of tin60-lead40 alloy may exhibit a rou surface caused by primary lead crystals. This is merely a cosmetic defect and do not affect the mechanical or electrical properties of the joints [Steen].

Solder with less than 58% tin, or certainly less than 55%, will show a frosty surface at shrinkage dimple, the area of frostiness increasing as the tin content decreases. At about 33% a below, the frostiness covers the entire surface. Addition of bismuth has a similar effect (see Chap 4.4.7).

12.3 SOLDERING DEFECTS ON PRINTED BOARDS

In practice, deviations from the ideal joint do occur, usually as a consequence of unrelated causes.

12.3.1 Classification of Defects*

The defects can be classified as follows:

(i) Major Defects:
   A major defect is a defect that is likely to result in failure or to reduce materially the usability of the unit of product for its intended purpose.
(ii) Minor Defects:
   A minor defect is a defect that is not likely to reduce materially the usability of the unit of product for its intended purpose, or is a departure from established standards that has little bearing on the effective use or operation of the unit.
(iii) Cosmetic Defects:
   A cosmetic defect is a deviation which does not affect the functioning or life of the product.

Major defects must always be repaired. The need to repair minor defects depends on specific requirements related to the desired level of reliability.
   Three classes are distinguished:

(i) Consumer equipment such as radio and TV sets;
(ii) Professional equipment such as measuring instruments, process-control systems and telecommunication units;
(iii) Equipment with the utmost reliability, as used in spacecraft and heart pacemakers.

Since by definition cosmetic defects have no effect on the functioning of the equipment, they need not be corrected. However, their correction is sometimes carried out if a certain appearance is required. Their presence should invite a closer investigation into their cause.

12.3.2 Enumeration of Generally-Occurring Defects

Apart from an incorrect quantity of solder in the joint, seven groups of defects in soldered joints are observed, as discussed in the following text.

---

* The definitions given of major and minor defects have been taken from the classification of defects in sampling standards [Spec.Ref.15] though this classification has a scope far beyond the inspection of solder joints.

12.3.2.1   NON-WETTING

Non-wetting is the failure of the solid metal surface to be wetted by molten solder, so that the original metal surface remains completely or partially visible (Figure 12.5 and Chapter 2.3). Non-wetting can occur on any of the parts to be joined. If non-wetting or poor wetting has been identified, the source of the trouble may not be apparent. The causes can be:

   (i) faults during the soldering process;
  (ii) incorrect material selection;
 (iii) contamination of surface to be soldered;
 (iv) too short a warming-up time for components having a high thermal demand;
  (v) faults during application of solder resist.

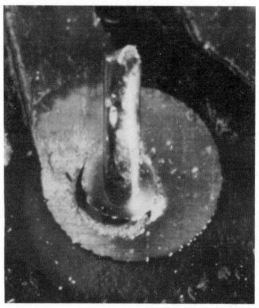

Fig. 12.5   A non-wetted solder land on a single-sided board, resulting in a joint having too small a volume of solder. The reduced strength of this joint has caused the joint to fracture (major defect, even before fracture is noticed). *Cf.* Fig. 8.33 showing the same effect but from a different cause.

12.3.2.2   DEWETTING

Dewetting is the withdrawal of molten solder from a metal surface which was initially wetted by solder (Figure 12.6). It is characterised by dispersed and often irregularly shaped areas of solder droplets, between which a thin coat of solder is left. Sometimes these areas and droplets have clear boundaries, but this is not always so (see Chapter 7.7.2). Dewetting can occur on either of the joint members. The causes can be (see also Chapter 2.3.3):

   (i) contamination of the surface to be soldered;
  (ii) contamination from the molten solder;
 (iii) contamination of the substrate to which an electrodeposit has been applied.

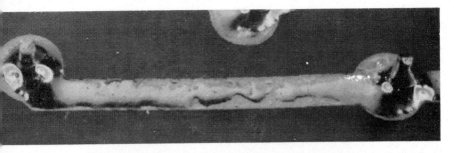

ig. 12.6 Dewetted conductor. Judged on its own, this dewetting of the conductor is merely a
smetic defect. However, the dewetting of conductors is often accompanied by dewetting of the
solder lands (see Fig. 12.7).

Dewetting is very evident at a high soldering temperature and a long soldering
ime. The soldering conditions and in particular the drainage path also influence
he occurrence of this phenomenon. Its presence indicates that the surface
ondition was not optimal from the soldering point of view, and may lead to
ther defects such as too small a quantity of solder in the joints (Figure 12.7).

ig. 12.7 Dewetted solder land on a single-sided board, resulting in a joint possessing an insufficient
olume of solder and thereby insufficient mechanical strength (insufficient reliability). The case
nown is a major defect. If dewetting occurs to a lesser degree than shown here, so that a larger solder
fillet is formed, then it is a minor defect or a cosmetic defect.

2.3.2.3   BRIDGING

Bridges (short-circuits) are connections between metal parts created by solder,
nd which are unwanted and not required in the design (see Figures 12.8 and
2.9).
The causes can be:

(i) design faults;
(ii) wrong process conditions;
iii) contaminated solder.

Bridges are major defects if they cause a short circuit between two conductors
hich should have a different potential. Bridges between conductors of the same

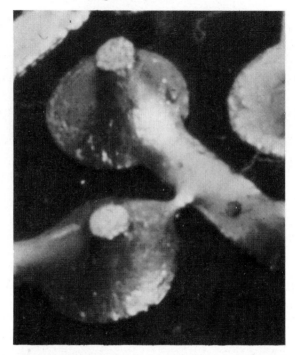

Fig. 12.8 Bridging (short-circuit) by solder between two conductors, due to insufficient distan
between them (major defect).

Fig. 12.9 A bridge between component terminations. This bridge is high enough above the printe
board to allow a conductor to pass underneath it (major defect). See also Fig. 8.28.

potential, *e.g.*, ground grids, are cosmetic defects (unless they cause hum b
providing an earth loop). Note that at times it is difficult to see whether a visib
soldered connection is a bridge or a solder covered conductor (Figure 8.26). Th
design should exclude such situations.

12.3.2.4   HOLES IN THE SOLDERED JOINT (SEE FIGURE 12.10)

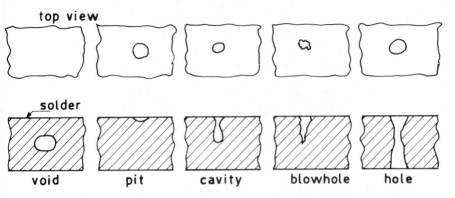

Fig. 12.10   Cross-sections of holes in the soldered joint.

A *void* is a space enclosed on all sides by the solder. Voids are not visible at the surface, but are frequently present (see Chapter 8.4.4). (Strictly speaking a void is empty.)

A *pit* is a relatively small recess in the solder surface, the bottom of which is visible from all angles of vision. It can be caused by shrinkage of the solder during solidification and is not marked as a defect.

A *cavity* is a deep recess in the solder surface.

A *blowhole* is a special type of cavity whose opening has an irregular and jagged form, without a smooth surface (Figure 12.11).

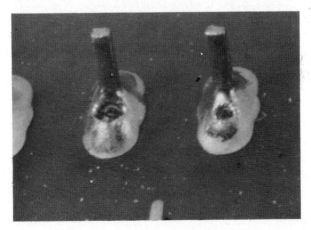

Fig. 12.11   Blowholes, likely to be encountered in soldered joints on printed boards with hole plating. In this case, the terminations and the solder lands are well wetted so that reworking is unnecessary (cosmetic defect).

A *hole* is a cavity which extends through the solder to the other side of the soldered joint (Figures 12.12 to 12.14).

The origin of voids, cavities, holes and blowholes is often associated with entrapped gas or flux. Gassing can occur with insufficiently predried printed

Fig. 12.12   Hole in the solder, caused by damage to the solder land in the vicinity of the hole (minor defect assuming a light component). This damage is often caused during hand insertion of components (see Chapter 8.3.1).

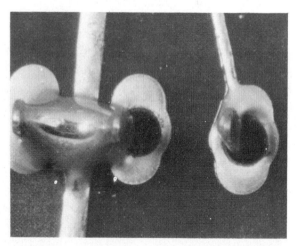

Fig. 12.13   Holes in the solder due to the solder lands not extending as far as the edges of the holes in the printed board (major defect), and to the gap between leads and solder lands being too large. To the left of the picture a bridge can be seen (major defect).

board material, via a defect in the plating of the hole wall. Bursting of a gas filled 'void' may result in a blowhole or a hole. Blowholes occur on printed boards with plated holes and can often be marked as cosmetic defects. Their occurrence calls for a study of the process conditions (see Chapter 8.1.3).

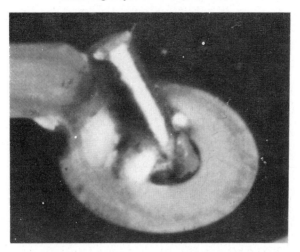

Fig. 12.14   Hole in the solder, due to encapsulation material on the component body extending onto the termination as far as the area to be soldered (major defect).

12.3.2.5   EXCESS SOLDER

Peaks, icicles or spikes (Figure 12.15), also called stalactites, consist of excess solder which has solidified in a long-drawn pointed form on solder lands, terminations or conductors. Similar defects can also occur on component terminations as a result of a circular cutting operation (Figure 9.30). Occasionally these defects are cosmetic defects, but in other cases their presence implies the risk of short-circuiting. In general, this type of defect requires correction if the permitted termination length is exceeded, or if the air insulation distance becomes too small. For high-voltage circuits it is especially important that spikes are not present (Figure 12.16).

The causes of excess solder are the same as those causing solder residues, mentioned in the following text.

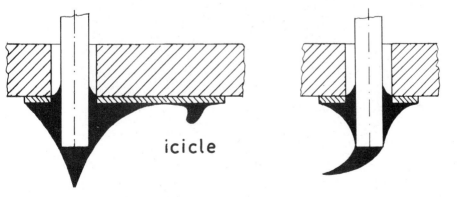

Fig. 12.15   Irregularities caused by excess solder.

Fig. 12.16 Solder spikes. The case shown is a cosmetic defect. If a spike is such that the component termination length is increased, the defect is, depending on the projecting length, a minor defect or a major defect (creepage distance inadmissibly small; risk of corona in high voltage circuits).

Fig. 12.17 Webbing. Webs are thin oxide threads with solder adhering to them. They are often difficult to detect and are sometimes above the surface of the printed board (major defect).

2.3.2.6   SOLDER RESIDUES

Solder residues can be distinguished as webs, skins and spatters.

A *web* is a solder residue adhering mainly to the printed board surface in the orm of one or more thin threads. Usually a number of solder particles can be ound on these threads (Figure 12.17).

A *skin* is a thin solder film which is sometimes left on the printed board surface fter soldering, connected to the conductors, for instance at a conductor junction Figure 12.18). Skins are also found on printed grid patterns (Figure 8.25).

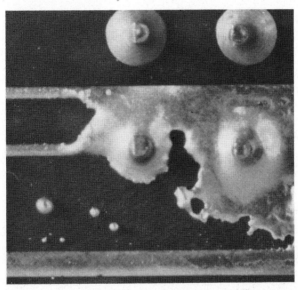

'ig. 12.18   Solder skin adhering to the printed board surface, producing short-circuits (major defect). Note also a number of solder balls (cosmetic defects).

'ig. 12.19   Solder spatters, which in several areas have almost caused short-circuits and certainly educe the creepage distance. Rating of the defect depends on the size of the spatters. The case shown here constitutes a minor defect.

A *spatter* (splash) is a separate solder residue that remains adhering to th surface of the board or embedded in flux residues. It is usually in the form of small skin or ball (Figure 12.19).

Solder residues can cause short-circuits immediately after soldering, or aft considerable time when residues have come loose and moved. Depending on th situation, the solder residues are major, minor or cosmetic defects. Webs a major defects. In the case of skins and spatters the reduction of the creepag distance is an important criterion.

The causes of solder residues can be:

(i)   Incorrect distribution of flux, resulting from maladjustment of fluxer transporting jig, or from board material that is badly wetted by flux;
(ii) Oxidation of solder at the position where the board loses contact with th solder bath or wave (also a fluxing fault);
(iii) Contamination of the solder.

12.3.2.7   DISTURBED SOLDERED JOINT

A disturbed soldered joint is a soldered joint in which the joint members hav moved with respect to each other during the solidifying time of the solder. Th results in an irregular, coarse and sometimes cracked surface (Figure 12.20). Th mechanical properties of such joints are poor and in consequence the joint is le reliable. Assessment is often difficult. If the surface of the joint shows cracks, is undoubtedly a major defect.

Fig. 12.20 Disturbed soldered joints, intentionally made by moving the wires during solidification o the solder. The appearance of the joints is irregular and not smooth (minor defect).

12.4   ASSESSMENT OF SOLDERED JOINTS ON PRINTED BOARDS

As a rule, assessment will be carried out with the unaided eye or with a illuminated or unilluminated magnifying glass having a 2 to 3 time magnification. Only in special cases, for a specific study of certain details, is necessary to use a higher magnification, *e.g.*, a stereoscopic microscope with magnification of 10 to 40 times.

The assessment of a soldered printed board can be subdivided into a number o phases.

First, a general inspection of the overall soldering result is performed. Al soldered joints should look alike. The protruding lengths of the terminations should be within the limits imposed. Apart from the soldering aspects, mounting aspects are also inspected, *e.g.*, missing components or serious out-of-true position of the components.

General inspection of the solder side of the printed board is followed by a general inspection of the component side as regards the amount of flux which has passed through the holes, and (in the case of printed boards with plated holes) the flow of solder into the holes.

After this general inspection of the soldered printed board, the joints should be studied in detail for defects by visually scanning the board. The observance of certain defects sometimes occurring systematically may offer some help: if, in a certain area, a defect is established more than once, similar areas on that printed board or on other printed boards will have an increased probability of failure and thus justify closer attention.

12.4.1   Printed Boards Without Hole Plating

In the case of printed boards without hole plating, the amount of solder per joint and the presence of holes in the joints are very important. However, no simple, general rule can be given as regards the need for correcting too much or too little solder. The same applies to wetting. This depends on the conditions of use of the end product.

12.4.1.1   AMOUNT OF SOLDER

Figure 12.21 illustrates soldered joints intentionally prepared to contain increasing quantities of solder from right to left. The centrally-located joints are to be considered optimal.

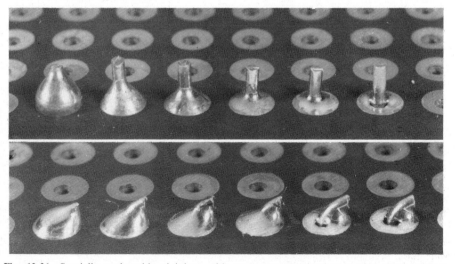

Fig. 12.21 Specially made soldered joints, with component terminations straight (top) or bent (bottom), on printed boards without hole plating (*cf.* Fig. 12.24). Suppose the joints are numbered 1 to 6 from left to right. The joints 1 and 2 are too large, but reworking is unnecessary because the contour of the component termination is still visible. The joints 6 constitute major defects. The joints 5 constitute minor defects. The joints 3 and 4 are to be considered optimal.

12.4.1.2 HOLES IN THE SOLDERED JOINTS

If component leads are soldered into holes in printed boards, the ideal situation is a complete enclosure of the leads by solder. This implies the absence of holes in the solder between the leads and the solder lands. None the less, deviations from the ideal situation do occur in practice. If a hole is found in a soldered joint, an important parameter is the fraction of the perimeter of the soldered joint that is covered by a closed solder surface, related to the forces expected to act on the joint in the conditions of use of the end product. For visual assessment, the size of the hole in the soldered joint is the major criterion.

Figure 12.22 constitutes a graphic aid for the rating of soldering defects, in which α is the angle subtended by portions of termination and solder land not joined by solder. In compiling this aid it has been assumed that wetting of the termination and solder land is adequate.

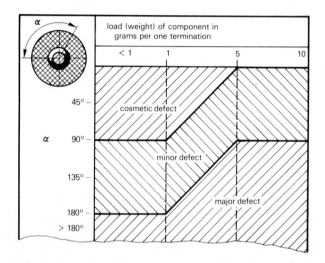

Fig. 12.22 Criteria for assessment of holes in soldered joints on printed board without hole plating, for soldered joints on which, except for the component's own weight, no other incidental forces are exerted. The figure indicates the influence of the component's mass. It does not claim to have a great accuracy and should not be taken to justify assigning separate criteria for all individual components.

Estimating the mass of components can be carried out with sufficient accuracy by using Figure 12.23. Because the components are shown full size (1:1) by comparing the actual component with the illustration the mass can be estimated.

If component terminations are bent at the pattern (foil) side of a printed board with an angle between the termination and the printed board smaller than 30°, so that along almost the entire length of the protruding termination solder is present between the termination and the printed conductor, holes in the soldered joints will usually be permissible.

Note: This case is not represented by the joints of Figure 12.21, because in these the angle between board and termination is too large, resulting in a deficient spreading along the length of the termination.

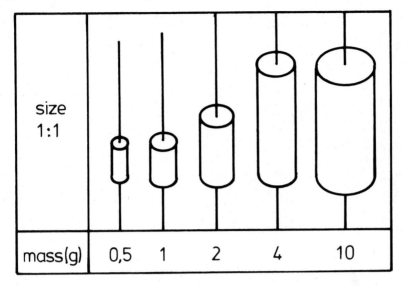

Fig. 12.23 Comparison diagram: sizes and masses of cylindrical components.

2.4.1.3 REWORK CRITERIA

In the foregoing Section, the holes in the joints have been evaluated merely from the point of view of the mechanical and electrical purposes of the joints. This is particularly important in instances in which no rework (touch-up) is carried out, for instance in the incoming inspection of soldered products.

In production practice, at the stage of visual inspection of soldered printed boards combined with rework, it may be too time-consuming to distinguish between the various degrees of severity of the defects. Simpler criteria must then be applied, for example the following:

(i)   With protruding straight terminations, no holes are allowed;
(ii) With bent terminations, holes are permitted if the full length of the bent part of the termination is soldered to the solder land or the conductor.

2.4.2 Printed Boards with Plated Holes

If the joints have been designed according to the rules given in Chapter 8, and if the specific soldering distance (see Chapter 3.4) of the separate components is fully observed, the solder will flow into the plated holes up to or over the rim on the component side of double-sided boards. Since it is virtually impossible to realise the same thermal conditions for every single solder joint, deviations will still be possible for joints with unfavourable thermal conditions, which will result in holes not completely filled with solder. This is allowed, provided the plating of the hole wall is good, as practice shows that reworking of this kind of joint does not usually yield a quality improvement.

12.4.2.1   QUANTITY OF SOLDER

Figure 12.24 presents, from right to left, soldered joints intentionally made with increasing amounts of solder. The centrally-located joints are to be considered optimal.

Fig. 12.24   Joints similar to those of Fig. 12.21, but on boards with plated holes. Here the amount of solder is less critical and hardly ever a reason for rejection, even when solder fillets are absent (joint on extreme right). The same applies if the terminations in plated holes are bent.
Note: Do not confuse the examples shown here with incompletely filled holes resulting from insufficient wetting.

12.4.2.2   BLOWHOLES

In the assessment of blowholes the quality of the wetting of the termination in the region of the joint is as important as the size of the blowhole. If the termination has been well wetted, repair will be less frequently required. If printed boards need not satisfy stringent mechanical or thermal load requirements, blowholes having sizes equivalent to half the termination perimeter are permissible.

12.4.2.3   FILLING OF HOLES (DISREGARDING BLOWHOLES)

The ideal situation is that holes in the printed board are completely filled with solder showing a solder fillet on each side of the board (Figure 12.4). Deviations from this preferred shape can be tolerated [Keller *et al*, *cf*. Woodgate]. The solder in a plated hole is permitted to contain a cavity extending as far into the hole as a quarter of the board thickness from the top and the underside of the plated hole.

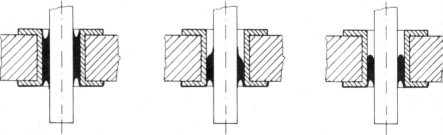

Fig. 12.25   Cross-sections of joints on printed boards with plated holes. For these holes wetting quality is to be preferred to solder quantity. Left: permitted; middle and right: not permitted (non wetting).

However, outside the area containing the cavity in the solder, the plated holes must be filled with solder through an angle of 360°, and the hole wall, component termination and hole edges must be completely wetted [*cf.* Spec. Ref.9]. The solder land on the solder side must also be completely wetted, whereas wetting of the solder land on the component side is not necessary (Figure 12.25 and 12.26).

At times inspection of the component side is not possible, in which case no cavity is permitted on the solder side. A fillet, however, is not necessary.

 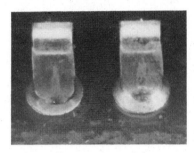

Fig. 12.26 Soldered IC terminations on the component side of a printed board with plated holes (complete IC left, detail right). The right-hand joint of the detail is good. The left-hand joint shows that the plated hole has not been completely filled. Inspection of the solder side of the board will be needed to determine whether this joint is acceptable or not.

12.4.3   Soldering-Defect Fault Finder

The soldering defects discussed in Chapter 12.3.2 have several causes [McGougan, Bernard, Pascoe]. In practice, it is often rather difficult to establish the cause in a particular case, because various causes may operate at the same time. The major causes of defects are inappropriate design of the pattern and insufficient thermal adaptation (see Chapters 8 and 3 respectively), but sudden changes in soldering quality on an unchanged design point to changed soldering conditions or changed materials. Table 12.1 may be of help in determining the causes of soldering defects. It shows the relationship between the various soldering defect types, as classified in this Chapter, and the soldering process conditions, by indicating under which Chapter/Section a detailed discussion is to be found. Where an intersection between line and column is left blank it can be assumed that little or no relationship exists.

12.5   ASSESSMENT OF HAND SOLDERED JOINTS

For soldered joints made with a soldering iron, the same requirements apply as for machine soldered joints. Briefly summarised these are:

(i)   The solder surface should be uniform and evenly bright;
(ii) The solder should have flowed thinly from the joint over the parts to be soldered;
(iii) The solder surface should be uninterrupted;
(iv) The soldered parts should remain recognisable within the joint;
(v)   The joint should contain a sufficient amount of solder.

Table 12.1

Soldering-Defect Fault Finder

Process Conditions / Soldering Defects	Thermal Aspects	Wettable Surfaces		Solder Flow					Soldering Process				
	Thermal Demand	Wettability	Flux (Activity)	Configuration of Conductors	Solder Contamination	Solder Oxidation	Deformation of Printed Board or Carrier	Solder Resist	Soldering Temperature Dwell Time	Flux Vapours	Predrying of Boards	Soldering Operation	Mounting, Jigging
Non-wetting Poor Wetting 12.3.2.1	3.4.1 3.4.2 7.3	4.2.5 6.1.2 6.3.5 6.4.3	2.3.1 5.1.1	8.3.1	4.4.5	4.5 9.1.2	8.1.1 8.1.2 8.3.4 9.6.4	8.3.5	3.1.2 9.1.1	8.3.4 9.2.7			
Dewetting 12.3.2.2		2.3.3 4.2.5 6.3.5 7.7.2			2.3.3								
Bridges 12.3.2.3			8.3.3 9.2	2.2.1 8.3.1 8.3.2 8.3.3	4.4.3	8.3.3	9.6.4	8.3.5				6.3.3 9.5.1	9.5.4
Holes 12.3.2.4	8.3.1	7.7.2	10.1.2	8.3.1 12.4.1						8.4.4 9.2.7	8.1.3		
Incorrect Solder Volume 12.3.2.5	12.4.2	12.4.2		2.2.1 8.3.1 12.4.2			9.6.4	8.3.5		8.3.4		9.5.4	
Solder Residues 12.3.2.6			8.3.2 8.3.2	8.3.2	4.4.1					8.3.2 9.2.7		9.5.4	
Disturbed Joints 12.3.2.7									11.3.1				9.5.4 9.6.3

Apart from these items there are several aspects which are more or less specific to the particular shapes of hand-soldered connections [Ellingson]. (See also Chapter 11.2.2.)

A typical defect which may occur in hand soldering is the cold soldered joint. Such a joint is the result of too low a soldering temperature or too short a contact time, so that it appears round and piled up, without the characteristic hollow shape of the solder fillet obtained after good spreading of the solder.

When soldering wires, the wire insulation must not extend into the joint and as a rule the insulation should remain 0,5 to 1 mm outside the joint. The insulation should remain clean and undamaged. If twisted conductors are soldered, the outer conductor strands should remain recognisable in the soldered joint (Figure 12.27). The flux residues of a good soldered joint should have a transparent, pale brown coloured appearance. It should be checked that the mechanical relief of the joints is and remains sufficient (no taut wires).

Imperfections formed during mechanical soldering of printed boards can be corrected by hand soldering. If holes insufficiently filled with solder are the consequence of faulty thermal design, reworking with the iron should generally be avoided, as in such a case the risk of thermal damage is high. For reworked joints on printed boards the same requirements apply as to other soldered joints.

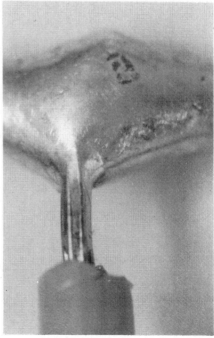

Fig. 12.27 Hand soldered connections of twisted conductors to a solid wire. The joint to the left is good and it can be easily inspected. The joint to the right cannot be assessed, because the strands are fully hidden by solder (major defect).

12.6   ASSESSMENT OF SOLDERED JOINTS OF SURFACE MOUNTED DEVICES

The visual aspects of good soldered joints, as discussed in Chapter 12.2, form the basis of the assessment of joints of surface mounted components. These joints obtain their strength completely from the coherency of the solder, contrary to those of leaded components which have the additional support of board material, *etc.*, surrounding the terminations, whereas these joints are in addition often very small. Good wetting of the surfaces is therefore the major criterion in the assessment.

If break tests are carried out to reveal the quality of the soldered joints of surface mounted components, it is usually found that it is not the joints that are ruptured, but the component itself, the substrate, or the bond between solder land and substrate (Figure 12.28). The best method is to perform cycling tests in which the solder is submitted to fatigue.

Fig. 12.28   Result of a break test of soldered joints of an SO-16 package, mounted on a printed board provided with simple straight conductors with a width of 0,75 mm and a thickness of 35 μm. The component was pushed from below through a hole in the board located at the centre of the component. The breaking force was about 140 N. Note that no damage to the soldered joints is recognisable (by courtesy of M.F. Verguld, Eindhoven).

Undesired bridges between juxtaposed terminations of one component are easily recognised in general, and the same is true for bridges between neighbouring leadless components.

A particular aspect that is not present with the leaded components mounted in holes is the possibility of the components being mounted next to the intended location on the solder lands (Figure 12.29). Misplacing of components is especially important for components, such as SOs and flatpacks, with small distances between their terminations, when a sideways shift readily gives too small an insulation distance.

Opinions concerning the visual requirements of soldered joints of surface

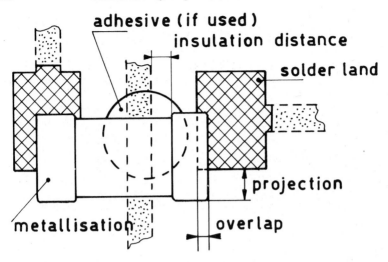

Fig. 12.29 Top view of a leadless component adhered on wide solder lands (with a conductor in between). A certain misplacing of the components is unavoidable owing to the various tolerances on components, support plates and mounting machine, and, if adhesive is applied before soldering, the tolerances of the location of the drop and of its diameter also come into play. Besides unwanted shift of the components, rotation is often observed (see Figure 12.31).

mounted components do not yet agree. The following paragraphs deal with leadless components, such as capacitors and resistors, with packages having very short leads, such as SOT-23, and with packages having many terminations, such as SO, VSO and flatpack. Various other types of components can be assessed, *mutatis mutandis*, along the same lines as given here, but no further elucidation is offered in the present text [see also Spec. Ref. 24 and (specially for chip carriers) Anon. Ref. 29].

12.6.1   Leadless Components

Multilayer chip capacitors have metallisation around the entire ends of the component, whereas chip resistors have no metallisation on their sides and sometimes not even on the whole head area, which calls for special attention. A special case is formed by two components, placed head to head with a connecting conductor. The two joints, one on each component, can readily flow together, forming a rigid connection between the two components, which is not desirable and can easily be avoided by good pattern design (see Figure 12.30).

12.6.1.1   MISPLACING

In the case of solder lands being wider than the component width, a rather large sideways shift of the components, up to a projecting distance of half the component width, is permissible (Figure 12.31), only considering joint strength and ignoring minimum insulation distances to neighbouring conductors and components. In the event of solder lands having a width of about half of that of the component metallisation, these lands must have a fillet across their full width.

If there is no overlap of the component metallisation on the solder land, a gap must be bridged during soldering, which may not happen or may produce a

Fig. 12.30 Soldered chip resistors, placed head to head. There is no metallisation on the side faces of these components nor right across the width of the top faces. Three joints shown are perfect and one is bad, because there is no complete fillet present, owing to smearing out of adhesive (by courtesy of A. den Haan, Eindhoven).

Fig. 12.31 Two leadless components placed out of accurate position, but within acceptable limits. Both the solder lands and the metallisation show good wetting. The adhesive drops between board and components can be recognised.

doubtful joint. An overlap just larger than nil is sufficient for wave soldering, but for reflow soldering an overlap larger than 0,25 mm is recommended (see following paragraph).

12.6.1.2   AMOUNT OF SOLDER

A requirement of good joints is that the part of the component metallisation not projecting past the edge of the solder land has a meniscus all along. The situation in Figure 12.30 is illustrative: the joint to the right has a width not much smaller than that of an approved joint on a small land, and yet has to be rejected because of the clearly visible wetting failure.

The amount of solder and the shape of the fillets of leadless components show large variations. After wave soldering the joints have in general a larger volume than after reflow soldering. In the former case the joints usually have a height (perpendicular to the board surface) equal to the thickness of the components. It is then irrelevant as to whether the fillet present between the component metallisation over the land and the land itself is convex or concave (Figure 12.32).

After reflow soldering, where only a limited quantity of solder is present, the height of the joint against the component metallisation should be a minimum of one third of the component thickness, and good wetting here implies that the meniscus is concave (see Figures 8.19 and 10.22).

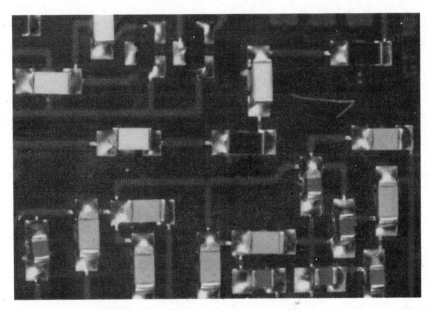

Fig. 12.32 Soldered components on a printed board with wide solder lands. During soldering the board was conveyed in the direction indicated by an arrow on the board, which can also be recognised from the different shapes of the fillets: leading fillets are smaller than trailing fillets which may even be convex (compare Figure 12.33).

12.6.2 SOT-23 Package

The outline and dimensions of the package have been shown in Figure 8.5. A typical soldering defect of wave-soldered SOT-23 packages is non-wetting despite adequate wettability of the surfaces. The cause of this defect is the obstruction of the solder flow by the component body, with the effect that the molten solder either does not come into contact with the termination and solder land at all or only to an insufficient degree (see Chapter 9.5.3.3).

12.6.2.1 MISPLACING

Good joints can be obtained only if the termination 'feet' of the package are positioned entirely within the periphery of the solder lands. In the case of wave soldering, the prior application of adhesive is critical in view of several tolerances, giving the risk of terminations being contaminated with adhesive with

Fig. 12.33   Part of a printed board provided with degassing holes. One termination of the component marked D3, had not obtained a correct solder fillet, because of the presence of adhesive between it and the solder land, although the visible parts of both the land and the termination have been wetted. The joint considered in fact provides a conductive connection, but its reliability is low. The two other SOT-23 packages have been mounted with considerable rotation, with the effect that the one at the top of the picture shows a lean joint with the foot of its component termination not fully positioned on the solder land.

the result that a fillet is not formed at all, as shown in Figure 12.33, or that only the extremity of the termination is soldered.

12.6.2.2   AMOUNT OF SOLDER

If the feet of the terminations are fully surrounded by solder, as shown in Figure 12.33 (see also Figure 12.35), there is no possibility of recognising the shape of the parts joined, which is a general requirement of soldered joints (Chapter 12.2.2), and moreover it is sometimes difficult to observe the wetting of the surfaces involved. In spite of these factors interfering with assessment, a large amount of solder is preferable to a small amount in terms of reliability in thermal cycling [Panousis *et al*]. A suitable quantity of solder is between 0,5 mg and 1 mg, using fairly large solder lands.

With smaller amounts of solder the shape of the terminations is visible and then wetting of the sides of the terminations gives the opportunity to assess the joints.

The requirement of shapes being recognisable has mainly been adopted to guarantee that the joints contain a minimum length of wire, but in the case of surface mounted components there is little doubt that the terminations are truly present.

12.6.3   SO-Packages and Flatpacks

These packages have rows of juxtaposed terminations with a width of about 0,4 mm and pitches of 1,27 mm, 1,00 mm and 0,762 mm for SO, flatpack and

VSO respectively. The leads of the SO are relatively short and rigid (Figure 12.34), whereas those of the VSO and flatpack are longer, and more flexible, having flat feet (see Figure 10.15).

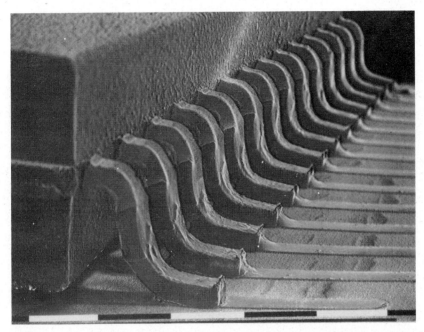

Fig. 12.34 SEM-picture of SO-package soldered on a printed board having small conductors with a width of 0,5 mm. The solder had been applied previously by electrodeposition in a layer of about 20 μm thickness, and reflowing was carried out by resistance heating, as in Figure 10.15. The amount of solder in the joint in the foreground is definitely insufficient. The scale in the picture indicates 1 mm.

12.6.3.1   MISPLACING

The maximum allowable sideways misplacing of the component depends on the insulation distance to be left. If no conductor is present between two lands of 0,5 mm width, the termination is allowed to project past the edge of the solder land for half of its width. With a wider solder land (usually up to 0,8 mm) the projection is accordingly smaller, assuming the same misplacing. An unwanted shift in the direction of the length of the terminations is not critical, as the solder lands are of adequate length.

12.6.3.2   AMOUNT OF SOLDER

The end of the terminations of an SO is curved, so that there is a wedge-shaped space between the under side of the terminations and the solder lands, which space is filled to an ever greater extent with solder if the amount of solder is increased. Figure 12.34 shows joints with very small quantities of solder; the first joint in the foreground has too little, whereas the second and third ones are just acceptable.

A larger amount of solder in the joint can be obtained by applying a solder cream, although of course there is a limit here. The joints shown in Figure 12.35, obtained with a solder cream screen printed on the substrate, are fat. Optimal joints are observed if there is a full meniscus at the sides of the terminations and a wetting of the 'heels' up to a height equal to the thickness of the termination (Figure 12.36); the amount of solder in a joint of an SO-termination is then about 0,5 mg. No requirements are placed on the cut edges of the ends of the terminations, but usually a meniscus is still present.

Fig. 12.35 Part of a thick-film hybrid circuit on an alumina substrate, with many conductors between neighbouring solder lands. The components were reflow soldered applying a hot-belt heating method and using a solder cream. The joints of the component leads are fat and contain about 0,75 mg of solder. The length of the SO-28 is about 18 mm.

The relevant part of the leads of VSOs and flatpacks is the under side of the feet. Because these feet are positioned flat on the solder lands a small amount of solder suffices to make a proper connection between a foot and a solder land. The wetting of the leads can be assessed at its true worth from the solder meniscus, however small, at the sides of the leads, whereas further requirements on the amount of solder on this type of component with flexible leads are usually more than is necessary.

The use of solder cream often implies the presence of small solder balls (satellites) embedded in the flux on the substrate surface between the conductors. In general these balls need not be removed for reasons of reduced insulation distance (see Figure 12.19).

Even if the wetting of the leads and the solder lands is excellent, it is still important to be aware of the possibility of one or more leads not being connected, because they had been inadvertently bent before soldering. If this is so, it is often at an end position.

g. 12.36 SEM-picture of soldered SO-lead, displaying a good wetting and a good quantity of lder. The surface of the joint shows some irregularities (no cracks) due to the presence of flux sidues. The solder was applied to the conductor by hot dipping of the board, and soldering was rformed by resistance heating in the same way as applies to Figure 12.34. The scale in the picture indicates 1 mm.

.7 REWORK OF SOLDERED JOINTS

The soldering defects observed after machine soldering, both the defects that nder the functioning of the assembly impossible immediately after soldering, d those that are expected to give problems during the life of the equipment, ust be corrected with the aid of a soldering iron. As previously mentioned, this tion of bringing a deviating product within the specification is called rework or uch-up and is in fact a repetition of a normal production process. The need for work just after machine soldering indicates that design and process conditions ere not good enough [Keller *et al*]. In general, this reworking should be limited incidental soldering defects which, even in a well controlled soldering process, nnot always be avoided. Rework is a costly operation because it consumes a nsiderable amount of time. Moreover, it is impossible to identify all faulty ints by visual inspection, however carefully this may be carried out. Therefore ore areas are reworked in practice than in fact need be, because the decision to work a specific area or not is taken so as to be on the safe side. This may in fect speed up the work because deciding whether to touch up a joint may take nger than actually doing it. The reliability of the final product depends on the nount of repair required, as some of the defects are inevitably overlooked and working can introduce new defects. The rework of the defects which have been tected does not guarantee them to be fully repaired. For instance, sometimes ey only seem to be repaired and the defects are merely disguised [Manko, redal]. If product or process deviations result in more defects than is thought permissible in a controlled process, this will have an adverse effect on the reliability of the finished product. A general large-scale reworking will never result in a quality level equal to that produced by a properly controlled mechanised process.

12.7.1   Amount of Rework

It is difficult to give general figures of the rework needed, because these depend on the actual situation and on the soldered product. Moreover, the definition of defects to be reworked is not always the same. Sometimes the rework figures are considered as confidential information, but otherwise many producers tend to give too optimistic information, not representative of their daily experiences.

In the discussions on rework it is necessary to distinguish clearly between different groups of 'defects', as shown in Figure 12.37.

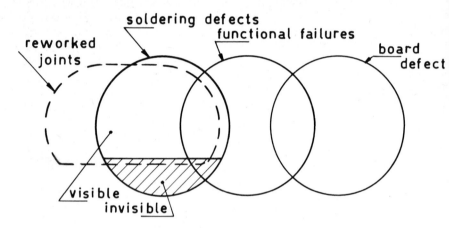

Fig. 12.37   Different groups of defects

Defects which make functioning impossible immediately after soldering (before reworking) arise from three sources, roughly giving equal numbers of defects:

(i)   board defects;
(ii) component defects (the defects being mostly invisible);
(iii) processing defects—placing defects and soldering defects.

Soldering defects are deviations from the ideal situation, that give either immediate functional failures or have a certain (non-zero) chance of becoming functional failures in the future. The estimation of this failure chance for various poor (non-ideal) joints is a difficult matter which is subject to continual discussion. In practice the soldering defects are defined by certain criteria, such as those given in Chapter 12.3.2. Only a few per cent (0-10%) of the soldering defects are immediate functional failures. Soldering defects and functional failures hence form very different groups. The same is true for the board defects and component defects.

About 10% of existing soldering defects are not found by visual inspection. These give immediate failures or remain as hidden soldering defects in the functioning end-product. For instance, 5% of the future functional defects will be caused by these hidden soldering defects. Only a proportion of these hidden defects could theoretically have been found by a more thorough visual inspection.

The soldering defects to be reworked may be divided into groups:

(i)   not soldered at all (40-60%);
(ii) insufficiently soldered (10-30%);
(iii) bridges (5-20%);
(iv) too much solder (0-10%).

The main causes of these defects are assignable to the design of the printed boards, and to a lesser extent to the soldering process.

After soldering and visual inspection, combined with rework, functional testing reveals mainly board and component defects. About 2% of the functional failures after rework are clear soldering defects, overlooked in inspection or insufficiently repaired.

From the above it is understandable that high quality cannot be brought into the product by reworking, but should be the result of an adequate design and correct processing before and during the machine soldering operation.

Process engineers should not aim chiefly at reworking the present defects, but at linking these with their causes, which should be removed.

Two examples are as follows:

Without careful processing, but avoiding elementary mistakes, in a certain production of single-sided printed boards (without hole plating) a soldering result was obtained with 25000 ppm rework. By taking a number of concerted measures this figure could be reduced to about 1000 ppm. Some of these measures, which are more or less equally effective, are:

(i)   Selection of optimal surface conditions (solderability) of solder lands;
(ii) Change of combined solder lands (having two or more component holes) to separate solder lands isolated by solder resist;
(iii) Automatic insertion of components wherever possible;
(iv) Consistent use of correct clearance between wire and hole (ratio of wire to hole diameter);
(v)   Use of optimal size of solder lands.

This level of 1000 ppm can be maintained in a good process with continual attention. It can in fact still be improved considerably. After visual inspection and rework the level of soldering defects is reduced to 250 ppm and after electrical testing to 50 ppm. These defects, still existing in a functioning equipment, would certainly have been reworked if they had been detected during inspection.

Note: The number of defects remaining after delivery can only be guessed, for instance from careful analysis of failures occurring after delivery or in accelerated life tests.

The second example is of double-sided boards with plated holes with about 1000 joints each, made for a highly professional application. A special and extensive inspection after delivery yielded that about 20 ppm of visual soldering

defects had been overlooked during earlier inspections, 40% being non-soldere
joints which had passed the functional examinations.

At a lower level than 1000 ppm of soldering defects the visual inspectic
becomes more and more difficult. Below 500 ppm visual inspection becom
almost impossible in common practice. Then there are so few defects present th
one does not know what to look for or how to do it. It is possible to look fc
usual defects by scanning the joints one by one, but this will soon cause 'ment:
defects' in those carrying out the inspection. Complete elimination of inspectic
and rework after soldering, simply leaving the soldering defects that do n
produce functional failures, is not reasonable at the 500 ppm level. To be able t
rely solely on electrical testing requires a quality level below 50 ppm defects. Thι
a gap exists in production practice (between 500 and 50 ppm) within which visuε
inspection is almost impossible and elimination of visual inspection
inadmissible.

12.7.2 Zero-Defect Soldering

The concept of 'zero-defect soldering' is often discussed. In order to place th
concept on a physically realistic basis, the probability of failure should t
quantified. The quality of soldered joints is determined by many parameter
each having a certain variability, assuming that the soldering defects are not tl
result of a systematic fault in the processing. The probability of occurrence of
defect, p, is the total number of defects divided by the total number of join
concerned. For a board with N joints, the average number of defects is pN
Under the assumed circumstances the defects show a Poisson distributioι
meaning that the fraction of boards with zero defects is given by e^{-pN}. For valuε
of $pN<0,2$, this fraction is about $1-pN$. In Figure 12.38 the probability of zerε

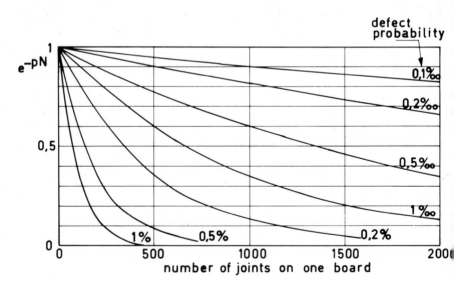

Fig. 12.38 Fraction of failure-free boards.

defect boards is given versus the number of joints on the board for several probabilities of defects (failures). With increasing numbers of joints on the board, the probability of failure must decrease proportionally to have the same fraction of boards without defects. The same is true for the fraction of boards with 1, 2, *etc.* defects, as is shown in Table 12.2.

Table 12.2

Poisson Distribution

	$pN=$	3	1	0,3	0,1	0,03
Fraction of boards with	0 defects	0,05	0,37	0,74	0,90	0,97
	1 defect	0,15	0,37	0,22	0,09	0,03
	2 defects	0,22	0,18	0,033	0,005	0,00
	3 defects	0,22	0,06	0,003	0,0002	0,00
	etc.					

Of course, if no soldering defects are present, true zero-defect soldering is achieved, but this is unrealistic as explained in Section 12.7.3.

If a desired fraction of boards without soldering defects is required, Table 12.2 indicates the maximum value of p to be permitted in production.

12.7.3 Statistical Analysis of Soldering Defects

Consider a statistical analysis of soldering defects on printed boards soldered in production. With soldering parameters termed as k_1, k_2, k_3, k_4, *etc.*, it is possible to investigate the soldering defects n_1, n_2, n_3, n_4, *etc.* For instance, n_2 is the number of bridges and k_3 is the soldering temperature. Because each n_i depends on each k_j, the following can be deduced:

$$n_1 = f_{11}.k_1 + f_{12}.k_2 + f_{13}.k_3 + \ldots$$
$$n_2 = f_{21}.k_1 + f_{22}.k_2 + f_{23}.k_3 + \ldots$$
$$n_3 = f_{31}.k_1 + f_{32}.k_2 + f_{33}.k_3 + \ldots$$
$$etc.$$

Defining ten parameters k and six types of soldering defects n produces a matrix of sixty factors f_{ij} describing the process. Some of the f-values are positive; others are negative or zero. The real situation is somewhat more complicated because higher order and mixing terms will also play a role.

In an experimental investigation the parameters k_1 to k_{10} must be varied, for instance set at 2 or 3 values. The number of separate experiments to be undertaken would then be very large (2^{10} or 3^{10}). The methods of statistical analysis help to set up a more realistic experimental scheme, in which the number of experiments is much smaller. This is possible because not all experiments have the same significance.

Once the experiments have been carried out for a certain design of board according to the prescribed combinations of process parameters, the evaluation of the matrix can be performed using a computer method in which that matrix is sought with the factors f_{ij} which best fits the experiments. The important factors automatically emerge quantitatively. Having available the matrix f_{ij}, the k-level can be selected so that a certain n-value is zero. However, no combination exist of k_1 to k_{10}, at which all defects n_1 to n_6 are zero. The most effective procedure i to minimise the weighed total number of defects. From such work it can be learn that, with the current state of technology, true defect-free soldering is not yet reality.

Another important result is obtained from the analysis of the experiments. Th matrices found depend strongly on the configuration of the conductors on th boards. Two types of boards that at first sight look the same produce totall different matrices. This means that a different combination of k_1 to k_{10} has to b selected for an optimal soldering result of another type of board. However, th results of the 'best' set of soldering conditions are only slightly better than thos of an 'average' set, showing the limited effect of the soldering parameters. Th configuration of the conductive pattern on the board and the joint design are th major factors determining the soldering quality (of course assuming that th soldering parameters are within common boundaries).

Within the existing technology a substantial reduction of soldering defects ca be achieved only by reconsidering the board design. However, the demands o the board design from the soldering point of view will certainly not coincide wit the designer's wishes for component density on the board, for maximum boar dimensions, *etc.*, so that a compromise will always be necessary.

REFERENCES

In view of the increasing use of computer-based literature scanning and search methods it is suggested that the word – **solder** – be used in the title of publications on soldering.

Authors

pages

Ackroyd, M. L., 'A Survey of Accelerated Techniques for Solderable Substrates', Publ. 531, Int. Tin Res. Inst.   248

Ackroyd, M. L., MacKay, C. A., 'Solders, Solderable Finishes and Reflowed Solder Coatings', Publ. 529, Int. Tin Res. Inst.; *Circuit World* 3, (2), 6-12 (1977).   106

Ackroyd, M. L., MacKay, C. A., Thwaites, C. J., 'Effect of Certain Impurity Elements on the Wetting Properties of 60% Tin-40% Lead Solders', *Metals Technology* 2, (2), 73-85 (1975).   106

Adamson, A. W., 'Physical Chemistry of Surfaces', Interscience, New York (1967).   14

Agniel, J. D., Val, C. M., 'Mounting of Micropackages in Vapour Phase Soldering and Study of Ageing Mechanism', Proc. Third European Hybrid Microelectronics Conf., Avignon, 435-455 (1981).   193

Ainsworth, P. A., 'Soft Soldering Gold Coated Surfaces', Publ. 431, Int. Tin Res. Inst.   193

Albom, S. E., Parsons, G. R., 'Precision Hot Gas Micro-Soldering Systems', *Electronic Prod.* 9, (4), 14, 16 (1980).   382

Allen, B. M., 'Discovering Soft-Soldering History', *The Metallurgist & Materials Technologist* 10, (10), 537-540 (1978).   2, 83

'New Prospects in Aluminium Soldering', Proc. Internepcon, Brighton, 179-183 (1975);   87

'Choice of Solder for Fine Wires and Thin Copper Films', *Wireless World* 78, 75-76 (1972);   117

'The Kinetics of the Soldering Process', *Electr. Pack. & Prod.* 21, (7), 288-290, 292, 294 (1981).   215

Allen, N., George, W. R., 'Standardizing Instruments for Soldering Assessment', *Weld. Metal Fabr.*, 47, (4), 267-271 (1979).   209

Ambrose, J., Barradas, R. G., Shoesmith, D. W., 'Investigations of Copper in Aqueous Alkaline Solutions by Cyclic Voltammetry', *Electroanal. Chem. & Interfacial Electrochem.*, 47, 47-64 (1973).   142

Amey, D. I., 'Integrated Circuit Package Selection: Pin grid arrays vs Chip Carriers'. *Electr. Pack. & Prod.* 22, (1), 262-268, 270, 272, 274, 276, 278 (1982).   278

Ammann, H. H., Farkass, I., 'Simulation of Thermal Stress Stimuli in the Testing of Printed Wiring Products', *IEEE Reliab. Physics Symp.*, 14th Ann. Proc. 141-146 (1976).   53

Andrade, A. D., Lampe, T., 'Inspection Techniques for Resistance Reflow Soldered Flatpack or Ribbon Leads', *Insulation/Circuits*, 21, (1), 32-34 (1975).   379

Andrich, E., 'Properties and Application of PTC Thermistors', *Electronic Appl. Comp., & Mat.* 26, (3), 123-144 (1965/1966).   393

Angal, R. D., Roy, D. L., 'The Surface Tension of Binary Liquid Alloys', *Z. Metallk.*, 73, (7), 428-432 (1982).   101

Anjard, R. P., 'Squeaking Solder Powder', *Microelectron Reliab.*, 21, (5), 749-750 (1981).   366

Antler, M., 'Gold-Plated Contacts: Effect of Heating on Reliability', *Plating*, 57, (6), 615-618 (1970).   193

Arnold, S. M., 'Repressing the Growth of Tin Whiskers', *Plating*, 53, (1), 96-99 (1966).   199

Berg, H., Hall, E., 'Dissolution Rates and Reliability Effects of Gold, Silver, Nickel and Copper in Lead Base Solders', *Ann. IEEE Proc. Rel. Phys.* (Symp.) **11**, 10-20 (1973). 113

Bernard, C., 'Wave Soldering Joint Quality Trouble Shooting Guide', *Insulation/Circuits*, **23**, (12), 23-25 (1977). 419

Bernard, C. D., 'Horizontal vs Inclined Conveyor Wavesoldering', *Circuits Manuf.*, **17**, (9), 53-55 (1977). 339

Bernier, D., 'Effect of Ageing on the Solderability of Various Plated Surfaces', *Plating*, **61**, (9), 842-845 (1974). 178

Bester, M. H., 'Wave Solder Process Controls', *Electr. Pack. & Prod.*, **21**, (12), 99-100, 102, 104, 106, 108 (1981). 349

Billing, B. G., 'PC Board Soldering Systems', *Electr. Pack & Prod.*, **23**, (1), 52-57 (1983). 349

Binnendyk, H. F., 'Economics of Functional Testing at Selected Levels', *Electronic Prod.*, **10**, (11), 63, 65 (1981). 400

Bircumshaw, L. L., 'The Surface Tension of Liquid Metals—Part V—The Surface Tension of the Lead-Tin Alloys', *Phil. Mag.*, **17**, 181-191 (1934). 101

Blasberg, H. J., 'Die Ausfallquoten von Bauelementen in Farbfernsehgeräten', *Funk-Technik*, **35**, (12), W456-W464 (1980). 305

Bogenschütz, A. F., Jostan, J. L., Mussinger, W., 'Galvanische Korrosionsschutzschichten für Elektronische Anwendungen', *Metalloberfläche*, **34**, 45-92, 93-136, 163-168, 187-194, 229-235, 261-308 (1980). 177, 194

Boggs, W. E., Kachik, R. H., Pellissier, G. E., 'The Effect of Alloying Elements on the Oxidation of Tin', *J. Electrochem. Soc.*, **110**, (1), 4-11 (1963). 145

Bohman, C. F., 'The Laser and Microsoldering', *Soc. Manuf. Eng.*, Tech. Paper AD 74-810. 378

Bondi, A., 'The Spreading of Liquid Metals on Solid Surfaces', *Chem. Rev.*, **52**, (2), 417-457 (1953). 17

Boogaerdt, C. A., de Mooij, H., 'Air Pollution from Soldering Fumes', *Ind. Medicine & Surgery*, **29**, 36-38 (1960). 87

Bornemann, A., ' "Tin Disease" in Solder Type Alloys', ASTM Spec. Techn. Publ. 189, 129-148 (1956). 93

Boynton, K. G., 'Oil in Wave Soldering', *Electronic Prod.*, **2**, (11), 60-62, 64 (1973). 339

Brando, E. E., Michalow, E. N., Tolstogusow, W. B., 'Zur Frage des Kontaktwinkels des Flüssigkeitstropfen auf der Oberfläche Deformierbarer Festkörper', *Z. Phys. Chem.*, Leipzig, **253**, (5/6), 369-378 (1973). 17

Braun, J. D., 'An Improved Soft Solder for Use with Gold Wire', *Trans. ASTM*, **57**, 568-571 (1964). 93

Bredal, E. P., 'Inspection can Reduce Touch-up', *Circuit Manuf.*, **21**, (9), 80, 82 (1981). 429

Bressler, R. G., 'On the Contour of Liquid-Vapor Interfaces in Capillary Grooves', *Trans. ASME*, (D-Basic), **93**, (1), 87-89 (1971). 20

Britton, S. C., 'Tin Versus Corrosion', Publ. 510, Int. Tin Res. Inst.; 144
'Spontaneous Growth of Whiskers on Tin Coatings: 20 Years of Observation', Publ. 487, Int. Tin Res. Inst. 197

Britton, S. C., Bright, K., 'An Examination of Oxide Films on Tin and Tin Plate', *Metallurgia*, **56**, 163-168 (1957). 144, 145

Britton, S. C., Clarke, M., 'Detection of Zinc Diffusion into Tin Coatings on Brass', *Trans. Inst. Metal Finish.*, **36**, 230-232 (1959);
'Effects of Diffusion from Brass Substrates into Electrodeposited Tin Coatings on Corrosion Resistance and Whisker Growth', *Trans. Inst. Metal Finish.*, **40**, 205-211 (1963). 180

Brodsky, W. L., Parker, F. D., Stafford, J. W., 'Reliability and Application of Leaded Plastic Chip Carriers', *Electr. Pack. & Prod.*, **21**, (11), 109-110, 112-114, 118, 120, 122 (1981). 277

Brothers, E. W., 'Intermetallic Compound Formation in Soft Solders', *Western Electric Eng.*, **25**, (2), 49-63 (1981). 93

Brous, J., 'Evaluation of Post-Solder Flux Removal', *Welding J. Res. Suppl.*, **54**, (12), 444S-448S (1975); 167
'Water-Soluble Flux and its Effect on PC Board Insulation Resistance', *Electr. Pack. & Prod.*, **21**, (7), 79-80, 82, 84-85, 86-87 (1981); also Proc. PC World Conv. II, Munich, Part II, 93-103 (1981). 160

Browne, L. T., 'Reflow Soldering of Hybrid Circuits', *Insulation/Circuits*, **21**, (9), 27-29 (1975). 371

Brus, G., Bentejac, R., Prevot, F., 'Analyse par chromatographie en phase gazeuse des produits résineux', *Ann. Fals. Exp. Chim.*, 1-16, Mai-Juin (1968). 151

Bud, P. J., 'Solderability and Corrosion Protection of PCBs', *Electronic Prod.*, **9**, (4), 25, 27, 29, 31; (5), 43, 45, 47, 49, 51 (1980); 187

'Solderability Assurance and Corrosion Protection of PWBs and Components', *Insulation/ Circuits*, **26**, (9), 20-23; (10), 49-51; (11), 31-35 (1980);   178

'General Review of Soldering as a Joining Technique', *Insulation/Circuits*, **23**, (3), 48-57 (1977);   28

'Wave Soldering Technique for the Soldering and Tinning of Coils, Windings and Wire', *Insulation/Circuits*, **20**, (4), 37-40; (5) 65-68 (1974);   333

'Mass Production Techniques Using the Principle of Wave Soldering', *Welding Journal*, **52**, (7), 431-439 (1973);   314

'Soldering, in-Line Lead Cutting and Cleaning of Printed Circuit Assemblies', *Manuf. Eng.*, 88-91, Oct. (1980).   346

Budrys, R. S., Brick, R. M., 'Variables Affecting the Wetting of Tin Plate by Sn-Pb-Solders', *Metall. Trans*, **2**, (1), 103-111 (1971).   149

Bulwith, R. A., 'Failure Analysis of Solder Joints', *Insulation/Circuits*, **24**, (2), 19-23 (1978);   81

'Blowholes and Voids: Causes and Cures', *Electr. Pack. & Prod.*, **16**, (11), 95-97, 99 (1976).   271, 316

Burge, P. S., Harries, M. G., O'Brien, I. M., Pepys, J., 'Respiratory Disease in Workers Exposed to Solder Flux Fumes Containing Colophony (Pine Resin)', *Clinical Allergy*, **8**, (1), 1-14 (1978); also, **10**, (2), 137-149 (1980).   167

Burge, P. S., Edge, G., Hawkins, R., White, V., Newman Taylor, A. J., 'Occupational Asthma in a Factory Making Flux-Cored Solder Containing Colophony', *Thorax*, **36**, (11), 828-834 (1981).   168

Burns, F., Zyetz, C., 'Laser Microsoldering', *Electr. Pack. & Prod.*, **21**, (5), 109-120 (1981).   379

Carleer, R., Francois, J. P., van Poucke, L. C., 'Determination of the Main, Minor and Trace Elements in Lead/Tin-Based Solder by Atomic Absorption Spectrophotometry', *Bull. Soc. Chim. Belge*, **90**, (4), 357-365 (1981).   129

Carslaw, H. S., Jaeger, J. C., 'Conduction of Heat in Solids', 2nd Edn., Clarendon Press, Oxford (1959).   58

Cassidy, M. P., Lin, K. M., 'Soldering Performance of Fluxes; a Study', *Electr. Pack. & Prod.*, **21**, (11), 153-154, 156, 158, 160 (1981); also *Electronic Prod.*, **11**, (4), 20-24, 26 (1982).   158

Cavanaugh, G. W., Langan, J. P. 'Tin-Lead Electrodeposits: The Effect of Impurities in the Solution', *Plating*, **57**, (4), 369-371 (1970).   184

Chadwick, D., Hashemi, T., 'Benzotriazole Adsorption on Copper Studied by X-ray Photoelectron Spectroscopy', *J. Electr. Spectr. & Rel. Phenom.*, **10**, 79-83 (1977).   196

Chu, T. Y., 'A Hydrostatic Model of Solder Fillets', *Western Electric Eng.*, **19**, (2), 31-42 (1975);   29

'A General Review of Mass Soldering Methods', *Insulation/Circuits*, **22**, (12), 73-75 (1976).   369

Clementson, J. J., Gilsing, C. P. G., Pol, G. H., 'The Compatibility of Electronic Components with Fluorocarbon Solvents in Cleaning Processes', Proc. Internepcon Europa, Brussels, 56-71, (1973).   164

Coffin, L. F., Tavernelli, J. F., 'The Cyclic Straining and Fatigue of Metals', *Trans. Met. Soc. AIME*, **215**, (5), 794-807 (1959).   122

Comerford, M. F., 'An Analysis of Some Important Parameters in Automatic Soldering', Proc. Nepcon East (1979);   298

'Removing Solder Bridges from Printed Circuit Boards', *Insulation/Circuits*, **27**, (4), 31-34 (1981).   335

Coombs, C. F., 'Printed Circuits Handbook' 2nd Edn., McGraw-Hill, New York (1979).   264, 399

Courtney, D., 'Health and Safety in Soft Soldering', *Brazing and Soldering* 3, 26-28, 32 (1982).   87, 168

Creydt, M., Fichter, R., 'Diffusion in Galvanisch Aufgebrachten Schichten und Weichloten Bei Temperaturen Zwischen 23°C und 212°C', *Metall*, **25**, (10), 1124-1127 (1971).   97, 99

Daebler, D. H., 'Specifying Solder Paste Materials for Stencilling Applications on Thick Film Circuits', *Electr. Pack. & Prod.*, **21**, (4), 99-*et seq*, (1981).   367

Damkjaer, A., 'Composition Analysis of Tin/Lead Platings on Printed Circuit Boards by the Beta-Backscatter Method', *Int. J. Appl. Rad. & Isotopes*, **27**, 631-636 (1976); 'Beta-Backscatter Gauge for Tin-Lead Analysis of Printed Circuit Boards', *Trans. Am. Nucl. Sci.*, **32**, 212-213 (1979).   128

Dance, F. J., 'Can PWBs Meet the Surface Mount Challenge?', *Electri·onics*, **29**, (5), 25-27; (6), 35-38 (1983).   278

Dance, F. J., Wallace, J. L., 'Clad Metal Circuit Board Substrates for Direct Mounting of Ceramic Chip Carriers', *Electr. Pack. & Prod.* **22**, (1), 229-232, 234, 236-237 (1982).   278

Engelmaier, W., 'Effects of Power Cycling on Leadless Chip Carrier Mounting Reliability and Technology', *Electr. Pack. & Prod.*, **23**, (4), 58-63 (1983). 276

Enos, H. I., Harris, G. C., Hedrick, G. W., 'Rosin and Rosin Derivates', Kirk-Othmer: Encyclopedia of Chemical Technology', **17**, 475-508, Interscience, New York (1968). 151

Erickson, D., 'Chip Carriers: Coming Force in Packaging', *Electr. Pack. & Prod.*, **21**, (3), 64-80 (1981); 276
'Solderability Test Systems', *Electr. Pack. & Prod.*, **20**, (5), 97 *et seq.* (1980); 205
'Automatic Component Insertion/Attachment Systems Review', *Electr. Pack. & Prod.* **22**, (1), 47-50, 52, 54, 56, 58, 60, 62 (1982). 263

Espy, P. N., 'Testing of Printed Circuit Board Solder Joints by Optical Correlation', NASA Techn. Report, NASA TR R-449 (1975). 401

Evans, C. J., 'Connector Finishes: Tin in Place of Gold', *IEEE Trans.*, Vol. CHMT-3, (2), 226-231 (1980). 193
'Fusible Alloys for Industry', *Tin and its Uses*, No. 133, 10-14 (1982). 124

Evans, U. R., 'The Corrosion and Oxidation of Metals', Arnold, London (1961). 145

Eyre, B. L., 'The Preparation of Tin and Tin Alloys for Micro-Examination', *Metallurgia*, **58**, 95-106 (1958); also, Publ. 282, Int. Tin Res. Inst. 90

Fashing, G. M., 'Weichlöten, Lote und Flussmittel in der Elektrotechnik', *Feinwerktechnik*, **73**, (12), 519-528 (1969). 124

Fennimore, J. E., 'Using Leadless Components Technology on Printed Wiring Boards', *Electr. Pack. & Prod.* **18**, (12), 128-132 (1978);
'Hermetic Ceramic Chip Carrier Implementation', *Electr. Pack. & Prod.*, **21**, (5), 172-181 (1981). 276

Fidos, H., Piekarski, K., 'Oxidation of Tin Coatings on Copper Wires', *J. Inst. Metals*, **101**, 95-96 (1973). 97, 145

Fidos, H., Schreiner, H., 'Feuerverzinnung von Kupferschaltdrähten', *Metall* **61**, (3), 225-228 (1970). 185

Fisher, H. J., Phillips, A., 'Viscosity and Density of Liquid Lead-Tin and Antimony-Cadmium Alloys', *J. Metals*, **6**, (9), 1060-1070 (1954). 102, 103

Fishman, D., Cooper, N., 'Mounting Leadless Chip Carriers onto Printed Circuit Boards', *Hybrid Circuits*, No 1, 38-43 (1982). 277

Fletemeyer, W., 'Chip Components can be Flow-Soldered on Both Sides of a Board to Boost Density', *Electron. Design* (USA), **28**, (2), 90-91 (1980). 342

Flint, O., 'Surface Tension of Liquid Metals', *J. Nuclear Mat.*, **16**, 233-248 (1965). 16, 101

Flot, R., Gay, G., Jones, P., 'A Quantitative Method for Solderability Testing Using Computer Aided Wetting Balance Method', Proc. Int. Conf. on Soft Soldering and Welding in Electronics and Precision Mechanics, Munich (1981); *DVS Berichte*, **71**, 115-120 (1981). 235

Fornara, R. E., Kleiner, E., 'Zur Prüfung der Weichlotbarkeit von Metallischen Halbzeugen', *J. Mat. Techn.*, **2**, (5), 252-253 (1971). 237

Frankenthal, R. P., Siconolfi, D. J., 'AES Study of Tin-Lead Alloys: Effects of Ion Sputtering and Oxidation on Surface Composition and Structure', *J. Vac. Sci. Technol.*, **17**, (6), 1315-1319 (1980); also, *Surf. Sci.*, **104**, (1), 205-211 (1980). 145

Frankland, H. G., Sawyer, N. J., Sanderson, I. S., 'Solder Joints', Determining Causes of Cracking in Conformal Coated Solder Joints; Measuring the Stresses in the Joints; Techniques of Strengthening the Joints.
Insulation/Circuits **17**, (1), 21-27; (2), 33-37; (3), 51-59 (1971). 304, 308

Franz, A., Tappe, G., 'Checking the Thermal Expansion for Epoxy-Glass Laminates for PCs and Multilayer Boards; *Electronic Engng.*, **43**, (Oct) 37-39 (1971). 269

Friedrich, D., Schreiner, H., 'Zur Technologie der Feuerdickverzinnung von Schaltdrähten', *Metall*, **27**, (12), 1187-1195 (1973); **29**, (9), 886-894 (1975). 186

Friedrich, D., Knott, U., Schmitt-Thomas, G., 'Diffusionsvorgänge beim Weichlötprozess unter Besonderer Berücksichtigung des Wellenlötverfahrens', Proc. Int. Conf. on Soft Soldering and Welding in Electronics and Precision Mechanics, Munich (1981); *DVS Berichte*, **71**, 11-15 (1981). 46, 98

Fuchs, F. J., 'Fluxless Ultrasonic Soldering Prevents Flux Residues Problems', *Assembly Engng.*, **21**, (11) 12-16 (1978);
'Ultrasonics in Electronic Soldering Application', *Electr. Pack. & Prod.*, **19**, (11), 124-132 (1979). 46

Furuta, N., Hamamura, K., 'Growth Mechanism of Proper Tin-Whiskers', *Jap. J. Appl. Phys.*, **8**, (12), 1404-1410 (1969). 198

Gamalski, J., 'Standardization for Soldering', Proc. Int. Conf. on Soft-Soldering and Welding in Electronics and Precision Mechanics, Munich (1981); *DVS Berichte* **71**, 141-143 (1981). 8

bhardt, E., Köstlin, K., 'Über die Eigenschaften Metallischer Schmelzen', *Z. Metallk.*, **48**, (12), 636-641 (1957). 102

tten, J. R., Senger, R. C., 'Immersion Wave Soldering Process', *IBM J. Res. Dev.*, **26**, (3), 379-382 (1982). 318

ade, G. H., Post, H. R., 'Ageing of Solder Standards', *Appl. Spectroscopy*, **22**, (2), 123 (1968). 89

aessgen, R., 'Electronic Grade Solder Paste: Characteristics and Application', *Solid State Technol.*, **24**, (4), 54-55 (1981). 364

olachev, S. M., Kudryavtsev, V. S., Ovseevich, V. L., 'The Hydrostatic Model of the Redistribution of the Tin-Lead Alloy in the Melting of the Coating of Printed Circuit Boards', *Welding Prod. (Svar. Proiz.)*, **27**, (2), 41-44 (1981). 187

oldman, I. B., 'Differential Thermal Analysis as an Aid to Solder Flux Characterization', *Insulation/Circuits*, **27**, (3), 41-44 (1981). 134

oldmann, L. S., Krall, B., 'Measurement of Solder-Flux-Vapor Surface Tension by a Modified Maximum Bubble Pressure Technique', *Rev. Sci. Instr.*, **47**, (3), 324-325 (1976). 101

onzalez, H. M., 'Component Mounting Methods and Their Effect on Solder Joint Cracking', *Insulation/Circuits*, **23**, (11), 19-24 (1977). 306, 308

öber, H., Erk, S., Grigull, U., 'Grundgesetze der Wärmeübertragung', Springer, Berlin (1963). 61

ühl, W., Grühl, U., 'Über die Oxydation von flüssigem Zinn', *Metall.*, **6**, (7,8), 177-182 (1952). 110

umbel, E. J., 'Statistical Theory of Extreme Values and Some Practical Applications', Nat. Bur. Standards, Appl. Math. Series 33 (1954); also, Statistics of Extremes, Columbia University Press, New York (1967). 247

utbier, E. A., Moy, P. H., Dominick, J. C., 'Dissolution Rates of Fine Magnet Wire in Molten Tin-Lead Solders', *Insulation/Circuits*, **25**, (1), 19-23 (1979). 117

agstrom, R. A., Wild, R. N., 'Evaluation of Solders for IBM System/4 Pi Computers', Proc. Internepcon, Brighton 271-286 (1969). 119

all, P. M., Condra, L. W., 'Aging of Solder Connections to Ti-Pd-Au Films', *IEEE Trans.* Vol. CHMT-2, (3), 279-283 (1979). 93

ansen, M., Anderko, K., 'Constitution of Binary Alloys', McGraw-Hill, New York (1958) (Supplements in 1965 and 1969). 127

arding, W. B., Pressly, H. B. 'Soldering to Gold Plating', Tech. Proc. 50th Ann. Conf. Am. Electropl. Soc., 90-106 (1963). 193

argis, B. M., Westervelt, D. J., 'High Lead Count Packages and Interconnection Alternatives', *Electr. Pack. & Prod.*, **21**, (9), 82-86, 88, 89 (1981). 278

arman, A. C., 'Rapid Tin-Nickel Intermetallic Growth: Some Effects on Solderability', Proc. Internepcon, Brighton, 42-49 (1978). 99, 100

arman, G. G., 'The Use of Acoustic Emission as a Test Method for Electronic Interconnections and Joints', Proc. Int. Conf. on Soft-Soldering and Welding in Electronics and Precision Mechanics, Munich (1981); *DVS Berichte*, **71**, 104-110 (1981). 401

arper, C. A., 'Handbook of Materials and Processes for Electronics', McGraw-Hill, New York (1970). 172, 266

artland, S., Hartley, R. W., 'Axisymmetric Fluid-Liquid Interfaces', Elsevier, Amsterdam (1976). 29

artmann, H. J., 'Flussmittelfreies Löten von Schichtschaltungen', Int. Conf. on Soldering, Brazing and Welding in Electronics, Munich (1976); *DVS Berichte*, **40**, 24-30 (1976); 'Extended Application of Wetting Balance for the Evaluation of Flux-free Soldering Processes' (in German), Int. Conf. on Soldering, Brazing and Welding in Electronics, Munich (1976); *DVS Berichte*, **40**, 149-156 (1976). 34, 217

asson, J. C., 'Open-Tube-Column Gas Chromatography of Rosin Fluxes', *Anal. Chem.*, **44**, (9), 1586-1589 (1972). 151

aug, K. Th., 'Untersuchungen über die Zeitstandfestigkeit von Weichlötverbindungen', *Schweissen u Schneiden*, **17**,(5), 200-207 (1965). 120

eller, M., Schmidt, E. R., 'The Economics of Testing Discrete Axial Components at Incoming Inspection', *Electr. Pack. & Prod.*, **20**, (10), 89, 90, 92, 94 (1980). 400

enneke, E. G., Reifsnider, K. L., Stinchcomb, W. W., 'Thermography—An NDI Method for Damage Detection', *J. Metals*, **31**, (9), 11-15 (1979). 401

errmann, G., (Editor), 'Handbuch der Leiterplattentechnik', 2nd Edn, Leuze, Saulgau/Württ. (1982). 264

ill, J. A., Rippere, R. E., Murphy, C. B., 'Thermal Analysis of Soldering Flux Components', *Insulation*, **9**, (2), 31-32 (1963). 134

Hobbins, N. D., Roberts, R. F., 'An Ellipsometric Study of Thin Film Formed on Copper by Benzotriazole and Benzimidazole', *Surface Technol.*, **9**, 235-239 (1979).   1§

Hofmann, W., 'Lead and Lead Alloys', Springer Verlag, Berlin (1970).   1◖

Holmes, P. J., Loasby, R. G., 'Handbook of Thick Film Technology', Electrochemical Publications, Ayr (1976).   116, 2◖

Honda, Y., 'MELF Resistors Facilitate High Density Mounting', *J. Electr. Engng.*, **17**, April 56-61 (1980).   2⁷

Howard, R. T., 'Optimization of Indium-Lead Alloys for Controlled Collapse Chip Connection Application', *IBM J. Res. Develop.* **26**, (3), 372-378 (1982).   1⁷

Howes, M. A. H., Saperstein, Z. P., 'The Reaction of Lead-Tin Solders with Copper Alloys', *Welding J. Res. Suppl.*, **48**, (2), 80S-85S, (1969).   1▮

Howie, F. H., Hondros, E. D., 'The Surface Tension of Tin-Lead Alloys in Contact with Fluxes', *J. Mat. Science* **17**, (5), 1434-1440 (1982).   1◖

Ilnoya, K., Asakawa, S., Hotta, K., Burson, J. H., 'Liquid Surface Profiles in Contact with Symmetric Solid Surfaces', *Powder Technol.*, **1**, 28-32 (1967).   2

Ijiri, K., Ueda, A., 'Chip Resistors Facilitate Increased Densities', *J. Electr. Engng.*, **17**, (April), 44-47 (1980).   2⁷

Ivlev, V. I., Yudin, V. A., 'Thermal EMF of Lead-Tin Alloys', *High Temp. R. (Templofizika Vysokikikh Temperatur)*, **19**, (4), 562-565 (1981).   1℃

Jafri, A., 'Fighting Whisker Growth in the Communication Industry', *Plating*, **60**, (4), 358-361 (1973).   1§

Jawitz, M. W., 'Trouble Shooting Manual for Printed Circuit Production', *Insulation/Circuits (suppl.)*, **22**, (4), 5-38 (1976).   2◖

Jellison, J. L., Johnson, D. R., Hoskin, F. M., 'Statistical Interpretation of Meniscograph Solderability Tests', *IEEE Trans.* Vol. PHP-**12**, (2), 126-133 (1976).   206, 2▮

Johannessen, J. S., Grande, A. P., 'Auger Depth Profiling and Analysis of Defects in Tinplate Surfaces', *Mat. Sci. and Eng.*, **42**, 321-327 (1980).   3

Johnson, C., 'Fused Flux Coating on Solder Preforms Reduces Cracking and Sticking', *Electr. Pack. & Prod.* **22**, (11), 23-24 (1982).   3◖

Jol, A. C., 'The Effect of Flux Behaviour on Printed Board Characteristics', Proc. Int. Conf. on Soft Soldering and Welding in Electronics and Precision Mechanics, Munich (1981); *DVS Berichte*, **71**, 131-134 (1981).   14

Jones, W. R. D., Davies, J. B., 'The Viscosity of Lead, Tin and Their Alloys', *J. Inst. Metals*, **86**, 164-166 (1957/58).   10

Jostan, J. L., 'Whiskerbildung bei Zinn, Zinn-Blei-Legierungen, Silber und Gold', *Galvanotechnik*, **71**, (9), 946-955 (1980).   1§

Karnowski, M. M., Rosenzweig, A., 'The Gold-Tin-Lead Alloys', *Trans. Metall. Soc.* AIME, **242**, (11), 2257-2261 (1968).   1℃

Karpel, S., 'Mass-Soldering Equipment for the Electronics Industry', 'Part 1, Wave Soldering;' 'Part 2, Drag and Dip Soldering', *Tin & Its Uses*, No. 127, 1-6; No. 128, 1-6 (1981). 'Part 3, Vapour Phase Soldering', *Tin & Its Uses* No. 130, 1-4 (1981) also, Publ. 612, Inst. Tin. Res. Inst.   349, 38

Kaufman, A. B., 'Proper Design and Materials Eliminate Causes of A-C Current Leakage in Soldering Irons', *Insulation/Circuits*, **22**, (1), 14-16 (1976).   3§

Kawakatsu, I., Osawa, T., 'Wettability of Liquid Tin on Solid Copper', *Trans. Japan Inst. Metals*, **14**, (2), 114-119 (1973).   ▮

Kay, P. J., MacKay, C. A., 'The Growth of Intermetallic Compounds on Common Basic Materials Coated with Tin and Tin-Lead Alloys', *Trans. Inst. Metal Finish.*, **54**, 68-74 (1976);   ℭ

'Barrier Layers Against Diffusion', *Trans. Inst. Metal Finish.*, **57**, 169-174 (1979).   9

Keil, A., 'Über das Kriechverhalten Einiger Weichlote', *Metall*, **11**, (9), 740-742 (1957).   1▮

Keller, J., 'Improving PWB Reliability while Cutting Soldering and Cleaning Costs', *Assembly Engng*, **24**, (5), 14-17; (6) and (7) (1981);   16

'Soldering without Shorts – Joints are Auto ND Tested', Proc. Ann. Reliability and Maintenability Symp. Philadelphia, 283-288 (1981).   3³

Keller, J., Keller, J. D., Keller, R. L., 'PWB Work Centres Save $ Billions', *Assembly Engng*, **22**, (2) 14-17; (3) 12-15; (4) 20-27 (1979).   42

Keller, J. D., 'Can the US Afford the "Cosmetic Look" in Soldered Joints?', *Assembly Engng*, **16**, (10) 32-35; (11) 38-41 (1973);   4℃

'Process Control – Key to Reliable Wave Soldering', *Assembly Engng*, **12** (5) 50-54; (6) 40-45 (1969).   3³

Langan, J. P., Souzis, L., 'The Functional Approach to Soldering', *Welding J.,* **56**, (1), 13-17 (1977).

Lashko, S. V., Lymar, P. I., Lashko, N. F., 'The Effect of Magnesium Additions on the Properties of Tin-Lead Brazing Alloys', *Welding Prod. (Svar. Proiz.),* **27**, (10), 35-37 (1980).

Lashko, S. V., Nagapetyan, I. G., 'Special Features in the Filling of a Horizontal Gap with a Soldering Alloy during Isothermal Contact', *Welding Prod. (Svar. Proiz.),* **27**, (8), 32-34 (1980).

Lashko, S. V., Perekrestova, R. A., 'Effects of a Solder Layer on the Ductility of Copper and Brass at 20°C', *Automatic Welding (Avt. Svarka),* **29**, (11), 29-31 (1976).

Latin, A., 'The Influence of Fluxes on the Spreading Power of Tin Solders on Copper', *Trans. Faraday Soc.,* **34**, (2), 1384-1395 (1938).

Lea, C., 'The Physical Basis of Wettability in Metallic Systems', Proc. 8th Int. Vacuum Congress, Cannes, Vol. II, 467-470 (1980).

'Soldering: An Irreplaceable Joining Technique?' *Brazing and Soldering* **3**, 24-25 (1982).

Lee, I. W. H., 'Screenable Solder Paste', *Welding J.* **56**, (10), 32-36 (1977).

van de Leest, R. E., Krijl, G., 'A Tungstate Conversion Coating on Tin', *Thin Solid Films* **72**, 237-246 (1980).

Lehner, K., Safran, M., v. Schau, P., Weise, G., 'Insulation Distances on Printed Circuit Boards', *Nachrichten Technische Zeitschrift,* **27**, (11), 433-439 (1974).

Leinauer, H., Müller, H., 'Weichlöttechnik-Parameter-Definitionen', *Feinwerktechnik u Messtechnik,* **85**, (6), 253-257 (1977).

Lenz, E., 'Anforderungen an die Weichlötnormen aus der Sicht einer Automatischen Fertigung in der Elektroindustrie', *Feinwerktechnik u Micronic,* **76**, (3), 123-129 (1972). 106, 174, 186,

Lenz, E., Kramer, P., 'Werkstofftechnische Voraussetzungen für den Automatisierten Lötprozess in der Elektrotechnik', *Feinwerktechnik* **74**, (7), 273-282 (1970). 175,

Leonida, G., 'Handbook of Printed Circuit Design, Manufacture, Components and Assembly', Electrochemical Publications, Ayr.(1981). 263, 264,

Leven, S. S., 'Screening Procedure for Adhesion Degradation due to Solder Leaching in Thick-Film Hybrid Microcircuits', *Solid State Technol.,* **20**, (3), 39-44 (1977).

Lin, K. M., Harry, T. R., 'High Performance Instrument for Solder Wetting Studies', *Western Electric Eng.,* **26**, (2), 11-19 (1982).

Lindner, K., 'Rationelle IC-Montage Mittels Impulslöten', Proc. Int. Conf. on Soft-Soldering and Welding in Electronics and Precision Mechanics, Munich (1981); *DVS Berichte,* **71**, 45-51 (1981).

Livingstone, J. D., 'Precipitation and Superconductivity in Lead-Tin and Lead-Cadmium Alloys', *J. Appl. Phys.,* **34**, 3028-3036 (1963).

Loeffler, J. R., 'N/C Laser Soldering. Fast-Low Cost-no Rejects', *Assembly Engng,* **20**, (3) 32-34 (1977).

Long, J. B., 'Tin and Tin Alloy Coatings for Printed Circuits', *Insulation/Circuits,* **22**, (5), 17-22 (1976);

'A Critical Review of Solderability Testing', *J. Electrochem. Soc.,* **122**, (2), 25C-32C (1975).

Lore, A. M., 'Cleaning Copper Chemically—A Comparison', *Insulation/Circuits,* **26**, (3), 41-44 (1980) 173,

Lunt, M., 'Multi Factory Aspects of Static Sensitive Device Usage', *Electronic Prod.,* **10**, (4), 21-25 (1981)

Lyman, J., 'Packaging; Chip Carriers, Pin-grid Arrays Change the PC-Board Landscape', *Electronics,* **54**, (29 Dec.), 66-75 (1981);

'Sized Solder Bumps Make Solid Joints', *Electronics,* **54**, (3 Nov.), 46, 48 (1981)

MacKay, C. A., 'Surface Finishes and Their Solderability', *Weld. Metal Fabr.* **47**, (1), 55-62 (1979); 145, 177,

'Solder Creams and How to Use Them', Proc. Internepcon, Brighton, 61-67 (1980);

Electr. Pack. & Prod., **21**, (2), 116 *et seq.* (1981).

'Causes and Effects of Solder Contamination', *Electri·onics,* **29**, (3), 44-48; (4), 41-44; (5), 51-53 (1983).

MacKay, C. A., Audette, D. A., 'Gauging Flux Performance, Reading the Label won't do', *Circuits Manuf.,* **22**, (5), 40, 42, 44, 65, 66 (1982). 145,

Majumdar, S. R., Michael, D. H., 'The Equilibrium and Stability of Two Dimensional and Asymmetric Pendent Drops', *Proc. R. Soc.* London, A **351**, 89-115; 117-127 (1976).

Manko, H., 'Understanding the Solder Wave and Its Effects on Solder Joints', *Insulation/Circuits*, **24**, (1), 45-49 (1978); 334, 339
'Eliminate Poor Solderability: Don't Bury It Under Solder', *Insulation/Circuits*, **22**, (2), 27-30 (1976). 429

Mansveld, J. F., Jans, J. M., 'The PD-R Method of Manufacturing Printed Circuit Boards', *Plating & Surface Finish.*, **66**, (1), 14-17 (1979). 264

Mattera, L., 'Components Reliability', *Electronics*, **48** (2 Oct) 91-98; (30 Oct) 87, 94 (1975). 305

Mayhew, A. J., Wick, G. R., 'Solderability and Contact Angle', Proc. Internepcon, Brighton, 45-55 (1971). 235

Maykuth, D. J., 'Learning the Science of Soldering. Solder Training Courses in the USA and Canada', *Tin & Its Uses*, No. 132, 1-4 (1982). Also *Brazing & Soldering*, (4), 31-33 (1983). 395

McBride, M. E., 'The Wicking Method of Solder Removal', *Insulation/Circuits*, **26**, (13), 25-28 (1980). 398

McCarthy, T. J., MacKay, C. A., Thwaites, C. J., 'Effect of Surface Contamination of Copper, Arising From Water Rinsing on Solderability', *Circuit World*, **6**, (4), 6-9 (1980). 196

McGougan, C. J., 'Everyman's Guide to Quality Flowsoldering', *Electronic Prod.*, **2**, (4), (1973). 419

McMillan, I. D., 'Infra Red Solder Fusing', *Electronic Prod.*, **5**, (5), 41, 42, 44 (1976). 189, 377

McNutt, J. E., Andes, G. E., 'Relationship of The Contact Angle to Interfacial Energies', *J. Chem. Phys.*, **30**, (5), 1300-1303 (1959). 17

Messner, G. M., 'Impact of New Devices on PCB Design and Material Selection', *IPC Techn. Rev.* 11-19, Jan. (1983); also IPC-TP-427. 278

Metzger, W., Schmitz, M., 'Über die Vermeidung von Whiskerbildung bei Zinn-Niederschlägen', *Galvanotechnik*, **59**, (10), 827-828 (1968). 199

Miedema, A. R., den Broeder, F. J. A., 'On The Interfacial Energy in Solid-Liquid and Solid-Solid Metal Combinations', *Z. Metallk.*, **70**, (1), 14-20 (1979). 18

Miller, C., 'Soldering with Light', *Photonics Spectra,* **17**, (5), 83, 84, 86 (1983). 378

Missel, L., 'Shelf Life Improvement of Electroplated Solder', *Metal Finish.*, **68**, (6), 85-89 (1970). 183

Mitchell, J. P., Welsher, T. L., 'Conductive Anodic Filament Growth in Printed Circuit Materials', Proc. Printed Circuit World Conv. II, Munich, Part I, 80-93 (1981). 141

Miura, N., Fuura, Y., Kazami, A., 'High Power Hybrid IC on Insulated Metal Substrates', Proc. of 1st Conf. on Solid State Devices, Tokyo (1969) (suppl. to *J. Jap. Soc. Appl. Phys.*, **39**, 211-217 (1970)). 263

Mohler, J. B., 'Soldering Properties of Metal Surfaces', *Plant Eng.*, (14 Oct) 136-137; (28 Oct) 109-110; (11 Nov) 153-154 (1976). 175

van der Molen, T., 'Water Soluble Fluxes vs. Rosin Fluxes for Soft Soldering of Electronic Devices', *Insulation/Circuits*, **23**, (5), 32-38 (1977). 158

Molenaar, A., Coumans, J. J. C., 'Autocatalytic Tin Deposition', *Surface Technol.*, **16**, (3), 265-275 (1982). 178

Mollendorf, J. C., 'The Applicability of Approximate and Exact Transient Heat Transfer Analyses to Heating Processes Used to Solder Multilayer Circuit Boards', *IEEE Trans.*, Vol. PHP-11, (2), 96-104 (1975). 53

Moore, J., 'A Solder Reflow Review', *Insulation/Circuits*, **24**, (3), 49-52 (1978). 187

Mulholland, W. A., Willyard, D. L., 'Soldering to Thin Film Hybrid Microcircuits', *Welding J. Res. Suppl.*, **53**, (10), 466S-474S (1975). 115

Munford, J. W., 'The Influence of Several Design and Material Variables on the Propensity for Solder Joint Cracking', *IEEE Trans.*, Vol. PHP-11, (4), 296-304 (1975). 307

Murr, L. E., 'Interfacial Phenomena in Metals and Alloys', Addison-Wesley, New York (1975). 14

Naguib, H. M., MacLaurin, B. K., 'Silver Migration and the Reliability of Pd/Ag Conductors in Thick-Film Dielectric Crossover Structures', *IEEE Trans.*, Vol. CHMT-2, (2), 196-207 (1979). 142

Nakajima, M., 'SOLBOT Automated Equipment Overcomes PC Board Soldering Problems', *J. Electr. Engng.*, **16**, (Sept) 41-43 (1979). 330

Nelson, G. C., Borders, J. A., 'Surface Composition of a Tin-Lead Alloy', *J. Vac. Sci. Technol.*, **20**, (4), 939-942 (1982). 145

Nesse, T., 'Die Zeitstandfestigkeit von Weichlötverbindungen bei Verwendung von Sonderweichloten', *Feinwerktechnik u Micronic*, **76**, (3), 134-138 (1973). 123

Nicotera, E. T., 'Gold Plating: Evaluation of the Alternatives', *Electr. Pack. & Prod.*, **14**, (12), 31-39 (1974). 193

446   Cited Authors

ahn, A., Down, W. H., 'Protecting the Solderability of DIP Leads', *Circuits Manuf.* **23**, (3), 68-71 (1983). 185

athore, H. S., Yih, R. C., Edenfeld, A. R., 'Fatigue Behavior of Solders Used in Flip-Chip Technology', *J. Testing & Eval.*, **1**, (2), 170-178 (1973). 122

ayleigh, Lord, 'Intensity of Light Reflected From Water and Mercury', Collected Scientific Papers IV, 13-14 (1892-1901). 21

efaie, Mah El, 'Chip-Package Substrate Cushions Dense High-Speed Circuitries', *Electronics*, **55**, (14 July) 135-141 (1982). 277

eichenecker, W. J., 'Thermal Expansion of the Copper-Tin Intermetallic Compound Cu_6Sn_5 in the Temperature Range $-180°C$ to $+200°C$', *Insulation/Circuits*, **27**, (11), 109-111 (1981);
'Thermal Expansion of the Copper-Tin Intermetallic Compound Cu_3Sn in the Temperature Range $-195°C$ to $+300°C$', *Welding J. Res. Suppl.*, **60**, (10), 109S-111S (1981);
'Copper-Tin Intermetallic Compound Cu_6Sn_5. Electrical Conductivity in the Temperature Range $-195°C$ to $+150°C$', *Tin & Its Uses*, No. 130, 14-16 (1981);
'Electrical Conductivity of Copper-Tin Intermetallic Compound Cu_3Sn in the Temperature Range $-195°C$ to $+150°C$', *Welding J. Res. Suppl.*, **59**, (10), 308S-310S (1980). 105

esendes, J., 'Production Techniques with S.O. Packages', *Electr. Pack. & Prod.*, **22**, (3), 115-117, 121-122, 124-125, 128 (1982). 276

ickabaugh, L. J., 'An Ionic Contamination Detection System (ICDS) with Improved Performance for Quantizing Residual Ionic Species', *IEEE Trans.*, Vol. CMHT-2, (1), 134-139 (1979). 167

iedel, W., 'Über die Struktur und die Eigenschaften Elektrolytisch Abgeschiedener Zinn-Blei-Legierungen', *Metalloberfläche*, **23**, (2), 42-44 (1969). 178

oberts, D. F. T., 'A Mechanism of Solder Dewetting', Proc. Internepcon, Brighton, 50-54 (1978); 185
'The Globule Test – is it Reliable', *Brazing and Soldering,* **4**, 28-30 (1983). 221

othschild, B. F., 'Electroplating of Solderable Coatings', *Metal Finish.*, **78**, (5), 35-41 (1980); also, (short version): *Metal Progress*, **119**, (7), 25-29 (1981). 177, 194

ossi, F. L., Vernier, T. E., Val, C. M., 'Capabilities and Limits of Ceramic Chip Carrier Computer Model for Thermal and Mechanical Behaviour', Proc. ISHM, Los Angeles, 267-275 (1979). 276

ubin, W., 'Xersin Flux', *Electronic Prod.*, **8**, (6), 43-52 (1979);
'A New Flux for Electronics Soldering', *Insulation/Circuits*, **26**, (1), 27-28 (1980);
'Some Recent Advances in Flux Technology', *Brazing & Soldering*, **2**, 24-28 (1982); also *Welding J.,* **61**, (10), 39-44 (1982); 154
'Environmental Effects of Fumes Created during Soldering', *Brazing and Soldering,* **3**, 22-23 (1982). 168

ubin, W., Allen, B. M., 'The Chemistry and Behaviour of Fluxes', *Trans. Inst. Metal Finish.*, PC Suppl., **50**, 133-137 (1972). 146

ubin, W., Lovering, D. G., 'The Application of Thermal Analysis in Solder Flux Studies', *Brazing & Soldering*, **1**, 27-28, 32 (1981); also *Electr. Pack. & Prod.*, **22**, (3), 133-136 (1982); 134
'Fluxes', Chapter 8 (pp. 185-222) of: 'Molten Salt Technology', (Lovering, D. G., Editor) Plenum, New York (1982). 169

uhl, R. H., Netz, D., Heckman, R., 'Reducing Solder Shorts in Wave Soldering', *Electronic Prod.*, **6**, (3), 8, 10, 13 (1977). 298

ydwansky, F. C., 'Chips, DIPs and PWBs', *Circuits Manuf.*, **21**, (9), 54-58, 60, 62 (1981). 275

abo, J. G., 'Detection of Anions With Silver Chromate-Impregnated Paper', *Chemist-Analyst*, **54**, 110 (1965). 137

t. Louis, J., Thumm, M., Ribot, P., Gale, G. N., 'Low Cost Chip Carriers for the 1980s', *IEEE Trans.* Vol. CMHT-4, (2), 205-209 (1981). 277

aperstein, Z. P., Howes, M. H., 'Mechanical Properties of Soldered Joints in Copper Alloys', *Welding J. Res. Suppl.*, **48**, (8), 317S-327S (1969). 93, 119

ax, N. I., 'Dangerous Properties of Industrial Materials', Reinhold, New York (1968). 168

cagnelli, H. J., D'Erchia, F. J., Wittenberg, A. M., 'Forced Hot Air Fusing of Solder Plated Circuits', *Welding J.*, **54**, (10), 718-724 (1975). 384

carlett, J. A. 'Unsoldering PCBs Without Damage', *Electronics & Power*, **26**, (9), 715-718 (1980).
'Printed Circuit Boards for Microelectronics' 2nd Edn, Electrochemical Publications, Ayr (1980). 294

charf, W. D., 'Installing an Aqueous Cleaner, a User's View of the Shake-Down Process', *Circuits Manuf.*, **21**, (11), 26, 28, 30, 32, 34 (1981). 165

Schmitt-Thomas, K. G., Hager, H., 'Schadenmechanismen an Weichlötverbindungen unter Thermischen Wechselbeanspruchungen', *Schweissen u Schneiden*, **29**, (12), 487-490 (1977). 16

Schmitt-Thomas, K. G., Hammer, M., 'Bildung Intermetallischer Phasen bei Weichlötverbindungen und ihre Bedeutung für das Bruchverhalten', *Schweissen u Schneiden*, **29**, (7), 258-262 (1977). 9

Schmitt-Thomas, K. G., Maier, W., 'Investigation of Soft-Soldered Joints by Aid of Acoustic Emission Analysis', Paper 23, BABS Conference, London (1979). 46

Schmitt-Thomas, K. G., Zahel, H. M., 'Untersuchungsverfahren zur Erfassung der Wirkung von Verunreinigingen in Weichlotbädern' *Metall*, **37**, (1), 43-49 (1983) 16

Schneider, A. F., 'Flux Choices for Soldering Printed Wiring Assemblies', *Electr. Pack. & Prod.*, **20**, (7), 89-108 (1980). 31

Schoenthaler, D., 'Solder Fusing With Forced Convection Liquid Heating', *Western Electric Eng.*, **19**, (2), 11-23 (1975);
'Solder Fusing With Heated Liquids', *Welding J. Res. Suppl.*, **53**, (11), 498S-509S (1974); 38
'Solder Coating Thickness Considerations for Hot Gas Solder Levelling', *Insulation/ Circuits*, **24**, (12), 39-43 (1978); 18
'Reflow Soldering With Radiant Heating', Paper 5/2 Symp. Record; Int. Electr. Circuit Pack. Symp., Aug. (1969). 37
'Soldering Surface Mounted Chip Carriers to Printed Circuits', *Western Electric Eng.* **27**, (1), 73-79 (1983). 27

Schouten, G., 'A Figure of Merit for Solderability', *Philips Telecom. Rev.*, **38**, (3), 131-138 (1980). 21

Schuessler, P., 'Water-Soluble Flux Technology', *Insulation/Circuits*, **27**, (13), 88-91 (1981). 16

Schuster, J. L., Chilko, R. J., 'Ultrasonic Soldering of Aluminium Heat Exchangers', *Welding J.*, **57**, (10), 711-717 (1975). 4

Schwaneke, A. E., Lee, A. Y., Falke, W. L., 'Interfacial Compositions of Solders and Fluxes on Aluminium', *Welding J. Res. Suppl.*, **53**, (10), 446S-453S (1974). 17

Schwaneke, A. E., Falke, W. L., Miller, V. R., 'Surface Tension and Density of Liquid Tin-Lead Alloys', *J. Chem. Eng. Data*, **23**, (4), 298-301 (1978). 10

Scriven, L. E., Sternling, C. V., 'The Marangoni Effect', *Nature*, **187**, (16 July) 186-188 (1960). 20, 3

Sharples, P., 'An Independent Investigation Into the Reduction of Wear of Soldering Bits', *Ind. Electronics*, 30-34, Oct. (1962). 39

Shawki, G. S. A., El-Sabbagh, A. A. S., 'Shear Strength of Brazed and Soldered Joints', *Welding J. Res. Suppl.*, **54**, (8), 276S-279S (1975). 11

Shelepaev, A. G., 'Variation in the Electrical Resistance of Soldered Joints', *Measurement Techniques (Izmeritel'naya Technika)*, **18**, (7), 1068-1069 (1975). 10

Shipley, J. F., 'Influence of Flux, Substrate and Solder Composition on Solder Wetting', *Welding J. Res. Suppl.*, **54**, (10), 357S-362S (1975). 13

Shoji, Y., Uchida, S., Ariga, T., 'Dissolution of Solid Copper into Molten Tin-Lead Alloys Under Static Conditions', *Trans. Japan Inst. Metals*, **21**, (12), 819-823 (1980); 98, 11
'Dissolution of Solid Copper Cylinder in Molten Tin-Lead Alloys under Dynamic Conditions', *Metall. Trans. B.*, **13**B, (Sept), 439-445 (1982). 10

Sidhu, A., 'Lot- und Flussmittelauswahl Unter dem Gesichtspunkt der Geringsten Arbeitsplatzbelastung', Proc. Int. Conf. on Soft-Soldering and Welding in Electronics and Precision Mechanics, Munich (1981); *DVS Berichte* **71**, 134-137 (1981). 8

Siedle, A. R., Velapoldi, R. A., Erickson, N., 'The Reaction of Copper Metal with Benzotriazole', *Surface Science*, **3**, 229-235 (1979). 19

Skoog, D. A., West, D. M., 'Principles of Instrumental Analysis', 2nd Edn, Holt, Rinehart and Winson, City (1980). 12

Slattery, J. A., White, C. E. T., 'A Primer on the Use of Solder Creams in Hybrid Assembly', *Electr. Pack. & Prod.*, **21**, (10), 146-156 (1981). 36

Smithells, C. J., 'Metals Reference Book', 5th Edn, Butterworths, London (1976). 88, 101, 103, 107, 12

Southwell, R. V., 'An Introduction to the Theory of Elasticity', Dover, New York (1961), (Oxford Univ. Press 1941). 27

Spector, M., 'Porcelain Coated Steel Substrates for High Density Component Interconnection', *Insulation/Circuits*, **25** (1), 15-17 (1979). 26

Spergel, J., 'Tin Transformation of Tinned Copper Wire', *ASTM Spec. Tech. Publ.*, No. 319, 83-92 (1962). 9

Spigarelli, D. J., 'Vapor Phase Fusion Eliminates Fluxing and Post-Cleaning of Printed Wiring Boards', Proc. Internepcon, Brighton, 58-60 (1980). 34, 18

'Design and Process Considerations for Soldering Surface Mounted Components', El. Comp. Conf., San Diego (1982) — 390

Sprengling, G. R., 'Chemical Stripping of Coils' (Part 1), *Insulation/Circuits*, **26**, (2), 25-28 (1980). — 117

Stafford, J. W., 'Chip Carriers—Their Application and Future Direction', *Electr. Pack. & Prod.*, **20**, (7), 135-136, 138-141 (1980); also, *IEEE Trans.*, Vol. CHMT-4, (2), 195-199 (1981). — 276

Stayner, R. A., 'Soldering With Oil', *Electr. Pack. & Prod.*, **14**, (3), 103-106 (1974). — 319, 339

Steen, H., 'Dendritic Patterns on Soldered Joints on Printed Circuit Boards', Proc. Conf. on Soft Soldering and Welding in Electronics and Precision Mechanics, Munich (1981); *DVS Berichte*, **71**, 5-10 (1981). — 404

Stone, K. R., Duckett, R., Muckett, S., Warwick, M., 'Mechanical Properties of Solders and Soldered Joints', *Brazing & Soldering*, (4), 20-27 (1983). — 120

Stoneman, A. M., MacKay, C. A., Thwaites, C. J., Mackowiak, J., 'Oxidation of Molten Solder Alloys Under Simulated Wave-Soldering Conditions', *Metals Technol.*, **5**, (4), 126-132 (1978). — 111

Strauss, R., 'Machine Soldering: The State of the Art as Presented at Productronica 81', *Brazing & Soldering*, **2**, 38-41 (1982). — 340, 349

Studnick, W. R., Foune, C. C., 'Testing for Corrosivity in Activated Liquid Soldering Fluxes', *Western Electric Eng.*, **17**, (1), 3-8 (1973);
'Do Residues From Today's Fluxes Corrode Copper on PW Boards?', *Circuit Manuf.*, **13**, (4), 34-38 (1973). — 136

Swanson, P. W., 'Soldering Sensitive Components', *Electronic Prod.*, **9**, (4), 19, 21 (1980). — 397

Swartzell, J. C., 'Etching Parameters: Their Individual and Collective Impact on High Density Circuit Production', Proc. PC World Convention II, Munich, Part II, 16-22 (1981); also *Circuit World*, **8**, (1), 21-23 (1981). — 281

Sylvester, J. A., 'Hand or Manual Soldering', *Insulation/Circuits*, **21**, (11), 76-84 (1975). — 393

Tabelev, V. D., Rossoshinskii, A. A., Ivanova, L. R., 'The Connection Between Oxidation and Flow of POS-61 Solder', *Automatic Welding (Avt. Svarka)*, **34**, (5), 37-38 (1981). — 17

Takasago, H., Takada, M., Adachi, K., Onishi, Y., 'Reverse Mode Reflow Soldering Technique', Proc. Int. Microelectronics Conf., Tokyo 278-283 (1982). — 363

Takeno, S., 'Applications of Chip Coils Expanding', *J. Electr. Engng*, 19, (Jan), 86-88 (1982). — 274

Tamura, A., Tachibana, Y., Itakura, S., 'Some Considerations on Solder Flow-up into Plated-Through Holes', *Welding J. Res. Suppl.*, **52**, (10), 441S-445S (1973). — 82

Taylor, B. E., Slutsky, J., Larry, J. R., 'Technology of Electronic Grade Solder Pastes', *Solid State Technol.*, **24**, (9), 127-135 (1981). — 364

Tresh, H. R., Crawley, A. F., 'The Viscosities of Lead, Tin and Pb-Sn Alloys', *Metall. Trans.* **1**, 1531-1535 (1970). — 102

Thwaites, C. J., 'Towards Better Soldering via an Integrated Production Scheme', Publ. 549, Int. Tin Res. Inst.;
'The Philosophy of Quality Control in Soldering Operations', *Circuit World*, **1**, (3), 30-36 (1975); — 5
'Testing for Solderability', *British Weld. J.*, **12**, (11), 543-550 (1965); — 149
'Glycol as Solvents in Zinc Chloride Soldering Fluxes', *Sheet Metal Ind.*, **38**, 583-587, 594 (1961); — 159
'Practical Hot-Tinning', Publ. 575, Int. Tin Res. Inst.; — 185
'Some Experiments on the Hot-Tinning of Small Parts', *Metallurgia*, **64**, 117-124 (1961); — 186
'A New Solderability Test Apparatus', Publ. 344, Int. Tin Res. Inst.; — 228
'The Solderability of Some Tin, Tin Alloy and Other Metallic Coatings', Publ. 304, Int. Tin Res. Inst.; — 236
'Solderability and Some Factors Affecting It', *Brazing & Soldering*, **1**, 15-18 (1981); — 251
'The Attainment of Reliability in Modern Soldering Techniques for Electronic Assemblies', Rev. 166, *Int. Metall. Reviews*, 17, (Sept) 149-174 (1972). — 314

Thwaites, C. J., Hampshire, W. B., 'Mechanical Strength of Selected Soldered Joints and Bulk Solder Alloys', Publ. 524, Int. Tin Res. Inst. — 120

Thwaites, C. J., MacKay, C. A., 'Some Effects of Abrasive Cleaning on the Solderability of Printed Circuits', *Metal Finish. Journal*, (9), 291-294 (1968); also Publ. 386, Int. Tin Res. Inst. — 37, 183

Tissier, G., Le Gressus, C., Bouygues, J., 'Surface Phenomena in Electronics Interconnection Technology – A Review', *IEEE Trans.* Vol. CHMT-5, (2), 217-224 (1982). — 142

Tompkins, H. G., 'The Interaction of Some Atmospheric Gases With a Tin-Lead Alloy', *J. Electrochem. Soc.*, **120**, (5), 651-654 (1973). — 145

Tu, K. N., 'Interdiffusion and Reaction in Bimetallic Cu-Sn Thin Films', *Acta Metall.*, **21**, (4), 347-354 (1973). — 199

White, D. W. G., 'The Surface Tension of Liquid Metals and Alloys', *Metall. Rev.*, **13**, No. 124, 73-96 (1968).   14

Whitley, J. H., 'The Tin Commandments', *Plating & Surface Finish.*, **68**, (10), 38-39 (1981).   193

Wild, R. N., 'Effects of Gold on Solder Properties', Proc. Internepcon, Brighton, 27-32 (1968);   108
'Some Fatigue Properties of Solders and Solder Joints', Proc. Internepcon, Brighton (1975); also, *Welding J. Res. Suppl.*, **51**, (11), 521S-526S (1972);   122
'Properties of Some Low Melt Fusible Solder Alloys', Proc. Internepcon, Brighton, 81-91 (1971).   124

Williams, R., 'De-Wetting of Fused Tin/Lead Plated Printed Wiring Boards', *Circuit World*, **1**, (1), 37-39 (1974).   37, 155

Williams, W. L., 'Gray Tin Formation in Soldered Joints Stored at Low Temperatures', *ASTM Spec. Tech. Publ.*, No. 189, 149-158 (1956).   93

Wolf, H. J., 'Induktives Weichlöten von Leiterplatten', *ZIS Mitt.*, 413-418 April (1973).   383

Wolters, J., 'Zur Geschichte der Löttechnik', Spec. Publ., Degussa (1975).   83

Woodgate, R., 'The Use of Resistivity Meters in PC Cleaning Systems', *Electr. Pack. & Prod.*, **20**, (10), 191-192, 194 (1980);   165
'Considerations in High-Speed Component Lead Cutting', *Electr. Pack. & Prod.*, **20**, (7), 63-64, 66-67 (1980);   346
'Solder Joint: Quality or Not?' *Circuits Manuf.*, **21**, (11), 22, 24 (1981).   418
Computer-Controlled Soldering is a Fiction', *Circuits Manuf.*, **22**, (6), 26, 28, 30 (1982).
'Computer Controlled Soldering – Fact or Fiction', Proc. Internepcon, Brighton, 219-221 (1982).   351

Yost, F. G., 'Soldering to Gold Films', *Gold Bull.*, **10**, 94-100 (1977).   115

Young, T., 'An Essay on the Cohesion of Fluids', *Trans. Roy. Soc. (Philosophical)*, **95**, 65-87 (1805).   16

Zado, F. M., 'Effects of NonIonic Water Soluble Flux Residues', *Western Electric Eng.*, **27**, (1), 41-48 (1983)   160
'Increasing the Soldering Efficiency of Noncorrosive Rosin Fluxes', *Western Electric Eng.*, **27**, (1), 22-29 (1983).   101
'The Theory and Practice of High Efficiency Soldering With Noncorrosive Rosin Soldering Fluxes', Proc. Printed Circuit World Conv. II, Munich, Part I, 154-161 (1981).   154, 335

Zakraysek, L., 'Whisker Growth From a Bright Acid Tin Electrodeposit', *Plating & Surface Finish.*, **64**, (3), 38-42 (1977).   199

Zimmerman, R. H., 'Measuring Plating Thickness', *Metal Finish.*, **59**, (5), 67-73 (1961).   186

Zürn, H., Nesse, T., 'Beitrag Zum Zeitstandverhalten von Lötverbindungen aus Zinn-Weichloten bei Raumtemperature', *Schweissen u Schneiden*, **18**, (1), 2-10 (1966);   120
'Die Metallurgischen Vorgänge Beim Weichlöten von Kupfer und Kupferlegierungen und das Festigkeitsverhalten der Lötverbindungen', *Metall*, **20**, (11), 1144-1151 (1966).   93

Anonymous

References cited in this section are those where no specific author is credited with the contribution.
In the text they appear, for example, as [Anon. Ref.1].

pages

A.1   'Solderability Tester for PTH's Performs Solder Globule Test Automatically',
       Insulation/Circuits, **23,** (1), 17-18 (1977).   226

A.2   'Photographic Guide to Soldering Quality', Publ. 555, Int. Tin Res. Inst., (31 pages,
       20 photographs in colour).   402

A.3   'QS-Manual', Post Office Telecommunication, The Post Office, London (3 booklets)
       (1972).   402

A.4   Insulation/Circuits Forum: 'What Direction Will Wave Soldering Take in the 80's?',
       Insulation/Circuits, **26,** (2), 14 (1980).   333

A.5   'Copper-Tin Intermetallics', *Circuits Manuf.,* **20,** (9), 60-62, 64 (1980).   401

A.6   'Yag-laser Inspection of Solder Joints Would Speed Processing of PC Boards', *Laser
       Focus,* **16,** (6), 42 (1980).   401

A.7   'Laser/Thermal Technique Speeds Solder Joint Inspection', *Electr. Pack. and Prod.,*
       21, (10), 16, 18 (1981).   401

A.8   'Flux Effects Test Pin Contacts', *Electronic Prod.,* **8,** (4), 29 (1979).   157

A.9   'The Manual Soldering of High-Reliability Electrical Connections', Europ. Space
       Res. Centre, Noordwijk, the Netherlands, ESRO PSS-14/QRM-O8P Issue, No. 1
       (Estec);
       'Requirements for Soldered Electrical Connections', NASA R and QA Manual NHB
       5300.4 (3A-1) (1976);
       'How to Make Soldered Connections to Terminals', *Insulation/Circuits,* **26,** (3),
       69-74; (6), 33-38 (1980).   397

A.10   'High Reliability Soldering Training Manual', General Electric Space Division, Valley
       Forge Space Techn. Center, P.O. Box 855, Philadelphia, Pennsylvania, USA.   396

A.11   'Film and Trainee Handbook: Basic Soldering for Electronics', Pace Inc., 9329 Fraser
       Street, Silver Spring, Maryland 20910, USA.   397

A.12   'Development of Highly Reliable Soldered Joints for Printed Boards', (final report)
       pp. 400 (1968), Westinghouse Defense and Space Center, Aerospace Div., Baltimore,
       Maryland, USA.   303, 307, 402

A.13   Series on: 'Soldering of Aluminium', *Welding J.,* **51,** (1972) starting p. 571, and **52,**
       (1973).   176

A.14   'Preventing PCB Dewetting', *Circuits Manuf.,* **16,** (5), 46-50 (1976).   37, 185

A.15   'Eliminating Smoke Problems During Wave Soldering', *Insulation/Circuits,* **25,** (5),
       25-26 (1979).   320

A.16   Selective Plating, Especially on Lead Frames, Spec. Issue of *The Western Electric
       Eng.,* **22,** (2), (1978).   178

A.17   'Neue Möglichkeiten Beim Feuerverzinnen, Feuerverbleien, Feuerkadmieren und
       Anderem von Massenteilen', *Metall,* **21,** (8), 822-825 (1967).   186

A.18   'Guide to Wave Soldering Equipment', *Insulation/Circuits,* **23,** (2), 38-46 (1977). 349

A.19   'Modification and Repair for Printed Boards and Assemblies', IPC-R-700 B (1977).   399

A.20   'Acoustical Microscopy, Non-Destructive Analysis of Internal Microstructure',
       Circuits Manuf., **19,** (6), 36-42 (1979).   401

A.21   Film: 'The Right Connection: Towards Better Soldering', (a 23 minute colour film
       with sound), Int. Tin. Res. Inst.   5

A.22   'Solderability Evaluation of Thick and Thin Fused Coatings', IPC-TR-461 (1979).   108

A.23   'New Punch Technology Greatly Increases Soldering Reliability', *J. Electr. Eng.,* **11,**
       (Oct), 61-62 (1974).   284

A.24   'Philips Group Opens Push to Surface Mount Technology – Dedicates New SMD
       Center', *Electr. Pack. & Prod.,* **22,** (3), 15-16 (1982).   279

A.25   'One-shot Temperature Indicators', *Assembly Eng.,* **22,** (12), 14-15 (1979).   327

A.26   'Guidelines for Printed Board Component Mounting', IPC-CM-770 B (1980).   263, 272

A.27   'Metallography of Tin and Tin Alloys', Publ. No. 580, Int. Tin. Res. Inst.   90

A.28   Several Feature Articles on 'Chip-type Components' of various Authors in *J. Electr.
       Engng.,* **20,** (Jan), 30-58 (1983).   274

A.29   (Proposal) 'Guidelines for Surface Mounting and Interconnecting Chip Carriers',
       IPC-CM-78 (1983).   423

Specifications

pecifications cited in the text appear, for example, as [Spec.Ref. 1].

.1 'Basic Environment Testing Procedures for Electronic Components and Electronic Equipment', Test T – Soldering, Publication 68-2-20, IEC (1979).
8, 154, 155, 219, 222, 228, 232, 239, 243, 248, 250, 252, 259

.2 'Recommended Methods of Test for Volume and Surface Resistivity of Electrical Insulating Materials', Publication 93, IEC (1958). 139

.3 'General Requirements and Measuring Methods for Printed Wiring Boards', Publication 326, IEC (1970). 294

.4 Printed Boards, Part 2: 'Test Methods', Publication 326-2, IEC (1976).

.4a First Supplement to Publ. 326-2 (1976), Publication 326-2A, IEC (1980). 243, 248

.5 'Basic Environmental Testing Procedures for Electronic Components and Electronic Equipment', Test Ca; Damp heat steady state, Publication 68-2-3, IEC (1969). 139, 248

.6 'Insulation Co-ordination within Low-Voltage Systems Including Clearances and Creepage Distances for Equipment', Publication 664, IEC (1980). 293

.7 'Terms and Definitions for Printed Circuits', Publication 194, IEC (1975);
'Terms and Definitions, Standard Specification ANSI/IPC-T-50B (1980). 264

.8 'Solderability Test Methods for Printed Wiring Boards', Standard Specification (Interim Final) IPC-S-804, Nov. (1981). 228, 232, 238

.9 'General Requirements for Soldering Electronic Interconnections', Standard Specification ANSI/IPC-S-815A (1980). 140, 165, 317, 396, 419

.10 'Printed Wiring Assemblies', MIL-Spec, MIL-P-28809A (1981). 164

.11 'Flux, Soldering, Liquid (Rosin Base)', Military Spec. MIL-F-14256D (1975). 137, 138

.12 'Test Methods for Electronic and Electrical Component Parts', Method 208C, Solderability, Military Standard MIL-STD-202E (1975). 238, 254

.13 'Solderability Test Standard', ANSI/EIA-RS-178B (1973). 254

.14 'Storage of Printed Boards', IVF – Resultat (Sweden) 76635 (1976). 195

.15 'Sampling Procedures and Tables for Inspection by Attributes', ISO 2859 (1974);
'Sampling Plans and Procedures for Inspection by Attributes', Publication 410, IEC (1973); (see also national standards: MIL-STD 105D; NF X06-022; DIN 40080; BS 6001; NEN 10410; etc.) 405

.16 'Meniscograph Solderability', Method 2022, MIL-STD-883B (1977). 259

.17 'Solder, Tin Alloy: Tin-Lead Alloy; and Lead Alloy', Federal Specification QQ-S-571E (1972). 151

.18 'Alliages et Flux Utilisés Pour l'Exécution de Brasages Tendres', Norme Française NF C90-550 (1977). 139, 145, 235

.19 'Specification for Electroplated Coatings of Tin/Lead Plating', British Standards Inst., BS 6137 (1982); also: 'Zinnüberzüge auf Eisen- und Kupferwerkstoffen', Deutsche Norm DIN 50965 (1982). 178

.20 'Soft Soldered Joints-Determination of Shear Strength', ISO Int. Stand. 3683 (1978). 119

.21 'Various Standards for Solder Alloys', taken up in Table 4.1. 85

.22 'Various Standards for Alloys and Fluxes', taken up in Table 5.11. 170

.23 'Various Standards for Test Methods for Solderability', taken up in Table 7.8. 260

.24 'Specification for Custom-built integrated circuits of assessed quality: Generic data and methods of tests', British Standards Inst. BS 9450 (1975) and amendments No. 1 (1970) and No. 2 (1980). 423

Abbreviations used

NSI	American National Standards Institute
STM	American Society for Testing of Materials
IN	Deutsches Institut für Normung
IA	Engineering Department Electronic Industries Association
C	International Electrotechnical Commission
C	Institute for Interconnecting and Packaging Electronic Circuits
O	International Organisation for Standardisation
F	Institutet för Verkstadsteknisk Forskning

BIBLIOGRAPHY OF BOOKS ON SOFT SOLDERING (1760-1983)

Compiled by B. M. Allen

This bibliography has been arranged in chronological order of the earlies edition, subsequent editions being shown, with details of any change in title or authorship, under the dates of the first.

The bibliography has been compiled from the catalogues of The Britisl Museum; Patent Office, London; Metals Society, London; Science Museum South Kensington, London; British Non-Ferrous Metals Technology Centre Wantage, Oxon.; International Tin Research Institute, Greenford, Middlesex Lead Development Association, London; Deutsches Museum, Munich Humboldt University, Berlin; Deutsche Staatsbibliothek, Berlin. The assistance of the staff of these libraries, and of Dr Maronna of Humboldt University ir searching the two Berlin based establishments is gratefully acknowledged.

Note:
The decision as to whether a work should be included in this list was necessarily somewha arbitrary. The criteria used were that the work should exist as a separate volume however short, that i must contain a substantial section on soldering *per se* rather than a short passage incidental to some other subject, that it is not a reprint from a periodical, and that, if published by a solde manufacturer, it should be more than merely a catalogue. Books specifically on soldering history or aluminium soldering are listed separately. Unpublished theses are excluded.

1760   KLEIN, Johann Georg Friedrich, 'Ausführliche Beschreibung . . . der Metalllothe und Löthungen', p. 200; 2 plates, Berlin, Verlag des Buchladens der Realschule.

1844   THON, Christian Friedrich Gottlieb, 'Die Löth-Kunst', p. xvi + 78; 5 plates, Neue Schauplatz der Künste und Handwerke, No. 137, Weimar, B. Fr. Voigt,
        1858   2nd Edn, p. xvi + 83; 5 plates.
        1863   'Legir- und Löthkunst', 3rd Edn, p. x + 107; 55 figures in 6 plates.
        1871   4th Edn, p. 172; 60 figures.
        1880   WILDBERGER, Andr., 'Die Legir- und Löthkunst', 5th Edn, p. xii + 216; 61 figures in 4 plates.
        1895   WÜST, Fritz, 'Legir- und Löthkunst', 6th Edn, p. viii + 106; 33 figures.
        1908   7th Edn, p. viii + 183; 50 figures, Leipzig, B. F. Voigt.
        1923   8th Edn, p. 100.

1880   SCHLOSSER, Edmund, 'Das Löthen und die Bearbeitung der Metalle', p. xvi + 232; 2' figures, A. Hartlebens chemische-technische Bibliothek No. 73, Wien, Pest, Leipzig,
        1891   2nd Edn, p. viii + 246; 25 figures.
        1905   3rd Edn, p. viii + 229; 35 figures.
        1916   'Das Löten und Schweißen', 4th Edn, p. viii + 260; 65 figures.

1880   Wildberger, see under 1844 THON

1893   EDWINSON, George, 'Metal Working for Amateurs Part I: Brazing and Soldering', p. viii + 56; 54 figures, London, Warlock and Bowden.

1894   PROBERT, W., 'The Art of Soldering', p. 30, Birmingham, W. B. Hill & Co.

1895   Wüst, see under 1844 THON

1900   BOLAS, Thomas, 'Soldering, Brazing and the Joining of Metals', Useful Arts and Handicrafts, Ed. H. Snowden-Ward, Book 19 (Vol. 2), p. 24; 11 figures, London, Dawbarn and Ward,
     1910   BOLAS, Bernard D., 4th Edn.
     1940   GENTRY, George, Revised and enlarged Edn, p. 84, London, Percival Marshall.

1904   HASLUCK, Paul Nooncree, 'Soldering, Brazing and Riveting', 9th Ch. of 'Metalworking, a Book of Tools, Materials and Processes for the Handyman', p. 38; 61 figures, London, Cassell.

1910   Bolas, B. D., see under 1900 BOLAS

1910   THATCHER, Edward, 'Simple Soldering both Hard and Soft', p. 76, New York, Spon and Chamberlain, London, E. & F. N. Spon.

1911   SEIFERT, Paul, 'Schweißen und Löten', p. iv + 282, 'Bibliothek der gesamten Technik', No. 154,
     1920   2nd Edn, p. 208; 158 figures, 'Bibliothek der gesamten Technik'. No. 263.

1912   HOBART, James Francis, 'Soft Soldering, Hard Soldering and Brazing', p. xiii + 190; New York, Van Nostrand,
     1919   2nd Edn, p. xiii + 190; 62 figures.

1916   JONES, Bernard Edward, 'Soldering, Brazing and Welding', p. iv + 156; 78 figures, 'Work' Handbooks, London, Cassell, reprinted 1917, 1918, 1919, 1920, 1921.

1920   YATES, Raymond Francis, 'Home Soldering and Brazing', p. 122, London, Henry Frowde and Hodder & Stoughton.

1920   WERNER, Eugen, 'Das Löten', p. iv + 51; 33 figures, Lübeck, Ch. Coleman.

1927   BURSTYN, Walther,
     1940   2nd Edn.
     1944   'Das Löten', 3rd Edn, p. 48; 74 figures, Werkstattbücher, No. 28, Berlin, Springer-Verlag.
     1954   von LINDE, R., 4th Edn, p. 68; 50 figures, Berlin, Göttingen, Heidelberg, Springer-Verlag.

1927   CLAUS, Willi and LÜDER, Erich, 'Löten und Lote', p. 36; 16 figures, AWF 207, Berlin, AWF,
     1936   LÜDER, Erich, 2nd Edn, p. 66; 33 figures.

1929   NIGHTINGALE, S. J., 'Soft Solders and Soldered Joints', p. 98; 44 figures, Birmingham, British Non-Ferrous Metals Research Association (privately circulated),
     1932   'Tin Solders', first published edition.
     1942   NIGHTINGALE, S. J. and HUDSON, O. F., 2nd Edn, p. xii + 105; 53 figures, London, British Non-Ferrous Metals Research Association.

1934   FRANKLIN, Eric, 'Soldering, Brazing and Welding', 'Work' Handbooks, London, Cassell (see also under 1916 JONES),
     1954   2nd Edn, p. 168.

1936   Lüder, see under 1927 CLAUS and LÜDER.

1937   HEYNEMANN, J., 'Lötmittel und Löten', p. iv + 47; 23 figures, Leipzig, Dr Max Jänecke Verlagsbuchhandlung.

1940   Gentry, see under 1900 BOLAS.

1942   Hudson, see under 1929 NIGHTINGALE.

1943 TAYLOR, Louie S., 'Successful Soldering', p. xii + 76; 2 figures, 24 plates, New York, McGraw-Hill.

1948 McKEOWN, J., 'The Properties of Soft Solders and Soldered Joints', p. xx + 118; 56 figures, London, British Non-Ferrous Metal Research Association.

1948 LEWIS, W. R., 'Notes on Soldering', London, Tin Research Institute,
1959   2nd English Edn, p. 100; 47 figures.
1959   'Notes sur les soudures d'étain', p. 107, Brussels, Centre d'Information de l'Etain.
1961   'Soldeo blando', p. 112, London, Tin Research Institute.
1963   'Weichlöt-Handbuch', p. 110, Düsseldorf, Zinn-Informations Büro.

1949 YERKOW, C., 'Fundamentals of Soft Soldering', p. 96, Peoria Ill, Manual Arts Press.

1950 MEBS, R. W. and ROESER, Wm. F., 'Solders and Soldering', p. 12; 10 figures, National Bureau of Standards, Washington, DC.

1952 KHRENOV, K. K., 'Svarka, rezka i paika metallov', Moscow, Mashgiz,
1958   CHRENOV, K. K., 'Schweißen, Schneiden und Löten von Metallen', p. 440, Halle/Sa., Marhold Verlag.

1952 LÜDER, Erich, 'Handbuch der Löttechnik', p. 440; 457 figures, Berlin, Verlag Technik.

1952 Anon., 'The Welding, Brazing and Soldering of Copper and its Alloys', London, CDA No. 147,
1958   6th revised imp., p. 193; 81 figures.

1953 THEWS, Edmund Richard, 'Metallurgie, Technologie und Anwendung der Weichlote', p. 240; 58 figures, Berlin-Grünewald, Metall-Verlag.

1954 von Linde, see under 1927 BURSTYN.

1954 BARBER, Clifford L., 'Solder, its Fundamentals and Usage', Kester Solder Co.,
1961   2nd Edn, p. v + 86; 28 figures.
1965   3rd Edn, p. v + 85; 28 figures.

1955 TURPIN, A. R., 'Soldering and Brazing', Hemel Hempstead, Model and Allied Publications,
1963   revised Edn, p. 88; 30 figures, reprinted 1967, 1970.

1956 Various authors, 'Symposium on Solder', p. v + 190, Philadelphia, ASM STP 189.

1958 KRIST, T., 'Schweissen-Schneiden-Löten-Tabellen der Praxis', p. 613; 1500 figures, Darmstadt, Technik-Tabellen-Verlag.

1958 Chrenov, see under 1952 KHRENOV.

1959 LASHKO, Nikolai Fedorovich and LASHKO-AVAKYAN, Sof'ya Vasil'evna, 'Paika metallov', Moscow, Mashgiz,
1961   WALD, Adolf (translator), 'Brazing and Soldering of Metals', p. vi + 410; 159 figures, Jerusalem, Israel Programme for Scientific Translations.
1977   LASHKO, N. F. and LASHKO, S. V., 'Paika metallov', 2nd Edn, p. 328; 54 figures, Moscow, Mashinostroenie.

1959 AWS Committee on Brazing and Soldering, 'Soldering Manual', p. ix + 170; 79 figures, New York, American Welding Society,
1978   2nd Edn, revised, p. ix + 149; 52 figures.

1961 Wald, see under 1959 LASHKO and LASHKO-AVAKYAN.

1962 SZÜCS, Tibor and TÓTH, Endre, 'Lágyforrasztás', p. v + 154; 48 figures, Budapest, KGM Müszaki Tájékoztató és Propaganda Intézet.

1962 RUŽA, Viliam, 'Spájkovanie kovov v priemysle', Bratislava, SVTL (in Slovak)
1978   KLUNA, Jindřich (translator), 'Pájení', p. 395; 269 figures, Prague, SNTL. (in Czech)

1963 LAKEDOMONSKY, A. V. and KHRYAPIN, V. E., 'Spravochnik payalshchika', Moscow, Mashgiz.

63   Various authors, 'Papers on Soldering – (1962)', p. v + 92,. Philadelphia, ASTM STP 319.

63   CHURCHILL, S. Collard, 'Soldering and Brazing Technology', Vol. 1: Soldering, p. 147; 66 figures, London, Machinery Publishing Co.

65   MANKO, Howard Herman, 'Solders and Soldering', p. xv + 323; 177 figures, New York, McGraw-Hill,
      1979   2nd Edn, p. xv + 350; 158 figures.

65   FÜLLENBACH, H., LANGE, H., PARTHEY, H., STRANSKI, J. N., 'Metallurgische und Technologische Untersuchungen an Weichloten', p. 67; 15 figures, Forschungsberichte des Landes NRW, Nr. 1421, Köln, Westdeutscher Verlag.

65   LANCASTER, J. F., 'Brazing, Soldering and Adhesive Jointing', Ch. V of 'The Metallurgy of Welding, Brazing and Soldering', London, George Allen and Unwin,
      1970   2nd Edn, p. 26; 9 figures.
      1981   3rd Edn.

66   LÜDER, Erich, 'Löten', p. 72; 63 figures, Munich, Carl Hauser Verlag.

67   LAUBMEYER, Günther and KUPKE, Wolfgang, 'Weichlöten in der Elektronik', p. 144; 80 figures, Berlin, Fachverlag Schiele and Schön.

67   National Aeronautics and Space Administration, 'Soldering Electrical Connections', A Handbook, p. v + 66; 72 figures, 4th Edn, of NSA SP 5002.

68   DEZETTEL, Louis M., 'ABC's of Electrical Soldering', Indianapolis, Howard W. Sams,
      1968   English Edn, Slough, W. Foulsham.
      1972   Revised English Edn, p. 128; 120 figures, Slough, W. Foulsham.

68   van der HOEK, F.,
      1972   'Soldering and Brazing', Ch. 3 of 'Philips Precision Engineering Handbooks' Ed. A. Davidson, No. 5 – Joining Techniques, p. 121; 49 figures, London, Macmillan.

69   ALLEN, Bernard Michael, 'Soldering Handbook', p. v + 120; 61 figures, London, Iliffe,
      1971   'Practical Soldering' (= Part 1 of 'Soldering Handbook'), p. 24; 28 figures, Hemel Hempstead, Multicore Solders Ltd.
      1973   SZABÓ Miklôs (translator), 'Forrasztási Zsebkönyv', p. 134, 61 figures, Budapest, Müszaki Könyvkiadó,
      1976   'Handajukeno Handobutsuku', p. 127; 61 figures, Osaka, Nihon Superior.

69   Anon., 'Löten von Kupfer und Kupferlegierungen', p. 111; 59 figures, Berlin, Deutsches Kupfer-Institut.

70   Educational Systems Ltd., 'Solders and Fluxes', p. 189, London, Newnes-Butterworth.

72   Various authors, 'Löten', p. 224; 109 figures, Grundlagen der Schweißtechnik No. 7, Berlin, VEB Verlag Technik.

73   Szabó, see under 1969 ALLEN.

73   Various authors, 'Praktisk Lödbarhetsprovning', p. 39, Stockholm, Sveriges Makanförbund.

73   MARTIN, Louis F., 'Fluxes, Solders and Welding Alloys', p. 280; 8 figures, Park Ridge, Noyes Data Corporation.

73   GRAM, Niels, 'Bogen om loddetin', p. 80; 29 figures, Glostrup, Paul Bergsøe & Søn A/S,
      1977   'The Bergsøe Solder Book', p. 45; 27 figures, Vojens, Paul Bergsøe & Søn A/S.

74   MÜLLER, B. F., 'Weichlöten', p. 39; 43 figures, 'Blaue Reihe' Vol. 127, Bern and Stuttgart, Verlag 'Technische Rundschau' im Hallwag Verlag.

74   TANAKA, W., 'Handazuke Gijutsu', p. 359; 162 figures, Tokyo, Sogu Denshi Syuppan sha.

75   THWAITES, Colin J. and BARRY, B. T. K., 'Soldering', p. 29; 35 figures, Engineering Design Guides No. 07, Oxford, University Press.

76   Anon., 'Solders and Soldering', p. 15; 11 figures, New York, Lead Industries Association.

1976   SCHMIDTKE, Hans, 'Löttechnik in der Elektrotechnik', p. 45; 69 figures, Fachschriftenverlag Aargauer Tagblatt AG, Aarau, Schweiz.

1976   Various authors, 'Löten und Schweißen in der Elektronik', p. 171, Düsseldorf, DVS Berichte Band 40.

1977   THWAITES, Colin J., 'Soft Soldering Handbook', p. 117; 80 figures, Greenford International Tin Research Institute.

1978   Klůna, see under 1962 RUŽA.

1978   ROSENTHAL, Murray P., 'Mini/Micro Soldering and Wire Wrapping', p. 112; 87 figures Rochelle Park, NJ, Hayden Book Co. Inc.

1978   STRAUSS, Rudolf, 'Das Löten für den Praktiker', p. 110; 66 figures, 'RPB-Electronic-Taschenbücher' No. 112, Munich, Franzis-Verlag.

1979   RADOMSKI, Tadeusz and CISZEWSKI, Andrzej, 'Lutowanie', p. 444; 228 figures, Warsaw, Wydawnictwa Naukowo-Techniczne.

1979   Various authors, Third International Brazing and Soldering Conference, Preprints, p. 449, London, BABS/Metals Society.

1981   LEONIDA, Giovanni, 'Handbook of Printed Circuit Design, Manufacture, Components and Assembly', p. 569; 393 figures, Ayr, Electrochemical Publications Ltd.

1981   OLESEN, S. T., 'Loddebarhed af Elektronikkomponenter', p. 80; 24 figures, ECR-113, Hørsholm, Elektronikcentralen.

1981   Various authors, 'Weichlöten und Schweissen in Elektronik und Feinwerktechnik, Soft Soldering and Brazing in Electronic and Precision Mechanics', p. 144, Düsseldorf, DVS-Berichte Band 71.

1982   THWAITES, C.J., 'Capillary Joining-Brazing and Soft Soldering', p. 211; 76 figures, John Wiley and Sons Limited.

1983   WOODGATE, R.W., 'Handbook of Machine Soldering', p. 224, 114 figures, John Wiley and Sons Limited

SOLDERING HISTORY

1936   MARYON, Herbert, 'Soldering and Welding in the Bronze and Early Iron Ages', p. 36; 11 figures, Cambridge, Mass., Fogg Art Museum.

1954   BAUERT-KEETMAN, Ingrid, 'Das Löten im Wandel der Jahrtausende', p. 32, Wuppertal, Wilhelm Paff.

1975   WOLTERS, Jochem, 'Zur Geschichte der Löttechnik', p. 79; 14 figures, Hanau, Degussa.

ALUMINIUM SOLDERING

1942   KAUFMANN, H., 'Praktische Anleitung für die Ausführung von Aluminium-Hart- und Weichlötungen', p. 62, Berlin-Südende, Klett.

1957   Anon., 'Soldering Aluminium', London, Aluminium Federation Bulletin 23,
1968   2nd Edn, p. 40; 16 figures.

1965   Anon., 'Soldering Alcoa Aluminium', p. 126; 41 figures, Pittsburgh, Aluminium Company of America.

1971   Various authors, 'Aluminium Soldering Handbook', p. 72; 58 figures, New York, Aluminium Association,
1976   2nd Edn.

1977   KLOCK, H. and SCHOER, H., 'Schweißen und Löten von Aluminiumwerkstoffen', p. vii + 168; 152 figures, 'Fachbuchreihe Schweißtechnik' No. 70, Düsseldorf, DVS.

SOLDERING TERMS

For definition of terms see also Spec. Ref. 7 and 8.

English	Dutch	French	German	Swedish
ctivated flux	geaktiveerd vloei-middel	flux activé	aktiviertes Fluss-mittel	aktiverat fluss
ctivity	aktiviteit	activité	Aktivität	aktivitet
geing	oudering	vieillissement	Alterung	åldring
lloy	legering	alliage	Legierung	legering
arrier layer	tussenlaag	barrière de diffusion	Sperrschicht	spärrskikt
ath	bad	bain	Bad	bad
oard	paneel, kaart	carte, panneau	Leiterplatte	mönsterkort
razing	hardsolderen	brasage fort	Hartlöten	hårdlödning
ridging	brugvorming	pontage	Brückenbildung	överbryggning
arrier	paneeldrager	support	Träger	lödfixtur
hip component	chip onderdeel	composant chipse	Chip-Bauelement	chip
leaning	wassen	nettoyage	Reinigung	tvättning
oating	bedekking	dépot revêtement	Überzug	skikt
old soldered joint	koude las	point de soudure froid	kalte Lötstelle	kallödning
olophony	kolofonium	colophane	Kolophonium	kolofonium
omponent	onderdeel	composant	Bauteil	komponent
onductor (track)	geleider (spoor)	conducteur (piste)	Leiterbahn	ledare
ontact angle	randhoek	angle de contact	Kontaktwinkel	vätvinkel
onveyor	transporteur	convoyeur	Transport Einrichtung	transportbana
ored wire (flux cored wire)	harskernsoldeer	fil à flux incorporé	Röhrenlöt	flussfyllt lod
rater (blowhole)	krater	cratère (= soufflure)	Ausbläser	krater
ut edge	snijrand	bord de coupe	Schnittkante	snittkant
e-soldering	de-solderen	dessoudage	Auslöten	avlödning
ewetting	ontvochtiging	retrait de mouillage	Entnetzung	vätningsåtergång
ip soldering	dompelsolderen	soudage au trempé	Tauchlöten	dopplödning
ipping speed limit	kritische dompelsnelheid	vitesse limite d'immersion	Grenztauchge-schwindigkeit	högsta väthastighet
issolution	oplossen	dissolution	Auflösung	upplösning
rag soldering	sleepsolderen	soudage à la traine	Schlepplöten	släplödning
ross formation	dros-vorming	formation de crasses	Krätzebildung	slaggbildning
well time	verblijftijd	durée d'immersion	Verweilzeit	dopptid
namel copper wire	lakdraad	fil de cuivre émaillé	Wickeldraht	lacktråd
dge connector	randconnector	connecteur encartable	Steckverbinder	anslutningsdon

459

English	Dutch	French	German	Swedish
epoxy glass fibre laminate	epoxy glas weefsel plaat	stratifié verre epoxy	Epoxydglashart-gewebe	epoxy glas lamin
fillet	kegel	filet	Lötkegel	lodfyllning
flux	vloeimiddel	flux	Flussmittel	fluss
flux cored wire	harskernsoldeer	fil à flux incorporé	Röhrenlot	flussfyllt lod
foam flux	schuimvloei-middel	flux en mousse	Schaumflussmittel	skumfluss
fusible alloy	smeltlegering	alliage fusible	Schmelzlegierung	smältlegering
globule tester	globule tester	appareil d'essai à la goutte	Kugelprüfgerät	lodkuleprovare
hot dip tinning	vuurvertinnen	étamage au trempé	Feuerverzinnen	varmvörtenning
icicles	pegels	drapeaux	Lotzapfen	lodtapp
immersion depth	dompeldiepte	profondeur d'immersion	Tauchtiefe	doppdjup
impurities	verontreinigingen	impuretés	Verunreinigungen	föroreningar
joint = soldered joint	verbinding	joint soudé	Lötstelle	lödförbindning
lead (wire)	draad	conducteur	Draht	tråd
lead (element)	lood	plomb	Blei	bly
levelling	(levelling)	nivelage	(Levelling)	(levelling)
magnet wire	wikkeldraad	fil de bobinage	Spulendraht	lindningstråd
manual soldering	handsolderen	soudage manuel	Handlöten	hand lödning
melting point	smeltpunt	température de fusion	Schmeltzpunkt	smältpunkt
metallised hole = plated hole	gemetalliseerd gat	trou metallisé	Durchkontaktie-rung	metallerat hål
non-wetting	niet-bevochtiging	non-mouillage	keine Benetzung	ickevätning
nozzle	uitstroomtoren	buse	Düse	munstycke
passivation	passivering	passivation	Passivierung	passivering
phenolic paper laminate	hardpapier	stratifié papier-phenolique	Phenolharz-Hartpapier	Fenolpappers-laminat
plated (through) hole	gemetalliseerd gat	trou métallisé	Durchkontaktie-rung	metallerat hål
preforms	(preforms) ringetjes	préforme	Lotformteile	formlod
preheating	voorverwarmen	préchauffage	Vorheizen	förvärmning
preserving coat	beschermlaag	vernis de protection	Schutzlack	skyddsskikt
printed (circuit) board	paneel met gedruk-te bedrading	carte imprimée	Leiterplatte	mönsterkort
reflow soldering	reflow solderen	soudage par refusion	Reflow-Löten	omsmältnings-lödning
reliability	betrouwbaarheid	fiabilité	Zuverlässigkeit	tillförlitlighet
residues (flux-)	resten	résidue de flux	Rückstände	flussrest
resin flux	hars vloeimiddel	flux résineux	Harzflussmittel	lödharts
resistance to soldering heat	weerstand tegen soldeertemperatuur	résistance à la chaleur de soudage	Lötwärmebeständ-igkeit	motstånd mot lödvärme
rework	nasolderen	retouche	Nacharbeit	omarbeta
rosin flux	hars vloeimiddel	flux résineux	Kolophonium-flussmittel	lödharts
rotary dip	(rotary dip)	trempage par rotation	Drehtauchen	(rotary dip)
soft-soldering	zachtsolderen	soudage (brasage tendre)	Weichlöten	mjuklödning
solder (alloy)	soldeer	alliage d'apport	Lotlegierung	lod
solder cream	soldeerpasta	crème à souder	Lotpaste	lodpasta
solder defect	soldeerfout	soudure défectueuse	Lötfehler	lödfel

English	Dutch	French	German	Swedish
solder land	soldeervlak	plage de soudage	Lötauge	lödställe
solder meniscus	meniskus	menisque	Lotmeniskus	menisk
solder resist	soldeerafscherm-lak	vernis épargne de soudage	Lötstoplack	lödmask
solderability	soldeerbaarheid	soudabilité	Lötbarkeit	lödbarhet
soldered joint	soldeerverbinding	joint soudé	Lötverbindung	lödförbindning
soldering	solderen	souder	löten	lödning
soldering iron	soldeerbout	fer à souder	Lötkolben	lödkolv
soldering time	soldeertijd	temps de soudage	Lötzeit	lödtid
spatter	spetter	éclaboussure		lodstänk
specimen	proefstuk	éprouvette	Probe	prov(föremål)
spreading	spreiding	étalement	Ausbreitung	utbredning
steam ageing	oudering in stoom	vieillissement en vapeur d'eau	Dampfalterung	åldring i ånga
storage	opslag	stockage	Lagerung	lagring
surface tension	oppervlakte spanning	tension de surface	Oberflächen-spannung	ytspänning
tag	soldeeroog	cosse	Lötfahne	anslutningsstift
termination	uitloper	sortie	Anschluss	uttag
thermal demand	benodigde hoeveel-heid warmte	(appel thermique)	Warmebedarf	värmebehov
track (conductor)	spoor (geleider)	piste (conducteur)	Leiterbahn	ledare
touch up (rework)	nasolderen	retouche (de soudage)	nachlöten	bättring
voids	gallen, holten	manques	Löcher	por
warp	kromming	vrillage	Krummung	varp
wave soldering	golfsolderen	soudage à la vague	Schwallöten	våglödning
webbing	spinragvorming	toile d'araignée	Gewebe	(webbing)
wettability	bevochtigbaarheid	mouillabilité	Benetzbarkeit	vätbarhet
wetting	bevochtiging	mouillage	Benetzung	vätning
wetting balance	bevochtigings-balans	balance de mouillage	Benetzungswaage	meniscograf

Subject Index

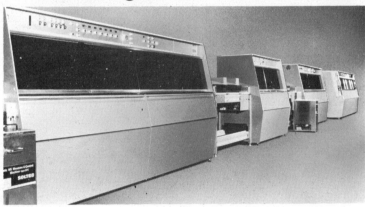

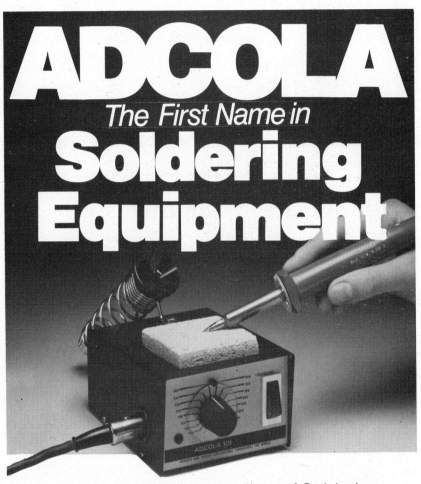

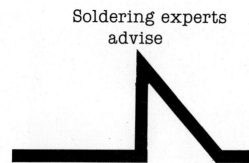

GALDEN

Inert perfluorinated fluids for vapour phase reflow soldering

■ GALDEN LS, for usual solder alloys with tin/lead ratios ranging from 45/55 to 95/5.

■ GALDEN HS, extends the application area of vapour phase reflow soldering to higher melting solder alloys, such as 96·5 Sn/3·5 Ag, 99 Sn/1 Sb, 95 Sn/5 Sb.

Properties		GALDEN LS	GALDEN HS
Operating temperature	°C	220–235	250–256
	°F	428–455	482–509
Liquid density (20°C–68°F)	g/ml	1·82	1·84
Average molecular weight		800	900
Heat of vaporization	cal/g	15	15
Specific heat	cal/g°C	0·24	0·24
Thermal conductivity	mW/m°C	70	70
Kinematic viscosity (20°C–68°F)	cSt	5	9
Surface tension (20°C–68°F)	dyne/cm	18	18

GALDEN* fluids exhibit high thermal and chemical stability, complete compatibility with electronic materials, high oxidation resistance, non flammability, low toxicity.

* = registered trade mark

UNITED STATES
Montedison Usa Inc.»
1114 Avenue of the Americas –
New York, N.Y. 10036 –
Tel. (212) 764.0260 –
Telex Montedison 223447-66312 –
Cable Montedison N.Y.

JAPAN
Nippon Montedison KK
Montedison Bldg. 1-3-2 Aobadai –
Meguro Ku – Tokyo 153
Tel. (03) 462.0551 –
Telex Gabbro J 02-423851 –
Cable Gabbronip Tokyo

GERMANY (WEST)
Montedison (Deutschland) G.m.b.H.
Head Office:
Postfach 5626 – Frankfurter Strasse 33–35 –
D-6236 Eschborn Bei Frankfurt –
Tel. 492-0 – Telex MCH 4-18305 –
Cable Montedison Frankfurt
Branch Office:
Bruehlhofstrasse 5 – 7022 Echterdingen
Eleinfeleden –
Tel. 796.004/8 – Telex 041 – 7255131
Oberstasse, 6 – 403 Ratingen –
Tel. 25071/3 – Telex 8-585-083 –
Cable Montedison Ratingen

UNITED KINGDOM
Montedison (U.K.) Ltd.
7/8 Lygon Place – Ebury Street –
London SW1 W OJR –
Tel. 01-730.3405 –
Telex 918743 Montedison –
Cable Montedison London SW1

FRANCE
Montedison France S.A.
Tour Franklin – Quartier Boildieau –
Puteaux (Hauts de Seine) –
Cedex 11 – 92081 Paris – La Défense –
Tel. 776.41.16 –
Telex Monted 620232-620574 –
Cable Montefrance Puteaux Paris

MONTEDISON GROUP

 MONTEFLUOS

Via Principe Eugenio 1/5 – 20155 Milano (Italy)
Telephone: (02) 63331 – Cables MONTEFLUOS MI
Telex: 310679 MONTEDISON I PER MONTEFLUOS

♯♯ REGISTERED TRADE MARK OF MONTEDISON S.p.A